# Student, Parent, Teacher
# Internet Resources

**Science Online** **ca7.msscience.com**

Access your Student Edition on the Internet so you don't need to bring your textbook home every night. You can link to features and get additional practice with these Online Study Tools.

Check out the following features on your
**Online Learning Center:**

## Study Tools

- **Concepts In Motion**
  - Interactive Tables
  - Interactive Time Line
  - Animated Illustrations
- Lesson Self-Check Quizzes
- Chapter Test Practice
- Standardized Test Practice

- Vocabulary PuzzleMaker
- Interactive Tutor
- Multilingual Science Glossary
- Study to Go
- Online Student Edition
- **BrainPop** BrainPop Movies

## Extensions

- Virtual Labs
- Microscopy Links
- Periodic Table Links
- Career Links

- Prescreened Web Links
- WebQuest Project
- Science Fair Ideas
- Internet Labs

## For Teachers

- Teacher Bulletin Board
- Teaching Today, and much more!

# Safety Symbols

These safety symbols are used in laboratory and field investigations in this book to indicate possible hazards. Learn the meaning of each symbol and refer to this page often. *Remember to wash your hands thoroughly after completing lab procedures.*

| SAFETY SYMBOLS | HAZARD | EXAMPLES | PRECAUTION | REMEDY |
|---|---|---|---|---|
| DISPOSAL | Special disposal procedures need to be followed. | certain chemicals, living organisms | Do not dispose of these materials in the sink or trash can. | Dispose of wastes as directed by your teacher. |
| BIOLOGICAL | Organisms or other biological materials that might be harmful to humans | bacteria, fungi, blood, unpreserved tissues, plant materials | Avoid skin contact with these materials. Wear mask or gloves. | Notify your teacher if you suspect contact with material. Wash hands thoroughly. |
| EXTREME TEMPERATURE | Objects that can burn skin by being too cold or too hot | boiling liquids, hot plates, dry ice, liquid nitrogen | Use proper protection when handling. | Go to your teacher for first aid. |
| SHARP OBJECT | Use of tools or glassware that can easily puncture or slice skin | razor blades, pins, scalpels, pointed tools, dissecting probes, broken glass | Practice common-sense behavior and follow guidelines for use of the tool. | Go to your teacher for first aid. |
| FUME | Possible danger to respiratory tract from fumes | ammonia, acetone, nail polish remover, heated sulfur, moth balls | Make sure there is good ventilation. Never smell fumes directly. Wear a mask. | Leave foul area and notify your teacher immediately. |
| ELECTRICAL | Possible danger from electrical shock or burn | improper grounding, liquid spills, short circuits, exposed wires | Double-check setup with teacher. Check condition of wires and apparatus. Use GFI-protected outlets. | Do not attempt to fix electrical problems. Notify your teacher immediately. |
| IRRITANT | Substances that can irritate the skin or mucous membranes of the respiratory tract | pollen, moth balls, steel wool, fiberglass, potassium permanganate | Wear dust mask and gloves. Practice extra care when handling these materials. | Go to your teacher for first aid. |
| CHEMICAL | Chemicals that can react with and destroy tissue and other materials | bleaches such as hydrogen peroxide; acids such as sulfuric acid, hydrochloric acid; bases such as ammonia, sodium hydroxide | Wear goggles, gloves, and an apron. | Immediately flush the affected area with water and notify your teacher. |
| TOXIC | Substance may be poisonous if touched, inhaled, or swallowed. | mercury, many metal compounds, iodine, poinsettia plant parts | Follow your teacher's instructions. | Always wash hands thoroughly after use. Go to your teacher for first aid. |
| FLAMMABLE | Open flame may ignite flammable chemicals, loose clothing, or hair. | alcohol, kerosene, potassium permanganate, hair, clothing | Avoid open flames and heat when using flammable chemicals. | Notify your teacher immediately. Use fire safety equipment if applicable. |
| OPEN FLAME | Open flame in use, may cause fire. | hair, clothing, paper, synthetic materials | Tie back hair and loose clothing. Follow teacher's instructions on lighting and extinguishing flames. | Always wash hands thoroughly after use. Go to your teacher for first aid. |

 **Eye Safety** Proper eye protection must be worn at all times by anyone performing or observing science activities.

 **Clothing Protection** This symbol appears when substances could stain or burn clothing.

 **Animal Safety** This symbol appears when safety of animals and students must be ensured.

 **Handwashing** After the lab, wash hands with soap and water before removing goggles.

# Focus On
# Life Science

Glencoe Science

CALIFORNIA GRADE 7

NATIONAL GEOGRAPHIC

ca7.msscience.com

**Glencoe**

New York, New York    Columbus, Ohio    Chicago, Illinois    Peoria, Illinois    Woodland Hills, California

## Glencoe Science

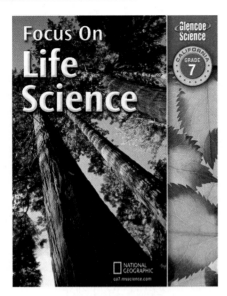

### Focus On Life Science

Redwood trees can live over 200 years and grow to heights over 90 meters tall. There are three members of the redwood family—coast redwoods, giant sequoias, and dawn redwoods.

### Science Online ca7.msscience.com

Check out the following features on your **Online Learning Center:**

**Study Tools**
- Concepts In Motion
  - Interactive Tables
  - Interactive Time Line
  - Animated Illustrations
- Lesson Self-Check Quizzes
- Chapter Test Practice
- Standardized Test Practice
- Vocabulary PuzzleMaker
- Interactive Tutor
- Multilingual Science Glossary
- Study to Go
- Online Student Edition
- BrainPop Movies

**Extensions**
- Virtual Labs
- Microscopy Links
- Periodic Table Links
- Career Links
- Prescreened Web Links
- WebQuest Project
- Science Fair Ideas
- Internet Labs

**For Teachers**
- Teacher Bulletin Board
- Teaching Today, and much more!

**Glencoe**

The *McGraw·Hill* Companies

Send all inquiries to:
Glencoe/McGraw-Hill
8787 Orion Place
Columbus, OH 43240-4027

ISBN-13: 978-0-07-879434-6
ISBN-10: 0-07-879434X

Printed in the United States of America.

1 2 3 4 5 6 7 8 9 10 079/043 11 10 09 08 07

# Contents in Brief

**Introduction to Investigation and Experimentation** . . . . . . . . . . . . . . . . . . . . . . . . 2

7.a, 7.b, 7.c, 7.d, 7.e

## Unit 1
**Cell Biology** . . . . . . . . . . . . . . . . . . . . . . **42**

Chapter 1 **Cell Structure and Function** . . . . . . . 44

1.a, 1.b, 1.c, 1.d, 2.e, 7.a, 7.c, 7.d, 7.e

Chapter 2 **From a Cell to an Organism** . . . . . . . 84

1.c, 1.e, 1.f, 5.a, 7.a, 7.d, 7.e

## Unit 2
**Reproduction and Genetics** . . . . . . . . . . . **120**

Chapter 3 **Reproduction of Organisms** . . . . . . 122

2.a, 2.b, 5.f, 7.a, 7.b, 7.c, 7.d, 7.e

Chapter 4 **Genetics** . . . . . . . . . . . . . . . . . . . . . 168

2.b, 2.c, 2.d, 7.a, 7.b, 7.c, 7.e

## Unit 3
**Evolution—Change Over Time** . . . . . . . . . **204**

Chapter 5 **The Process of Evolution** . . . . . . . . 206

3.a, 3.b, 3.e, 7.a, 7.b, 7.c, 7.d

Chapter 6 **Evolution—Evidence of Change** . . 240

3.a, 3.c, 3.d, 4.c, 4.e, 4.f, 7.c, 7.d, 7.e

## Unit 4
**Earth and Life History** . . . . . . . . . . . . . . . **278**

Chapter 7 **The Age of Earth** . . . . . . . . . . . . . . 280

4.a, 4.c, 4.d, 7.c, 7.d

Chapter 8 **The History of Life on Earth** . . . . . 312

4.b, 4.e, 4.g, 7.a, 7.c, 7.d

## Unit 5
**Structure, Function, and Physical Properties in Living Systems** . . . . . . . . . . . **354**

Chapter 9 **The Musculoskeletal System and Levers** . . . . . . . . . . . . . . . . . . . . . 356

5.a, 5.c, 6.h, 6.i, 7.a, 7.c, 7.d

Chapter 10 **The Cardiopulmonary System and Pressure** . . . . . . . . . . . . . 388

5.b, 6.j, 7.a, 7.c, 7.e

Chapter 11 **The Eye and Light** . . . . . . . . . . . . . . 424

5.g, 6.a, 6.b, 6.c, 6.d, 6.e, 6.f, 6.g

Chapter 12 **The Ear and Sound** . . . . . . . . . . . . . 468

5.g, 7.b, 7.d, 7.e

Chapter 13 **The Human Reproductive System** . . . . . . . . . . . . . . . . . . . . . . . . 500

5.d, 5.e, 7.a, 7.b, 7.c, 7.d

# Teacher Advisory Board

The California Science Teacher Advisory Board provided valuable input in the development of the 2007 edition of *Focus On Life Science.* They helped create the scope and sequence of the Student Edition, provided content and pedagogical comments, and provided feedback for the Teacher Wraparound Edition.

**Charles Beecroft**
8th Grade Science
  Teacher
Columbia School District
Redding, CA

**Douglas Fisher**
Director of Professional
  Development
City Heights Educational
  Collaborative
San Diego, CA

**Patricia Juárez**
Coordinator III
Sacramento City Unified
  School District
Sacramento, CA

**Tom Castro**
Science Teacher
Martinez JHS/
  Martinez USD
Martinez, CA

**Mindi Fisher**
Leadership Team
  Administrator
Peninsula Union School
  District
Samoa, CA

**Kathy Molnar**
Professional
  Development Mentor
Etiwanda School District
Etiwanda, CA

**Lisa L. Cordes**
Science Department
  Chair
Rivera Middle School/
  El Rancho USD
Pico Rivera, CA

**Frederick W. Freking**
Faculty Advisor
University of California,
  Los Angeles
Los Angeles, CA

**Carol Orton**
Teacher
Bernardo Heights
  Middle School
San Diego, CA

**Justin Cunningham
EdD**
Coordinator, Small
  School District Services
San Diego, County Office
  of Education
San Diego, CA

**Nancy Frey**
Associate Professor of
  Literacy
San Diego State
  University
San Diego, CA

**Joycalyn Peoples**
Science Specialist
Riverside Unified School
  District
Riverside, CA

**Richard Filson**
Science Department
  Chair
Edison High School,
  Stockton Unified
  School District
Stockton, CA

**Maria C. Grant**
Teacher
Hoover High School/
  San Diego City School
  and San Diego State
  University
San Diego, CA

**Wendi L. Rodriguez**
Teacher
Heritage/Snowline JUSD
Phelan, CA

**Bruce Fisher**
Distinguished Teacher
  in Residence
Humboldt State
  University
Arcata, CA

**Patrick Horton**
Science Teacher
Day Creek Intermediate
  School
Etiwanda, CA

**Gladys Sorensen**
Science Department
  Chair
Patrick Henry Middle
  School
Grenada Hills, CA

**Patty Horton**
Professional
  Development Provider
Etiwanda School District
Etiwanda, CA

**Granger B. Ward**
California
  Superintendent and
  Former Science Teacher
San Diego, CA

# Acknowledgements

## Authors

Science Online Learn more about the authors at ca7.msscience.com.

**Juli Berwald, PhD**
Science Writer
Austin, TX

**Douglas Fisher, PhD**
Director of Professional
    Development and
    Professor
City Heights Educational
    Collaborative, San
    Diego State University
San Diego, CA

**Kimberly Fekany Lee,
PhD**
Science Writer
Weschester, IL

**Keith Olin Mann, PhD**
Associate Professor of
    Geology
Ohio Wesleyan University
Delaware, OH

**Donna L. Ross, PhD**
Associate Professor of
    Science Education
San Diego State University
San Diego, CA

**Dinah Zike, MEd**
Educational Consultant
Dinah-Might Activities,
    Inc.
San Antonio, TX

**NATIONAL GEOGRAPHIC**

**National Geographic**
Education Division
Washington, D.C.

## Series Consultants

Content consultants reviewed the chapters in their area of expertise and provided suggestions for improving the effectiveness of the science instruction.

### Science Consultants

**Richard Allen, PhD**
University of California,
    Berkeley
Berkeley, CA

**Karamjeet Arya, PhD**
San Jose State University
San Jose, CA

**Teaster Baird, PhD**
San Francisco State
    University
San Francisco, CA

**Natalie Batalha, PhD**
San Jose State University
San Jose, CA

**Robin Bennett, MS**
University of Washington
Seattle, WA

**William B. N. Berry,
PhD**
University of California,
    Berkeley
Berkeley, CA

**Diane Clayton, PhD**
NASA
Santa Barbara, CA

**Susan Crawford, PhD**
California State University
Sacramento, CA

**Stephen F. Cunha, PhD**
Humboldt State University
Arcata, CA

**Jennifer A. Dever, PhD**
University of San Francisco
San Francisco, CA

**Alejandro Garcia, PhD**
San Jose State University
San Jose, CA

**Alan Gishlick, PhD**
National Center for
    Science Education
Oakland, CA

**Juno Hsu, PhD**
University of California,
    Irvine
Irvine, CA

**Martha Jagucki, MS**
Geologist
Columbus, OH

**Lee Kats, PhD**
Pepperdine University
Malibu, CA

**Christopher Kim, PhD**
Chapman University
Orange, CA

**Monika Kress, PhD**
San Jose State University
San Jose, CA

**Steve Lund, PhD**
University of Southern
    California
Los Angeles, CA

**Michael Manga, PhD**
University of California,
    Berkeley
Berkeley, CA

**Kate Schafer, PhD**
Aquamarine Research
Mountain View, CA

**Julio G. Soto, PhD**
San Jose State University
San Jose, CA

# Acknowledgements

**Dr. Edward Walton**
California Polytechnical
  Institute
Pomona, CA

**VivianLee Ward**
National Health Museum
Washington, DC

### Math Consultant

**Grant Fraser, PhD**
California State
  University
Los Angeles, CA

### Reading Consultant

**ReLeah Cossett Lent**
Author/Educational
  Consultant
Alford, FL

### Safety Consultant

**Jeff Vogt, MEd**
Federal Hocking Middle
  School
Stewart, OH

## Series Teacher Reviewers

Each Teacher Reviewer reviewed at least two chapters, providing feedback and suggestions for improving the effectiveness of the science instruction.

**Joel Austin**
Roosevelt Middle School
San Francisco, CA

**Nicole Belong**
Coronado Middle School
Coronado, CA

**Patrick Brickey**
Lakeview Junior High School
Santa Maria, CA

**Mary Pilles Bryant**
Henry J. Kaiser High School
Fontana, CA

**Edward Case**
Washington Academic Middle
  School
Sanger, CA

**Monaliza Chian**
E. O. Green Junior High School
Oxnard, CA

**Valesca Lopez Dwyer**
Park View Middle School
Yucaipa, CA

**Kathryn Froman**
North Davis Elementary School
Davis, CA

**Brian Gary**
Margaret Landell Elementary
Cypress, CA

**Jeanette George-Becker**
Roosevelt Elementary School
San Gabriel, CA

**Bret Harrison**
Frank Ledesma Elementary
Soledad, CA

**Rick Hoffman**
Kastner Intermediate School
Fresno, CA

**Kimberly Klein**
Barstow Intermediate School
Barstow, CA

**David Kulka**
South Peninsula Hebrew Day
  School
Sunnyvale, CA

**Christina Lambie**
Highland Elementary School
Richmond, CA

**Kathleen Magnani**
Center Junior High School
Antelope, CA

**Tara McGuigan**
Monroe Clark Middle School
San Diego, CA

**Shelia Patterson**
K–12 Alliance-California
Oceano, CA

**Sharon Pendola**
St. Albans Country Day School
Roseville, CA

**Lori Poublon-Ramirez**
Herman Intermediate School
San Jose, CA

**Martha Romero**
E. O. Green Junior High School
Oxnard, CA

**Arlene Sackman**
Earlimart Middle School
Earlimart, CA

**Rex Scates**
Herman Intermediate School
San Jose, CA

**Robert Sherriff**
Winston Churchill Middle School
Carmichael, CA

**Maria Mendez Simpson**
School Programs Coordinator/
  Birch Aquarium
La Jolla, CA

**Lorre Stange**
Laytonville Elementary School
Laytonville, CA

**Louann Talbert**
Laytonville Middle School
Laytonville, CA

**Gina Marie Turcketta**
St. Joan of Arc School
Los Angeles, CA

# Table of Contents

**Introduction to Investigation and Experimentation**.................... 2   7.a, 7.b, 7.c, 7.d, 7.e

   **What is science?** ........................2   7.c

   **Tools of the Life Scientist**.................7   7.a, 7.b, 7.c, 7.d, 7.e

   **Case Study: The Diabetes Generation** ......34   7.a, 7.c

---

## Unit 1 Cell Biology.................................................42

**Chapter 1**
**Cell Structure and Function** .............. 44   **California Standards**

**Lesson 1** Cells and Life ........................48   1.a, 7.a, 7.c

**Lesson 2** The Cell............................56   1.a, 1.b, 1.c, 2.e, 7.c

**Lesson 3** Cells and Energy .....................68   1.d, 7.a, 7.c, 7.d, 7.e

  Standards Assessment ......................... 82–83

**Chapter 2**
**From a Cell to an Organism**............... 84

**Lesson 1** The Cell Cycle and Cell Division ........88   1.c, 1.e, 7.a

**Lesson 2** Levels of Organization..................98   1.f, 5.a, 7.d, 7.e

  Standards Assessment ....................... 116–117

**Read on Your Own**.......................118

**Unit Test** ...............................119

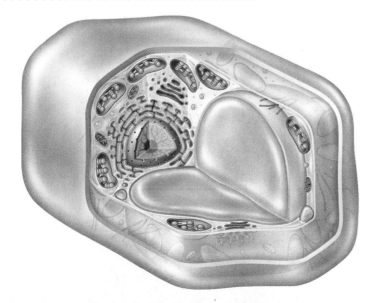

*A plant cell*

# Table of Contents

## Unit 2 Reproduction and Genetics . . . . . . . . . . . . . . . . . . . . . . . . . . . . . . .120

### Chapter 3
**Reproduction of Organisms** . . . . . . . . . . . . . **122**

**California Standards**

**Lesson 1** Sexual Reproduction and Meiosis . . . . . .126    2.b, 7.d

**Lesson 2** Plant Reproduction . . . . . . . . . . . . . . . . . .134    2.a, 5.f, 7.b

**Lesson 3** Animal Reproduction . . . . . . . . . . . . . . .143    2.a, 2.b, 7.c

**Lesson 4** Asexual Reproduction . . . . . . . . . . . . . . .151    2.a, 7.a, 7.c, 7.d, 7.e

Standards Assessment . . . . . . . . . . . . . . . . . . . . . . . **166–167**

### Chapter 4
**Genetics** . . . . . . . . . . . . . . . . . . . . . . . . . . . . . **168**

**Lesson 1** Foundations of Genetics . . . . . . . . . . . . . .172    2.b, 2.d

**Lesson 2** Understanding Inheritance . . . . . . . . . . .182    2.c, 2.d, 7.a, 7.b, 7.c, 7.e

Standards Assessment . . . . . . . . . . . . . . . . . . . . . . . **200–201**

**Read on Your Own** . . . . . . . . . . . . . . . . . . . . . . **202**
**Unit Test** . . . . . . . . . . . . . . . . . . . . . . . . . . . . . **203**

## Unit 3 Evolution—Change Over Time . . . . . . . . . . . . . . . . . . . . . . . . . . 204

### Chapter 5
**The Process of Evolution** . . . . . . . . . . . . . . . . **206**

**Lesson 1** Natural Selection . . . . . . . . . . . . . . . . . . . .210    3.a, 3.b, 7.c

**Lesson 2** Adaptation and Extinction . . . . . . . . . . . .219    3.a, 3.e, 7.a, 7.b, 7.c

Standards Assessment . . . . . . . . . . . . . . . . . . . . . . . **238–239**

*Camellia saluenensis*

# Table of Contents

**Chapter 6**
**Evolution—Evidence of Change** ........ 240

California Standards

**Lesson 1** Fossils and Evolution.................244       3.c, 4.c, 4.e, 7.d

**Lesson 2** Biological Evidence ..................252       3.c

**Lesson 3** Evolution and Plate Tectonics.........257       3.a, 4.f

**Lesson 4** Classifying Organisms...............262       3.d, 7.c, 7.d, 7.e

Standards Assessment ....................... 274–275

Read on Your Own..................... 276
Unit Test .............................. 277

**Unit 4 Earth and Life History**...................................278

**Chapter 7**
**The Age of Earth** ...................... 280

**Lesson 1** Relative Ages of Rocks................284       4.a, 4.c, 7.d

**Lesson 2** Absolute Ages of Rocks ..............293       4.d, 7.c, 7.d

Standards Assessment ....................... 310–311

**Chapter 8**
**The History of Life on Earth** .............312

**Lesson 1** Geologic Time and Mass Extinctions ...316       4.b, 4.e, 4.g, 7.a

**Lesson 2** Early Earth History ..................325       4.b, 4.e, 4.g, 7.d

**Lesson 3** Middle and Recent Earth History ......332       4.b, 4.e, 4.g, 7.a

Standards Assessment ....................... 350–351

Read on Your Own..................... 352
Unit Test .............................. 353

*Sandstone wave in
Paria Canyon*

# Table of Contents

## Unit 5 Structure, Function, and Physical Properties in Living Systems . .354

**California Standards**

### Chapter 9
**The Musculoskeletal System and Levers . . . . . . . . . . . . . . . . . . . . . . . . . 356**

Lesson 1   The Musculoskeletal System . . . . . . . . . . 360        5.a, 5.c, 6.h, 7.a, 7.c

Lesson 2   The Body and Levers . . . . . . . . . . . . . . . . 368        6.h, 6.i, 7.a, 7.c, 7.d

Standards Assessment . . . . . . . . . . . . . . . . . . . . . . 386–387

### Chapter 10
**The Cardiopulmonary System and Pressure . . . . . . . . . . . . . . . . . . . . . . . . 388**

Lesson 1   The Pulmonary-Circulatory System . . . .392        5.b, 7.c

Lesson 2   Pressure and the Body . . . . . . . . . . . . . . .405        5.b, 6.j, 7.a, 7.c, 7.e

Standards Assessment . . . . . . . . . . . . . . . . . . . . . . 422–423

### Chapter 11
**The Eye and Light . . . . . . . . . . . . . . . . . . . . . 424**

Lesson 1   What is light? . . . . . . . . . . . . . . . . . . . . . .428        6.a, 6.e

Lesson 2   Light and Matter . . . . . . . . . . . . . . . . . . .435        6.b, 6.c, 6.f, 6.g

Lesson 3   Using Lenses. . . . . . . . . . . . . . . . . . . . . . .443        6.d

Lesson 4   The Eye and Vision . . . . . . . . . . . . . . . . .450        5.g, 6.b, 6.d, 6.e

Standards Assessment . . . . . . . . . . . . . . . . . . . . . . 466–467

### Chapter 12
**The Ear and Sound . . . . . . . . . . . . . . . . . . . . . 468**

Lesson 1   Sound . . . . . . . . . . . . . . . . . . . . . . . . . . . .472        5.g, 7.b

Lesson 2   The Ear and Hearing. . . . . . . . . . . . . . . . .480        5.g, 7.b, 7.d, 7.e

Standards Assessment . . . . . . . . . . . . . . . . . . . . . . 498–499

*Galápagos ground finch*

# Table of Contents

**Chapter 13**
**The Human Reproductive System** . . . . . . . . **500**

**Lesson 1**  Reproductive Systems . . . . . . . . . . . . . . . .504          5.d, 7.a

**Lesson 2**  Development Before Birth . . . . . . . . . . . .515          5.e, 7.a, 7.b, 7.c, 7.d

Standards Assessment . . . . . . . . . . . . . . . . . . . . . . . **530–531**

Read on Your Own . . . . . . . . . . . . . . . . . . . . . **532**
Unit Test . . . . . . . . . . . . . . . . . . . . . . . . . . . . . . **533**

**At-Home Standards Practice** . . . . . . . . . . . . . . . . . . . . . . . . . . . . . . . . . . . **534**

**Student Resources** . . . . . . . . . . . . . . . . . . . . . . . **552**

**Science Safety Skill Handbook** . . . .**554**

**Technology Skill Handbook** . . . . . . .**557**

**Math Skill Handbook**
   **Math Review** . . . . . . . . . . . . . . . . . . . . . . . .**561**
   **Science Applications** . . . . . . . . . . . . . . . . .**571**

**Reference Handbook**
   **Using a Calculator** . . . . . . . . . . . . . . . . . . .**576**
   **Understanding Scientific Terms** . . . . . . . . .**577**

**Use and Care of a Microscope** . . . . . . . . . . . .**579**
**Diversity of Life: Classification of**
   **Living Organisms** . . . . . . . . . . . . . . . . . . . .**580**
**Periodic Table of the Elements** . . . . . . . . . .**584**

**English/Spanish Glossary** . . . . . . . . .**586**

**Index** . . . . . . . . . . . . . . . . . . . . . . . . . . . . .**601**

**Credits** . . . . . . . . . . . . . . . . . . . . . . . . . . .**613**

*California Poppies*

# BrainPOP Movies

To view BrainPOP Movies go to **ca7.msscience.com**. *The features listed here correlate to their respective chapter's science content.*

## BrainPOP Movies

| Title | Chapter-Lesson |
|-------|----------------|
| Bacteria | 1-3 |
| Cell Structures | 1-2 |
| Mitosis | 2-1 |
| Cell Specialization | 2-2 |
| Seed Plants | 3-2 |
| Heredity | 4-2 |
| Fossils | 6-1 |
| How Joints Work | 9-2 |
| Circulatory System | 10-1 |
| Color | 11-1 |
| Eye | 11-4 |
| Fertilization and Birth | 13-2 |

# Real World Science

*The features listed here correlate to their respective chapter's science content.*

| Chapter/Page | Science & Career | Science & Technology | Science & History | Science & Society |
|---|---|---|---|---|
| **1** *76–77* | From Cells to Organelles | Confocal Laser Scanning Microscopy | Golgi's "Black" Reaction | Putting Organisms to Good Use |
| **2** *110–111* | David Burgess, PhD | Healing Burns with Artificial Skin | Walther Flemming | Sign Up, Save Lives |
| **3** *160–161* | Lions and Tigers and Bears, Oh My! | Producing Disease-Free Plants | Ernest Everett Just and Parthenogenesis | Animal Cloning— Yes or No? |
| **4** *194–195* | Making New Plant Breeds | Genetic Engineering | Luther Burbank's Legacy | Genetically-Modified Plants |
| **5** *232–233* | You can be an evolutionary biologist! | A Molecular Clock | Counting Coprolites | Habitat Degradation and Extinction |
| **6** *268–269* | Studying Bacterial Evolution | Observe Evolution in Action | Early Hypothesis of Evolution | The Galápagos Islands—An Evolution Museum |
| **7** *304–305* | Studying the Rocks of Earth | It's looking at the small stuff and changing it. | Carving Rocks Through History | The State Mineral and Its History |
| **8** *344–345* | You can study ancient life! | How old is it? | The "Age of the Fishes" | Changing Climate and Our World |
| **9** *380–381* | You can be an athletic trainer! | Checking Out Your Knees | Archimedes, Levers, and the Human Body | Artificial People? |
| **10** *416–417* | A Surgical Pioneer | Have a Heart | The Blood Course of a Horse | Asthma in California |
| **11** *460–461* | So You Want to be a Lighting Technician | High-Tech Help for the Blind | The Invention of Eyeglasses | The Impact of the Lightbulb on Society |
| **12** *492–493* | Become a Speech Therapist | Cochlear Implants | Good Vibrations | Noise Pollution |
| **13** *524–525* | The Science of Reproductive Endocrinology | Ovarian Tissue Transplant | The First Test-Tube Baby | STDs—Sexually Transmitted Diseases |

# Labs

## Labs

| | | | California Standards |
|---|---|---|---|
| **Chapter 1** | Exploring the Unknown | 74–75 | 1.b, 7.a, 7.c, 7.d, 7.e |
| **Chapter 3** | Plant Propagation | 158–159 | 2.a, 7.a, 7.c, 7.e |
| **Chapter 6** | Classifying the Students in Your Class | 266–267 | 3.d, 7.c, 7.d, 7.e |
| **Chapter 11** | Can a cow eye teach you about your eyes? | 458–459 | 5.g |

## Design Your Own Labs

| | | | |
|---|---|---|---|
| **Chapter 2** | Design an Organ | 108–109 | 5.a, 7.d, 7.e |
| **Chapter 4** | What makes you unique? | 192–193 | 2.d, 7.a, 7.b, 7.c, 7.e |
| **Chapter 5** | Can you apply the principles of natural selection to island species? | 230–231 | 3.b, 7.b, 7.c |
| **Chapter 7** | Erosion Stoppers | 302–303 | 7.c, 7.d |
| **Chapter 9** | Build Your Own Levers | 378–379 | 6.h, 6.i, 7.a, 7.c, 7.d |
| **Chapter 10** | What happens when the cardiopulmonary system breaks down? | 414–415 | 5.b, 6.j |
| **Chapter 13** | A Healthy Pregnancy | 522–523 | 5.e, 7.a, 7.b, 7.c, 7.d |

## Use the Internet Labs

| | | | |
|---|---|---|---|
| **Chapter 8** | How has California changed over geologic time? | 342–343 | 7.a, 7.d |
| **Chapter 12** | Animal Hearing | 490–491 | 5.g, 7.b, 7.e |

## Launch Labs

| | | | California Standards |
|---|---|---|---|
| **Chapter 1** | What are we made of? | 45 | 7.a, 7.d |
| **Chapter 2** | When is division not a math problem? | 85 | 1.a, 7.a, 7.d |
| **Chapter 3** | How does reproduction happen? | 123 | 2.a, 7.d |
| **Chapter 4** | How well can you predict? | 169 | 2.d, 7.c |
| **Chapter 5** | What attracts insects to certain flowers? | 207 | 3.a |
| **Chapter 6** | Can you make an animal evolve? | 241 | 3.a, 3.d |
| **Chapter 7** | What is Earth's surface like? | 281 | 4.a, 7.e |

# Launch Labs (continued)

**California Standards**

| | | | |
|---|---|---|---|
| **Chapter 8** | How are events unscrambled? *Try at Home* | 312 | 4.e., 4.g, 7.c |
| **Chapter 9** | Is it easy to lift? | 357 | 5.c, 7.a |
| **Chapter 10** | Does your pulse change? | 389 | 5.b, 7.c |
| **Chapter 11** | Can you make a rainbow? | 425 | 6.e |
| **Chapter 12** | How many sounds can you make? | 469 | 5.g, 7.e |
| **Chapter 13** | Is it a boy or a girl? | 501 | 2.b, 7.c |

# MiniLabs

**California Standards**

| | | | |
|---|---|---|---|
| **Chapter 1** | How can you model a cell? | 65 | 1.b, 7.d |
| | How can you see photosynthesis? *Try at Home* | 73 | 1.d, 7.c |
| **Chapter 2** | What's in a tissue? | 103 | 5.a, 7.d |
| **Chapter 3** | What does meiosis look like? | 132 | 2.b, 7.d |
| | What's in a flower? | 138 | 5.f, 7.d |
| | How do yeast reproduce? | 153 | 2.a, 7.a, 7.c, 7.d |
| **Chapter 5** | How does the shape of a bird's beak determine what it eats? | 214 | 7.c |
| | How can your population have the strongest, longest-lasting survivors? *Try at Home* | 228 | 3.a, 7.a |
| **Chapter 6** | How do fossils form? | 249 | 3.c, 7.d |
| | How can you use a dichotomous key? *Try at Home* | 264 | 3.d, 7.d |
| **Chapter 7** | How does Earth change over time? *Try at Home* | 292 | 7.d |
| **Chapter 8** | What makes the best fossils? | 327 | 7.d |
| | What happened here? *Try at Home* | 340 | 7.c |
| **Chapter 9** | How do bones and muscles interact? *Try at Home* | 366 | 5.c, 7.a |
| **Chapter 10** | How does the cardiopulmonary system work? *Try at Home* | 412 | 5.b, 6.j, 7.a |
| **Chapter 11** | Why does the pencil look broken? *Try at Home* | 438 | 6.c |
| | How does the image change? | 444 | 6.d |
| | How do you see colors in the dark? *Try at Home* | 454 | 5.g |
| **Chapter 12** | How does an ear hear? | 489 | 5.g, 7.d |

# Labs

## DataLabs

**California Standards**

| | | | |
|---|---|---|---|
| **Chapter 1** | How can you observe DNA in a cell? | 54 | 1.a, 7.a, 7.c |
| **Chapter 2** | How does your garden grow? (Try at Home) | 96 | 1.c, 7.a |
| **Chapter 3** | How fast do they grow? | 148 | 2.a, 7.c |
| **Chapter 4** | Peas, Anyone? (Try at Home) | 176 | 2.d |
| | Can you see a genotype? | 191 | 2.d |
| **Chapter 5** | How many bird species live near you? (Try at Home) | 229 | 7.c |
| **Chapter 6** | Data Collection | 255 | 3.c |
| **Chapter 7** | How long until it's all gone? | 300 | 7.c |
| **Chapter 8** | Which organisms return first following a catastrophic event? (Try at Home) | 324 | 7.c |
| **Chapter 9** | What is the mechanical advantage of a lever? | 376 | 6.i, 7.d |
| **Chapter 10** | How does illness affect the cardiopulmonary system? (Try at Home) | 404 | 5.b, 7.c |
| **Chapter 11** | Can you identify waves in the electromagnetic spectrum? (Try at Home) | 434 | 6.a |
| **Chapter 12** | How loud and how low can you go? (Try at Home) | 477 | 5.g, 7.b |
| **Chapter 13** | Which hormones control ovulation? (Try at Home) | 509 | 5.d, 7.a |
| | Can folic acid prevent birth defects? (Try at Home) | 402 | 5.e, 7.a |

(Try at Home) **This lab might be performed at home.**

# Math and Language Arts

*The California Science, Math and Language Arts correlations for these features can be found on the referenced page.*

## Get Ready to Read

**Chapter 1** Preview .......................... 46
**Chapter 2** Identify the Main Idea .............. 86
**Chapter 3** New Vocabulary ................... 124
**Chapter 4** Monitor......................... 170
**Chapter 5** Visualize ....................... 208
**Chapter 6** Questioning .................... 242
**Chapter 7** Make Predictions ................ 282
**Chapter 8** Identify Cause and Effect.......... 314
**Chapter 9** Make Connections................ 358
**Chapter 10** Summarize...................... 390
**Chapter 11** Compare and Contrast ........... 426
**Chapter 12** Make Inferences ................. 470
**Chapter 13** Take Notes ..................... 502

## Target Your Reading

**Chapter 1** .................................. 47
**Chapter 2** .................................. 87
**Chapter 3** ................................. 125
**Chapter 4** ................................. 171
**Chapter 5** ................................. 209
**Chapter 6** ................................. 243
**Chapter 7** ................................. 283
**Chapter 8** ................................. 315
**Chapter 9** ................................. 359
**Chapter 10** ................................. 391
**Chapter 11** ................................. 427
**Chapter 12** ................................. 471
**Chapter 13** ................................. 503

## Applying Math

**Chapter 1** Cell Volume and Surface Area ........ 67
**Chapter 2** Probability and the Cell Cycle ........ 97
**Chapter 3** Life Span Conversions.............. 150
**Chapter 4** Probabilities and Inheritance........ 181
**Chapter 5** The Accommodations of the HMS *Beagle* ...................... 218
**Chapter 6** Converting Time Ranges of Fossils into Years ...................... 261
**Chapter 7** Measuring Mineral Production in California ...................... 301
**Chapter 8** Scientific Notation and Age of Meteorites ...................... 341
**Chapter 9** Degree of Joint Rotation ........... 377
**Chapter 10** Blood Pressure Variations .......... 413
**Chapter 11** Scientific Notation ................ 433
**Chapter 12** City Noise and Bar Graphs ......... 479
**Chapter 13** Hormone Levels and a Box-and-Whisker Plot.............. 514

# A Guide to California Standards

## For Students and Their Families

### What is the purpose of the California Content Standards?

Content standards were designed to encourage the highest achievement of every student, by defining the knowledge, concepts, and skills that students should acquire at each grade level.

## This Guide Contains:

**Science Content Standards, Grade 7 and Correlations . . . xix**

**Math Content Standards, Grade 7 . . . . . . . . . . . . . . . . . . xxv**

**English-Language Arts Content Standards, Grade 7 . . . xxviii**

California State Capitol Building, Sacramento

# California Science Content Standards

## Grade 7 Focus On Life Science

The science curriculum in grade seven emphasizes the study of life sciences. A foundation in modern biological sciences, with an emphasis on molecular biology, is essential for students who will become public school science teachers, college and university science professors and researchers, and specialists in technological fields.

Another definitive reason for a focus on life science in grade seven is the students' own biological and behavioral transition into early adolescence. Young adolescents make decisions that may have an enormous influence on their lives. The study of life science provides a knowledge base on which adolescents can make well-informed and wise decisions about their health and behavior. The relevance of the curriculum to students' lives helps students to maintain an interest in science and to expand their knowledge of the natural sciences. Items within the text that relate to a Science Content Standard will be represented like this:  5.a

## California Science Content Standards
### Correlated to *Focus On Life Science*

| Science Content Standards | Page Numbers |
| --- | --- |
| **Cell Biology** | |
| 1. All living organisms are composed of cells, from just one to many trillions, whose details usually are visible only through a microscope. As a basis for understanding this concept: | |
| **1.a** Students know cells function similarly in all living organisms. | **50–54, 56–63,** 134–159 |
| **1.b** Students know the characteristics that distinguish plant cells from animal cells, including chloroplasts and cell walls. | **58, 61, 62,** 74 |
| **1.c** Students know the nucleus is the repository for genetic information in plant and animal cells. | **54, 60,** 89, 96 |
| **1.d** Students know that mitochondria liberate energy for the work that cells do and that chloroplasts capture sunlight energy for photosynthesis. | 61, **68–72,** 73 |
| **1.e** Students know cells divide to increase their numbers through a process of mitosis, which results in two daughter cells with identical sets of chromosomes. | **88–94,** 153–159, 515 |
| **1.f** Students know that as multicellular organisms develop, their cells differentiate. | **100–102,** 153–159 |

**Bold page numbers** indicate in-depth coverage of standard.

# California Science Content Standards

| Science Content Standards | Page Numbers |
|---|---|
| **Genetics** | |

**2. A typical cell of any organism contains genetic instructions that specify its traits. Those traits may be modified by environmental influences. As a basis for understanding this concept:**

| | | |
|---|---|---|
| **2.a** | Students know the differences between the life cycles and reproduction methods of sexual and asexual organisms. | 126–128, 148, **134–159** |
| **2.b** | Students know sexual reproduction produces offspring that inherit half their genes from each parent. | **126–132**, 173, 175, 178–179, **182–184**, 501 |
| **2.c** | Students know an inherited trait can be determined by one or more genes. | 174–180, **184–188**, 192–193 |
| **2.d** | Students know plant and animal cells contain many thousands of different genes and typically have two copies of every gene. The two copies (or alleles) of the gene may or may not be identical, and one may be dominant in determining the phenotype while the other is recessive. | **175**, 176, **177–179**, 191–193 |
| **2.e** | Students know DNA (deoxyribonucleic acid) is the genetic material of living organisms and is located in the chromosomes of each cell. | 54, **60, 89,** 128–133, 177 |

| **Evolution** | |
|---|---|

**3. Biological evolution accounts for the diversity of species developed through gradual processes over many generations. As a basis for understanding this concept:**

| | | |
|---|---|---|
| **3.a** | Students know both genetic variation and environmental factors are causes of evolution and diversity of organisms. | **215, 220–223,** 241, **257–259** |
| **3.b** | Students know the reasoning used by Charles Darwin in reaching his conclusion that natural selection is the mechanism of evolution. | **210–217** |
| **3.c** | Students know how independent lines of evidence from geology, fossils, and comparative anatomy provide the bases for the theory of evolution. | **244–256** |
| **3.d** | Students know how to construct a simple branching diagram to classify living groups of organisms by shared derived characteristics and how to expand the diagram to include fossil organisms. | 262–263, **264, 266–267** |
| **3.e** | Students know that extinction of a species occurs when the environment changes and the adaptive characteristics of a species are insufficient for its survival. | 219, **224–227, 318–323,** 324, 327 |

**Bold page numbers** indicate in-depth coverage of standard.

# California Science Content Standards

| Science Content Standards | Page Numbers |
| --- | --- |
| **Earth and Life History (Earth Sciences)** | |
| 4. Evidence from rocks allows us to understand the evolution of life on Earth. As a basis for understanding this concept: | |
| 4.a Students know Earth processes today are similar to those that occurred in the past and slow geologic processes have large cumulative effects over long periods of time. | 284–285 |
| 4.b Students know the history of life on Earth has been disrupted by major catastrophic events, such as major volcanic eruptions or the impacts of asteroids. | 318–323, 330–331, 334–337, 339 |
| 4.c Students know that the rock cycle includes the formation of new sediment and rocks and that rocks are often found in layers, with the oldest generally on the bottom. | 246, 249, 286–291 |
| 4.d Students know that evidence from geologic layers and radioactive dating indicates Earth is approximately 4.6 billion years old and that life on this planet has existed for more than 3 billion years. | 293–299 |
| 4.e Students know fossils provide evidence of how life and environmental conditions have changed. | 247–250, 316–317, 325–339 |
| 4.f Students know how movements of Earth's continental and oceanic plates through time, with associated changes in climate and geographic connections, have affected the past and present distribution of organisms. | 257–259 |
| 4.g Students know how to explain significant developments and extinctions of plant and animal life on the geologic time scale. | 316–323, 325–339 |

**Bold page numbers** indicate in-depth coverage of standard.

# California Science Content Standards

| Science Content Standards | Page Numbers |
|---|---|
| **Structure and Function in Living Systems** | |
| **5.** The anatomy and physiology of plants and animals illustrate the complementary nature of structure and function. As a basis for understanding this concept: | |
| **5.a** Students know plants and animals have levels of organization for structure and function, including cells, tissues, organs, organ systems, and the whole organism. | **100–106,** 108–109, **364–365** |
| **5.b** Students know organ systems function because of the contributions of individual organs, tissues, and cells. The failure of any part can affect the entire system. | 106, 108–109, 389, **392–396, 400, 401–402, 410,** 412, 414–415 |
| **5.c** Students know how bones and muscles work together to provide a structural framework for movement. | 357, **360–367** |
| **5.d** Students know how the reproductive organs of the human female and male generate eggs and sperm and how sexual activity may lead to fertilization and pregnancy. | **504–509,** 510–511, **512–513** |
| **5.e** Students know the function of the umbilicus and placenta during pregnancy. | 515–516, **517–523** |
| **5.f** Students know the structures and processes by which flowering plants generate pollen, ovules, seeds, and fruit. | **138–141** |
| **5.g** Students know how to relate the structures of the eye and ear to their functions. | **450–454,** 456, 458–459, 469, **474–476, 482–493** |

**Bold page numbers** indicate in-depth coverage of standard.

# California Science Content Standards

| Science Content Standards | Page Numbers |
|---|---|
| **Physical Principles in Living Systems (Physical Sciences)** | |
| **6. Physical principles underlie biological structures and functions. As a basis for understanding this concept:** | |
| **6.a** Students know visible light is a small band within a very broad electromagnetic spectrum. | **430–431**, 432, 434 |
| **6.b** Students know that for an object to be seen, light emitted by or scattered from it must be detected by the eye. | 431, 441, **450–453** |
| **6.c** Students know light travels in straight lines if the medium it travels through does not change. | **428**, 438–439, **440** |
| **6.d** Students know how simple lenses are used in a magnifying glass, the eye, a camera, a telescope, and a microscope. | 444, 446–448, 451–452, 456 |
| **6.e** Students know that white light is a mixture of many wavelengths (colors) and that retinal cells react differently to different wavelengths. | 425, **439, 454–455** |
| **6.f** Students know light can be reflected, refracted, transmitted, and absorbed by matter. | **435–436, 438, 440–441**, 443–445, 451, 452 |
| **6.g** Students know the angle of reflection of a light beam is equal to the angle of incidence. | **440–441**, 447 |
| **6.h** Students know how to compare joints in the body (wrist, shoulder, thigh) with structures used in machines and simple devices (hinge, ball-and-socket, and sliding joints). | 362–363, 369, 378–379 |
| **6.i** Students know how levers confer mechanical advantage and how the application of this principle applies to the musculoskeletal system. | 368–379 |
| **6.j** Students know that contractions of the heart generate blood pressure and that heart valves prevent backflow of blood in the circulatory system. | 407–409, 412, 414–415 |

**Bold page numbers** indicate in-depth coverage of standard.

# California Science
# Content Standards

| Science Content Standards | Page Numbers |
|---|---|
| **Investigation and Experimentation** | |
| 7. Scientific progress is made by asking meaningful questions and conducting careful investigations. As a basis for understanding this concept and addressing the content in the other three strands, students should develop their own questions and perform investigations. Students will: | |
| **7.a** Select and use appropriate tools and technology (including calculators, computers, balances, spring scales, microscopes, and binoculars) to perform tests, collect data, and display data. | 7–13, 17, 31, 38, 39, 41, **54, 74–75, 96, 158–159, 192–193, 228, 342,** 357, **366, 378–379, 412, 414–415, 509, 519, 522–523** |
| **7.b** Use a variety of print and electronic resources (including the World Wide Web) to collect information and evidence as part of a research project. | 13, 17–19, 77, 110–111, 160–161, **192–193,** 194, **230–231,** 268–269, 477, **490–491, 522–525** |
| **7.c** Communicate the logical connection among hypotheses, science concepts, tests conducted, data collected, and conclusions drawn from the scientific evidence. | 5, 6, 14–16, 20–21, 28–33, 36–41, 54, **73–75, 158–159,** 169, **192–193, 214, 229, 230–231,** 268–269, 300, **302–303, 324,** 308, **378–379,** 389, 402, **404, 414–415, 477, 490–491, 522–523,** 591 |
| **7.d** Construct scale models, maps, and appropriately labeled diagrams to communicate scientific knowledge (e.g., motion of Earth's plates and cell structure). | 11, 23, **74–75,** 103, **108–109, 132, 138, 249,** 268–269, 292, **302–303, 327, 342, 376, 378–379, 489,** 522–523 |
| **7.e** Communicate the steps and results from an investigation in written reports and oral presentations. | 20–21, 28–33, **74–75, 108–109, 158–159, 192–193,** 268–269, **414–415,** 469, 490–491 |

**Bold page numbers** indicate in-depth coverage of standard.

# California Math Content Standards

Items within the text that relate to a Math Content Standard will be represented like this: **MA7: NS 1.0**

## Number Sense

**MA7: NS 1.0** Students know the properties of, and compute with, rational numbers expressed in a variety of forms:

**MA7: NS 1.1** Read, write, and compare rational numbers in scientific notation (positive and negative powers of 10) with approximate numbers using scientific notation.

**MA7: NS 1.2** Add, subtract, multiply, and divide rational numbers (integers, fractions, and terminating decimals) and take positive rational numbers to whole-number powers.

**MA7: NS 1.3** Convert fractions to decimals and percents and use these representations in estimations, computations, and applications.

**MA7: NS 1.4** Differentiate between rational and irrational numbers.

**MA7: NS 1.5** Know that every rational number is either a terminating or repeating decimal and be able to convert terminating decimals into reduced fractions.

**MA7: NS 1.6** Calculate the percentage of increases and decreases of a quantity.

**MA7: NS 1.7** Solve problems that involve discounts, markups, commissions, and profit and compute simple and compound interest.

**MA7: NS 2.0** Students use exponents, powers, and roots and use exponents in working with fractions:

**MA7: NS 2.1** Understand negative whole-number exponents. Multiply and divide expressions involving exponents with a common base.

**MA7: NS 2.2** Add and subtract fractions by using factoring to find common denominators.

**MA7: NS 2.3** Multiply, divide, and simplify rational numbers by using exponent rules.

**MA7: NS 2.4** Use the inverse relationship between raising to a power and extracting the root of a perfect square integer; for an integer that is not square, determine without a calculator the two integers between which its square root lies and explain why.

**MA7: NS 2.5** Understand the meaning of the absolute value of a number; interpret the absolute value as the distance of the number from zero on a number line; and determine the absolute value of real numbers.

## Algebra and Functions

**MA7: AF 1.0** Students express quantitative relationships by using algebraic terminology, expressions, equations, inequalities, and graphs:

**MA7: AF 1.1** Use variables and appropriate operations to write an expression, an equation, an inequality, or a system of equations or inequalities that represents a verbal description (e.g., three less than a number, half as large as area A).

**MA7: AF 1.2** Use the correct order of operations to evaluate algebraic expressions such as $3(2x + 5)^2$.

**MA7: AF 1.3** Simplify numerical expressions by applying properties of rational numbers (e.g., identity, inverse, distributive, associative, commutative) and justify the process used.

**MA7: AF 1.4** Use algebraic terminology (e.g., variable, equation, term, coefficient, inequality, expression, constant) correctly.

**MA7: AF 1.5** Represent quantitative relationships graphically and interpret the meaning of a specific part of a graph in the situation represented by the graph.

**MA7: AF 2.0** Students interpret and evaluate expressions involving integer powers and simple roots:

**MA7: AF 2.1** Interpret positive whole-number powers as repeated multiplication and negative whole-number powers as repeated division or multiplication by the multiplicative inverse. Simplify and evaluate expressions that include exponents.

**MA7: AF 2.2** Multiply and divide monomials; extend the process of taking powers and extracting roots to monomials when the latter results in a monomial with an integer exponent.

**MA7: AF 3.0** Students graph and interpret linear and some nonlinear functions:

**MA7: AF 3.1** Graph functions of the form $y = nx^2$ and $y = nx^3$ and use in solving problems.

**MA7: AF 3.2** Plot the values from the volumes of three-dimensional shapes for various values of the edge lengths (e.g., cubes with varying edge lengths or a triangle prism with a fixed height and an equilateral triangle base of varying lengths).

# California Math Content Standards

**MA7: AF 3.3** Graph linear functions, noting that the vertical change (change in y-value) per unit of horizontal change (change in x-value) is always the same and know that the ratio ("rise over run") is called the slope of a graph.

**MA7: AF 3.4** Plot the values of quantities whose ratios are always the same (e.g., cost to the number of an item, feet to inches, circumference to diameter of a circle). Fit a line to the plot and understand that the slope of the line equals the quantities.

**MA7: AF 4.0 Students solve simple linear equations and inequalities over the rational numbers:**

**MA7: AF 4.1** Solve two-step linear equations and inequalities in one variable over the rational numbers, interpret the solution or solutions in the context from which they arose, and verify the reasonableness of the results.

**MA7: AF 4.2** Solve multistep problems involving rate, average speed, distance, and time or a direct variation.

## Measurement and Geometry

**MA7: MG 1.0 Students choose appropriate units of measure and use ratios to convert within and between measurement systems to solve problems:**

**MA7: MG 1.1** Compare weights, capacities, geometric measures, times, and temperatures within and between measurement systems (e.g., miles per hour and feet per second, cubic inches to cubic centimeters).

**MA7: MG 1.2** Construct and read drawings and models made to scale.

**MA7: MG 1.3** Use measures expressed as rates (e.g., speed, density) and measures expressed as products (e.g., person-days) to solve problems; check the units of the solutions; and use dimensional analysis to check the reasonableness of the answer.

**MA7: MG 2.0 Students compute the perimeter, area, and volume of common geometric objects and use the results to find measures of less common objects. They know how perimeter, area, and volume are affected by changes of scale:**

**MA7: MG 2.1** Use formulas routinely for finding the perimeter and area of basic two-dimensional figures and the surface area and volume of basic three-dimensional figures, including rectangles, parallelograms, trapezoids, squares, triangles, circles, prisms, and cylinders.

**MA7: MG 2.2** Estimate and compute the area of more complex or irregular two-and three-dimensional figures by breaking the figures down into more basic geometric objects.

**MA7: MG 2.3** Compute the length of the perimeter, the surface area of the faces, and the volume of a three-dimensional object built from rectangular solids. Understand that when the lengths of all dimensions are multiplied by a scale factor, the surface area is multiplied by the square of the scale factor and the volume is multiplied by the cube of the scale factor.

**MA7: MG 2.4** Relate the changes in measurement with a change of scale to the units used (e.g., square inches, cubic feet) and to conversions between units (1 square foot = 144 square inches or $[1 \text{ ft}^2] = [144 \text{ in}^2]$, 1 cubic inch is approximately 16.38 cubic centimeters or $[1 \text{ in}^3] = [16.38 \text{ cm}^3]$).

**MA7: MG 3.0 Students know the Pythagorean theorem and deepen their understanding of plane and solid geometric shapes by constructing figures that meet given conditions and by identifying attributes of figures:**

**MA7: MG 3.1** Identify and construct basic elements of geometric figures (e.g., altitudes, midpoints, diagonals, angle bisectors, and perpendicular bisectors; central angles, radii, diameters, and chords of circles) by using a compass and straightedge.

**MA7: MG 3.2** Understand and use coordinate graphs to plot simple figures, determine lengths and areas related to them, and determine their image under translations and reflections.

**MA7: MG 3.3** Know and understand the Pythagorean theorem and its converse and use it to find the length of the missing side of a right triangle and the lengths of other line segments and, in some situations, empirically verify the Pythagorean theorem by direct measurement.

**MA7: MG 3.4** Demonstrate an understanding of conditions that indicate two geometrical figures are congruent and what congruence means about the relationships between the sides and angles of the two figures.

**MA7: MG 3.5** Construct two-dimensional patterns for three-dimensional models, such as cylinders, prisms, and cones.

# California Math Content Standards

**MA7: MG 3.6** Identify elements of three-dimensional geometric objects (e.g., diagonals of rectangular solids) and describe how two or more objects are related in space (e.g., skew lines, the possible ways three planes might intersect).

## Statistics, Data Analysis, and Probability

**MA7: SP 1.0 Students collect, organize, and represent data sets that have one or more variables and identify relationships among variables within a data set by hand and through the use of an electronic spreadsheet software program:**

**MA7: SP 1.1** Know various forms of display for data sets, including a stem-and-leaf plot or box-and-whisker plot; use the forms to display a single set of data or to compare two sets of data.

**MA7: SP 1.2** Represent two numerical variables on a scatterplot and informally describe how the data points are distributed and any apparent relationship that exists between the two variables (e.g., between time spent on homework and grade level).

**MA7: SP 1.3** Understand the meaning of, and be able to compute, the minimum, the lower quartile, the median, the upper quartile, and the maximum of a data set.

## Mathematical Reasoning

**MA7: MR 1.0 Students make decisions about how to approach problems:**

**MA7: MR 1.1** Analyze problems by identifying relationships, distinguishing relevant from irrelevant information, identifying missing information, sequencing and prioritizing information, and observing patterns.

**MA7: MR 1.2** Formulate and justify mathematical conjectures based on a general description of the mathematical question or problem posed.

**MA7: MR 1.3** Determine when and how to break a problem into simpler parts.

**MA7: MR 2.0 Students use strategies, skills, and concepts in finding solutions:**

**MA7: MR 2.1** Use estimation to verify the reasonableness of calculated results.

**MA7: MR 2.2** Apply strategies and results from simpler problems to more complex problems.

**MA7: MR 2.3** Estimate unknown quantities graphically and solve for them by using logical reasoning and arithmetic and algebraic techniques.

**MA7: MR 2.4** Make and test conjectures by using both inductive and deductive reasoning.

**MA7: MR 2.5** Use a variety of methods, such as words, numbers, symbols, charts, graphs, tables, diagrams, and models, to explain mathematical reasoning.

**MA7: MR 2.6** Express the solution clearly and logically by using the appropriate mathematical notation and terms and clear language; support solutions with evidence in both verbal and symbolic work.

**MA7: MR 2.7** Indicate the relative advantages of exact and approximate solutions to problems and give answers to a specified degree of accuracy.

**MA7: MR 2.8** Make precise calculations and check the validity of the results from the context of the problem.

**MA7: MR 3.0 Students determine a solution is complete and move beyond a particular problem by generalizing to other situations:**

**MA7: MR 3.1** Evaluate the reasonableness of the solution in the context of the original situation.

**MA7: MR 3.2** Note the method of deriving the solution and demonstrate a conceptual understanding of the derivation by solving similar problems.

**MA7: MR 3.3** Develop generalizations of the results obtained and the strategies used and apply them to new problem situations.

# California English-Language Arts Content Standards

Items within the text that relate to an English-Language Arts Content Standard will be represented like this: **ELA7: R 1.4**

## Reading

### ELA7: R 1.0 Word Analysis, Fluency, and Systematic Vocabulary Development

#### Vocabulary and Concept Development

**ELA7: R 1.1** Identify idioms, analogies, metaphors, and similes in prose and poetry.

**ELA7: R 1.2** Use knowledge of Greek, Latin, and Anglo-Saxon roots and affixes to understand content-area vocabulary.

**ELA7: R 1.3** Clarify word meanings through the use of definition, example, restatement, or contrast.

### ELA7: R 2.0 Reading Comprehension (Focus on Informational Materials)

#### Structural Features of Informational Materials

**ELA7: R 2.1** Understand and analyze the differences in structure and purpose between various categories of informational materials (e.g., textbooks, newspapers, instructional manuals, signs).

**ELA7: R 2.2** Locate information by using a variety of consumer, workplace, and public documents.

**ELA7: R 2.3** Analyze text that uses the cause-and-effect organizational pattern.

#### Comprehension and Analysis of Grade-Level-Appropriate Text

**ELA7: R 2.4** Identify and trace the development of an author's argument, point of view, or perspective in text.

**ELA7: R 2.5** Understand and explain the use of a simple mechanical device by following technical directions.

#### Expository Critique

**ELA7: R 2.6** Assess the adequacy, accuracy, and appropriateness of the author's evidence to support claims and assertions, noting instances of bias and stereotyping.

### ELA7: R 3.0 Literary Response and Analysis

#### Structural Features of Literature

**ELA7: R 3.1** Articulate the expressed purposes and characteristics of different forms of prose (e.g., short story, novel, novella, essay).

#### Narrative Analysis of Grade-Level-Appropriate Text

**ELA7: R 3.2** Identify events that advance the plot and determine how each event explains past or present action(s) or foreshadows future action(s).

**ELA7: R 3.3** Analyze characterization as delineated through a character's thoughts, words, speech patterns, and actions; the narrator's description; and the thoughts, words, and actions of other characters.

**ELA7: R 3.4** Identify and analyze recurring themes across works (e.g., the value of bravery, loyalty, and friendship; the effects of loneliness).

**ELA7: R 3.5** Contrast points of view (e.g., first and third person, limited and omniscient, subjective and objective) in narrative text and explain how they affect the overall theme of the work.

#### Literary Criticism

**ELA7: R 3.6** Analyze a range of responses to a literary work and determine the extent to which the literary elements in the work shaped those responses.

## Writing

### ELA7: W 1.0 Writing Strategies

#### Organization and Focus

**ELA7: W 1.1** Create an organizational structure that balances all aspects of the composition and uses effective transitions between sentences to unify important ideas.

**ELA7: W 1.2** Support all statements and claims with anecdotes, descriptions, facts and statistics, and specific examples.

**ELA7: W 1.3** Use strategies of note taking, outlining, and summarizing to impose structure on composition drafts.

#### Research and Technology

**ELA7: W 1.4** Identify topics; ask and evaluate questions; and develop ideas leading to inquiry, investigation, and research.

**ELA7: W 1.5** Give credit for both quoted and paraphrased information in a bibliography by using a consistent and sanctioned format and methodology for citations.

**ELA7: W 1.6** Create documents by using word-processing skills and publishing programs; develop simple databases and spreadsheets to manage information and prepare reports.

#### Evaluation and Revision

**ELA7: W 1.7** Revise writing to improve organization and word choice after checking the logic of the ideas and the precision of the vocabulary.

### ELA7: W 2.0 Writing Applications (Genres and Their Characteristics) Using the writing strategies of grade seven outlined in Writing Standard 1.0, students:

**ELA7: W 2.1** Write fictional or autobiographical narratives:

   a. Develop a standard plot line (having a beginning, conflict, rising action, climax, and denouement) and point of view.

   b. Develop complex major and minor characters and a definite setting.

   c. Use a range of appropriate strategies (e.g., dialogue; suspense; naming of specific narrative action, including movement, gestures, and expressions).

**ELA7: W 2.2** Write responses to literature:

   a. Develop interpretations exhibiting careful reading, understanding, and insight.

   b. Organize interpretations around several clear ideas, premises, or images from the literary work.

   c. Justify interpretations through sustained use of examples and textual evidence.

**ELA7: W 2.3** Write research reports:

   a. Pose relevant and tightly drawn questions about the topic.

   b. Convey clear and accurate perspectives on the subject.

c. Include evidence compiled through the formal research process (e.g., use of a card catalog, Reader's Guide to Periodical Literature, a computer catalog, magazines, newspapers, dictionaries).

d. Document reference sources by means of footnotes and a bibliography

**ELA7: W 2.4**   Write persuasive compositions:

a. State a clear position or perspective in support of a proposition or proposal.

b. Describe the points in support of the proposition, employing well-articulated evidence.

c. Anticipate and address reader concerns and counterarguments.

**ELA7: W 2.5**   Write summaries of reading materials:

a. Include the main ideas and most significant details.

b. Use the student's own words, except for quotations.

c. Reflect underlying meaning, not just the superficial details.

## Written and Oral English Language Conventions

### ELA7: WO 1.0   Written and Oral English Language Conventions

#### Sentence Structure

**ELA7: WO 1.1**   Place modifiers properly and use the active voice.

#### Grammar

**ELA7: WO 1.2**   Identify and use infinitives and participles and make clear references between pronouns and antecedents.

**ELA7: WO 1.3**   Identify all parts of speech and types and structure of sentences.

**ELA7: WO 1.4**   Demonstrate the mechanics of writing (e.g., quotation marks, commas at end of dependent clauses) and appropriate English usage (e.g., pronoun reference).

#### Punctuation

**ELA7: WO 1.5**   Identify hyphens, dashes, brackets, and semicolons and use them correctly.

#### Capitalization

**ELA7: WO 1.6**   Use correct capitalization.

#### Spelling

**ELA7: WO 1.7**   Spell derivatives correctly by applying the spellings of bases and affixes.

## Listening and Speaking

### ELA7: LS 1.0   Listening and Speaking Strategies

#### Comprehension

**ELA7: LS 1.1**   Ask probing questions to elicit information, including evidence to support the speaker's claims and conclusions.

**ELA7: LS 1.2**   Determine the speaker's attitude toward the subject.

**ELA7: LS 1.3**   Respond to persuasive messages with questions, challenges, or affirmations.

#### Organization and Delivery of Oral Communication

**ELA7: LS 1.4**   Organize information to achieve particular purposes and to appeal to the background and interests of the audience.

**ELA7: LS 1.5**   Arrange supporting details, reasons, descriptions, and examples effectively and persuasively in relation to the audience.

**ELA7: LS 1.6**   Use speaking techniques, including voice modulation, inflection, tempo, enunciation, and eye contact, for effective presentations.

#### Analysis and Evaluation of Oral and Media Communications

**ELA7: LS 1.7**   Provide constructive feedback to speakers concerning the coherence and logic of a speech's content and delivery and its overall impact upon the listener.

**ELA7: LS 1.8**   Analyze the effect on the viewer of images, text, and sound in electronic journalism; identify the techniques used to achieve the effects in each instance studied.

### ELA7: LS 2.0   Speaking Applications (Genres and Their Characteristics) Using the speaking strategies of grade seven outlined in Listening and Speaking Standard 1.0, students:

**ELA7: LS 2.1**   Deliver narrative presentations:

a. Establish a context, standard plot line (having a beginning, conflict, rising action, climax, and denouement), and point of view.

b. Describe complex major and minor characters and a definite setting.

c. Use a range of appropriate strategies, including dialogue, suspense, and naming of specific narrative action (e.g., movement, gestures, expressions).

**ELA7: LS 2.2**   Deliver oral summaries of articles and books:

a. Include the main ideas of the event or article and the most significant details.

b. Use the student's own words, except for material quoted from sources.

c. Convey a comprehensive understanding of sources, not just superficial details.

**ELA7: LS 2.3**   Deliver research presentations:

a. Pose relevant and concise questions about the topic.

b. Convey clear and accurate perspectives on the subject.

c. Include evidence generated through the formal research process (e.g., use of a card catalog, Reader's Guide to Periodical Literature, computer databases, magazines, newspapers, dictionaries).

d. Cite reference sources appropriately.

**ELA7: LS 2.4**   Deliver persuasive presentations:

a. State a clear position or perspective in support of an argument or proposal.

b. Describe the points in support of the argument and employ well-articulated evidence.

# Reading for Information

When you read *Focus On Life Science*, you are reading for information. Science is nonfiction writing—it describes real-life events, people, ideas, and technology. Here are some tools that *Focus On Life Science* has to help you read.

## Before You Read

By reading **The BIG Idea** and **Main Idea** prior to reading the chapter or lesson, you will get a preview of the coming material.

On the first page of each chapter you will find **The BIG Idea**. The Big Idea is a sentence that describes what you will learn about in the chapter.

### CHAPTER 10

# The Cardiopulmonary System and Pressure

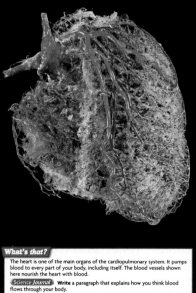

**The BIG Idea**
The pulmonary-circulatory system, driven by pressure generated by the heart, functions as a whole to supply oxygen to and remove carbon dioxide from your cells.

**LESSON 1** 3.b, 7.c
The Pulmonary-Circulatory System
**Main Idea** The pulmonary and circulatory systems work together to transport oxygen to your cells and to remove carbon dioxide from your cells.

**LESSON 2**
3.b, 6.j, 7.a, 7.c, 7.e
**Pressure and the Body**
**Main Idea** Pressure allows us to breathe and keeps blood flowing throughout the circulatory system.

**What's that?**
The heart is one of the main organs of the cardiopulmonary system. It pumps blood to every part of your body, including itself. The blood vessels shown here nourish the heart with blood.
**Science Journal** Write a paragraph that explains how you think blood flows through your body.

388

Source: Chapter 10, p. 388

**The BIG Idea** is divided into Main Ideas. Each lesson of the chapter has a **Main Idea** that describes the focus of the lesson.

### LESSON 1

**Science Content Standards**
**3.b** Students know organ systems function because of the contributions of individual organs, tissues, and cells. The failure of any part can affect the entire system.
**7.c** Communicate the logical connection among hypotheses, science concepts, tests conducted, data collected, and conclusions drawn from the scientific evidence.

**Reading Guide**

**What *You'll* Learn**
▶ **Investigate** the pulmonary and circulatory systems.
▶ **Describe** the interaction of the pulmonary and circulatory systems.
▶ **Explain** how problems can occur in the pulmonary and circulatory systems.

**Why *It's Important***
Understanding how these systems work will help you decrease your risks for diseases.

**Vocabulary**
| | |
|---|---|
| pulmonary system | atrium |
| breathing | ventricle |
| lungs | artery |
| pneumonia | capillary |
| suffocation | vein |
| asthma | heart attack |
| circulatory system | stroke |
| | heart |

**Review Vocabulary**
**respiration:** a series of chemical reactions that transforms the energy in food molecules to usable cellular energy (p. 68)

## The Pulmonary-Circulatory System

**Main Idea** The pulmonary and circulatory systems work together to transport oxygen to your cells and to remove carbon dioxide from your cells.

**Real-World Reading Connection** Take a deep breath. Notice how your chest expands. Every time you breathe, air enters and exits your lungs. At the same time, your heart is constantly beating. How do these events happen and why are they necessary for survival?

### The Pulmonary System

You may already know that we, like all animals, need oxygen to live. We get oxygen from the air we breathe. We also need to rid our bodies of carbon dioxide. Recall from Chapter 1 that carbon dioxide is a waste product of cellular respiration. How do we take in oxygen and remove carbon dioxide? Our **pulmonary system** (PUL muh nar ee • SIHS tehm) contains tissues and organs specialized for taking in oxygen and removing carbon dioxide from our bodies and for exchanging oxygen and carbon dioxide. The pulmonary system is also often referred to as the respiratory system. **Figure 1** highlights the organs and tissues of the pulmonary system. Take a deep breath. Think about where you feel the air moving through your body. Look at **Figure 1** and trace the path you think the air follows.

**Figure 1** The pulmonary system includes all the passageways that bring air in and out of the body.

Right lung
Left lung
Heart

392 Chapter 10

Source: Chapter 10, Lesson 1, p. 392

## Other Ways to Preview

- Read the chapter title to find out what area of science you will study.

- Skim the photo, illustrations, captions, graphs, and tables.

- Look for key terms that are boldfaced and highlighted.

# Reading for Information

The Get Ready to Read section allows you to learn, practice, and apply a reading skill before you start reading the chapter's first lesson. Target Your Reading will help you keep the main idea in focus as you read the chapter.

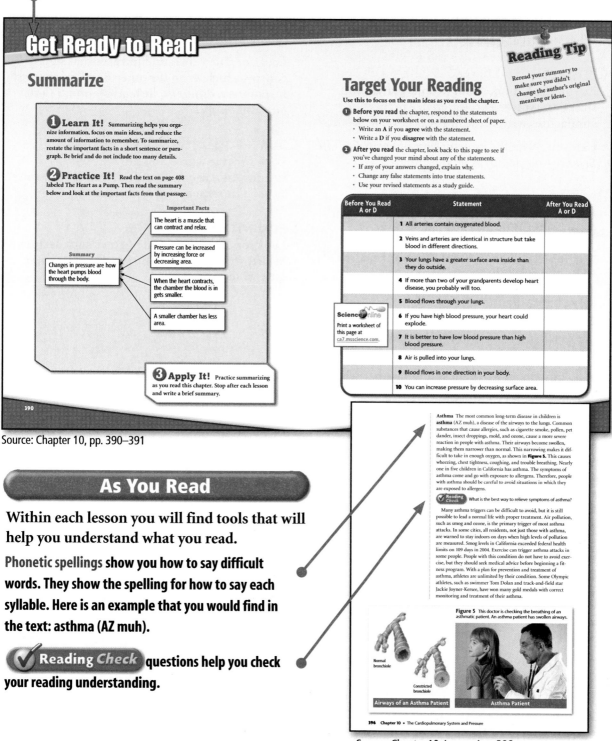

## Get Ready to Read

### Summarize

**1 Learn It!** Summarizing helps you organize information, focus on main ideas, and reduce the amount of information to remember. To summarize, restate the important facts in a short sentence or paragraph. Be brief and do not include too many details.

**2 Practice It!** Read the text on page 408 labeled The Heart as a Pump. Then read the summary below and look at the important facts from that passage.

**Important Facts**

The heart is a muscle that can contract and relax.

Pressure can be increased by increasing force or decreasing area.

When the heart contracts, the chamber the blood is in gets smaller.

A smaller chamber has less area.

**Summary**

Changes in pressure are how the heart pumps blood through the body.

**3 Apply It!** Practice summarizing as you read this chapter. Stop after each lesson and write a brief summary.

390

### Reading Tip

Reread your summary to make sure you didn't change the author's original meaning or ideas.

### Target Your Reading

Use this to focus on the main ideas as you read the chapter.

**1 Before you read** the chapter, respond to the statements below on your worksheet or on a numbered sheet of paper.
- Write an **A** if you **agree** with the statement.
- Write a **D** if you **disagree** with the statement.

**2 After you read** the chapter, look back to this page to see if you've changed your mind about any of the statements.
- If any of your answers changed, explain why.
- Change any false statements into true statements.
- Use your revised statements as a study guide.

**Science Online**
Print a worksheet of this page at ca7.msscience.com.

| Before You Read A or D | Statement | After You Read A or D |
|---|---|---|
| | **1** All arteries contain oxygenated blood. | |
| | **2** Veins and arteries are identical in structure but take blood in different directions. | |
| | **3** Your lungs have a greater surface area inside than they do outside. | |
| | **4** If more than two of your grandparents develop heart disease, you probably will too. | |
| | **5** Blood flows through your lungs. | |
| | **6** If you have high blood pressure, your heart could explode. | |
| | **7** It is better to have low blood pressure than high blood pressure. | |
| | **8** Air is pulled into your lungs. | |
| | **9** Blood flows in one direction in your body. | |
| | **10** You can increase pressure by decreasing surface area. | |

Source: Chapter 10, pp. 390–391

## As You Read

Within each lesson you will find tools that will help you understand what you read.

**Phonetic spellings** show you how to say difficult words. They show the spelling for how to say each syllable. Here is an example that you would find in the text: asthma (AZ muh).

✔ **Reading Check** questions help you check your reading understanding.

**Asthma** The most common long-term disease in children is **asthma** (AZ muh), a disease of the airways to the lungs. Common substances that cause allergies, such as cigarette smoke, pollen, pet dander, insect droppings, mold, and ozone, cause a more severe reaction in people with asthma. Their airways become swollen, making them narrower than normal. This narrowing makes it difficult to take in enough oxygen, as shown in **Figure 5**. This causes wheezing, chest tightness, coughing, and trouble breathing. Nearly one in five children in California has asthma. The symptoms of asthma come and go with exposure to allergens. Therefore, people with asthma should be careful to avoid situations in which they are exposed to allergens.

✔ **Reading Check** What is the best way to relieve symptoms of asthma?

Many asthma triggers can be difficult to avoid, but it is still possible to lead a normal life with proper treatment. Air pollution, such as smog and ozone, is the primary trigger of most asthma attacks. In some cities, all residents, not just those with asthma, are warned to stay indoors on days when high levels of pollution are measured. Smog levels in California exceeded federal health limits on 109 days in 2004. Exercise can trigger asthma attacks in some people. People with this condition do not have to avoid exercise, but they should seek medical advice before beginning a fitness program. With a plan for prevention and treatment of asthma, athletes are unlimited by their condition. Some Olympic athletes, such as swimmer Tom Dolan and track-and-field star Jackie Joyner-Kersee, have won many gold medals with correct monitoring and treatment of their asthma.

**Figure 5** This doctor is checking the breathing of an asthmatic patient. An asthma patient has swollen airways.

Normal bronchiole

Constricted bronchiole

**Airways of an Asthma Patient**

**Asthma Patient**

**396** Chapter 10 • The Cardiopulmonary System and Pressure

Source: Chapter 10, Lesson 1, p. 396

# Reading for Information

## Other Skills to Exercise as You Read

### Question
- What is the **Main Idea**?
- What is **The BIG Idea**?

### Connect
- As you read, think about people, places, and situations you've encountered. Are there any similarities with those in *Focus On Life Science*?
- Can you relate the information in *Focus On Life Science* to other areas of your life?

### Predict
- Predict events or outcomes by using clues and information you already know.
- Change your prediction as you read and gather new information.

### Visualize
- Create a picture in your mind about what you are reading. Picture the setting—for example, a laboratory, a roller coaster, or a mountain.
- A mental image can help you remember what you read for a longer time.

### Compare and Contrast Sentences
- Look for clue words and phrases that signal comparison, such as *similar to, just as, both, in common, also,* and *too.*
- Look for clue words and phrases that signal contrast, such as *on the other hand, in contrast to, however, different, instead of, rather than, but,* and *unlike.*

### Cause-and-Effect Sentences
- Look for clue words and phrases such as *because, as a result, therefore, that is why, since, so, for this reason,* and *consequently.*

### Sequential Sentences
- Look for clue words and phrases such as *after, before, first, next, last, during, finally, earlier, later, since,* and *then.*

## After You Read

Follow up your reading with a summary and an assessment of the material to evaluate if you understood the text.

### Summarize
- Describe **The BIG Idea** and how the details support it.
- Describe the **Main Idea** and how the details support it.
- Use your own words to explain what you read.
- Complete the Summary Activity at the end of the lesson.

### Assess
- What was **The BIG Idea**?
- What was the **Main Idea**?
- Did you learn anything new from the material?
- Can you use this new information in other school subjects or at home?
- What other sources could you use to find out more information about the topic?

# Previewing Your Textbook

Follow the tour through the next few pages to learn about using your textbook, *Focus On Life Science*. This tour will help you understand what you will discover as you read *Focus On Life Science*. Before you begin reading, take the tour so that you are familiar with how this textbook works.

## Unit Preview

**West-Coast Events Time Line** See significant events that occurred on the West Coast of the United States and compare them to events that occurred around the world.

**World Events Time Line** See significant events that occurred around the world and compare them to events that occurred on the West Coast.

**Science Online** A visual reminder to explore online tools to learn more about a scientist's career.

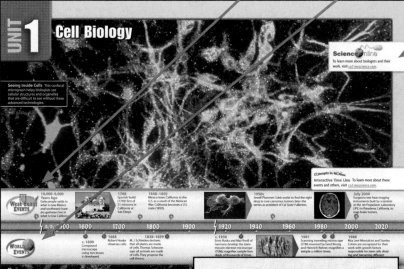

Source: Unit 1, pp. 42–43

## Unit Review

**Reading on Your Own** a listing of books recommended by the California State Board of Education

**Unit Test** multiple-choice questions and written-response questions that review the unit

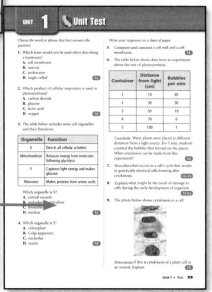

Source: Unit 1, pp. 118–119

# Previewing Your Textbook

## Chapters

**The BIG Idea** The Big Idea is a sentence that describes what you will learn about in the chapter.

**Main Idea** The Main Ideas support the Big Idea. Each lesson of the chapter has a Main Idea that describes the focus of the lesson.

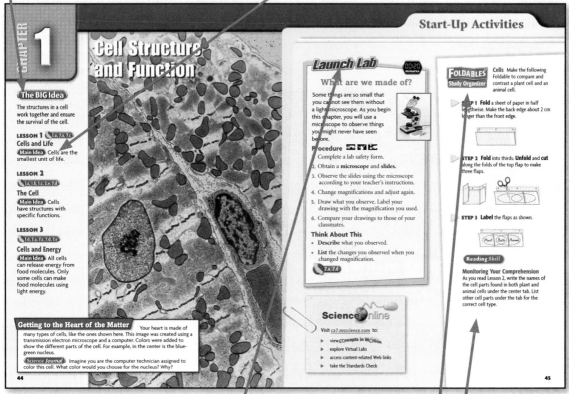

Source: Chapter 1, pp. 44–45

**Launch Lab** a short investigation that introduces the chapter's subject

**Foldables™ Study Organizer** an easy way to take notes as you read the chapter and a valuable tool for review

**Reading Skill** This is a reading skill that you will practice throughout the chapter.

# Previewing Your Textbook

## Lessons

**Main Idea** The Big Idea is supported by Main Ideas. Each lesson of the chapter has a Main Idea that describes the focus of the lesson.

**Science Content Standards** a listing of the California Science Content Standards that are covered within the lesson

 **Reading Check** a question that tests your reading comprehension

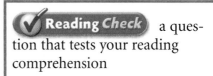 **Visual Check and Caption Questions** questions found throughout the lesson about important graphs, photos, or illustrations

### LESSON 1

 **Science Content Standards**

**1.a** Students know cells function similarly in all living organisms.
**7.a** Select and use appropriate tools and technology (including calculators, computers, balances, spring scales, microscopes, and binoculars) to perform tests, collect data, and display data.
**7.c** Communicate the logical connection among hypotheses, science concepts, tests conducted, data collected, and conclusions drawn from the scientific evidence.

**Reading Guide**

**What You'll Learn**
▶ **Summarize** the cell theory.
▶ **Identify** the characteristics of life.
▶ **Explain** the importance of water in a cell.
▶ **Describe** the four basic substances of a cell.

**Why It's Important**
Learning about cells will help you understand how living organisms function.

**Vocabulary**
light microscope
cell theory
homeostasis
protein
nucleic acid
lipid
carbohydrate

**Review Vocabulary**
**cell:** basic structural and functional unit of all organisms (Grade 5)

#### Cells and Life

**Main Idea** Cells are the smallest unit of life.

**Real-World Reading Connection** People once thought Earth was flat because they did not have tools to discover that it is round. People also had many wrong ideas about living things on Earth. They did not have the tools to observe very small living things.

**Early Ideas About Cells**

Most cells are so small, as shown in **Figure 1**, that you cannot see them without some type of magnifying device. There even was a time when people did not know that cells existed. People also once believed that an egg contained a miniature version of an adult organism. They thought the organism's structures just had to increase in size as the organism grew.

**Early Microscopes**

After the invention of the light microscope, around 1600, ideas about living things changed. A **light microscope** uses light and has one or more lenses that enlarges an image of something.

**Figure 1 Cell Size** Most cells can only be seen using some type of microscope.

Electron microscope

| 0.1 nm | 1 nm | 10 nm | 100 nm |

Atoms
Amino acids
DNA
Viruses

1 billion nanometers (nm) = 1 meter
1 million micrometers (μm) = 1 meter
100 centimeters (cm) = 1 meter
1,000 meters (m) = 1 kilometer (km)

**48** Chapter 1 • Cell Structure and Function

Source: Chapter 1, Lesson 1, p. 48

## Lesson Review

**What have you learned about cells and life?**

You have read in this lesson that

• a light microscope is needed to see most cells;
• a cell is the smallest unit of a living organism;
• the cell theory was developed after many observations by scientists;
• for something to be a living thing, it must have all the characteristics of life;
• all living things depend on water for their survival; and
• cells contain four basic substances—proteins, nucleic acids, lipids, and carbohydrates.

### LESSON 1 Review

**Summarize**

Create your own lesson summary as you organize an **outline**.

1. **Scan** the lesson. Find and list the first red main heading.
2. **Review** the text after the heading and list 2–3 details about the heading.
3. **Find** and list each **blue** subheading that follows the red main heading.
4. **List** 2–3 details, key terms, and definitions under each **blue** subheading.
5. **Review** additional red main headings and their supporting **blue** subheadings. List 2–3 details about each.

**ELA7: W 2.5**

**Using Vocabulary**

1. Use the term *homeostasis* in a sentence. **1a**
2. Distinguish between ribonucleic acid and a protein. **1a**

**Understanding Main Ideas**

3. Which characteristic of life is shown when you squint in bright light? **1a**
   A. growth and development
   B. reproduction
   C. organization
   D. responses
4. **Assess** the importance of the invention of the microscope to science. **1a**
5. **Summarize** the cell theory in your own words. **1a**
6. **Give** an example for each of the four basic substances of a cell. **1a**

**Standards Check**

7. **Explain** why water is important to cells. **1a**

**Applying Science**

8. **Critique** the following statement: A kite is a living thing. **1a**
9. **Organize** Copy and fill in the graphic organizer below. In each of the smaller ovals, list a characteristic of life. **1a**

Characteristics of Life

 **Science Online**
For more practice, visit **Standards Check** at ca7.mssscience.com.

Lesson 1 • Cells and Life **55**

Source: Chapter 1, Lesson 1, p. 55

**Summarize** Use this exercise to help you create your own summary of the lesson's content.

**Self Check** A series of questions to check your understanding of the lesson's material.

# Previewing Your Textbook

## Hands-On Science

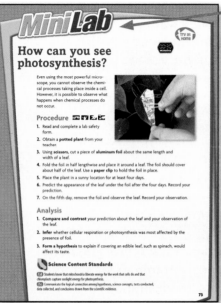

Source: Chapter 1, p. 73

**MiniLab** These investigations emphasize the lesson's content. MiniLabs are located in either a margin, like the one shown here, or on a full page. The California Science Content Standards that correlate to the material are listed.

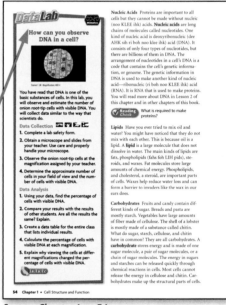

Source: Chapter 1, p. 54

**DataLab** These investigations emphasize the lesson's content by using mathematical analysis. DataLabs are located in either a margin or on a full page, as shown here. The California Science Content Standards and the California Mathematics Content Standards that correlate to the material are listed.

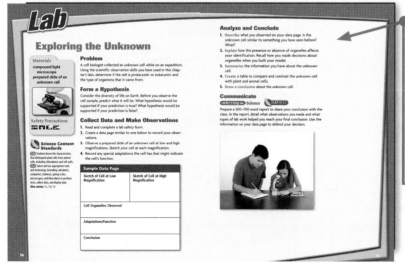

Source: Chapter 1, pp. 74–75

**Lab** Full-length investigations emphasize the chapter's content. Included are Labs, Design Your Own Labs or Use the Internet Labs. The California Science Content Standards that correlate to the material are listed.

# Previewing Your Textbook

## Special Features

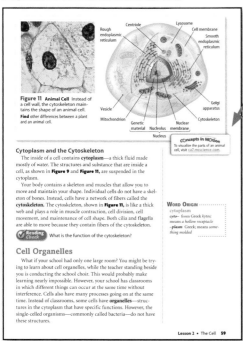

Source: Chapter 1, Lesson 2, p. 59

**Concepts in Motion** interactive art or diagrams that can be accessed through the Glencoe Web site to help you build understanding of concepts

**Real-World Science** Four connections with science are made in this feature: Science and Career, Science and Technology, Science and History, and Science and Society. These four connections will help you practice written and oral presentation skills.

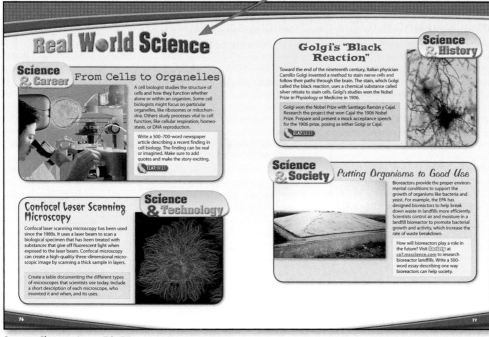

Source: Chapter 1, pp. 76–77

# Previewing Your Textbook

##  Standards Review

**Linking Vocabulary and Main Ideas** a concept map to assist you in reviewing your vocabulary

**Using Vocabulary** a variety of questions that will check your understanding of vocabulary definitions

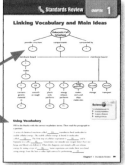

Source: Chapter 1, p. 79

**Understanding Main Ideas** multiple-choice questions

**Applying Science** short-answer and extended-response questions to practice higher-level thinking skills

**Cumulative Review** short-answer questions covering material from earlier in the unit

Source: Chapter 2, pp. 114–115

**Writing in Science** an exercise to practice writing skills; the California English/Language Arts Content Standards that correlate to the material are listed

**Applying Math** a series of questions that practice math skills related to the chapter; the California Mathematics Content Standards that correlate to the material are listed

##  Standards Assessment

**Standards Assessment** multiple-choice questions to review the California Science Content Standards covered in the chapter

Source: Chapter 1, pp. 82–83

# Scavenger Hunt

*Focus On Life Science* contains a wealth of information. The secret is to know where to look to learn as much as you can.

As you complete this scavenger hunt, either on your own or with your teachers or family, you will quickly learn how the textbook is organized and how to get the most out of your reading and study time.

1. How many units are in the book? How many chapters?

2. On what page does the glossary begin? What glossary is online?

3. In which Student Resource at the back of your book can you find a listing of Laboratory Safety Symbols?

4. Suppose you want to find a list of all the Launch Labs, MiniLabs, DataLabs, and Labs, where do you look?

5. How can you quickly find the pages that have information about geneticist Gregor Mendel?

6. What is the name of the table that summarizes the key concepts and vocabulary of a chapter? On what page in Chapter 4 are these two things located?

7. In which Student Resource at the back of your book can you find information on unit conversion? What are the page numbers?

8. On what page can you find **The BIG Idea** for Chapter 1? On what page can you find the **Main Idea** for Chapter 1, Lesson 2?

9. What feature at the start of each unit provides insight into a scientist's work?

10. What study tool shown at the beginning of a chapter can you make from notebook paper?

11. **Concepts In Motion** are interactive animations. Where do you go to interact with the animation?

12. What activities at the beginning of each chapter will help improve your reading?

# Introduction to
# Investigation and Experimentation

**What is science?** Science is the process of studying nature at all levels, from the farthest reaches of space to the smallest particle of matter, and the collection of information that is learned through this process. Every day, scientists ask questions about the natural world and propose explanations based on evidence they gather. This evidence can then be used by other scientists to answer their own questions about the natural world.

## What is life science?

**Life science**, or biology, is the scientific study of living things. Life scientists study the structures, functions, and histories of organisms and the interactions of organisms with their environments. Today, knowledge of how living things grow, reproduce and change is expanding rapidly. This knowledge is leading to advancements in medicine, agriculture and environmental management. Familiarize yourself with the topics in the Introduction to Investigation and Experimentation to help you conduct your own investigations of topics in life science.

# Table of Contents

## What is science? . . . . . . . . . . . . . . . . . . . . . . . . . . . . . . . . 4
- The Branches of Science
- Scientific Methods
- Scientific Theories
- Scientific Laws

## The Tools of the Life Scientist . . . . . . . . . . . . . . 7

### Lab and Field Study Tools . . . . . . . . . . . . . . . . . . . . . . . . . . . . 7
- Science Journal
- Rulers and Metersticks
- Thermometers
- Beakers
- Test Tubes
- Graduated Cylinder
- Compound Microscope
- Triple-Beam Balance
- Computers and the Internet

### Tools of Scientific Thinking . . . . . . . . . . . . . . . . . . . . . . 14
- Observations
- Hypotheses and Predictions
- Inferring
- Finding Useful Resources
- Identifying Fact and Opinion
- Evaluating Evidence and Explanations
- Writing a Lab Report
- Making an Oral Presentation
- Drawing Diagrams
- Constructing Scale Models

### Data Analysis Tools . . . . . . . . . . . . . . . . . . . . . . . . . . . . . . . . 24
- Making Data Tables
- Making Line Graphs
- Making Bar Graphs
- Making Circle Graphs

### Designing a Controlled Experiment . . . . . . . . . . . . . . . . . . 28
- Asking Scientific Questions
- Writing a Hypothesis and Prediction
- Defining Variables and Constants
- Experimental Group and Control Group
- Measuring the Dependent Variable
- Writing a Procedure
- Determining Materials
- Recording Observations
- Analyzing Results
- Drawing Conclusions
- Analyzing Error

## Case Study: The Diabetes Generation . . . . . . . . . . . . . . 34
- Obesity on the Rise
- The History of Diabetes
- Fat is a Problem for Insulin
- Collecting Data From Humans
- Reversing the Diabetes Trend

# The Branches of Science

There are an infinite number of questions to ask about the natural world. However, these questions are often organized into different fields of study. The chart below lists three areas of science that you will study in middle school.

## Earth Science

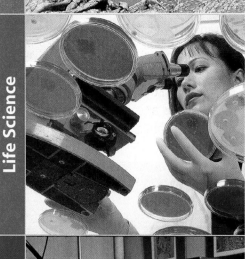

Volcanologists are Earth scientists that study volcanoes. This team of student volcanologists is studying patterns in cooled volcanic lava. This team of volcanologists is studying a hot volcano lava tube in Kilauea, Hawaii.

**Earth scientists ask questions such as:**

- What makes the ocean salty?
- What causes an earthquake?
- Why are there more earthquakes in California than in Arizona?
- How are mountains formed?
- What causes a tsunami?

## Life Science

Microbiologists are life scientists that ask questions about organisms that are too small to see with the naked eye. This microbiologist is studying the growth of bacteria in order to find out which medicine can treat a disease.

**Life scientists ask questions such as:**

- What causes plants to grow?
- How do diseases spread in a population?
- Why do some whales beach themselves, but others do not?

## Physical Science

Electron microscopists are physical scientists that observe objects at magnifications up to 800,000 times their actual size. This electron microscopist is using a scanning electron microscope at the University of California, Berkeley to observe the structure of an ant's head.

**Physical scientists ask questions such as:**

- Why does the sunlight melt snow?
- Why are some buildings damaged more than others during earthquakes?
- What makes up stars?
- What causes acid rain to form?

**7.c** Communicate the logical connection among hypotheses, science concepts, tests conducted, data collected, and conclusions drawn from the scientific evidence.

# Scientific Methods

You might think that science is only about facts and discoveries. But, science is also about the skills and thought processes required to make discoveries. There is no one scientific method used by scientists. Instead, scientific methods are based on basic assumptions about the natural world and how humans understand it.

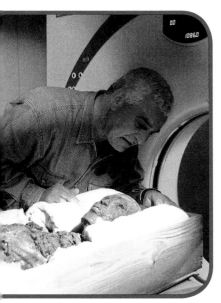

**Improved tools and techniques enable scientists to learn more about ancient remains. Zahi Hawass, chairman of Egypt's Supreme Council for Antiquities, examines the mummy of King Tutankhamen before it undergoes a CAT scan.**

## Assumptions of Scientific Methods

**1. There are patterns in nature.**

Science assumes that there are patterns in nature. Patterns are characteristics or interactions between things that repeat over and over. Patterns can be observed using the five human senses—sight, hearing, touch, smell, and taste.

**2. People can use logic to understand an observation.**

Science assumes that an individual can make an observation and then create a series of logical steps in order to find a valid explanation for the observation. This series of steps can then be communicated to others.

**3. Scientific discoveries are replicable.**

Something that is replicable in science can be repeated over and over again. If a scientist claims to have made a discovery using a certain set of steps in his or her investigation, another scientist should be able to repeat the same steps and get the same result. This ensures that scientists provide reliable evidence to support their claim.

## Scientific methods cannot answer all questions.

Questions that deal with your feelings, values, beliefs, and personal opinions cannot be answered using scientific methods. Although people sometimes use scientific evidence to form arguments about these topics, there is no way to find answers for them using scientific methods. Good science is based on carefully crafted questions and objectively collected data.

### Questions Science Cannot Answer

The following are examples of questions that cannot be answered by science.

- Which band has the best songs?
- Why do bad things happen?
- What does it mean to be a good person?

**7.c** Communicate the logical connection among hypotheses, science concepts, tests conducted, data collected, and conclusions drawn from the scientific evidence.

# Scientific Theories

Using scientific methods to ask questions about the natural world has led to the formation of scientific theories. A **scientific theory** is explanation of things or events that is based on knowledge gained from many observations and investigations. They are independently tested by many scientists and are objectively verified. However, even the best scientific theory can be rejected if new scientific discoveries reveal new information.

## How is a scientific theory different from a common theory?

| Scientific Theory | Common Theory |
|---|---|
| • A scientific theory is an explanation for an observation supported by evidence from many scientific investigations. | • A common theory is a collection of related ideas that one supposes to be true. |
| • Strength of a scientific theory lies solely in the accuracy of its predictions. | • Strength of a theory is based on the clarity of the explanation, not necessarily objectively obtained evidence. |
| • A scientific theory is modified or rejected if new evidence makes the theories predictions no longer true. | • A common theory may or may not be modified or rejected when presented with new evidence. |
| • A scientific theory must be rejectable. | • A common theory does not have to be rejectable. |

# Scientific Laws

A rule that describes a pattern in nature is a **scientific law.** For an observation to become a scientific law, it must be observed repeatedly. The law then stands until someone makes observations that do not follow the law. A law helps you predict that an apple dropped from arm's length will always fall to Earth. A scientific law, unlike a scientific theory, does not attempt to explain *why* something happens. It simply describes a pattern.

**7.a** Select and use appropriate tools and technology (including calculators, computers, balances, g scales, microscopes, and binoculars) to perform tests, collect data, and display data.

**7.e** Communicate the steps and results from an investigation in written reports and oral presentations.

**Tools of the Life Scientist:**
**Lab and Field Study Tools**

# Lab and Field Study Tools

Lab and field study tools are physical tools that help you make better observations during scientific investigations. These tools enable you to measure the amounts of liquids, measure how much material is in an object, and observe things that are too small or too far away to be seen with the naked eye. Learning how to use them properly will help you when designing your own investigations.

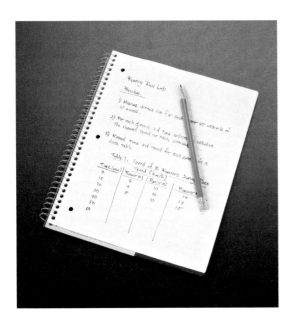

### Science Journal  **Use a Science Journal to record questions, procedures, observations, and conclusions from your investigations.**

**TIP**  Your Science Journal can be a spiral-bound binder, a loose-leaf notebook, or anything that will help you record and save information.

**TIP**  It is important that you keep your Science Journal organized. An organized journal will enable you to find information that you have collected in the past.

**TIP**  Write down the date when you are recording information in your Science Journal, and leave extra space to go back to later.

### Rulers and Metersticks  **Use metric rulers and metersticks to measure length or distance.**

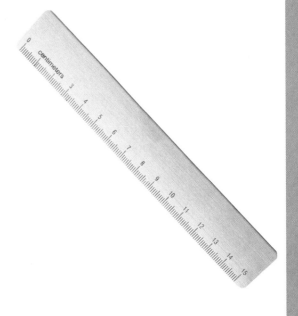

**TIP**  Metric units of measurement for length include kilometers (km), meters (m), centimeters (cm), and millimeters (mm). The unit of measurement you choose to use will depend on the distance or length you need to measure. For example, a meterstick would be best to measure the length of your classroom. However, a 10-cm ruler would be the best tool to measure the length of a maple leaf.

**TIP**  Estimate one decimal place beyond the markings on the ruler. For a meterstick, measure to the nearest 0.1 cm.

## Tools of the Life Scientist:
### Lab and Field Study Tools

**7.a** Select and use appropriate tools and technology (including calculators, computers, balances, spring scales, microscopes, and binoculars) to perform tests, collect data, and display data.

## Thermometers  Use a thermometer to measure the temperature of a substance.

**TIP**  The metric unit of measurement for temperature is degrees Celsius (°C).

**TIP**  When measuring a liquid that is being heated from the bottom, do not let the thermometer rest on the bottom of the container. This will result in an inaccurate reading.

**SAFETY**  Be careful when transporting a glass thermometer. Glass thermometers are very fragile and are easily broken if dropped or bumped.

## Beakers  Use a beaker for holding and pouring liquids.

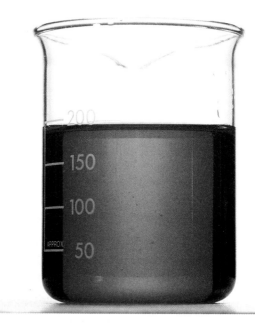

**TIP**  Use a graduated cylinder instead of a beaker to measure the volume of a liquid. The lines on the side of a beaker are not accurate.

**SAFETY**  Use a beaker that holds about twice as much liquid as you are measuring to avoid overflow.

**TIP**  Use a hot plate to keep a substance warmer than room temperature.

**SAFETY**  Use goggles to protect your eyes when working with liquids in the lab.

**SAFETY**  Use gloves to protect your hands when working with liquids in the lab.

**7.a** Select and use appropriate tools and technology (including calculators, computers, balances, spring scales, microscopes, and binoculars) to perform tests, collect data, and display data.

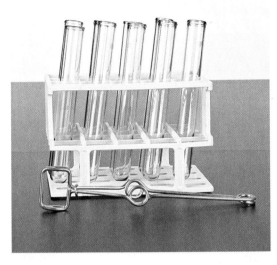

## Test Tubes  Use a test tube to study small samples of solids, liquids and gases.

**TIP** Use a test-tube rack to keep your test tubes upright and organized.

**SAFETY** Since liquids can spill or splash from test tubes, use small amounts of liquids and keep the mouth of the test tube pointed away from you and other people.

**SAFETY** Use a test-tube holder if you are heating the substance in a test tube or if the substance in the test tube is dangerous to touch.

**SAFETY** Do not put a stopper in a test tube if you are heating it.

## Graduated Cylinder  Use a graduated cylinder to measure the volume of a liquid.

### Using a Graduated Cylinder

**1.** Place the graduated cylinder on a level surface so that your measurement will be accurate.

**2.** To read the scale on a graduated cylinder, make sure to have your eyes at the same level as the surface of the liquid.

**3.** The surface of the liquid in a graduated cylinder will be curved—this curve is called a meniscus. Read the line at the bottom of the meniscus.

**TIP** A 10-mL graduated cylinder will measure a small volume of liquid more precisely than a 100 mL graduated cylinder.

**TIP** Estimate one decimal place beyond the markings on the graduated cylinder. For a 100-mL graduated cylinder, estimate to the nearest 0.1 mL.

**TIP** You can use a graduated cylinder to find the volume of a solid object by measuring the increase in a liquid's level after the object is submerged in the liquid.

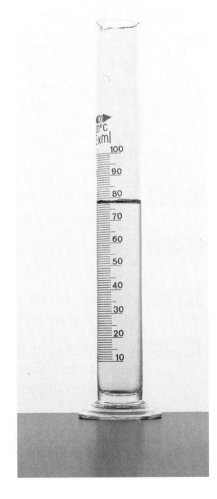

**7.a** Select and use appropriate tools and technology (including calculators, computers, balances, spring scales, microscopes, and binoculars) to perform tests, collect data, and display data.

## Compound Microscope  Use a compound microscope to study very small objects that cannot be observed with the naked eye.

### Using a microscope

1.  Adjust the diaphragm so that you can see a bright circle of light through the eyepiece.

2.  Turn the nosepiece to click the low power lens into place.

3.  Place the slide on the stage. Be sure it is centered over the hole in the stage.

4.  Using the coarse adjustment knob, slowly lower the lens and focus on the specimen.

5.  Switch to the high-power lens.

6.  Use the fine adjustment knob to focus on the specimen with the high-power lens.

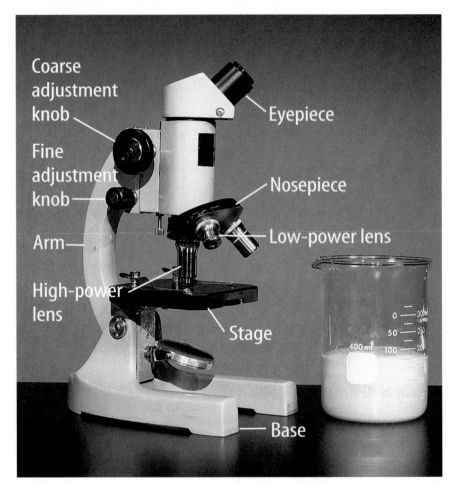

Coarse adjustment knob

Fine adjustment knob

Arm

High-power lens

Eyepiece

Nosepiece

Low-power lens

Stage

Base

**SAFETY**  Be sure not to touch the slide with the lens of the microscope. Doing so can cause the slide and coverslip to shatter and can damage the lens.

**SAFETY**  When carrying a microscope, always hold it underneath the base with one hand and hold the arm of it with your other hand.

**TIP**  Always adjust the coarse adjustment with the microscope on lowest power. This makes it easier to focus on the sample and not damage any part of the microscope.

**TIP**  Use as little light as you possibly can to give better contrast of the sample (which will make it easier to see). If the light is too bright or too dark then you might not be able to see the sample.

**7.a** Select and use appropriate tools and technology (including calculators, computers, balances, spring scales, microscopes, and binoculars) to perform tests, collect data, and display data.

**7.d** Construct scale models, maps, and appropriately labeled diagrams to communicate scientific knowledge (e.g., motion of Earth's plates and cell structure).

## Making a Wet-Mount Slide

To view an object with a compound microscope, the object must first be mounted on a slide using a technique called "wet mount."

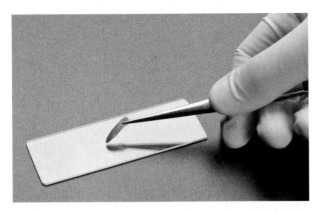

**1.** Place the specimen on the center of the slide.

**2.** Place a drop of water on the specimen.

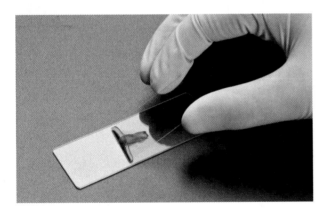

**3.** Place a cover slip on the slide.

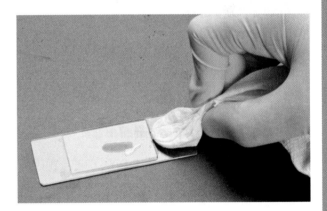

**4.** Dry excess water and draw out air bubbles with a paper towel.

## Drawing a Specimen

Drawings of specimens record what you see in the microscope's field of view. You don't need to be an art expert to create a drawing. Just make your drawing simple and clear. All drawings should be labeled with the specimen name and the magnification used.

**TIP** Write all labels outside the circle.

**TIP** Use a pencil so you can erase if needed.

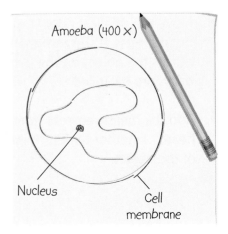

Amoeba (400 ×)

Nucleus

Cell membrane

**7.a** Select and use appropriate tools and technology (including calculators, computers, balances, spring scales, microscopes, and binoculars) to perform tests, collect data, and display data.

## Triple-Beam Balance Use a triple beam balance to measure the mass, or amount of material contained in an object.

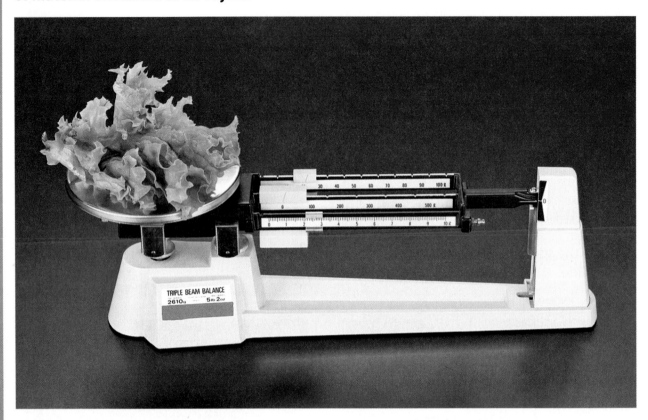

## Using a Triple-Beam Balance

1. When nothing is on the pan, make sure the pointer of the balance and the riders are at zero.

2. Place the object you want to measure on the pan. The pointer will rise above the zero mark.

3. Adjust the riders to bring the pointer back down to zero. To do this, start by moving the largest rider (100 g) away from the pan one notch at a time. If moving the largest rider causes the pointer to fall below zero, set the largest rider back at the previous notch. Then, move the next smaller rider (10 g) in the same way.

4. Move the smallest rider (1 g) until the pointer rests at the zero mark. This means the object on the pan and the riders are balanced.

5. Add the measurements from the three beams together to determine the mass of the object.

### Think Like a Scientist

Use a triple beam balance to measure the mass of your pencil. If you measured it's mass on the Moon would it be the same? Why or why not? Perhaps you have heard that the terms mass and weight mean different things? Do you know the difference?

**7.a** Select and use appropriate tools and technology (including calculators, computers, balances, spring scales, microscopes, and binoculars) to perform tests, collect data, and display data.

**7.b** Use a variety of print and electronic resources (including the World Wide Web) to collect information and evidence as part of a research project.

**Tools of the Life Scientist:**
**Lab and Field Study Tools**

# Computers and the Internet

**Use a computer to collect, organize and store information about a topic you are researching. That information can be an article you found on the Internet or data from an experiment you performed.**

## Using Spreadsheet Programs

Use a spreadsheet program to create data tables and graphs.

**TIP** Think about how to organize your data before you begin entering data.

**TIP** Columns are assigned letters and rows are assigned numbers. Each point where a row and column intersect is called a cell, and is labeled according to where it is located. For example: column A, row 1 is A1.

**TIP** To edit text in a cell, activate the cell by clicking on it.

**TIP** When using a spreadsheet program to create a graph, make use of the type of graph that best represents the data.

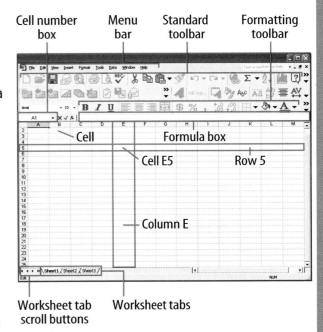

Cell number box    Menu bar    Standard toolbar    Formatting toolbar

Cell    Formula box

Cell E5    Row 5

Column E

Worksheet tab scroll buttons    Worksheet tabs

## Using Search Engines

Use a web browser to search for information resources on the Internet.

Navigation buttons    Address bar    Loading indicator

Link indicator

**TIP** Enclose phrases in quotes to narrow your search results. For example, "global warming".

**TIP** Use Boolean operators to further modify a search.

- **and**—narrows a search by requiring all terms to appear in document. For example, "global warming" *and* oceans.

- **or**—broadens a search by at least one of the terms joined by it to appear in the document. For example, "global warming" *or* "climate change."

- **and not**—limits a search by excluding documents whether they meet the other criteria of the search or not. For example, "global warming" *and* oceans *and not* **California.**

**7.c** Communicate the logical connection among hypotheses, science concepts, tests conducted, data collected, and conclusions drawn from the scientific evidence.

# Tools of Scientific Thinking

Scientific thinking tools are techniques that help you to refine your questions, make useful observations, and think critically about scientific information. As you work in the lab, refer to this guide to help you understand the nature of science.

## Observations

An **observation** is an act of watching something and taking note of what occurs. Although observing often refers to vision, all five human senses can be used to make observations. You make observations in order to ask questions and make informed hypotheses. You also make observations when you collect data in an experiment. There are two types of observations:

### Qualitative Observations

**Qualitative observations** are descriptions of the natural world using words.

### Qualitative Observations

**Qualitative observations** are expressed as numbers.

---

**EXAMPLE**

A student wanted to know if her cat preferred to eat one brand of dry cat food over another. She put equal quantities of each brand in identical bowls in front of her cat during feeding time. At the end of feeding time, she recorded how much of each type of food her cat had eaten using words. Then she measured the mass of the remaining cat food in each bowl.

**Cat Food Preference**

| | Photograph | Qualitative Observations | Quantitative Observations |
|---|---|---|---|
| **Brand A** | | Some food eaten | Mass of food remaining = 24 g |
| **Brand B** | | All food eaten | Mass of food remaining = 0 g |

---

**7.c** Communicate the logical connection among hypotheses, science concepts, tests conducted, data collected, and conclusions drawn from the scientific evidence.

**Tools of the Life Scientist:**
**Tools of Scientific-Thinking**

## Hypotheses and Predictions

A **hypothesis** is a tentative explanation or an answer to a question that can be tested with a scientific investigation to describe *what* will happen and *why* it will happen.

A **prediction** is a forecast of what will happen next in a sequence of events, but it does not explain why something happens.

---

**EXAMPLE**

Imagine you have two daisies in your classroom. One looks healthy while the other is turning brown. You notice that the healthy-looking daisy receives a lot of sunlight, and the unhealthy daisy receives less sunlight. You know both plants are given the same amount of water every day.

**What is one hypothesis that could be used to investigate why one daisy is healthy and the other is not?**

| | |
|---|---|
| **1.** Start by asking a question. | **1. Question:** Why is one daisy healthy and the other is not? |
| **2.** Document what you already know from prior observations. | **2. Observations:** The healthy-looking daisy receives a lot of sunlight. The unhealthy daisy receives little sunlight. |
| **3.** Write a hypothesis which tentatively explains your observation. | **3. Hypothesis:** The daisy is not healthy because it is not receiving enough light to grow. |
| **4.** Write a prediction that can be used to test your hypothesis. | **4. Prediction:** If I provide the unhealthy daisy with the same amount of sunlight as the healthy daisy, it will become healthier. |

---

**TIP** The results of an experiment do not *prove* that a hypothesis is correct. Instead, the results of an experiment either *support or do not support* the hypothesis. This is because scientific inquiry is uncertain. You cannot be sure that you are aware of everything that could have affected the results of your experiment.

**TIP** An experiment is not a failure if the results do not support your hypothesis. In the experiment above, if the unhealthy plant does not improve after providing it with more light, you can eliminate that as the cause of the problem and revise your hypothesis.

**7.c** Communicate the logical connection among hypotheses, science concepts, tests conducted, data collected, and conclusions drawn from the scientific evidence.

# Inferring

An **inference** is a logical conclusion based on the information that is available to you. Your prior knowledge and observations help you make inferences.

**TIP** It is important to distinguish between observations and inferences. Descriptions are observations. However, when you offer an explanation for that observation, you are making an inference.

**EXAMPLE**

It is easy to trick yourself into making an inference without adequate evidence to support it. Look at the two photographs shown below. Based on what you see, you might infer that the cat knocked over the plant. However, you need to carefully note your observations first.

| **Photo 1 Observations** | **Photo 2 Observations** |
| --- | --- |
| • the plant is upright<br>• the cat is near the plant | • the plant lying sideways on the floor<br>• the cat is absent from the image |

**TIP** When making an inference, be certain to use accurate data and observations. Analyze all the data you have collected. Then, based on everything you know, explain or interpret what you have observed.

**7.a** Select and use appropriate tools and technology (including calculators, computers, balances, spring scales, microscopes, and binoculars) to perform tests, collect data, and display data.

**7.b** Use a variety of print and electronic resources (including the World Wide Web) to collect information and evidence as part of a research project.

# Finding Useful Resources

In any scientific investigation, you might find that you need background information about how others have asked and answered similar scientific questions. Finding useful print and electronic resources is an important skill that you develop as you perform scientific investigations.

## Print Resources

**Print resources** are books, newspapers, popular magazines, and peer-reviewed journals. Print resources are available at your local library and can be searched using the library's card catalog.

**TIP** You are more likely to find useful information for scientific inquiry at the library than on the Web. Most print resources have been edited and peer reviewed by experts who ensure that the document is accurate and useful.

**TIP** Most public libraries have electronic card catalogs that make it easier to find useful information quickly.

**TIP** If you find a useful book or journal article, check the works-cited pages for the author's references. These documents might be useful to you as well.

**TIP** If you get stuck or have a question, librarians will be happy to help you find what you need.

## Internet Resources

**Internet resources** are Web pages and other electronic documents that are available to anyone with a computer and Internet connection. These documents can be found using keyword searches on internet search engines or by browsing hyperlinks on Web pages.

**TIP** Use specific keywords when you search the Web.

**TIP** When performing a Web search, enclosing phrases with quotes can narrow your search to the most relevant pages.

**TIP** When using a search engine, the first hit in your search results is not always the best. Search results are arranged by popularity, not by relevance to your topic.

**TIP** Information obtained from the Web is more likely to be biased than print resources. Information from government or educational institution Web sites is usually more reliable than a personal Web site.

**Tools of the Life Scientist:**
**Tools of Scientific-Thinking**

**7.b** Use a variety of print and electronic resources (including the World Wide Web) to collect information and evidence as part of a research project.

## Identifying Fact and Opinion

With so much information available to you through books, magazines and the internet, it can be challenging to find resources that contain objective, factual information. When searching for science resources on a topic, carefully evaluate what you are reading to determine if the author is stating facts or opinions.

> **Facts** are measurements, observations, and theories that can be strictly defined and evaluated for their validity through objective investigation.
>
> **EXAMPLE**
>
> **Fact:** The shortest route on foot between my house and my school measures 2.7 km.
>
> **Opinions** are personal views, feelings, or claims about a topic. Opinions cannot be proved true or false.
>
> **EXAMPLE**
>
> **Opinion:** The distance between my home and my school is too far to walk.

### Human Activities and the Envrionment

**OPINION**
Look for words that express beliefs or feelings. The word *unfortunately* indicates that an opinion is being expressed.

Making fuel economy standards for passenger automobiles more strict is the only effective way to decrease our consumption of fossil fuels in the United States. The enactment of Corporate Average Fuel Economy (CAFE) standards in 1975 resulted in a 95-percent increase of cars' average fuel economy over the following decade. Unfortunately, the popularity of gas-hogging sport-utility vehicles and trucks since the early 1990s has caused American drivers to return to their pattern of fossil fuel misuse. Since then, transportation energy consumption has increased by 1.8 percent per year, faster than any other major category of energy use. Raising federal fuel economy standards by 5 percent annually until 2012 and by 3 percent per year after that could save 67 billion barrels of oil over the next 40 years. Because American consumers insist on purchasing vehicles that are less fuel-efficient, tightening these standards might be the only way to prevent fossil fuels reserves from running out in the near future.

**FACT**
Sentences containing measurements and statistics are more likely to be facts.

**TIP** Scientific evidence often is used to argue an opinion. Even reliable sources of information such as science magazines and newspapers sometimes publish articles that mix opinions with fact based content.

**TIP** Just because a statement is presented as fact, it is not necessarily accurate. Once you have separated facts from opinions, check the facts against other resources to ensure that the information is commonly accepted.

**7.c** Communicate the logical connection among hypotheses, science concepts, tests conducted, data collected, and conclusions drawn from the scientific evidence.

**Tools of the Life Scientist:**
**Tools of Scientific-Thinking**

# Evaluating Evidence and Explanations

Whether you are reading science articles and lab reports or drawing conclusions from data you have collected in a lab, it is essential to think critically about the data and the scientific explanations presented to you. **Critical thinking** means comparing what you already know with the explanation you are given in order to decide if you agree with it or not.

## Evaluating Scientific Evidence

Start by evaluating the quality of the evidence presented to you. Valid scientific investigations contain quantitative or qualitative evidence called **data.** Data can be descriptions, tables, graphs, or labeled drawings. Data are used to support or refute the investigation's hypothesis. When evaluating data from an investigation ask the following questions:

- **Does the journal article or lab report contain data?** A proper scientific investigation always contains data to support an explanation.

- **Are the data precise?** Data used to support an explanation should be exact. Quantitative observations or detailed descriptions and drawings of events are much better than vague descriptions of events. Imprecise phrases such as "a lot" and "a little" do not accurately describe an event because it's impossible to know to what that description is being compared. Vague descriptions lead to incorrect explanations.

- **Have the results of the experiment been repeated?** If a friend told you he could hit a home run, but he was unable to do it while you watched, would you believe him? Probably not. Likewise, scientific data are more reliable when the investigator has repeated an experiment several times and consistently produced the same results. Scientific evidence is considered to be even more reliable when multiple investigators try the same experiment and get the same results.

 **Think Like a Scientist**

Why do you think scientific evidence is more reliable when different investigators try the same experiment rather than the same investigator performing the experiment multiple times?

## Evaluating Scientific Explanations

Having good data is the first step to providing a good explanation for the data. However, it's easy to make a mistake and accidentally arrive at the wrong conclusion. When evaluating an inference or a conclusion, ask yourself the following questions:

- **Does the explanation make sense?** Be skeptical! There need to be logical connections between the investigator's question, hypothesis, predictions, data, and conclusions. Read the information carefully. Can the investigator reasonably draw his or her conclusion from the results of the experiment?

- **Are there any other possible explanations?** Since it is virtually impossible to control every variable that could affect the outcome of an experiment, it's important to think of other explanations for the results of an experiment. This is particularly true when the data are unusual or unexpected.

**7.c** Communicate the logical connection among hypotheses, science concepts, tests conducted, data collected, and conclusions drawn from the scientific evidence.

**7.e** Communicate the steps and results from an investigation in written reports and oral presentations.

# Writing a Lab Report

How would you know what your friends are thinking if you didn't communicate? Likewise, scientists share the results of their investigations. Part of being a science student involves learning to communicate the outcome of your investigations clearly and effectively.

## Written Reports

Written reports use text, data tables, graphs, and drawings in an organized manner to state clearly the topic you investigated and to explain your findings. Written reports can be used to communicate the results of a lab or a more involved investigation such as a Design Your Own Lab or a science fair project.

### EXAMPLE

The format below shows the basic organization of a good lab report. Depending on the complexity of your investigation, you might need to add more information.

**Problem**
State exactly what problem the investigation is attempting to solve or what question the investigation is attempting to answer.

**Form a Hypothesis**
Describe what you thought would happen and why.

**Procedure**
Describe the steps you took in a logical manner.

**Results**
Organize your data into a table so that the information is easy to read and analyze.

**Analyze and Conclude**
Support any answers to questions with the data from your table. The conclusions you draw from the investigation should be based on your analysis of the data. Also, include notes about measuring errors or problems you encountered that could affect your conclusions.

**7.c** Communicate the logical connection among hypotheses, science concepts, tests conducted, data collected, and conclusions drawn from the scientific evidence.

**7.e** Communicate the steps and results from an investigation in written reports and oral presentations.

**Tools of the Life Scientist:**
**Tools of Scientific-Thinking**

# Making an Oral Presentation

Oral presentations are a convenient way to communicate the results of your investigation to several people at once.

### Organize your presentation.

**Problem**  State exactly what problem the investigation is attempting to solve or what question the investigation is attempting to answer.

**Hypothesis**  Describe what you thought would happen and why.

**Procedure**  Proceed in a very logical manner, telling what you did step by step.

**Results**  Explain both your controls and variables. Use graphs to summarize your data.

**Conclusion**  State the conclusions you can validly draw from the investigation and support them with data from the investigation. Describe any measuring errors or problems you encountered that could affect your conclusions.

**Questions**  When you are finished, ask your audience if they have any questions about your investigation. If you don't know the answer to a question, admit that you don't know and indicate that you will check into the matter.

---

**TIP**  Use visuals.

Visuals illustrate points so they are easier to understand, reinforce major ideas in your presentation, and keep the audience focused. They also will help guide you as you speak.

### What are visuals?
- graphs and charts
- maps, photos, and drawings
- models
- video/film

### What media are used?
- poster display
- transparencies/slides
- video projection/projector
- blackboard/whiteboard
- computer presentation programs

**TIP**  Practice your presentation.

Be sure to rehearse your presentation before you face your audience. Rehearsing will help you remember your presentation when you are presenting it to the class, and it will help you to relax. Dress neatly and stand up straight.

- Don't chew gum or candy.
- Stand to the side of your display.
- Speak loudly enough to be heard by the audience.
- Make eye contact with the audience.
- If you have a partner, be sure you share equally in the presentation.

**7.d** Construct scale models, maps, and appropriately labeled diagrams to communicate scientific knowledge (e.g., motion of Earth's plates and cell structure).

# Drawing Diagrams

A **diagram** is a scientific illustration that explains a process or the logical relationship between objects or ideas.

**EXAMPLE**

This diagram is a visual representation of the process of photosynthesis.

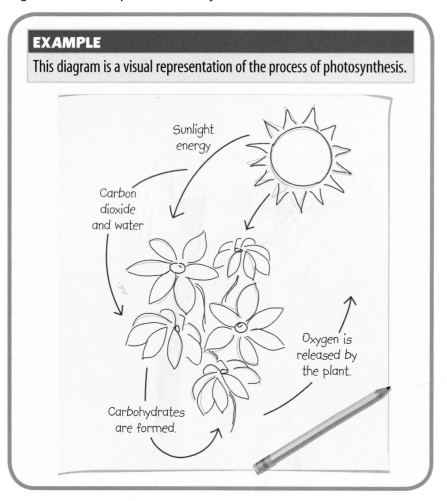

**TIP** Useful diagrams often are not realistic drawings. For most diagrams it is better to make simple, clear drawings in order convey to the viewer how the parts relate to each other or how the process works.

**TIP** Carefully label diagrams so the viewer does not accidentally misinterpret the information you present.

**TIP** Use diagrams during oral presentations to help your audience understand the design of your experiment.

**Think Like a Scientist**

Describe your daily routine using a diagram.

1. List the events that take place in your day.

2. Connect the events using arrows.

**7.d** Construct scale models, maps, and appropriately labeled diagrams to communicate scientific knowledge (e.g., motion of Earth's plates and cell structure).

**Tools of the Life Scientist:**
**Tools of Scientific-Thinking**

# Constructing Scale Models

A **scale model** is a three-dimensional representation of an object that is proportionately larger or smaller than the object itself. Scale models are often used to show the structure of an object and how parts of that structure fit together.

**EXAMPLE**

This architecture class is constructing the scale model of a bridge. Pieces are carefully measured and crafted so that they represent a realistic bridge.

**TIP** Scale models do not have to be made of the same material as the full-scale object. Choose a material that is easy to measure, cut, and bend precisely when you are constructing a scale model.

## Understanding Scale

When building a scale model, you need to determine how much smaller or larger your model will be than the object you are representing. A **scale** is a ratio of the measurements of original object to the measurements of model. For example if a model of a car was made at a scale of 1/100, then the actual car would be 100 times larger than the model. That means that if the car were 10 m long, the model of the car would be 10 cm long.

**TIP** Having a scale ensures that you don't make certain parts of the model too large or too small relative to other parts.

# Data Analysis Tools

Use data analysis tools to help you organize your data and display patterns in your results.

## Making Data Tables

Data tables help you organize and record the measurements you make. A data table displays information in rows and columns so that it is easier to read and understand.

---

### EXAMPLE

Suppose you were competing in a 50-km bicycle race. You planned to keep a pace of 10 km/h. In order to know if you stayed on pace or not, you had a friend record your time at every 10 km.

### Construct the Data Table

| | |
|---|---|
| **Step 1.** | Think about the variables you plan to investigate. Then, organize the data table into columns and rows. |
| **Step 2.** | Create headings that describe the variable and the corresponding unit of measurement. |
| **Step 3.** | Give the data table a title and a number. |

**Your data can be organized like this:**

**Table 1 Bicycle Race Data**

| Distance (km) | Time (h) |
|---|---|
| 0 | 0 |
| 10 | 0.75 |
| 20 | 2 |
| 30 | 3.5 |
| 40 | 4 |
| 50 | 5 |

**Or like this:**

**Table 2 Bicycle Race Data**

| Distance (km) | 0 | 10 | 20 | 30 | 40 | 50 |
|---|---|---|---|---|---|---|
| Time (h) | 0 | 0.75 | 2 | 3.5 | 4 | 5 |

---

 **Think Like a Scientist**

Study the types of graphs discussed in the pages ahead. Which type of graph would be appropriate for displaying the bicycle race data—a line graph, bar graph or circle graph? Why?

# Making Line Graphs

## A line graph shows a relationship between two variables that change continuously.

- Line graphs are good for showing how an independent variable affects a dependent variable or showing how a variable changes over time.
- Both variables in a line graph must be numbers.

### EXAMPLE

Suppose you measured the temperature of the air from sea level to the top of the highest mountain in the world. You measured air temperature in 1,000-m increments from 0 m to 7,000 m. What would a graph of these data look like?

| Air Temperature and Altitude | |
|---|---|
| **Air Temperature (°C)** | **Altitude (m)** |
| 15 | 0 |
| 7.5 | 1,000 |
| 0 | 2,000 |
| −7.5 | 3,000 |
| −15 | 4,000 |
| −22.5 | 5,000 |
| −30 | 6,000 |
| −37.5 | 7,000 |

### Construct the Graph

| | |
|---|---|
| **Step 1.** | Use the horizontal x-axis for the independent variable (altitude) and the vertical y-axis for the dependent variable (air temperature). |
| **Step 2.** | Draw the x- and y-axes using a scale that contains the smallest and largest values for each variable. Label each axis. |
| **Step 3.** | To plot the first data point, find the x-value (0) on the x-axis. Imagine a line rising vertically from that place on the axis. Then, find the corresponding y-value (15) on the y-axis. Imagine a line moving horizontally from that place on the axis. Make a data point where the two imaginary lines intersect. Repeat this process for the remaining data. |
| **Step 4.** | Connect the data points with lines. |
| **Step 5.** | Title the graph. |

### Interpreting Line Graphs

What can you say about the relationship between altitude and air temperature?

- As altitude increased, temperature decreased.
- Air temperature changed about the same amount every 1,000 m.

**TIP**  Be sure to examine the scale of a graph carefully. The scale of a graph can give a distorted picture of the data.

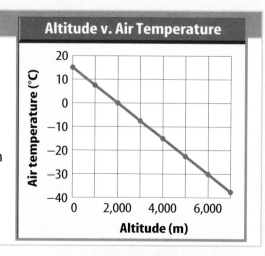

**Altitude v. Air Temperature**

## Making Bar Graphs

**A bar graph uses rectangular blocks, or bars, of varying sizes to represent and compare quantitative data.** The length of each bar is determined by the amount of the variable you are measuring.

### EXAMPLE

Suppose you measured the total rainfall for each month of the year in Los Angeles. You collected the rainfall data in the following data table.

| Monthly Rainfall in Los Angeles | |
| --- | --- |
| **Month** | **Rain (cm)** |
| January | 6.1 |
| February | 6.4 |
| March | 5.1 |
| April | 1.8 |
| May | 0.3 |
| June | 0 |
| July | 0 |
| August | 0.5 |
| September | 0.8 |
| October | 0.8 |
| November | 4.6 |
| December | 4.3 |

### Constructing the Graph

| | |
| --- | --- |
| **Step 1.** | Use the horizontal x-axis for the category (month) and the vertical y-axis for the measured variable (rain). |
| **Step 2.** | Draw the x- and y-axes. Evenly space the category names below the x-axAis. Use a scale that contains the smallest and largest values for the measured variable. Then, label each axis. |
| **Step 3.** | To draw the first bar, find the first category name (January) below the x-axis. Then, draw a bar up to the measured value for that category (6.1) on the y-axis. Repeat this process for the remaining data. |
| **Step 4.** | Title the graph. |

### Interpreting Bar Graphs

- Los Angeles received the most rainfall in February.

- Los Angeles received no measurable rain in both June and July.

- Question to ask: *Does Los Angeles usually receive no rain in June and July?* To find out, compare rainfall amounts for June and July to the recorded rainfall for those months in the past several years.

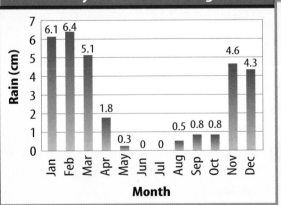

**Monthly Rainfall in Los Angeles**

## Making Circle Graphs

**A circle graph, or pie graph, is used to show some fixed quantity is broken down into parts.** The circular pie represents the total. The slices represent the parts and usually are presented as percentages

### EXAMPLE

Suppose you want to find out what portion of the recyclable waste your family recycles is aluminum, glass, plastic and paper in a single month. Every week before the recyclables are collected you measure the mass of aluminum, glass, plastic and paper in the bin. You add up the total mass for each category and create the following data table. Now, what portion does each category represent?

### Recyclable Material Used in One Month

| Material Type | Mass (kg) |
| --- | --- |
| Aluminum | 1 |
| Glass | 3 |
| Plastic | 2 |
| Paper | 6 |

### Constructing the Graph

| | |
| --- | --- |
| **Step 1.** | Find the total of the measured variable (mass) by adding together the values for all of the categories: **1 kg + 3 kg + 2 kg + 6 kg = 12 kg** |
| **Step 2.** | Calculate the number of degrees of a circle that the first category's value (1) represents. To do this, write a fraction comparing the measured value with the total for all categories (1/12). Then multiply this fraction by 360° **(1/12) × 360° = 30°.** Repeat this process for the remaining categories. |
| **Step 3.** | Draw a circle. Use a protractor to draw the angle (number of degrees) for each category. |
| **Step 4.** | Color and label each section of the graph. |
| **Step 5.** | Title the graph. |

### Interpreting Circle Graphs

- In the time measured, 50 percent of the total mass of your family's recycled waste was paper.

- <u>Questions to ask:</u> *What factors could have caused this outcome? Did your family recycle more paper than usual? Is this amount typical?* Only further investigation will tell you.

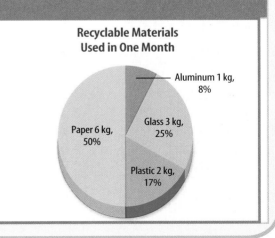

Recyclable Materials
Used in One Month

Aluminum 1 kg, 8%
Glass 3 kg, 25%
Plastic 2 kg, 17%
Paper 6 kg, 50%

**7.c** Communicate the logical connection among hypotheses, science concepts, tests conducted, data collected, and conclusions drawn from the scientific evidence.

**7.e** Communicate the steps and results from an investigation in written reports and oral presentations.

# Designing a Controlled Experiment

In this section you will apply your lab skills, scientific thinking skills, and data analysis skills to the task of designing your own controlled experiment. A controlled experiment is a type of scientific investigation that tests how one thing affects another. Use this section to help you with Design Your Own Labs and science projects.

## Asking Scientific Questions

Scientific investigations often begin when someone observes an event in nature and wonders why or how it occurs. To begin designing an experiment, questions need to be refined into specific questions that can be answered with the time and resources available to you.

### EXAMPLE

Many antibacterial soap products have appeared on grocery store shelves in recent years. Antibacterial soaps are products that have chemical additives that are known to kill bacteria. However, questions have been raised about the effectiveness of such soaps when compared to traditional soaps that do not contain antibacterial additives. You decide to investigate this controversy by performing a controlled experiment.

**Question:**
Are antibacterial soaps better than regular soaps?

**Observations:**
- Antibacterial soaps contain chemicals designed to kill microorganisms.
- Antibacterial soaps are often advertised to kill bacteria during hand-washing better than regular soaps.

**Refined Question:**
Are hand soaps containing antibacterial additives more effective at killing bacteria during hand-washing than soaps that do not contain anti-bacterial additives?

**7.c** Communicate the logical connection among hypotheses, science concepts, tests conducted, data collected, and conclusions drawn from the scientific evidence.

**7.e** Communicate the steps and results from an investigation in written reports and oral presentations.

**Tools of the Life Scientist:**
**Designing a Controlled Experiment**

# Writing a Hypothesis and Prediction

A **hypothesis** is a tentative explanation that can be tested with a scientific investigation. It uses your prior knowledge and observations to predict what will happen and why. A **prediction** is a statement of what will happen next in a sequence of events—in this case, your experiment. If the results of the experiment match the prediction, the hypothesis is considered to be supported.

Hypothesis:
Hands washed with anti-bacterial soap will have fewer remaining bacteria than hands washed with soaps without anti-bacterial additives because anti-bacterial soaps contain chemicals that are designed to kill bacteria.

Prediction:
If Group A washes their hands with antibacterial soap and Group B washes their hands with non-antibacterial soap, then samples taken from Group A will grow fewer bacterial colonies than samples taken from Group B.

# Defining Variables and Constants

To test a prediction, you need to identify variables and constants you want to use in your experiment. Variables and constants are factors you think could affect the outcome of your experiment.

## Variables

A **variable** is any factor that can have more than one value. In controlled experiments, there are two types of variables—independent variables and dependent variables.

The **independent variable** is the factor you want to test. It is manipulated or changed by the investigator to observe how it affects a dependent variable.

A **dependent variable** is the factor you measure or observe during an experiment.

## Constants

To test how the independent variable affects the dependent variable, you need to keep all other factors the same for each test. The factors that remain the same are called **constants**. Without constants, two independent variables could change at the same time and you won't know which variable affected the dependent variable.

Independent Variable: soaps with or without antibacterial additives

Dependent Variable: number of bacterial colonies grown on nutrient agar in 1 week

Constants: same washing time, same water temperature, same sink, same sampling technique

**Tools of the Life Scientist:**
Designing a Controlled Experiment

**7.c** Communicate the logical connection among hypotheses, science concepts, tests conducted, data collected, and conclusions drawn from the scientific evidence.

**7.e** Communicate the steps and results from an investigation in written reports and oral presentations.

# Experimental Group and Control Group

A controlled experiment has at least two groups—a control group and an experimental group. The **experimental group** is used to study the effect of a change in the independent variable on the dependent variable. The **control group** contains the same factors as the experimental group, but the independent variable is not changed. Without a control, it is impossible to know if your experimental observations result from the variable you are testing or some other factor.

Experimental group:
Test subjects who wash their hands with soap with or without antibacterial additives

Control group:
Test subjects who wash their hands with tap water only

# Measuring the Dependent Variable

Before you write a procedure, think about what kind of data you need to gather from the dependent variable to know how it relates to the changes you make to the independent variable. Dependent variables can be measured qualitatively or quantitatively.

## Qualitative Measurement

**Qualitative measurements** of the dependent variable use words to describe what you observe in your experiment. Qualitative measurements are easy to make. For some investigations, qualitative data might be the only kind of data you can collect.

## Qualitative Measurement of Bacteria Colonies

Independent Variable
Use of antibacterial or non-antibacterial soaps

Dependent Variable
Colony density judged visually: Low (none to little growth), Medium (spotty growth), High (growth covers plate)

## Quantitative Measurement

**Quantitative measurements** of the dependent variable use numbers to describe what you observe in your experiment. In most experiments, quantitative measurements will provide you with greater precision in your data than qualitative measurements.

## Quantitative Measurement of Bacteria Colonies

Independent Variable
Use of antibacterial or non-antibacterial soaps

Dependent Variable
Colony density by count of individual bacterial colonies

c Communicate the logical connection among hypotheses, science concepts, tests conducted, data
d, and conclusions drawn from the scientific evidence. 7.e Communicate the steps and results
investigation in written reports and oral presentations. 7.a Select and use appropriate tools and
logy (including calculators, computers, balances, spring scales, microscopes, and binoculars) to perform tests, collect data, and display data.

**Tools of the Life Scientist:**
Designing a Controlled Experiment

# Writing a Procedure

A procedure is a set of instructions that you use to gather the data you need to answer your question. Each step in the experiment's procedure should be clear and easy to follow. Record your procedure in your Science Journal so you can execute it with precision.

Procedure

Step 1  To ensure the objectivity, have a lab partner pour the contents of each type of soap into identical pump bottles and label the bottles Group A and Group B.

Step 2  Randomly assign 15 test subjects to group A, group B, and control (no soap)—5 subjects per group.

Step 3  Give each test subject one pump of their assigned soap. Allow hand-washing for 1 minute and rinsing for 15 seconds. Subjects in control group wash with water only.

Step 4  After hand-washing, rub a sterile cotton swab against the palm of the subject's hand for 5 seconds. Open a fresh petri dish and streak the agar from side to side twice. Seal the dish with tape and label it with the subject's group name. Repeat this process for all 15 subjects.

Step 5  Incubate samples at room temperature for 24 hours.

Step 6  After incubation, count the number of bacterial colonies on each sealed dish and record it in a data table.

Step 7  Calculate the average number of bacterial colonies for each group.

Step 8  Reveal which soap was group A and which soap was group B.

Step 9  Sterilize used agar plates with bleach and dispose.

# Determining Materials

Carefully examine each step in your procedures. Determine what materials and tools are required to complete each step.

1. 15 petri dishes with nutrient agar
2. liquid hand soaps - traditional and antibacterial
3. 2 sterilized opaque plastic pump bottles
4. sterilized cotton swabs to collect bacteria samples
5. masking tape to seal petri dishes
6. sink for test subjects to wash hands

15 test subjects

**7.c** Communicate the logical connection among hypotheses, science concepts, tests conducted, data collected, and conclusions drawn from the scientific evidence.

**7.e** Communicate the steps and results from an investigation in written reports and oral presentations.

## Recording Observations

Once your procedure has been approved, follow the steps in your procedure and record your data. As you make observations, note anything that differs from your intended procedure. If you change a material or have to adjust the amount of time you observe something, write that down in your Science Journal.

### Fig. 1. Number of Bacterial colonies after 24 hours

| Sample | Group A | Group B | Control |
|--------|---------|---------|---------|
| 1 | 15 | 25 | 45 |
| 2 | 39 | 37 | 29 |
| 3 | 27 | 42 | 63 |
| 4 | 34 | 34 | 37 |
| 5 | 45 | 17 | 78 |
| Average | 32 | 31 | 50 |

## Analyzing Results

To summarize your data, look at all of your observations together. Look for meaningful ways to present your observations. Presenting your data in the form of a graph is a powerful tool to communicate patterns in your data.

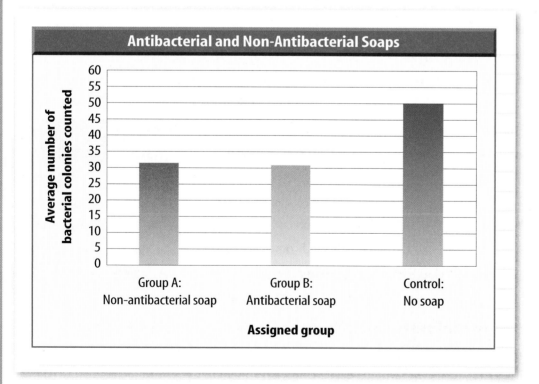

**Antibacterial and Non-Antibacterial Soaps**

Average number of bacterial colonies counted

Group A: Non-antibacterial soap

Group B: Antibacterial soap

Control: No soap

**Assigned group**

**7.c** Communicate the logical connection among hypotheses, science concepts, tests conducted, data collected, and conclusions drawn from the scientific evidence.

**7.e** Communicate the steps and results from an investigation in written reports and oral presentations.

**Tools of the Life Scientist:**
**Designing a Controlled Experiment**

## Drawing Conclusions

To draw conclusions from your experiment, examine the data tables and graphs you have created. Describe trends you see in the data. Then, compare the results to your prediction and hypothesis. Determine if the results support or do not support your hypothesis. Use evidence in your results to support your determination.

> The average bacterial colony count for group A (antibacterial soap) was nearly identical to the colony count for group B (non-antibacterial soap). Although samples from both treatment groups grew fewer bacterial colonies than the group that washed their hands with water only, there is no data that supports the hypothesis that antibacterial soaps kill bacteria during hand washing better than non-antibacterial soaps. Therefore, the hypothesis is rejected.

## Analyzing Error

Error is a part of any scientific research. It's important to document anything that you changed in your procedure or could have caused uncertainty in your measurements. Be sure to include unanticipated factors or accidents that may have influenced your results and offer alternative explanations for your results.

> 1. Counting error may have occurred during bacteria colony counting. Some colonies were too close together to determine if it was one colony or more than one colony.
>
> 2. Sampling error may have resulted from small random variations in both water volume captured by swab and length of streak on plates.
>
> 3. Sampling error may have resulted from differences in initial bacteria count on each test subject's hands. Initial bacteria count was not measured.
>
> 4. Error may have resulted from variation in hand-washing technique from person to person. Uncontrolled factors such as vigorousness of washing and soap coverage on hands could have resulted in data variation. Future investigations will study the impact of these factors on sample bacteria count.
>
> Although these sources of error may have caused some variation in each sample, having multiple samples per group helped to insure that average bacteria count per group was reliable.

# Case Study: The Diabetes Generation

Since 1999, health professionals have criss-crossed the country in souped-up travel trailers, collecting data on the physical fitness of America's youth. They are interviewing children and teens about what they eat and how much exercise they get. The scientists give physical exams in the trailers decked out with all the tools you'd find in a doctor's office: scales, blood pressure cuffs, eye vision charts, and syringes to collect blood samples for testing.

## Obesity on the Rise

In 2004, scientists looked over the data they had collected in the first three years of the National Health and Nutrition Examination Survey. The study results alarmed everyone: the number of overweight children and teens shot up in the late 1980s. Four times as many youth weigh too much nowadays as they did in the 1960s. That's 1 out of every 7 kids with too much fat on his or her bones.

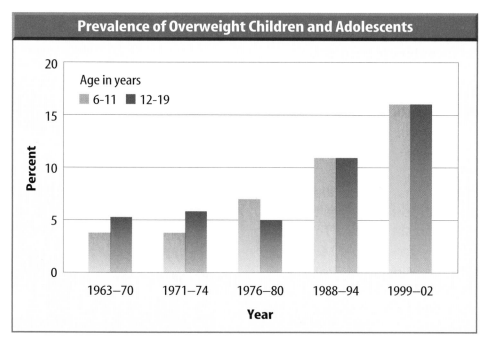

**Prevalence of Overweight Children and Adolescents**

Age in years
6-11   12-19

The results of the National Health and Nutrition Examination Survey revealed that the percentage of overweight children and young adults increased sharply starting in the late 1980s.

## Obesity and Diabetes

Researchers know that obesity can lead to diabetes. Sonia Caprio at Yale University in Connecticut and scientists she worked with wanted to know how many kids could develop diabetes. They conducted a study to find out how many children and teens have early signs of the disease.

## Diabetes and Sugar

People likely to develop diabetes have too much sugar in their blood. So, the scientists took blood from 167 obese children and teens and measured how much sugar each person carried. They found that almost a fourth of the study volunteers had unhealthy amounts of blood sugar. The scientists also found that 4 teens of the 167 volunteers had diabetes and weren't aware of it.

## The History of Diabetes

*Diabetes mellitus* is Greek, roughly meaning "water running through that is sweet." Diabetics are exceedingly thirsty and have to urinate a lot. Hence the "running through." And the urine passed by ancient diabetics attracted a lot of flies and ants, suggesting the urine contained something bugs like to eat—*mellitus* is Latin for honey.

### Diabetic Dogs

Although the disease goes back to ancient times, only in the last century have scientists found out how to treat diabetes. Dogs who lacked an organ called a pancreas suffered from the disease. Frederick Banting and Charles Best hypothesized that diabetes damaged a particular area of the pancreas.

### The Discovery of Insulin

To investigate this idea, the scientists removed the fluid from certain cells in the pancreatic organs of healthy dogs. Then they injected the fluid into diabetic dogs. The sick dogs that got the shots recovered from their disease. But if the scientists stopped giving the fluid to the recovering animals, the diabetes came back. The scientists concluded that whatever the dogs needed to fix the disease could be found in those pancreas cells.

Eventually, the team of scientists discovered a substance made by the pancreas that helped people use their blood sugar properly. Called insulin, this substance could be easily extracted from cows and given to diabetics to reduce the amount of sugar in their blood. The finding so improved the health of people with diabetes that Dr. Banting received the Nobel Prize in Medicine for the discovery.

**Scientists Frederick Banting and Charles Best studied diabetic dogs. Their research ultimately led to the discovery of insulin. Insulin is now used to treat diabetes in humans.**

## Fat is a Problem for Insulin

When people eat, their stomachs break down carbohydrates in food into a simple sugar called glucose—the same as table sugar—that tissues can use for fuel. But tissues need insulin to enable sugar to get inside cells, where the sugar is put to use.

In diabetics, muscle and some other tissues don't allow blood sugar to enter cells easily, even though insulin abounds. Some people who aren't diabetic still have trouble using sugar—these people are insulin resistant. Some scientists think a certain kind of fat prevents insulin from storing sugar, sending people with that kind of fat down the road to diabetes.

## Testing a Fat Hypothesis

To test the hypothesis that one kind of fat might make somone more prone to diabetes than another kind of fat, a group of researchers first experimented with young adult rats. Nir Barzilai, who works at the Albert Einstein College of Medicine in New York City, and his colleagues tested what kinds of fats might cause diabetes by removing fat from rats and seeing if the animals could use insulin any better.

The researchers performed surgery on three groups of rats. They trimmed fat from the abdomen of one group. This kind of fat is also called visceral fat. They removed an equal amount of fat from just under the skin of another group of rats. In the third group, the researchers pretended to perform surgery and wiggled fat around, but didn't remove any fat. Then the researchers let the rats recover for a few weeks.

In the next part of the experiment, the researchers had to figure out how sensitive the rats were to insulin. Healthy rats and people continually trickle sugar into their blood between meals. The sugar feeds all the tissues and gives people energy even when they're not eating. But if the amount of insulin in the blood rises suddenly, for example, if someone injected insulin into his blood, the body takes this as a sign that plenty of sugar is already coursing through the blood, and quickly stops trickling out sugar. Diabetics don't stop making sugar even when they have lots of insulin in their blood.

**Nir Barzilai and his colleagues learned about the relationship between visceral fat and insulin resistance by measuring how quickly rats with visceral fat and rats without visceral fat responded to injections of insulin.**

People and animals who are insulin resistant react to insulin in slow motion. When the rats healed up, the researchers tested how quickly the rats' responded to insulin. The team injected insulin into the blood of rats. Then they took a sample of blood every few minutes for 2 hours. In a laboratory, scientists measured the amount of sugar in the samples.

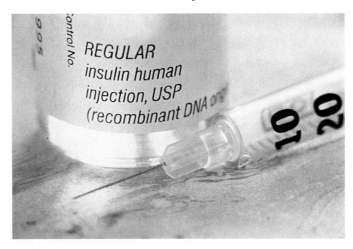

## Fat Experiment Results

The rats who had no fat removed had lots of sugar in their blood the whole time. These results meant they responded slowly to insulin. The rats who had the fat from under the skin taken out also responded slowly. But the rats who had their gut fat removed responded twice as fast to insulin as the other rats. Getting rid of visceral fat also got rid of the insulin resistance, so the researchers concluded that visceral fat causes insulin resistance in young rats.

## Fat and Insulin Resistance in Children

But does the same happen in children? Scientists at the University of Southern California (USC) in Los Angeles hypothesized that visceral fat in people might be contributing to insulin resistance in children in the same way that visceral fat does in rats. But scientists can't trim the fat from people like they can from rats. Instead, they predicted that kids with more fat in their gut would have more trouble using insulin.

Researchers at the University of Southern California measured the weights of 32 children between the ages of 8 and 13.

To investigate this possibility, USC researchers Michael Goran, Martha Cruz and Richard Bergman enlisted the help of 32 children between the ages of 8 and 13. The researchers gathered a variety of data: They weighed each child. They measured the different kinds of fat on the children's bodies. They also measured how well their bodies responded to insulin. Weighing is easy to do, but how did the researchers collect the other data?

## Collecting Data from Humans

Fat isn't easy to see with the naked eye. Fat lies under our skin and between our organs. And there are different ways to measure fat. One way uses calipers. A set of calipers are like pliers that measure fat by squeezing—and sometimes pinching!—a chunk of skin. But Goran and his colleagues needed different data. They needed to find out how much fat coated the organs in the stomach, where the fat is out of reach of calipers.

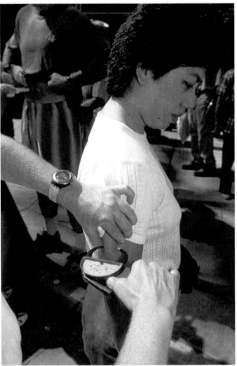

Calipers estimate body fat by measuring the amount of fat present underneath the skin.

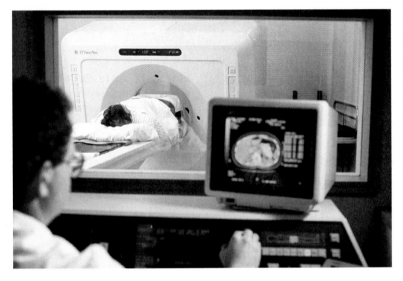

Scientists at the University of Southern California used a magnetic resonance imaging machine (MRI) like the one shown here to study the amount of fat present around internal organs. MRI allows researchers to view structures in the human body in great detail.

## Gathering Data Using MRI

So they decided to get an inside view using MRI, or magnetic resonance imagery. An MRI machine looks like a giant cube that takes up half a room and has a tube running through the middle. Technicians slide a person lying on her back partly or all the way into the tube. Inside, a powerful magnet scans her and creates an image of the different tissues in her body, much like X rays reveal bones inside a leg. Using an MRI scan of each child, the researchers measured how much fat each child had just under the skin and how much fat marbled through the organs.

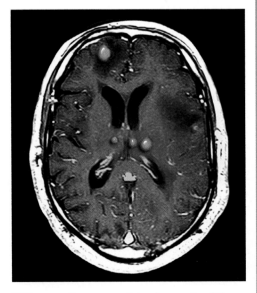

MRI scans allow research to view parts of the body in vivid detail.

## Measuring the Effects of Insulin

Then they had to figure out how sensitive the children's bodies were to insulin. Much like the scientists in the rat study, Goran's team injected insulin into the children's blood, which in healthy kids would cut the amount of sugar in their blood. Then they took a sample of blood every few minutes for three and a half hours. In a laboratory, scientists measured the amount of insulin and sugar in the samples.

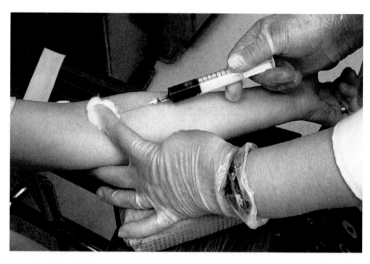

Goran's team of researchers took blood samples from the children in the study in order to measure the amount of sugar and insulin in their blood.

Then the researchers looked for relationships in the data they had collected. They compared the amount of each child's fat with how their bodies responded to insulin. The researchers found that children with more visceral fat took longer to stop pumping sugar into blood—children with more visceral fat were more insulin resistant than children with less visceral fat. But the researchers found that children with more fat under the skin were no more likely to be insulin resistant than children with less fat under their skin. The team concluded that visceral fat, but not other kinds of fat, contributed to insulin resistance, and possibly, diabetes.

## Reversing the Diabetes Trend

Many overweight people have high blood sugar and are insulin resistant. Scientists wondered if the road to diabetes could be reversed for some insulin resistant people by exercise and diet. A group of scientists at the National Institutes of Health started the Diabetes Prevention Program to find out. They took more than 3000 overweight adults from across the United States and divided them into smaller groups. Some they made exercise and eat better than they had been. Others they allowed to behave as they had previously.

After 3 years, the scientists checked the health of the volunteers. Those who exercised regularly and lost about 5% of their weight were far less likely to have diabetes than the other groups.

The Diabetes Prevention Program is helping adults reduce their risk of diabetes through improved diet and exercise.

## The Outlook for Obese Children

But those were adults. Can children seemingly destined to get diabetes benefit from exercise? Bernard Gutin at the Medical College of Georgia in Atlanta studies how exercise improves the health of children and teens. He hypothesized that working up a sweat every day would reduce bad fat in children, even if they didn't change their diet. He took 74 overweight children between the ages of 7 and 11 years of age. Some he made exercise for 40 minutes every day. The rest went about their daily routines. After 4 months, he measured visceral fat using MRI.

Although both groups of children gained visceral fat, the group that exercised gained much less visceral fat than the other group. The exercising group weighed less at the end of 4 months than the non-exercising group as well. He concluded from this experiment that exercise got children in better shape, even without changing their diets.

## Lesson Learned

Fortunately, all of the scientific data supports the hypothesis that most obese children can avoid diabetes. The best route to good health for all children and young adults involves a combination of improved diet and exercise. Staying away from foods high in fat and refined sugars, and getting exercise every day can make a major difference.

The researchers found that 40 minutes of exercise every day can reduce visceral fat in children.

For children and adults alike, studies show that a healthy diet combined with exercise is the most effective way to reduce the risks of both obesity and diabetes.

# UNIT 1 Cell Biology

**Seeing Inside Cells** This confocal micrograph helps biologists see cellular structures and organelles that are difficult to see without these advanced technologies.

## West-Coast Events

**10,000–9,000 Years Ago**
Early people settle in what is now Mexico and southward; hunters-gatherers live in what is now California.

**1769**
Spanish build (1769) first of 21 missions in California at San Diego.

**1848–1850**
Mexico loses California to the U.S. as a result of the Mexican War; California becomes a U.S. state (1850).

**A.D. 1500    1600    1700    1800    1900**

## World Events

**c. 1600**
Compound microscope using two lenses is developed.

**1665**
Robert Hooke observes cells.

**1838–1839**
M. J. Schleiden declares that all plants are made of cells. Thomas Schwann says all animals are made of cells. They propose the cell theory.

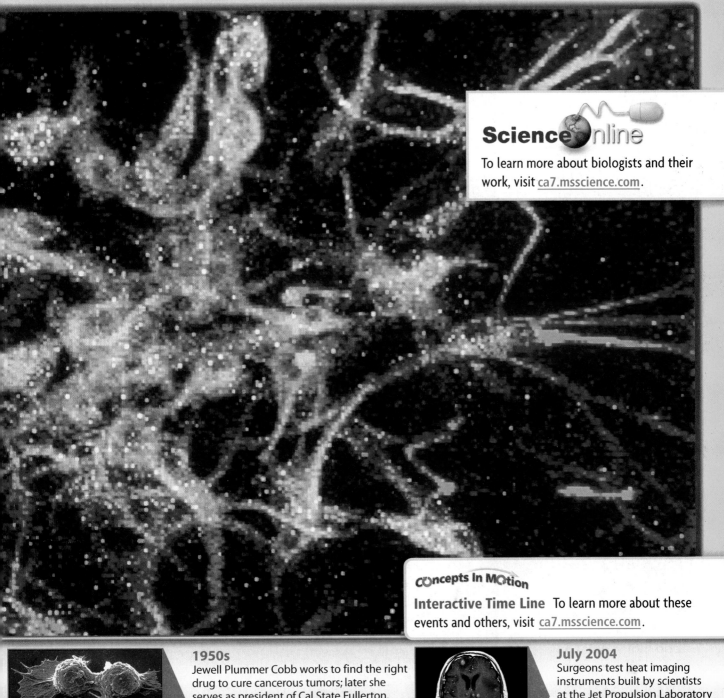

**Science Online**

To learn more about biologists and their work, visit ca7.msscience.com.

**Concepts In Motion**

**Interactive Time Line** To learn more about these events and others, visit ca7.msscience.com.

**1950s**
Jewell Plummer Cobb works to find the right drug to cure cancerous tumors; later she serves as president of Cal State Fullerton.

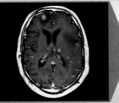

**July 2004**
Surgeons test heat imaging instruments built by scientists at the Jet Propulsion Laboratory (JPL) in Pasadena, California, to map brain tumors.

| 1920 | 1940 | 1960 | 1980 | 2000 | 2020 |

**c. 1930**
Ernst Ruska and Max Knoll of Germany develop the transmission electron microscope (TEM); magnifies sample hundreds of thousands of times.

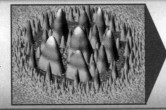

**1981**
Scanning tunneling microscope (STM) invented by Gerd Binnig and Heinrich Rohrer; magnifies a sample a million times.

**1986**
Rita Levi-Montalcini and Stanley Cohen are recognized for their work with growth factors responsible for stem cells dividing and becoming different kinds of cells.

# Cell Structure and Function

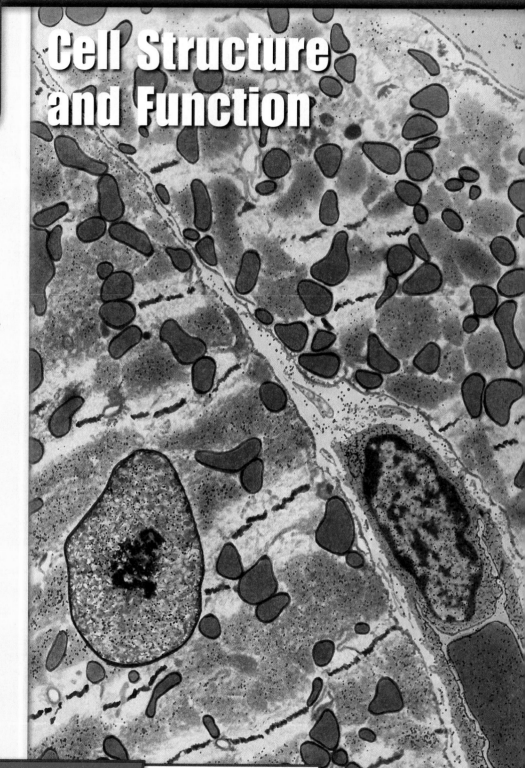

## The BIG Idea

The structures in a cell work together and ensure the survival of the cell.

**LESSON 1** 1.a, 7.a, 7.c

### Cells and Life

**Main Idea** Cells are the smallest unit of life.

**LESSON 2**

1.a, 1.b, 1.c, 2.e, 7.d

### The Cell

**Main Idea** Cells have structures with specific functions.

**LESSON 3**

1.d, 7.a, 7.c, 7.d, 7.e

### Cells and Energy

**Main Idea** All cells can release energy from food molecules. Only some cells can make food molecules using light energy.

## Getting to the Heart of the Matter

Your heart is made of many types of cells, like the ones shown here. This image was created using a transmission electron microscope and a computer. Colors were added to show the different parts of the cell. For example, in the center is the blue-green nucleus.

**Science Journal** Imagine you are the computer technician assigned to color this cell. What color would you choose for the nucleus? Why?

 minutes

## What are we made of?

Some things are so small that you cannot see them without a light microscope. As you begin this chapter, you will use a microscope to observe things you might never have seen before.

### Procedure

1. Complete a lab safety form.

2. Obtain a **microscope** and **slides.**

3. Observe the slides using the microscope according to your teacher's instructions.

4. Change magnifications and adjust again.

5. Draw what you observe. Label your drawing with the magnification you used.

6. Compare your drawings to those of your classmates.

### Think About This

- **Describe** what you observed.

- **List** the changes you observed when you changed magnification.

 7.a, 7.d

---

# Science Online

Visit ca7.msscience.com to:

▶ view **Concepts in Motion**

▶ explore Virtual Labs

▶ access content-related Web links

▶ take the Standards Check

---

**Cells** Make the following Foldable to compare and contrast a plant cell and an animal cell.

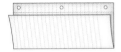 **STEP 1 Fold** a sheet of paper in half lengthwise. Make the back edge about 2 cm longer than the front edge.

**STEP 2 Fold** into thirds. **Unfold** and **cut** along the folds of the top flap to make three flaps.

**STEP 3 Label** the flaps as shown.

Plant  Both  Animal

 Reading *Skill*

**Monitoring Your Comprehension** As you read Lesson 2, write the names of the cell parts found in both plant and animal cells under the center tab. List other cell parts under the tab for the correct cell type.

# Get Ready to Read

## Preview

**①Learn It!** If you know what to expect before reading, it will be easier to understand ideas and relationships presented in the text. Follow these steps to preview your reading assignments.

1. Look at the title and any illustrations that are included.
2. Read the headings, subheadings, and anything in bold letters.
3. Skim over the passage to see how it is organized. Is it divided into many parts?
4. Look at the graphics—pictures, maps, or diagrams. Read their titles, labels, and captions.
5. Set a purpose for your reading. Are you reading to learn something new? Are you reading to find specific information?

**②Practice It!** Take some time to preview this chapter. Skim all the main headings and subheadings. With a partner, discuss your answers to these questions:

- Which part of this chapter looks most interesting to you?
- Are there any words in the headings that are unfamiliar to you?
- Choose one of the lesson standards check questions to discuss with a partner.

**③Apply It!** Now that you have skimmed the chapter, write a short paragraph describing one thing you want to learn from this chapter.

# Target Your Reading

Use this to focus on the main ideas as you read the chapter.

**Reading Tip**

As you preview this chapter, be sure to scan the illustrations, tables, and graphs. Skim the captions.

**1 Before you read** the chapter, respond to the statements below on your worksheet or on a numbered sheet of paper.

- Write an **A** if you **agree** with the statement.
- Write a **D** if you **disagree** with the statement.

**2 After you read** the chapter, look back to this page to see if you've changed your mind about any of the statements.

- If any of your answers changed, explain why.
- Change any false statements into true statements.
- Use your revised statements as a study guide.

| Before You Read A or D | Statement | After You Read A or D |
|---|---|---|
| | **1** All new cells come from preexisting cells. | |
| | **2** A microscope is needed to see most cells. | |
| | **3** Some living things do not require water to survive. | |
| | **4** Chromosomes are in the nucleus of every cell. | |
| | **5** Bacteria have specialized compartments called organelles. | |
| | **6** The cell wall and cytoplasm determine the shape of a cell. | |
| | **7** Oxygen is not required for cellular respiration. | |
| | **8** Cilia are short, hairlike cellular appendages. | |
| | **9** Most multicellular organisms are not dependent on photosynthesis. | |
| | **10** Plants cells are the only cells that can transform light energy. | |

**Science**nline

Print a worksheet of this page at ca7.msscience.com.

**Science Content Standards**

**1.a** Students know cells function similarly in all living organisms.

**7.a** Select and use appropriate tools and technology (including calculators, computers, balances, spring scales, microscopes, and binoculars) to perform tests, collect data, and display data.

**7.c** Communicate the logical connection among hypotheses, science concepts, tests conducted, data collected, and conclusions drawn from the scientific evidence.

## Reading Guide

### What *You'll Learn*

▶ **Summarize** the cell theory.

▶ **Identify** the characteristics of life.

▶ **Explain** the importance of water in a cell.

▶ **Describe** the four basic substances of a cell.

### Why *It's Important*

Learning about cells will help you understand how living organisms function.

### Vocabulary

light microscope
cell theory
homeostasis
protein
nucleic acid
lipid
carbohydrate

### Review Vocabulary

**cell:** basic structural and functional unit of all organisms (Grade 5)

# Cells and Life

**Main Idea** Cells are the smallest unit of life.

**Real-World Reading Connection** People once thought Earth was flat because they did not have tools to discover that it is round. People also had many wrong ideas about living things on Earth. They did not have the tools to observe very small living things.

## Early Ideas About Cells

Most cells are so small, as shown in **Figure 1,** that you cannot see them without some type of magnifying device. There even was a time when people did not know that cells existed. People also once believed that an egg contained a miniature version of an adult organism. They thought the organism's structures just had to increase in size as the organism grew.

## Early Microscopes

After the invention of the light microscope, around 1600, ideas about living things changed. A **light microscope** uses light and has one or more lenses that enlarges an image of something.

**Figure 1  Cell Size** Most cells can only be seen using some type of microscope.

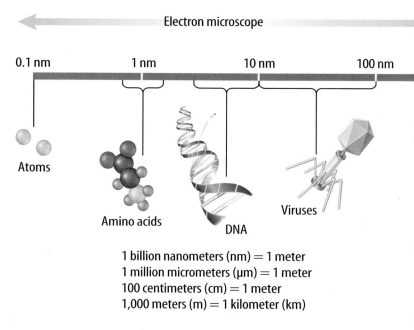

1 billion nanometers (nm) = 1 meter
1 million micrometers (µm) = 1 meter
100 centimeters (cm) = 1 meter
1,000 meters (m) = 1 kilometer (km)

## Modern Microscopes

Most of the structures within a cell are too small to be observed even with a light microscope. The best light microscopes can only enlarge images of objects up to about 1,500 times their original size. With the invention of the electron microscope in the 1930s, scientists were able to see most structures inside a cell, like those shown in **Figure 2.** An electron microscope can enlarge images 100,000 times or more. Improved types of electron microscopes include one that can produce images of atoms on or in surfaces of materials.

 **Figure 1** What is the smallest image size that can be detected by an electron microscope?

## The Cell Theory

Even after the invention of microscopes, scientists were only beginning to understand how cells relate to living things. In the 1830s, a German scientist observed that all plant parts are made of cells. Around the same time, another German scientist made the same observation about animals. Nearly two decades later, a German physician proposed that all cells come from preexisting cells. Together, these ideas became known as the **cell theory,** which is listed below.

- All organisms are made of one or more cells.
- The cell is the smallest unit of life.
- All new cells come from preexisting cells.

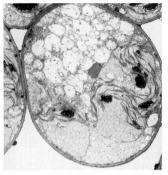

**Figure 2** Many of the details of a plant cell, such as the cell shown below, are visible only with an electron microscope.

TEM  Magnification: 17,000×

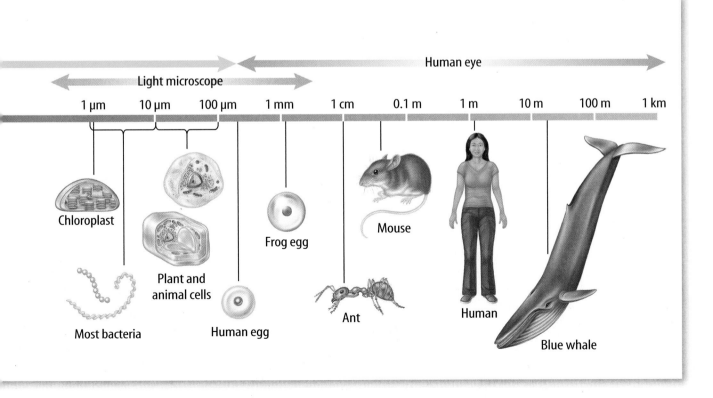

Human eye

Light microscope

1 μm   10 μm   100 μm   1 mm   1 cm   0.1 m   1 m   10 m   100 m   1 km

Chloroplast

Most bacteria

Plant and animal cells

Human egg

Frog egg

Ant

Mouse

Human

Blue whale

**Figure 3** Your environment includes living and nonliving things.
**Identify** the living or once-living things shown here.

# Characteristics of Life

Suppose your class took a field trip to a place like the one shown in **Figure 3.** Your teacher asks you to identify living and nonliving things in the environment. Could you complete this assignment? From observations and evidence gathered over time, scientists agree that all living things, or organisms, have common characteristics. Whether made of one cell or many cells, organisms are organized, respond, grow and develop, reproduce, maintain certain internal conditions, and use energy.

## Organization

The rooms and things in your home are organized in some way. The oven and refrigerator are in the kitchen, a sink and toilet are in the bathroom, and clothes and shoes are in the closets. Cells and organisms also are organized. Cells contain structures that have specialized functions similar to the way a house has rooms for different activities. Some organisms have a system of nerves controlled by a brain, much like a house has a system of electrical wires controlled by a circuit-breaker box. You will read more about the organization inside individual cells in the next lesson, and about the organization within organisms in Chapter 2.

**ACADEMIC VOCABULARY**

process (PRAH sehs)
*(noun)* a series of natural activities
*New cells form by the process of cell division.*

## Responses

If someone throws a ball at you, you might try to catch it. This is because you are able to respond to changes in your environment. Another example of the way living things respond is the way your body responds to an invasion by a disease-causing virus or bacterium. There are cells in your body that can recognize these invaders and respond with different **processes** to get rid of them.

 What characteristics are common to all organisms?

**Figure 4** The quino checkerspot butterfly, *Euphydryas editha quino,* undergoes many changes as it grows and develops from a caterpillar to an adult.

Caterpillar

Chrysalis

Butterfly

## Growth and Development

Humans grow and develop just as all organisms do. When organisms grow, they increase in size. Growth in multicellular organisms—organisms made of many cells—usually happens as the number of cells increases. An organism that is only one cell also grows because the cell increases in size.

Development includes all the changes that occur in an organism. For example, you might now be able to play a musical instrument or some sport that you could not play ten years ago. Some organisms have extraordinary changes over their lifetime, such as the butterfly shown in **Figure 4.**

## Reproduction

You read earlier in this lesson that all cells come from preexisting cells. The same is true for organisms. In order for organisms to continue to exist, they must reproduce and create offspring similar to themselves. Not every organism must reproduce. However, for a type of organism to continue to exist, reproduction must occur among some organisms of that type. Some organisms must have a mate to reproduce but others can reproduce without a mate.

## Homeostasis

Have you ever noticed that if you drink more water than usual, you have to use the restroom more often? That is because your body is maintaining **homeostasis** (hoh mee oh STAY sus) or trying to keep its internal conditions within certain limits. All organisms have the ability to maintain homeostasis, but the methods and needs vary depending on the organism and its environment. For example, many freshwater fish would not survive if placed in salt water because they would not be able to control the amount of salt in their bodies. A human maintains a body temperature of about 37°C by sweating, shivering, or changing the flow of blood.

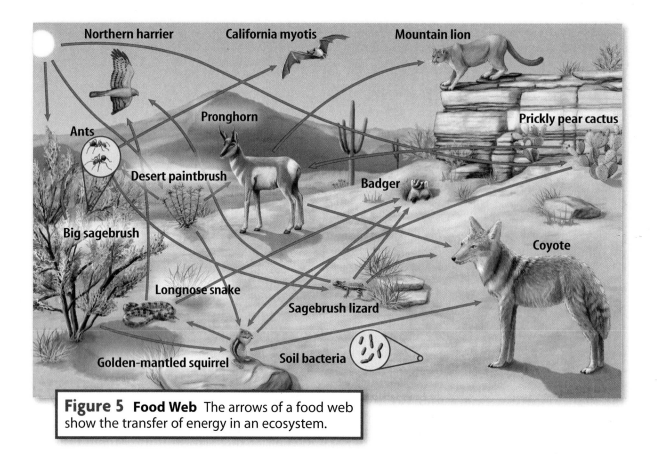

**Figure 5 Food Web** The arrows of a food web show the transfer of energy in an ecosystem.

## Energy

You use energy when you look at the pages of this book, sit at your desk, and when your heart pumps blood throughout your body. Cells continuously use energy to transport substances, make new cells, and perform chemical reactions. Our cells get energy from the food we eat. This energy originally came to Earth from the Sun, as shown in **Figure 5.** The Sun provides energy for nearly all the organisms on Earth. In Lesson 3, you will read about how plants use light energy to make food.

## Chemistry of a Cell

When you were younger, you might have played with some kind of building blocks. You probably made many things using different sizes and shapes of blocks. In a similar way, a cell can make different things using atoms and molecules as its building blocks. You might recall from another science class that atoms combine to make molecules. Most of the molecules in living things are made from six kinds of atoms: sulfur, nitrogen, potassium, hydrogen, oxygen, and carbon. The molecules in cells can combine in many ways to make different substances that are used for thousands of different functions.

**SCIENCE USE V. COMMON USE**

**energy**

*Science Use* the capacity of a physical or biological system to do work. *Our cells release energy from the food we eat.*

*Common Use* an imaginative or lively style. *His writing conveys great energy.*

 **Reading Check** What provides energy for many organisms on Earth?

## Water—The Main Ingredient

Have you ever wondered what you are made of? About two-thirds of your body's mass is water. Most of that water—67 percent—is inside cells and the rest surrounds cells. The water surrounding cells helps to maintain homeostasis because it helps to insulate your body. Water also can dissolve many different kinds of molecules. This enables your blood, which is mostly water, to transport substances throughout your body.

A unique property of water is that each water molecule has an area that is more negative—called the negative end—than the other area—called the positive end. As shown in **Figure 6,** the negative end of a water molecule is attracted to the positive end of another water molecule, similar to the way magnets are attracted to each other. This attraction is one reason why water can travel from the ground to leaves at the top of trees.

## Basic Substances

Besides water, cells contain substances that can be classified as proteins, nucleic acids, lipids, or carbohydrates. They also are called macromolecules. The prefix *macro-* means *large*. Macromolecules are large complex molecules usually made of long chains of smaller molecules.

**Proteins** The molecules necessary for nearly everything cells and organisms do are proteins, such as the examples listed in **Table 1.** There are thousands of different proteins. **Proteins** are folded chains or groups of folded chains of molecules called amino acids. Each protein has a specific sequence of amino acids within its chains. They must be folded correctly for the protein to function properly. Proteins have many functions in organisms and some proteins have the same function in different species of organisms.

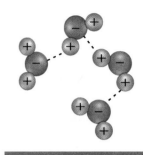

**Figure 6** The attraction among water molecules is shown here.

**Infer** how water molecules are able to move from the ground to the top of a tree.

**Water Molecules**

**WORD ORIGIN**

protein
from Greek *proteios;* means *the first quality*

| Table 1 Types of Proteins | |
|---|---|
| **Name** | **Function** |
| Keratin (KEH rih tihn) | Provides structural support for hair, horns, and feathers |
| Hemoglobin (HEE muh gloh bun) | Transports oxygen in the blood of animals with backbones |
| Casein (KAY seen) | Found in milk; a source of amino acids, phosphorus, and calcium when digested |
| Insulin (IHN suh lun) | Regulates the amount of sugar in the blood of animals with backbones |
| Amylase (AM uh lays) | Found in saliva; speeds up the breakdown of starch molecules |

## How can you observe DNA in a cell?

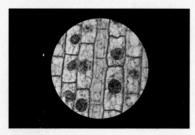

Stained LM  Magnification: 400×

You have read that DNA is one of the basic substances of cells. In this lab, you will observe and estimate the number of onion root-tip cells with visible DNA. You will collect data similar to the way that scientists do.

### Data Collection

1. Complete a lab safety form.

2. Obtain a microscope and slides from your teacher. Use care and properly handle your microscope.

3. Observe the onion root-tip cells at the magnification assigned by your teacher.

4. Determine the approximate number of cells in your field of view and the number of cells with visible DNA.

### Data Analysis

1. **Using** your data, find the percentage of cells with visible DNA.

2. **Compare** your results with the results of other students. Are all the results the same? Explain.

3. **Create** a data table for the entire class that lists individual results.

4. **Calculate** the percentage of cells with visible DNA at each magnification.

5. **Explain** why viewing the cells at different magnifications changed the percentage of cells with visible DNA.

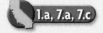 1.a, 7.a, 7.c

**Nucleic Acids** Proteins are important to all cells but they cannot be made without nucleic (noo KLEE ihk) acids. **Nucleic acids** are long chains of molecules called nucleotides. One kind of nucleic acid is deoxyribonucleic (dee AHK sih ri boh noo klee ihk) acid (DNA). It consists of only four types of nucleotides, but there are billions of them in DNA. The arrangement of nucleotides in a cell's DNA is a code that contains the cell's genetic information, or genome. The genetic information in DNA is used to make another kind of nucleic acid—ribonucleic (ri boh noo KLEE ihk) acid (RNA). It is RNA that is used to make proteins. You will read more about DNA in Lesson 2 of this chapter and in other chapters of this book.

 What is required to make proteins?

**Lipids** Have you ever tried to mix oil and water? You might have noticed that they do not mix with each other. This is because oil is a lipid. A **lipid** is a large molecule that does not dissolve in water. The main kinds of lipids are fats, phospholipids (fahs foh LIH pids), steroids, and waxes. Fat molecules store large amounts of chemical energy. Phospholipids, and cholesterol, a steroid, are important parts of cells. Waxes help reduce water loss and can form a barrier to invaders like the wax in our ears does.

**Carbohydrates** Fruits and candy contain different kinds of sugar. Breads and pasta are mostly starch. Vegetables have large amounts of fiber made of cellulose. The shell of a lobster is mostly made of a substance called chitin. What do sugar, starch, cellulose, and chitin have in common? They are all carbohydrates. A **carbohydrate** stores energy and is made of one sugar molecule, a pair of sugar molecules, or a chain of sugar molecules. The energy in sugars and starches can be released quickly through chemical reactions in cells. Most cells cannot release the energy in cellulose and chitin. Carbohydrates make up the structural parts of cells.

# What have you learned about cells and life?

You have read in this lesson that

- a light microscope is needed to see most cells;
- a cell is the smallest unit of a living organism;
- the cell theory was developed after many observations by scientists;
- for something to be a living thing, it must have all the characteristics of life;
- all living things depend on water for their survival; and
- cells contain four basic substances—proteins, nucleic acids, lipids, and carbohydrates.

## LESSON 1 Review

### Summarize

Create your own lesson summary as you organize an **outline.**

1. **Scan** the lesson. Find and list the first **red** main heading.

2. **Review** the text after the heading and list 2–3 details about the heading.

3. **Find** and list each **blue** subheading that follows the **red** main heading.

4. **List** 2–3 details, key terms, and definitions under each **blue** subheading.

5. **Review** additional **red** main headings and their supporting **blue** subheadings. List 2–3 details about each.

 ELA7: W 2.5

### Standards Check

#### Using Vocabulary

1. Use the term *homeostasis* in a sentence. `1.a`

2. Distinguish between ribonucleic acid and a protein. `1.a`

#### Understanding Main Ideas

3. Which characteristic of life is shown when you squint in bright light? `1.a`
   A. growth and development
   B. reproduction
   C. organization
   D. responses

4. **Assess** the importance of the invention of the microscope to science. `1.a`

5. **Summarize** the cell theory in your own words. `1.a`

6. **Give an example** for each of the four basic substances of a cell. `1.a`

7. **Explain** why water is important to cells. `1.a`

#### Applying Science

8. **Critique** the following statement: A kite is a living thing. `1.a`

9. **Organize** Copy and fill in the graphic organizer below. In each of the smaller ovals, list a characteristic of life. `1.a`

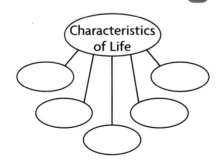

For more practice, visit **Standards Check** at ca7.msscience.com.

### Science Content Standards

**1.a** Students know cells function similarly in all living organisms.
**1.b** Students know the characteristics that distinguish plant cells from animal cells, including chloroplasts and cell walls.
**1.c** Students know the nucleus is the repository for genetic information in plant and animal cells.
**2.e** Students know DNA (deoxyribonucleic acid) is the genetic material of living organisms and is located in the chromosomes of each cell.
**7.d** Construct scale models, maps, and appropriately labeled diagrams to communicate scientific knowledge (e.g., motion of Earth's plates and cell structure).

## Reading Guide

### What *You'll Learn*

▶ **State** the role of the nucleus in a cell.

▶ **Compare and contrast** an animal cell and a plant cell.

▶ **Distinguish** between a prokaryotic cell and a eukaryotic cell.

### Why *It's Important*

Learning the functions of the parts of cells will help you understand how they are important in maintaining life.

### Vocabulary

cell membrane
cytoplasm
organelle
chromosome
mitochondrion
prokaryotic cell

cell wall
cytoskeleton
nucleus
ribosome
chloroplast
eukaryotic cell

# The Cell

**Main Idea** Cells have structures with specific functions.

**Real-World Reading Connection** Your body contains different structures that work together to keep you alive and healthy. For example, your skin protects your body, your stomach helps to digest food, and your brain controls your responses. Your cells also have structures that function in each cell.

## Cell Shape and Movement

Cells in your body have a variety of shapes and sizes, as shown in **Figure 7.** Different shapes relate to different functions. For example, a human red blood cell easily passes into the smallest blood vessels. A nerve cell can send signals over long distances within your body. Other organisms also have cells with shapes that relate to their functions. Some plant cells are hollow and make up tubelike structures that carry water and dissolved substances.

### Cell Membrane

Regardless of a cell's shape and function, every cell has a flexible covering that surrounds it called the **cell membrane.** A membrane can be made of one or more layers of linked molecules. The cell membrane protects the inside of a cell from the environment outside the cell. Because of its specific chemical makeup, the cell membrane is selectively permeable. This means the cell membrane does not allow all types of substances into the cell. As shown in **Figure 8,** some things cannot enter a cell and others cannot leave a cell.

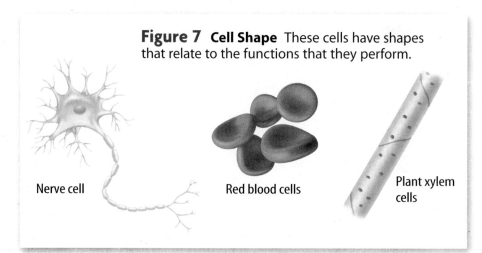

**Figure 7 Cell Shape** These cells have shapes that relate to the functions that they perform.

Nerve cell

Red blood cells

Plant xylem cells

# Visualizing the Cell Membrane

**Figure 8**
The cell membrane is a strong, flexible layer of phospholipids (gold) with protein doorways (purple). Molecules and substances enter and leave a cell by passing through the cell membrane in one of four ways.

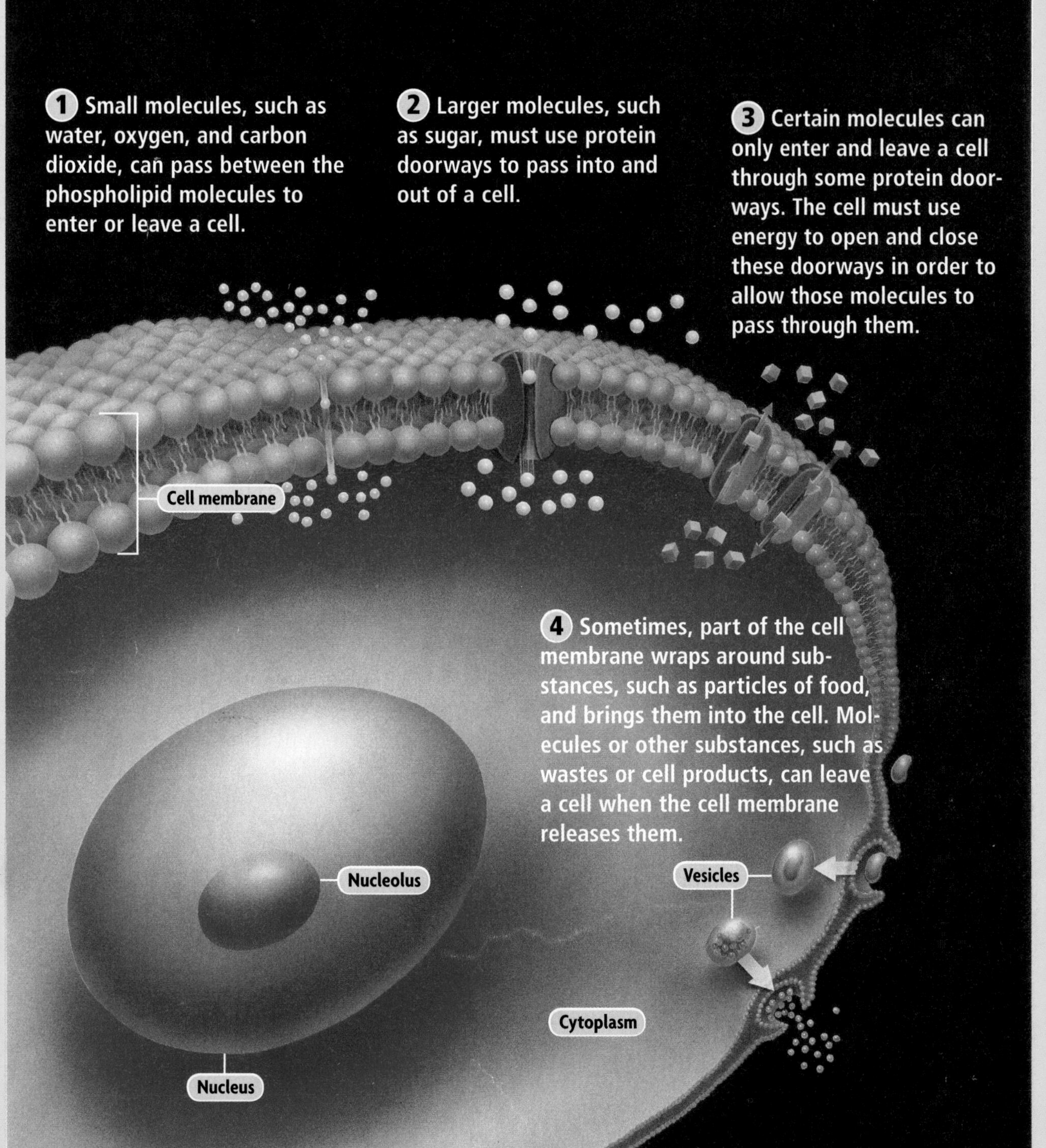

**1** Small molecules, such as water, oxygen, and carbon dioxide, can pass between the phospholipid molecules to enter or leave a cell.

**2** Larger molecules, such as sugar, must use protein doorways to pass into and out of a cell.

**3** Certain molecules can only enter and leave a cell through some protein doorways. The cell must use energy to open and close these doorways in order to allow those molecules to pass through them.

**4** Sometimes, part of the cell membrane wraps around substances, such as particles of food, and brings them into the cell. Molecules or other substances, such as wastes or cell products, can leave a cell when the cell membrane releases them.

Cell membrane

Nucleolus

Nucleus

Vesicles

Cytoplasm

*Contributed by National Geographic*

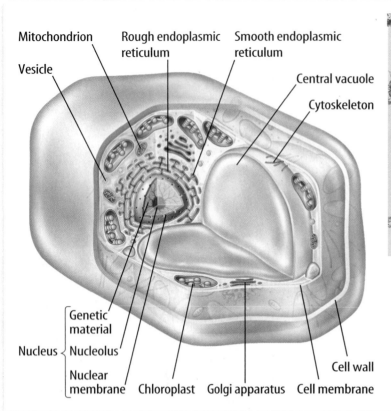

Mitochondrion
Rough endoplasmic reticulum
Smooth endoplasmic reticulum
Central vacuole
Cytoskeleton
Vesicle

Nucleus
- Genetic material
- Nucleolus
- Nuclear membrane

Chloroplast
Golgi apparatus
Cell membrane
Cell wall

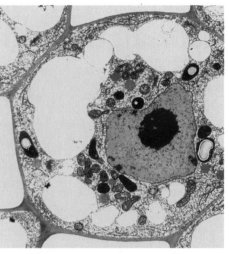

**Figure 9** **Plant Cell** The cell wall maintains the shape of a plant cell.

**COncepts In MOtion**
To visualize the parts of a plant cell, visit ca7.msscience.com.

## Cell Wall

Some cells, such as those in plants, fungi, and some bacteria, have a rigid **cell wall** that surrounds the cell outside its cell membrane. Plants and fungi can grow upward against the force of gravity because the rigid cell wall maintains the cell's shape, supports, and protects the cell. Substances can pass freely through a cell wall, unlike the cell membrane. Cell walls of plants, as shown in **Figure 9,** are made mostly of cellulose, a carbohydrate. Humans cannot digest cellulose, but cellulose is an important part of our diets. Cellulose stimulates the production of mucus in our intestines, which helps food travel smoothly through them.

## Cell Appendages

Some animals can run, hop, fly, or swim using appendages such as legs, wings, or fins. Cells can also have appendages. A flagellum (fluh JEH lum) (plural, flagella) is a tail-like appendage. Some single-celled organisms have one or more flagella. Many organisms produce sperm and each sperm moves by using its flagellum.

Cilia (SIH lee uh) (singular, cilium) are short, hairlike appendages. Cilia usually occur in large numbers on a cell, but a cell usually only has one flagellum. Some single-celled organisms move by the coordinated motion of cilia. Cilia also can be on the surface of a cell that does not move, as shown in **Figure 10.** In this case, the cilia help fluids move across the cell's surface.

**Figure 10** A respiratory cell has cilia that help move fluids across the cell's surface.

**Cilia**

Color-enhanced SEM Magnification: 1000×

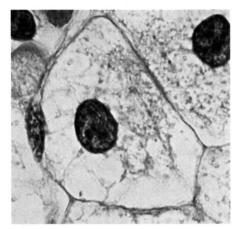
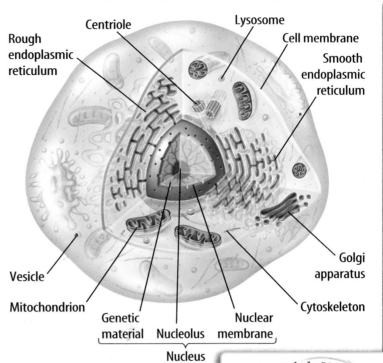

**Figure 11 Animal Cell** Instead of a cell wall, the cytoskeleton maintains the shape of an animal cell.

**Find** other differences between a plant and an animal cell.

Labels for figure: Rough endoplasmic reticulum, Centriole, Lysosome, Cell membrane, Smooth endoplasmic reticulum, Golgi apparatus, Cytoskeleton, Nuclear membrane, Nucleolus, Genetic material, Nucleus, Mitochondrion, Vesicle

**Concepts In Motion**
To visualize the parts of an animal cell, visit ca7.msscience.com.

## Cytoplasm and the Cytoskeleton

The inside of a cell contains **cytoplasm**—a thick fluid made mostly of water. The structures and substance that are inside a cell, as shown in **Figure 9** and **Figure 11,** are suspended in the cytoplasm.

Your body contains a skeleton and muscles that allow you to move and maintain your shape. Individual cells do not have a skeleton of bones. Instead, cells have a network of fibers called the **cytoskeleton.** The cytoskeleton, shown in **Figure 11,** is like a thick web and plays a role in muscle contraction, cell division, cell movement, and maintenance of cell shape. Both cilia and flagella are able to move because they contain fibers of the cytoskeleton.

 **Reading Check** What is the function of the cytoskeleton?

**Word Origin**

cytoplasm
*cyto–* from Greek *kytos;* means *a hollow receptacle*
*–plasm* Greek; means *something molded*

## Cell Organelles

What if your school had only one large room? You might be trying to learn about cell organelles, while the teacher standing beside you is conducting the school choir. This would probably make learning nearly impossible. However, your school has classrooms in which different things can occur at the same time without interference. Cells also have many processes going on at the same time. Instead of classrooms, some cells have **organelles**—structures in the cytoplasm that have specific functions. However, the single-celled organisms—commonly called bacteria—do not have these structures.

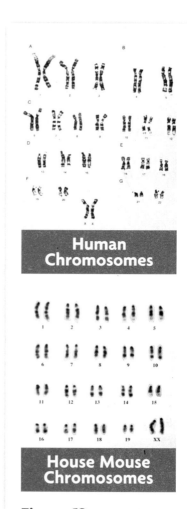

**Human Chromosomes**

**House Mouse Chromosomes**

**Figure 12** Each of these photos, called a karyotype, is of chromosomes removed from a nucleus.

## Nucleus—The Control Center

A large organelle inside many cells is the **nucleus,** as shown in **Figure 9** and **Figure 11** on the previous two pages. The nucleus (plural, nuclei) contains the genetic material—a chemical code for making all the molecules of a cell. Because of this, the nucleus often is called the control center of the cell. The nucleus is membrane-bound. That means it has a membrane surrounding it. Substances can pass into and out of the nucleus through small holes or pores in the nucleus' membrane. Inside the nucleus is the nucleolus. It helps make structures that make proteins.

The genetic material in the nucleus is made of long chains of DNA that are coiled into structures called **chromosomes.** Proteins in chromosomes also help the DNA coil. Cells in the same kind of organisms have the same number of chromosomes. For example, humans have 23 pairs of chromosomes in each cell but mice have 20 pairs in each cell, as shown in **Figure 12.**

## Manufacturing

A cell makes many kinds of molecules in order to perform different functions. You read in Lesson 1 that proteins are important molecules in cells. Proteins are built within small structures called **ribosomes.** A ribosome is different from other cell organelles because it is not surrounded by a membrane and is found in all cells. For a cell with a nucleus, ribosomes are made in the nucleolus and move into the cytoplasm through the nucleus' membrane. Ribosomes can be attached to an organelle called the endoplasmic reticulum (en duh PLAZ mihk • rih TIHK yuh lum). The endoplasmic reticulum (ER), as shown in **Figure 13,** is a highly-folded membrane that is connected to the nucleus' membrane. ER with ribosomes on its surface is called rough ER. Rough ER is important for making and modifying proteins. ER without ribosomes is called smooth ER. Smooth ER is important for making lipids and helps rid cells of chemicals and poisons.

**Figure 13** These electron micrographs show that ribosomes are attached to rough ER but are not attached to smooth ER.

**Relate** the presence of ribosomes on rough ER to its function.

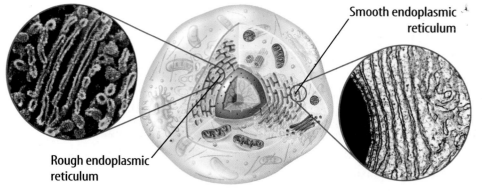

Smooth endoplasmic reticulum

Rough endoplasmic reticulum

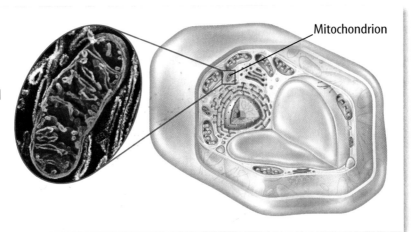

**Figure 14** Except for bacteria, all cells have mitochondria. They release the energy used by a cell and an organism.

Mitochondrion

## Energy Processing

Recall that using energy is a characteristic of life. There are two types of organelles that process the energy used by cells.

Chemical processes that release most of the energy used by a cell occur inside membrane-bound organelles called mitochondria. This energy is used for nearly all of a cell's and an organism's functions. A **mitochondrion** (mi tuh KAHN dree uhn) (plural, mitochondria), as shown in **Figure 14,** transforms the unusable energy in food molecules, into a form of usable energy. Mitochondria sometimes are called the power plants of a cell. Cells that require a lot of energy, such as muscle cells, have more mitochondria than cells that require less energy, such as skin cells.

 **Reading Check** What kind of cells require more mitochondria?

Some organisms, such as nearly all plants and some single-celled organisms, can make their own food. In plants, this happens in membrane-bound organelles called chloroplasts. A **chloroplast** (KLOR uh plast), as shown in **Figure 15,** uses light energy to make food—a type of sugar—from water and carbon dioxide. Some bacteria can make their own food, but they do not have chloroplasts.

**WORD ORIGIN**
mitochondria
from Greek *mitos* (means *thread*) and *khondrion* (means *little granule*)

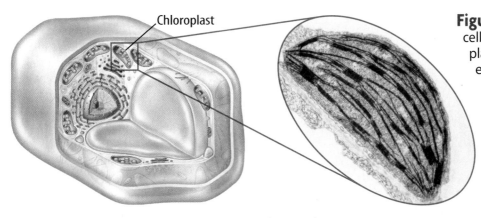

Chloroplast

**Figure 15** Only plant cells contain chloroplasts. They use light energy to make food.

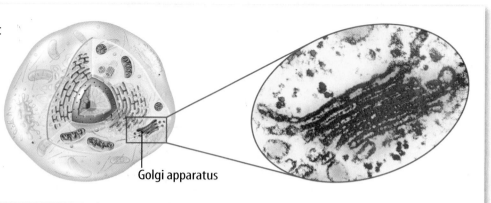

**Figure 16** Plant and animal cells contain Golgi apparatuses—flattened stacks of membranes.

Golgi apparatus

**ACADEMIC VOCABULARY**

modify (MAH deh fi)
*(verb)* to make minor changes. *The teacher modified her lesson to meet the needs of her students.*

## Processing, Transporting, and Storing

The Golgi apparatus, as shown in **Figure 16,** is like a processing factory for the cell. It makes, sorts, and ships molecules. The Golgi apparatus also **modifies,** stores, and directs the movement of molecules made in the ER. Some cells contain large numbers of Golgi apparatuses because the cells secrete substances that are needed by other cells or processes in an organism.

Within the cytoplasm are small, ball-like organelles called vesicles. A vesicle is made of membranes and transports or carries molecules throughout the cytoplasm. They carry substances to the cell membrane where they are released from the cell. Some vesicles form from the Golgi apparatus.

The storage organelles of a cell are vacuoles. Small vacuoles can contain food molecules, water, or waste products from the cell. An animal cell contains a special vacuole called the lysosome that stores digestive enzymes. A plant cell, like the one shown in **Figure 17,** has a large vacuole called the central vacuole. It stores water and other molecules important for a plant cell. The central vacuole enlarges when water enters a plant cell and shrinks when water leaves.

As you have just read, cells are organized and have specialized structures for different functions. Some cell structures are common to all cells, but other structures are found only in certain cell types, as shown in **Table 2** on the next page.

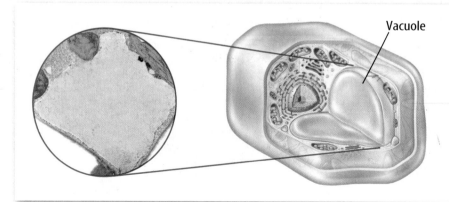

Vacuole

**Figure 17** Vacuoles are found in plant and animal cells and are used for the temporary storage of materials. The central vacuole is usually the largest organelle in a plant cell.

Concepts In Motion

**Interactive Table** To organize information about cell structures, visit Tables at ca7.msscience.com.

## Table 2 Cell Structure

| Cell Structure | Example | Function | Cell Type |
|---|---|---|---|
| Cell membrane | | regulates movement of substances into and out of a cell | all cells |
| Cell wall | | provides shape, protection, and support | plants, fungi, and some bacteria |
| Flagellum | | movement | some single-celled organisms and some sperm |
| Cilium | | movement | some single-celled organisms and some animal cells |
| Cytoskeleton | | cell shape and movement | all cells |
| Nucleus | | controls cell functions | most cells except bacterial cells |
| Ribosome | | site of protein production | all cells |
| Endoplasmic reticulum | | • smooth—makes lipids and gets rid of chemicals and poisons • rough—makes and modifies proteins | most cells except bacterial cells |
| Mitochondrion | | releases energy | most cells except bacterial cells |
| Chloroplast | | makes food | most plant cells |
| Golgi apparatus | | modifies, stores, and directs the movement of molecules made by ER | most cells except bacterial cells |
| Vesicle | | transports substances | most cells except bacterial cells |
| Lysosome | | stores digestive enzymes | most cells except plant and bacterial cells |
| Central vacuole | | stores water and plant substances | plant cells |

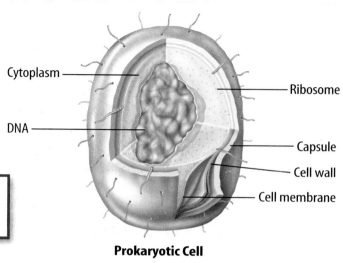

Cytoplasm

DNA

Ribosome

Capsule

Cell wall

Cell membrane

**Prokaryotic Cell**

**Figure 18** This single-celled organism has a cell membrane and DNA, but no organelles.

# Cell Types

You have read that not all cells have organelles. Scientists use this and other facts about cells to classify cells. A cell without a nucleus and most other organelles is classified as a **prokaryotic** (proh kayr ee AH tihk) **cell.** A cell with a nucleus and other organelles is classified as a **eukaryotic** (yew kayr ee AH tik) **cell.**

## Prokaryotic Cells

The first living things to inhabit Earth probably were prokaryotic cells. Evidence indicates that they were the only forms of life on Earth for billions of years. Like all cells, a prokaryotic cell has a cell membrane and DNA, as shown in **Figure 18.** Instead of pairs of chromosomes, a prokaryotic cell has a loop of DNA. Prokaryotic cells exist only as single-celled organisms. An organism that is one prokaryotic cell is called a prokaryote (proh KAYR ee oht). Many prokaryotes have cell walls and flagella.

Prokaryotes also are known as bacteria. Some bacteria harm humans, such as *Salmonella* (sal muh NEH la) bacteria that cause food poisoning. Other bacteria are beneficial to humans. Many antibiotics are produced using *Streptomyces* (strep tuh MI seez) bacteria. *Escherichia* (esch uh RIH kee uh) bacteria live in our intestines and protect us from infections caused by other harmful bacteria. They also help us digest food and absorb some nutrients.

Some bacteria in the environment are essential for decomposing dead organisms and recycling nutrients. Other bacteria can survive in extreme environmental conditions, such as extreme hot or cold temperatures or extreme salty conditions. For example, some bacteria, such as the type shown in **Figure 19,** can survive in temperatures up to 85°C (185°F).

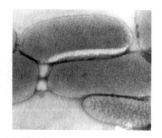

**Figure 19** *Thermus thermophilus* (THERM us • ther moh FIH lus) bacteria have been discovered near hydrothermal vents and in some hot springs.

 **Reading Check** How are bacteria beneficial to humans?

## Eukaryotic Cells

The plant and animal cells on pages 18 and 19 are examples of eukaryotic cells. Besides differences in their structures and components, eukaryotic cells are larger than prokaryotic cells, as shown in **Figure 20.** Protists, fungi, plants, and animals all are made of one or more eukaryotic cells so they are called eukaryotes (yew KAYR ee ohts). Many scientists suggest that the eukaryotic cell evolved as a result of one prokaryotic cell becoming part of another prokaryotic cell. Because mitochondria and chloroplasts contain their own DNA, scientists suggest that they might have been prokaryotic cells that became part of another prokaryotic cell. Over time, the mitochondrion and chloroplast lost the ability to exist on their own.

 **Visual Check** **Figure 20** Why do the yeast cells and *E. coli* appear similar in size when *E. coli* are really smaller?

**Figure 20 Size Comparison** Eukaryotic cells are much larger than prokaryotic cells.

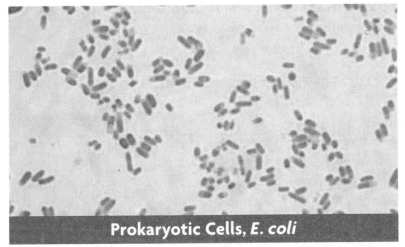

**Prokaryotic Cells, *E. coli***

Stained LM Magnification: 2000×

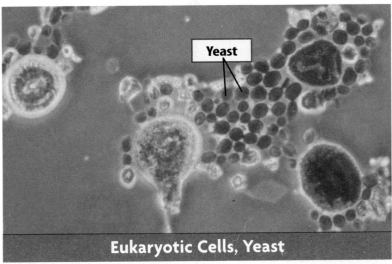

**Yeast**

**Eukaryotic Cells, Yeast**

Stained LM Magnification: 250×

 **MiniLab**

**How can you model a cell?**

00:15 minutes

**Procedure**

1. Complete a lab safety form.
2. Build the cell type that your teacher assigns your lab group, using available **materials.**
3. Briefly present your group's model to your class.

**Analysis**

1. **Explain** how you decided what to include in your cell model.
2. **Compare and contrast** this model and your drawings from the Launch Lab.
3. **Justify** structures you included in your cell model.

 **1.b, 7.d**

**WORD ORIGIN**
eukaryotic
from Greek *eu–* (means *well*) and *karyon* (means *nut, kernel*)

# What have you learned about the cell?

The parts of a cell have functions that ensure the survival of the cell. The cell membrane controls what enters and exits a cell. The cell wall and cytoskeleton determine the shape of a cell. Most cell organelles are membrane-bound. Chromosomes in a cell's nucleus contain genetic information.

Two cell types are prokaryotic and eukaryotic. Prokaryotic cells do not contain any membrane-bound organelles. Prokaryotic cells live in a wide range of environments and have various roles. Eukaryotic cells have a nucleus and other membrane-bound organelles. Eukaryotic cells have different roles in organisms.

# LESSON 2 Review

## Summarize

Create your own lesson summary as you write a **newsletter.**

1. **Write** this lesson title, number, and page numbers at the top of a sheet of paper.

2. **Review** the text after the red main headings and write one sentence about each. These will be the headlines of your newsletter.

3. **Review** the text and write 2–3 sentences about each **blue** subheading. These sentences should tell *who, what, when, where,* or *why* information about each headline.

4. **Illustrate** your newsletter with diagrams of important structures and processes next to each headline.

 ELA7: W 2.5

## Standards Check

### Using Vocabulary

1. Distinguish between a cell membrane and a cell wall. **1.b**

2. Use the term *chromosome* in a sentence.

### Understanding Main Ideas

3. Which organelle builds proteins? **1.a**

   A. mitochondrion
   B. ribosome
   C. chloroplast
   D. Golgi apparatus

4. **Evaluate** why each of these organelles is necessary for an animal cell: nucleus, mitochondria, endoplasmic reticulum, Golgi apparatus. **1.c, 1.d**

5. **Explain** the role of the cytoskeleton. **1.a**

6. **Construct** a concept map using the following terms: *cells, circular DNA, eukaryotic, nucleus, membrane-bound organelles, prokaryotic.* **2.e**

### Applying Science

7. **Form a hypothesis** about why organelles are surrounded by membranes. **1.a**

8. **Classify** You use a microscope and observe a cell with a nucleus and a cell wall. How would you classify it? Defend your answer. **1.b**

9. **Compare** Copy and fill in the graphic organizer below to compare the structures a plant cell to the structures of an animal cell. **1.b**

| Structure | Plant Cell (yes or no) | Animal Cell (yes or no) |
|---|---|---|
|  |  |  |

**Science Online**

For more practice, visit **Standards Check** at ca7.msscience.com.

# Applying Math

## Cell Volume and Surface Area

 1.g, 7.g

 MA7: MG 3.6

The cell membrane controls the type and quantity of substances that enter and leave a cell. As a cell grows, the surface area of its cell membrane and the volume inside the cell increase. When the surface area of a cell's membrane cannot process enough of the substances required by the cell's volume, the cell stops growing. If two cells have the same volume, the cell with the larger surface area can grow larger.

### Example

Find the surface areas and volumes of the two solids shown in the table. Which "cell" can grow larger?

**① Find the volume of each solid.**

|  | Solid 1 | Solid 2 |
|---|---|---|
|  | 2 cm, 2 cm, 2 cm | 2 cm, 1 cm, 4 cm |
| **What you know:** | $l = 2$ cm, $w = 2$ cm, $h = 2$ cm | $l = 2$ cm, $w = 4$ cm, $h = 1$ cm |
| **What you need to find:** | Volume, $V$ | $V$ |
| **Use this equation:** | $V_1 = lwh$ | $V_2 = lwh$ |
| **Substitute:** | $V_1 = 2 \times 2 \times 2$ or **8 cm³** | $V_2 = 2 \times 4 \times 1$ or **8 cm³** |

**Answer:** Both solids have the same volume.

**② Compare the surface areas of the solids.**

|  | Solid 1 | Solid 2 |
|---|---|---|
| **What you need to find:** | Surface area, $SA$ | $SA$ |
| **Use this formula:** | $SA_1 = 2lw + 2wh + 2lh$ | $SA_2 = 2lw + 2wh + 2lh$ |
| **Substitute:** | $SA_1 = (2 \times 2 \times 2) +$ $(2 \times 2 \times 2)$ or **24 cm²** | $SA_2 = (2 \times 4 \times 2) +$ $(2 \times 2 \times 1)$ or **28 cm²** |

**Answer:** *Solid 1* and *Solid 2* have the same volumes but *Solid 2* has a greater surface area than *Solid 1*. Therefore, *Solid 2* can grow larger.

---

### Practice Problems

1. What is the volume of a cube with a length of 3 cm, a width of 2 cm, and a height of 4 cm?

2. What is this cube's surface area?

Science Online
For more math practice, visit Math Practice at
ca7.msscience.com.

### Science Content Standards

**1.d** Students know that mitochondria liberate energy for the work that cells do and that chloroplasts capture sunlight energy for photosynthesis.
**Also covers:** 7.a, 7.c, 7.d, 7.e

## Reading Guide

### What *You'll Learn*

▶ **Compare and contrast** cellular respiration and photosynthesis.

▶ **Describe** the basic chemical reaction of photosynthesis.

▶ **Explain** the importance of pigments in photosynthesis.

▶ **Relate** photosynthesis to cellular respiration.

### Why *It's Important*

All organisms must transform and use energy in order to survive.

### Vocabulary

cellular respiration
ATP
glycolysis
fermentation
photosynthesis

### Review Vocabulary

**energy:** the capacity to do work (Grade 6)

# Cells and Energy

**Main Idea** All cells can release energy from food molecules. Only some cells can make food molecules using light energy.

**Real-World Reading Connection** When gasoline burns in a car engine, energy is released. It is transformed in many ways, making the car function as it should. Carbon dioxide, water vapor, and other waste gases from the burning gasoline exit through the exhaust pipe. Mitochondria are like engines in cells. Wastes are also produced when mitochondria release energy from food molecules.

## Cellular Respiration

Automobiles cannot use the crude oil that comes out of the ground as fuel. It must be processed and refined into gasoline or diesel fuel. As you read in the previous lesson, the energy stored in the food molecules is not in a form that cells can use. **Cellular respiration** is a series of chemical reactions that transforms the energy in food molecules to usable energy. The usable energy is in molecules of **ATP**—adenosine triphosphate (uh DEN uh seen • tri FAHS fayt).

### Reactions in the Cytoplasm

Cellular respiration happens in three steps. The first step is **glycolysis** (gli KAH lih sis) and it happens in a cell's cytoplasm. Glycolysis breaks down a glucose molecule—a type of sugar—into two smaller molecules, as shown in **Figure 21.** The chemical reactions of glycolysis require energy and release electrons that are used in the last step of cellular respiration.

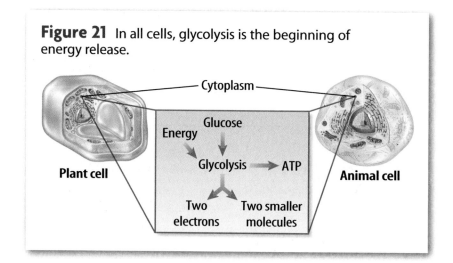

**Figure 21** In all cells, glycolysis is the beginning of energy release.

Cytoplasm

Plant cell

Energy
Glucose
Glycolysis ⟶ ATP
Two electrons
Two smaller molecules

Animal cell

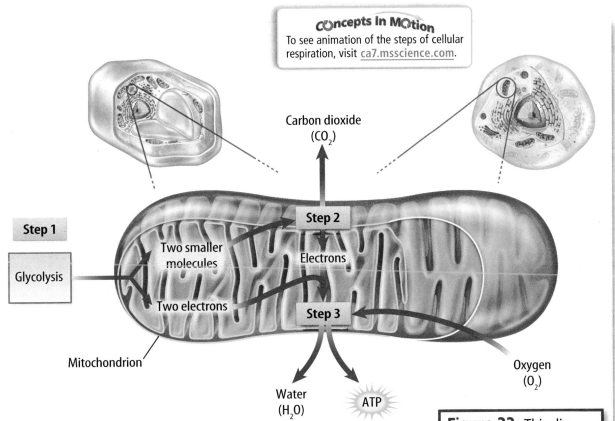

**C**Oncepts In M**O**tion
To see animation of the steps of cellular respiration, visit ca7.msscience.com.

Carbon dioxide $(CO_2)$

**Step 1**

Glycolysis

Two smaller molecules

**Step 2**

Electrons

Two electrons

**Step 3**

Mitochondrion

Water $(H_2O)$

ATP

Oxygen $(O_2)$

**Figure 22** This diagram illustrates the three steps of cellular respiration.

**Infer** Why can't prokaryotes perform cellular respiration?

## Reactions in Mitochondria

The second step of cellular respiration happens in mitochondria and uses the smaller molecules produced by glycolysis. The smaller molecules are broken down into molecules of carbon dioxide—a waste product—and more electrons are released.

The third and final step of cellular respiration requires the presence of oxygen, as shown in **Figure 22.** This step uses the electrons released during the first two steps. It produces large amounts of ATP—usable energy—and water—a waste product.

# Fermentation

Some cells can release energy from food molecules using a chemical process called **fermentation.** This process begins and ends in the cytoplasm and does not involve mitochondria or use oxygen. However, all types of fermentation produce fewer molecules of ATP than cellular respiration.

## Lactic Acid Fermentation

When our muscles use oxygen faster than our lungs and blood can deliver it to them for cellular respiration, they can release energy by lactic acid fermentation. This process releases energy from glucose and produces lactic acid and carbon dioxide as wastes. Cheese and yogurt are made using fungi and bacteria that perform lactic acid fermentation.

| Table 3 Processes that Release Cellular Energy | | | |
|---|---|---|---|
| Process | Oxygen Required | Number of ATP Molecules Available to a Cell | Waste Products |
| Cellular respiration | Yes | 36 | Water, carbon dioxide |
| Lactic acid fermentation | No | 2 | Lactic acid, carbon dioxide |
| Alcohol fermentation | No | 2 | Alcohol, carbon dioxide |

ACADEMIC VOCABULARY
evidence (EH vuh duhns)
(noun) an outward sign
*His sneezes and watery eyes were evidence of his allergies.*

### Alcohol Fermentation

Did you know that bread is made by using yeast? Why is yeast necessary? Yeast are single-celled fungi that can perform alcohol fermentation—another kind of fermentation that releases energy, as shown in **Table 3.** This kind of fermentation is similar to lactic acid fermentation except it produces ethanol (a kind of alcohol) instead of lactic acid. Like lactic acid fermentation, alcohol fermentation produces carbon dioxide but fewer ATP molecules than cellular respiration. Now do you know why yeast is needed to make the bread?

 **Table 3** Which process requires oxygen?

# Photosynthesis

You read in Lesson 1 that we get energy from the food that we eat. You also read that some organisms can make their own food using energy from the Sun or other light sources. **Photosynthesis** is a series of chemical reactions that makes food in these organisms.

### Light and Pigments

We see things because light reflects off them. Light from the Sun contains all colors: red, orange, yellow, green, blue, indigo, and violet. A rainbow is **evidence** of this. The color of an object is the result of that object reflecting only that color of light. The object absorbs the other colors of light. For example, a red shirt only reflects red light and absorbs all the other colors of light. The same is true for living things. Plants contain substances called pigments that reflect and absorb light. Chloroplasts contain the pigment chlorophyll that reflects green light. When leaves appear green, it is because they contain more chlorophyll than other pigments. Have you ever seen leaves change colors in the fall? This happens because the chlorophyll in leaves breaks down and is not replaced. So, you see colors reflected by the other pigments in leaves, like the yellow pigments in the grape leaves shown in **Figure 23.**

**Figure 23** When plants stop producing chlorophyll, the light reflected from other pigments can be seen.

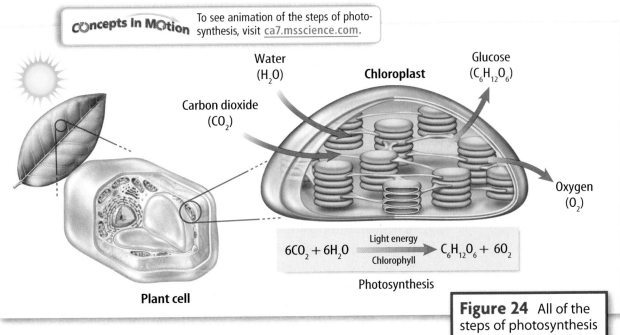

Concepts In Motion  To see animation of the steps of photo-synthesis, visit ca7.msscience.com.

Water ($H_2O$)

Carbon dioxide ($CO_2$)

Chloroplast

Glucose ($C_6H_{12}O_6$)

Oxygen ($O_2$)

$$6CO_2 + 6H_2O \xrightarrow[\text{Chlorophyll}]{\text{Light energy}} C_6H_{12}O_6 + 6O_2$$

Photosynthesis

Plant cell

**Figure 24** All of the steps of photosynthesis happen in chloroplasts.

## Reactions in Chloroplasts

The light energy absorbed by chlorophyll and other pigments powers the chemical reactions of photosynthesis. These reactions occur in chloroplasts. During photosynthesis, light energy, water, and carbon dioxide are used to make sugars. Photosynthesis also produces oxygen that is released into the atmosphere, as shown in **Figure 24.**

## Importance of Photosynthesis

The fruits and vegetables we eat grow because of photosynthesis. The cells of most organisms, even most bacteria, use sugars made by photosynthesis. Photosynthesis supplies Earth's atmosphere with oxygen, which we must have for our cells to perform cellular respiration. The carbon dioxide produced by organisms from cellular respiration would become toxic if it were not used during photosynthesis. **Figure 25** illustrates the important relationship between cellular respiration and photosynthesis.

**WORD ORIGIN**

photosynthesis
from German *photo* (means *light*) and *synthese* (means *synthesis*)

**Figure 25** Photosynthesis needs the products of cellular respiration and vice versa.

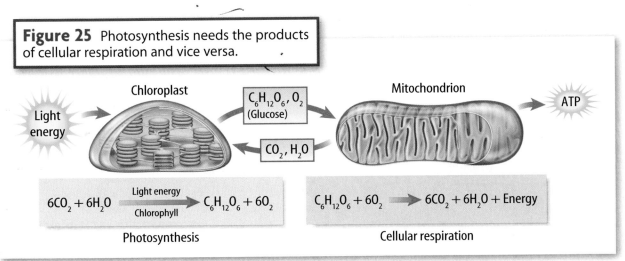

Light energy

Chloroplast

$C_6H_{12}O_6$, $O_2$ (Glucose)

$CO_2$, $H_2O$

Mitochondrion

ATP

$$6CO_2 + 6H_2O \xrightarrow[\text{Chlorophyll}]{\text{Light energy}} C_6H_{12}O_6 + 6O_2$$

Photosynthesis

$$C_6H_{12}O_6 + 6O_2 \longrightarrow 6CO_2 + 6H_2O + \text{Energy}$$

Cellular respiration

# What have you learned about cells and energy?

Cells perform cellular respiration and transform the unusable energy in large food molecules into usable energy in ATP molecules. Lactic acid fermentation and alcohol fermentation produce ATP molecules without the use of oxygen but fewer ATP molecules than cellular respiration. Light energy powers photosynthesis that produces sugars. Organisms that perform photosynthesis contain pigments that absorb light energy. Almost all organisms are dependent on photosynthesis. Cellular respiration and photosynthesis are important to most life on Earth.

# LESSON 3  Review

## Summarize

Create your own lesson summary as you design a **visual aid.**

1. **Write** the lesson title, number, and page numbers at the top of your poster.

2. **Scan** the lesson to find the **red** main headings. Organize these headings on your poster, leaving space between each.

3. **Design** an information box beneath each **red** heading. In the box, list 2–3 details, key terms, and definitions from each **blue** subheading.

4. **Illustrate** your poster with diagrams of important structures or processes next to each information box.

 ELA7: W 2.5

## Standards Check

### Using Vocabulary

1. Distinguish between cellular respiration and fermentation. **1.d**

2. In your own words, write a definition of *glycolysis*. **1.d**

### Understanding Main Ideas

3. What pigment in plants reflects green light? **1.d**

    **A.** DNA
    **B.** carbon dioxide
    **C.** lactic acid
    **D.** chlorophyll

4. **Relate** photosynthesis and cellular respiration. **1.d**

5. **List** the three steps of cellular respiration. **1.d**

6. **Give an example** of how fermentation is used in the food industry. **1.d**

7. **Sequence** Draw a graphic organizer like the one below to sequence the processes of cellular respiration. Describe each step in each box. **1.d**

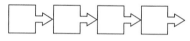

8. **Summarize** photosynthesis using an equation. **1.d**

### Applying Science

9. **Predict** what you think would happen if your cells could not perform lactic acid fermentation.

10. **Evaluate** the importance of plants to other organisms and the environment. **1.d**

11. **Form a hypothesis** about the differences in the air quality of a busy city and a forest. **1.d**

**Science Online**
For more practice, visit **Standards Check** at ca7.msscience.com.

# MiniLab

00:30 minutes

# How can you see photosynthesis?

Even using the most powerful micro-scope, you cannot observe the chemical processes taking place inside a cell. However, it is possible to observe what happens when chemical processes do not occur.

## Procedure

1. Read and complete a lab safety form.

2. Obtain a **potted plant** from your teacher.

3. Using **scissors,** cut a piece of **aluminum foil** about the same length and width of a leaf.

4. Fold the foil in half lengthwise and place it around a leaf. The foil should cover about half of the leaf. Use a **paper clip** to hold the foil in place.

5. Place the plant in a sunny location for at least four days.

6. Predict the appearance of the leaf under the foil after the four days. Record your prediction.

7. On the fifth day, remove the foil and observe the leaf. Record your observation.

## Analysis

1. **Compare and contrast** your prediction about the leaf and your observation of the leaf.

2. **Infer** whether cellular respiration or photosynthesis was most affected by the presence of foil.

3. **Form a hypothesis** to explain if covering an edible leaf, such as spinach, would affect its taste.

###  Science Content Standards

**1.d** Students know that mitochondria liberate energy for the work that cells do and that chloroplasts capture sunlight energy for photosynthesis.

**7.c** Communicate the logical connection among hypotheses, science concepts, tests conducted, data collected, and conclusions drawn from the scientific evidence.

# Lab

# Exploring the Unknown

## Materials

compound light microscope
prepared slide of an unknown cell

## Safety Precautions

## Science Content Standards

**1.b** Students know the characteristics that distinguish plant cells from animal cells, including chloroplasts and cell walls.

**7.a** Select and use appropriate tools and technology (including calculators, computers, balances, spring scales, microscopes, and binoculars) to perform tests, collect data, and display data.

**Also covers:** 7.c, 7.d, 7.e

## Problem

A cell biologist collected an unknown cell while on an expedition. Using the scientific observation skills you have used in this chapter's labs, determine if the cell is prokaryotic or eukaryotic and the type of organisms that it came from.

## Form a Hypothesis

Consider the diversity of life on Earth. Before you observe the cell sample, predict what it will be. What hypothesis would be supported if your prediction is true? What hypothesis would be supported if your prediction is false?

## Collect Data and Make Observations

1. Read and complete a lab safety form.
2. Create a data page similar to one below to record your observations.
3. Observe a prepared slide of an unknown cell at low and high magnifications. Sketch your cell at each magnification.
4. Record any special adaptations the cell has that might indicate the cell's function.

| Sample Data Page | |
|---|---|
| **Sketch of Cell at Low Magnification** | **Sketch of Cell at High Magnification** |
| | |
| **Cell Organelles Observed** | |
| **Adaptations/Function** | |
| **Conclusion** | |

## Analyze and Conclude

1. **Describe** what you observed on your data page. Is the unknown cell similar to something you have seen before? What?
2. **Explain** how the presence or absence of organelles affects your identification. Recall how you made decisions about organelles when you built your model.
3. **Summarize** the information you have about the unknown cell.
4. **Create** a table to compare and contrast the unknown cell with plant and animal cells.
5. **Draw a conclusion** about the unknown cell.

## Communicate

 **Science** **ELA7: W 2.3**

Prepare a 500–700-word report to share your conclusion with the class. In the report, detail what observations you made and what types of lab work helped you reach your final conclusion. Use the information on your data page to defend your decision.

# Real World Science

## Science & Career

## From Cells to Organelles

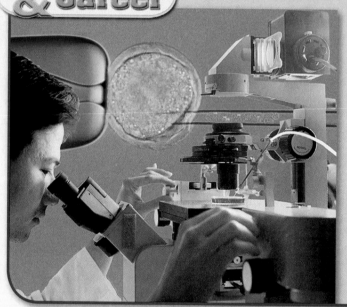

A cell biologist studies the structure of cells and how they function whether alone or within an organism. Some cell biologists might focus on particular organelles, like ribosomes or mitochondria. Others study processes vital to cell function, like cellular respiration, homeostasis, or DNA reproduction.

Write a 500–700-word newspaper article describing a recent finding in cell biology. The finding can be real or imagined. Make sure to add quotes and make the story exciting.

**ELA7:** W 2.1

## Confocal Laser Scanning Microscopy

## Science & Technology

Confocal laser scanning microscopy has been used since the 1980s. It uses a laser beam to scan a biological specimen that has been treated with substances that give off fluorescent light when exposed to the laser beam. Confocal microscopy can create a high-quality three-dimensional microscopic image by scanning a thick sample in layers.

Create a table documenting the different types of microscopes that scientists use today. Include a short description of each microscope, who invented it and when, and its uses.

# Golgi's "Black Reaction"

Toward the end of the nineteenth century, Italian physician Camillo Golgi invented a method to stain nerve cells and follow their paths through the brain. The stain, which Golgi called the black reaction, uses a chemical substance called silver nitrate to stain cells. Golgi's studies won the Nobel Prize in Physiology or Medicine in 1906.

Golgi won the Nobel Prize with Santiago Ramón y Cajal. Research the project that won Cajal the 1906 Nobel Prize. Prepare and present a mock acceptance speech for the 1906 prize, posing as either Golgi or Cajal.

ELA7: LS 2.1

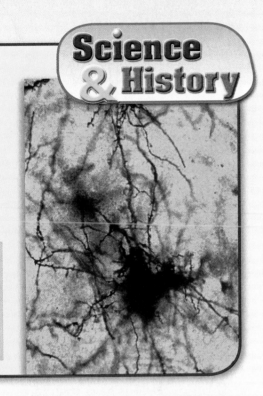

# Putting Organisms to Good Use

Bioreactors provide the proper environmental conditions to support the growth of organisms like bacteria and yeast. For example, the EPA has designed bioreactors to help break down waste in landfills more efficiently. Scientists control air and moisture in a landfill bioreactor to promote bacterial growth and activity, which increase the rate of waste breakdown.

How will bioreactors play a role in the future? Visit Society at ca7.msscience.com to research bioreactor landfills. Write a 500-word essay describing one way bioreactors can help society.

**The BIG Idea** The structures in cells work together and ensure the survival of the cell.

## Lesson 1 Cells and Life
`1.a, 7.a, 7.c`

**Main Idea** Cells are the smallest unit of life.

- A microscope is needed to see most cells.
- The cell is the smallest unit of a living organism.
- A living thing has all of the characteristics of life.
- Water is essential to all living things.
- Cells contain four basic substances: proteins, nucleic acids, lipids, and carbohydrates.

- **carbohydrate** (p. 54)
- **cell theory** (p. 49)
- **homeostasis** (p. 51)
- **light microscope** (p. 48)
- **lipid** (p. 54)
- **nucleic acid** (p. 54)
- **protein** (p. 53)

## Lesson 2 The Cell
`1.a, 1.b, 1.c, 2.e, 7.d`

**Main Idea** Cells have structures with specific functions.

- The cell membrane controls what enters and exits a cell.
- The cell wall and cytoskeleton determine the shape of a cell.
- The genetic information of a cell is in the chromosomes in the nucleus.
- The organelles of a cell have specialized functions.
- Prokaryotic cells do not contain membrane-bound organelles.
- Prokaryotic cells live in a wide range of environments and have various roles.
- Eukaryotic cells have a nucleus and other membrane-bound organelles.

- **cell membrane** (p. 56)
- **cell wall** (p. 58)
- **chloroplast** (p. 61)
- **chromosome** (p. 60)
- **cytoplasm** (p. 59)
- **cytoskeleton** (p. 59)
- **eukaryotic cell** (p. 64)
- **mitochondrion** (p. 61)
- **nucleus** (p. 60)
- **organelle** (p. 59)
- **prokaryotic cell** (p. 64)
- **ribosome** (p. 60)

## Lesson 3 Cells and Energy
`1.d, 7.a, 7.c, 7.d, 7.e`

**Main Idea** All cells can release energy from food molecules. Only some cells can make food molecules using light energy.

- Cells perform cellular respiration and make usable ATP energy from larger food molecules.
- Lactic acid fermentation and alcohol fermentation produce ATP without the use of oxygen.
- Light energy powers photosynthesis that produce sugars and oxygen.
- Photosynthesis and cellular respiration are related chemical reactions.

- **ATP** (p. 68)
- **cellular respiration** (p. 68)
- **fermentation** (p. 69)
- **glycolysis** (p. 68)
- **photosynthesis** (p. 70)

**STUDY TO GO** Download quizzes, key terms, and flash cards from ca7.msscience.com.

**Science**nline Interactive Tutor ca7.msscience.com

# Linking Vocabulary and Main Ideas

Use vocabulary terms from page 78 to complete this concept map.

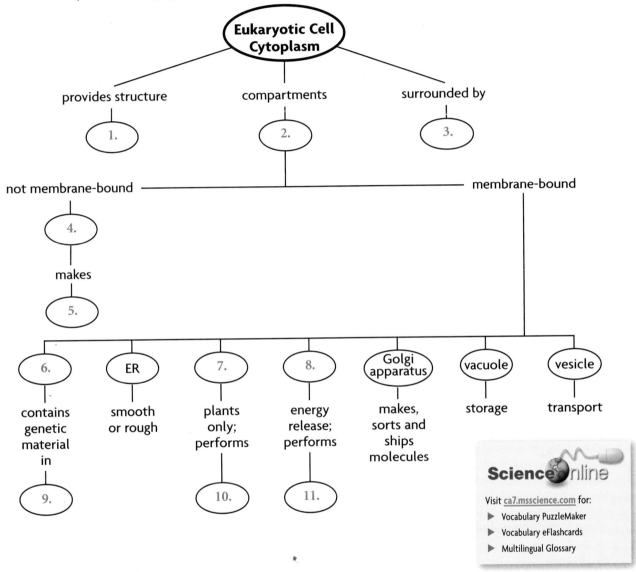

## Using Vocabulary

**Fill in the blanks with the correct vocabulary terms. Then read the paragraph to a partner.**

A series of chemical reactions called _____12._____ transforms food molecules to usable cellular energy. The usable cellular energy is found in molecules called _____13._____. The first step of cellular respiration is _____14._____, and it happens in a cell's _____15._____. Sometimes, our muscles use oxygen faster than our lungs and blood can deliver it. When this happens, our muscle cells can release energy by using a type of _____16._____. Some organisms can make their own food using energy from the Sun or other light sources by performing _____17._____.

# Understanding Main Ideas

*Choose the word or phrase that best answers the question.*

1. Which is not a characteristic of all living things?
   A. growth
   B. homeostasis
   C. response
   D. breathing                                    1.a

2. Which would enable you to study the membranes of a chloroplast?
   A. a light microscope                           7.a
   B. a telescope
   C. a hand lens
   D. an electron microscope

3. Some cells have structures that enable them to move from one place to another.

   What structures enable the cell shown above to move?
   A. flagella                                     1.a
   B. ribosomes
   C. cilia
   D. vesicles

4. What absorbs the light energy needed for photosynthesis?
   A. pigments
   B. cell walls
   C. mitochondria
   D. vacuoles                                     1.d

5. Which is produced during photosynthesis?
   A. carbon dioxide                               1.d
   B. glucose
   C. water
   D. lactic acid

6. Which can be observed only in a plant cell?
   A. cell membrane
   B. cell wall
   C. nucleus
   D. ribosome                                     1.b

7. What kind of cell would be most likely to live in an extremely hot spring?
   A. plant
   B. animal
   C. eukaryotic
   D. prokaryotic                                  1.a

8. Where are nucleic acids in a cell?
   A. cell membrane                                2.e
   B. cytoskeleton
   C. vacuole
   D. nucleus

9. Which process produces the most ATP?
   A. photosynthesis                               1.d
   B. cellular respiration
   C. lactic acid fermentation
   D. alcohol fermentation

10. Each organelle in a cell has a specific function.

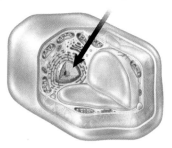

    What is the function of the organelle at the end of the arrow?
    A. stores genetic information                  1.c
    B. makes proteins
    C. cell structure and movement
    D. releases energy

 **Science** nline Standards Review ca7.msscience.com

## Applying Science

**11.** Pigments absorb and reflect different colors of light.

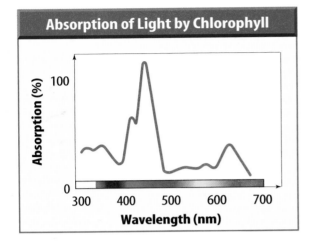

**Absorption of Light by Chlorophyll**

**Interpret** Use the graph above to explain why chlorophyll appears green. `1.d`

**12.** **Explain** how water helps an organism maintain homeostasis. `1.a`

**13.** **Give an example** of how organisms grow and develop. `1.a`

**14.** **Compare and contrast** a light microscope and an electron microscope. `7.a`

**15.** **Justify** the characteristic of life that you think is the most important for living organisms. `1.a`

**16.** **Distinguish** between a eukaryotic and prokaryotic cell. `1.a`

**17.** **Compare and contrast** a plant cell and an animal cell. `1.b`

**18.** **List** the steps of cellular respiration. `1.d`

**19.** **Compare** lactic acid fermentation and alcohol fermentation. `1.d`

**20.** **Determine** which energy-releasing process would be best if you needed a lot of energy. Explain. `1.d`

**21.** **Hypothesize** why plant cells contain more than one kind of pigment. `1.d`

## *WRITING in* Science

**22.** **Write** a paragraph that analyzes the following statement. "If we eat only meat, then we do not need plants." `ELA7: W 2.1`

## Applying Math

**23.** The height, width, and length of one solid are 3 cm, 4 cm, and 3 cm and, for another solid, 1 cm, 3 cm, and 12 cm. Find and compare the two volumes. `MA7: MG 2.1`

**Use the illustration below to answer question 24.**

**24.** Find the volume of each solid. `MA7: MG 2.1`

**25.** Two solids with the same volumes have the dimensions 1 cm × 3 cm × 8 cm and 4 cm × 2 cm × 3 cm. How do their surface areas compare? `MA7: MG 2.1`

**26.** What is the surface area of the solid with dimensions 2 cm × 4 cm × 5 cm? `MA7: MG 2.1`

**27.** What is the surface area of the solid with dimensions 2 cm × 2 cm × 8 cm? `MA7: MG 2.1`

A typical animal cell is shown below. Use this diagram to answer questions 1 and 2.

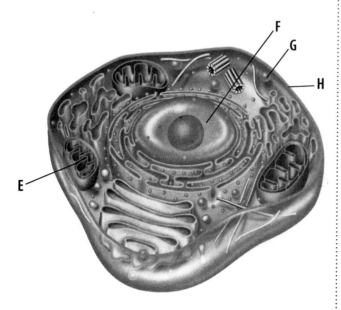

**1** Which letter corresponds to the organelle containing DNA?

**A** E

**B** F

**C** G

**D** H    2.e

**2** Which letter corresponds to the part of the cell that helps control what enters and leaves the cell?

**A** E

**B** F

**C** G

**D** H    1.a

**3** Which describes the function of the central vacuole in plant cells?

**A** It helps during reproduction.

**B** It helps regulate water content.

**C** It plays a key role in photosynthesis.

**D** It plays a key role in cellular respiration.    1.b

Use the diagram of the cell organelle to answer questions 4 and 5.

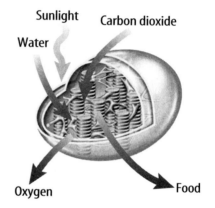

**4** Where might you find this organelle?

**A** in a brain cell

**B** in a hair cell

**C** in a plant cell

**D** in a bacterial cell    1.b

**5** What process is taking place in this organelle?

**A** cellular respiration

**B** photosynthesis

**C** food storage

**D** fermentation    1.d

**6** You exhale carbon dioxide that is a product of

**A** osmosis.

**B** DNA synthesis.

**C** photosynthesis.

**D** cellular respiration. `1.d`

**7** Which is needed for cellular respiration?

**A** oxygen

**B** lactic acid

**C** chlorophyll

**D** lipids `1.d`

**8** Which structure is part of a prokaryotic cell?

**A** chloroplast

**B** Golgi apparatus

**C** mitochondrion

**D** ribosome `1.a`

**9** The equation below represents photosynthesis.

chlorophyll
$$6CO_2 + 6H_2O + energy \rightarrow C_6H_{12}O_6 + 6O_2$$

**What energy transformation occurs?**

**A** light energy to chemical energy

**B** light energy to electrical energy

**C** light energy to mechanical energy

**D** light energy to nuclear energy `1.d`

**10** Which process releases the most energy?

**A** fermentation

**B** glycolysis

**C** photosynthesis

**D** cellular respiration `1.d`

The images below show the same organelle. Use these images to answer questions 11 and 12.

**11** What organelle is shown?

**A** chloroplast

**B** mitochondrion

**C** nucleus

**D** ribosome `1.d`

**12** What is its primary function?

**A** capturing light energy

**B** directing cell processes

**C** releasing energy

**D** making proteins `1.d`

**13** What do a bacterial cell, a plant cell, and a nerve cell have in common?

**A** cell wall and mitochondria

**B** cytoplasm and ribosomes

**C** nucleus and cell membrane

**D** flagella and chloroplasts `1.a`

### CHAPTER 2

# From a Cell to an Organism

### The BIG Idea

Nearly all the cells in an organism are genetically identical and are organized to work together.

**LESSON 1** 1.c, 1.e, 7.a
## The Cell Cycle and Cell Division

**Main Idea** The life of a cell usually includes periods of growth and reproduction.

**LESSON 2** 1.f, 5.a, 7.d, 7.e
## Levels of Organization

**Main Idea** From single-celled to multicellular organisms, all living things are organized.

### It's alive! It's alive!

The white root growing down into the soil will anchor the new plant that grows from this seed. Once, this seed was just cells in a flower on a California buckeye tree. If the new plant survives, it can grow to be a tree about 12 m tall.

**Science *Journal*** Predict what other functions the root might have for the new plant.

## When is division not a math problem?

Believe it or not, you started out as one cell. Obviously, you have grown. Cell division is why you grew.

### Procedure

1. Obtain a **numbered picture** from your teacher.

2. Use a **microscope** as instructed by your teacher and scan the **provided slide.** Find a cell that matches your numbered picture. Draw the cell in your lab notebook.

3. Move around the room and observe other cells. In your lab notebook, draw cells that are different from your cell.

### Think About This

- **Examine** What do your drawings show? Does the process look organized?

- **Predict** Where do you think this process might be happening right now?

1.a, 7.a, 7.d

### Science Online

Visit ca7.msscience.com to:

▶ view **Concepts in Motion**

▶ explore Virtual Labs

▶ access content-related Web links

▶ take the Standards Check

 **Cell Cycle** Make the following Foldable to organize the phases of the cell cycle.

 **STEP 1 Fold** a sheet of paper in half lengthwise.

 **STEP 2 Cut** along the top line and then every fifth or sixth line of the top flap to form seven tabs.

**STEP 3 Label** as shown.

Cell Cycle
Interphase
Prophase
Metaphase
Anaphase
Telophase
Cytokinesis

### Reading Skill

### Sequencing

As you read Lesson 1, write a description of what occurs in each phase of the cell cycle under the appropriate tab of your Foldable.

# Get Ready to Read

## Identify the Main Idea  ELA7: R.2.3

**① Learn It!** Main ideas are the most important ideas in a paragraph, a lesson, or a chapter. Supporting details are facts or examples that explain the main idea. Understanding the main idea allows you to grasp the whole picture.

**② Practice It!** Read the following paragraph. Draw a graphic organizer like the one below to show the main idea and supporting details.

> Single-celled eukaryotes include protists, like the amoeba shown in **Figure 9,** and some fungi. They are more complex than bacteria. Each single-celled eukaryote has a nucleus and other membrane-bound organelles. Membranes separate organelles and their specialized functions from each other. They also enable organelles to transport substances into and out of a cell.
>
> —from page 99

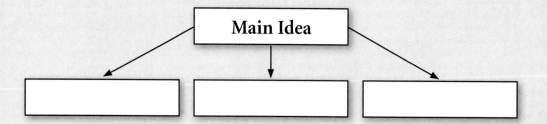

**③ Apply It!** Pick a paragraph from another section of this chapter and diagram the main idea as you did above.

**Reading Tip**

The main idea is often the first sentence in a paragraph, but not always.

# Target Your Reading

**Use this to focus on the main ideas as you read the chapter.**

**1** **Before you read** the chapter, respond to the statements below on your worksheet or on a numbered sheet of paper.

- Write an **A** if you **agree** with the statement.
- Write a **D** if you **disagree** with the statement.

**2** **After you read** the chapter, look back to this page to see if you've changed your mind about any of the statements.

- If any of your answers changed, explain why.
- Change any false statements into true statements.
- Use your revised statements as a study guide.

**Science** nline

Print a worksheet of this page at ca7.msscience.com.

| Before You Read A or D | Statement | After You Read A or D |
|---|---|---|
| | **1** All cell cycles are the same length of time. | |
| | **2** Interphase lasts longer than other phases of a cell's cycle. | |
| | **3** Mitosis produces two daughter cells. | |
| | **4** Chromosomes can be observed using a light microscope. | |
| | **5** A characteristic of all living things is that they grow and develop. | |
| | **6** Single-celled organisms have complex organization. | |
| | **7** Differentiated human cells can become another type of cell. | |
| | **8** Groups of similar cells that work together form tissues. | |
| | **9** Plants have organs that work together to perform functions. | |

### Science Content Standards

**1.c** Students know the nucleus is the repository for genetic information in plant and animal cells.

**1.e** Students know cells divide to increase their numbers through a process of mitosis, which results in two daughter cells with identical sets of chromosomes.

**7.a** Select and use appropriate tools and technology (including calculators, computers, balances, spring scales, microscopes, and binoculars) to perform tests, collect data, and display data.

### Reading Guide

#### What *You'll Learn*

▶ **Describe** the cell cycle.

▶ **Identify** the phases of mitosis.

▶ **Distinguish** among the cell cycle, mitosis, and cell division.

▶ **Explain** the importance of cell division.

#### Why *It's Important*

Learning how cells divide and grow will help you understand how all organisms grow.

#### Vocabulary

| | |
|---|---|
| cell cycle | anaphase |
| interphase | telophase |
| centromere | daughter cell |
| mitosis | cell plate |
| cytokinesis | homologous |
| prophase | chromosome |
| metaphase | sister |
| | chromatid |

#### Review Vocabulary

**eukaryotic cell:** a cell with a nucleus and other organelles (p. 64)

# The Cell Cycle and Cell Division

**Main Idea** The life of a cell usually includes periods of growth and reproduction.

**Real-World Reading Connection** A multicellular organism like yourself is made of trillions of cells. How are all of these cells made? How long does a cell live?

## The Cell Cycle

You probably are still growing, but not as fast as when you were younger. You might have entered the phase of development when your reproductive organs mature. All these phases are part of your life cycle. Similarly, cells have a life cycle called the **cell cycle.** The cell cycle, as shown in **Figure 1,** usually includes phases of growth and development and reproduction.

### Phases of the Cell Cycle

You'll spend most of your life growing and developing. Only a small portion of a human's life cycle is spent in the reproductive phase. The same is true for cells. The phase of a cell cycle when a cell is preparing to reproduce is called **interphase.** It usually lasts longer than other phases of the cell cycle. The phase when a eukaryotic cell reproduces is called the mitotic (mi TOH tik) phase. During the mitotic phase, the nucleus and cytoplasm of a cell divides, producing two new cells.

**Visual Check** **Figure 1** What processes are part of the mitotic phase?

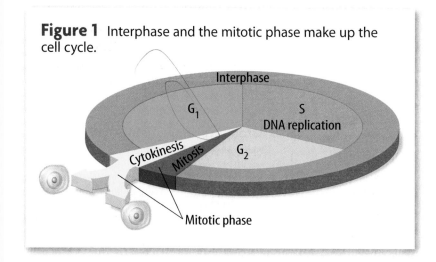

**Figure 1** Interphase and the mitotic phase make up the cell cycle.

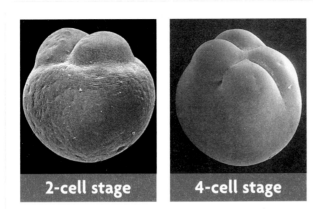
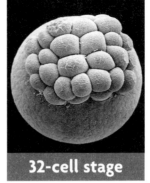
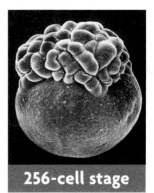

| 2-cell stage | 4-cell stage | 32-cell stage | 256-cell stage |

**Figure 2** The cell cycle for a newly fertilized zebra fish egg can be as short as 15 min.

## Length of a Cell Cycle

The length of time for the cell cycle is different for different types of organisms and cells. During the earliest stages of animal growth, the cell cycle can repeat quickly. For example, a zebra fish grows from a fertilized egg to 256 cells in just 2.5 h, as shown in **Figure 2.**

## Characteristics of Interphase

A cell performs specific functions during interphase. For example, a cell in your stomach might produce substances that help digest your food. A plant cell, such as the onion root cell shown in **Figure 3,** might perform cellular respiration during interphase.

Recall from Chapter 1 that a cell's nucleus contains chromosomes. During interphase, the chromosomes in the nucleus are like a bunch of thin spaghetti noodles. Each chromosome is so thin that it cannot be observed with a light microscope.

Also, you read that there are two sets of chromosomes in a nucleus. For each chromosome in one set of chromosomes, there is a similar chromosome in the other set of chromosomes. Scientists call each pair of similar chromosomes a pair of **homologous chromosomes** (huh MAH luh gus • KROH muh sohmz). Humans have 23 pairs of homologous chromosomes.

 How many sets of chromosomes are in a nucleus?

Imagine if you had two sets of instructions for making a pizza. The instructions are similar because they are both for making pizzas. However, they are not identical because the pizzas can have different toppings and crusts. The same is true for your homologous chromosomes; they have similar but not identical instructions.

**Figure 3** This cell is from the root of an onion and is in interphase.

**Infer** why the chromosomes are not visible in the cell's nucleus.

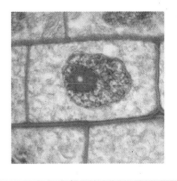

ACADEMIC VOCABULARY

establish (ih STAH blish)
(verb) to put beyond doubt
*Her time established that she was the faster runner.*

**Phases of Interphase** Scientists have **established** that interphase consists of three phases—G1, S, and G2. During G1 phase, a cell grows and carries out its usual cellular functions. Some cells remain in G1 and do not reproduce. For example, your muscle cells, some nerve cells, and red blood cells never reproduce. Injuries to nerve and muscle cells can result in a permanent loss of function because they are not replaced. Red blood cells are replaced because they are produced by certain cells in the center of some bones.

Growth continues into S phase. During S, however, the chromosomes inside a cell's nucleus replicate. This means that they make copies of themselves, as the diagram in **Figure 4** shows. The copies of a chromosome made during S phase are called **sister chromatids** (KROH muh tudz). Sister chromatids are held together at a region near the middle of each chromatid called the **centromere.** The replication of chromosomes during S phase ensures that the two new cells formed by cell division are identical.

**Visual Check** **Figure 4** How many centromeres are there for each replicated chromosome?

**Figure 4** A cell in G2 phase has an identical copy of each chromosome.

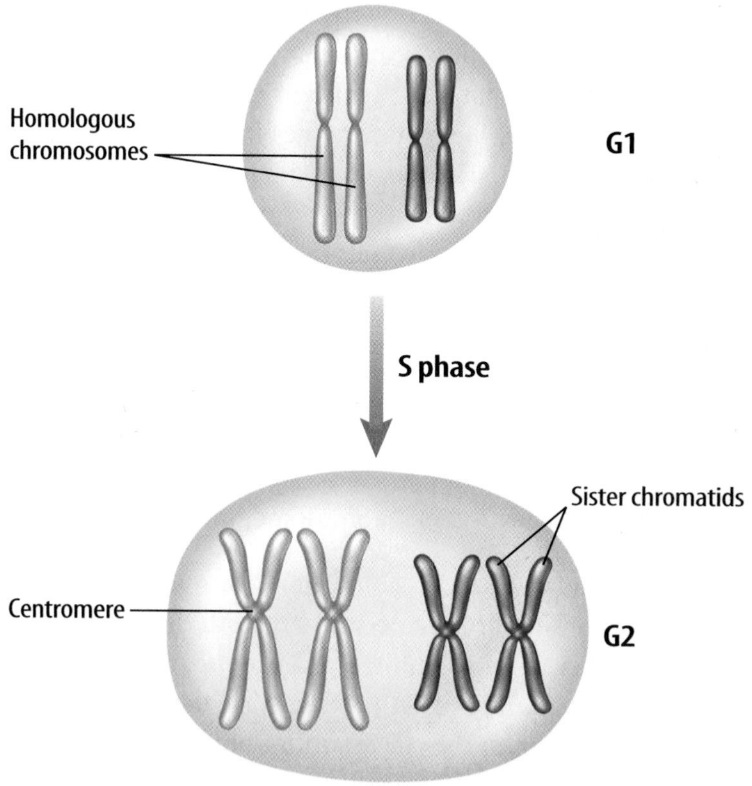

Homologous chromosomes

G1

S phase

Sister chromatids

Centromere

G2

| Table 1 Phases of the Cell Cycle | | |
| --- | --- | --- |
| **Phase** | **Stages** | **Description** |
| Interphase | G1 | Growth and cellular functions |
| | S | Growth and chromosome replication |
| | G2 | Growth and cellular functions; organelle replication |
| Mitotic phase | Mitosis | Nucleus divides. |
| | Cytokinesis | Cytoplasm divides. |

**Organelle Replication** A cell continues to grow and carry out cellular functions during the final phase of interphase, G2 phase. It also replicates organelles during this phase of interphase. Some organelles, such as mitochondria and chloroplasts, can duplicate themselves because they contain their own DNA. The major events of interphase and the cell cycle are summarized in **Table 1.**

**WORD ORIGIN**············

mitosis
from Greek *mitos* (means *warp thread*) and *osis* (means *act, process*)

# Mitosis and Cell Division

You read in Chapter 1 that eukaryotic cells have organelles and other structures. You also read that the control center of the cell is the nucleus. When new cells are made, it is important that the contents of the nucleus be copied correctly. The nucleus divides in a process called **mitosis** (mi TOH sus). The cytoplasm divides in a process called **cytokinesis** (si toh keh NEE sus). These events ensure that each new cell receives all it needs to function normally.

### Importance of Mitosis and Cell Division

As you read earlier in this lesson, a characteristic of all living things is that they grow and develop. Making more cells is one way multicellular organisms grow. They also grow because some cells increase in size.

Sometimes cells get old, wear out, and die. For example, everyone is constantly shedding old skin cells, as shown in **Figure 5.** New cells formed by mitosis and cell division replace these skin cells. Some cells, such as the ones that line your stomach, live only for a few days. Because of mitosis and cell division, new cells constantly replace these short-lived cells.

Some organisms reproduce by mitosis and cell division. These organisms produce offspring that are identical to the parent. You will read about this kind of reproduction in Chapter 3.

 How do multicellular organisms grow?

**Figure 5** We lose about 30,000–40,000 dead skin cells every minute. Cell divisions replace skin cells.

Color-enhanced SEM Magnification: 1000×

**Cell Division** Have you ever fallen and scraped your knee? The scrape heals because new cells are made to replace the cells that were damaged or lost. These new cells are made by mitosis and cell division.

It is important to understand that the processes of mitosis and cell division do not produce all cells. For example, a different kind of cell division produces sperm cells or egg cells from reproductive cells. You will read about this kind of cell division in Chapter 3.

## Phases of Mitosis

Mitosis is a continuous process. However, mitosis has four recognizable phases or stages, as shown in **Figure 6.**

**Prophase** The first phase of mitosis is **prophase.** Two major events happen during prophase. First, the DNA that makes up a replicated chromosome twists into tight coils. Have you ever twisted a rubber band so tightly that it coiled around itself? This is similar to what happens to chromosomes during prophase. Once the replicated chromosomes coil, they can be observed with a light microscope. The other major event during prophase is that the membrane around the nucleus breaks apart. After this happens, chromosomes can move to other areas of a cell.

 **Figure 6** Why can you see the chromosomes in the nucleus of the cell during prophase?

**Metaphase** During the second stage of mitosis, **metaphase**, the replicated chromosomes move to the middle of the cell. The pairs of sister chromatids line up end-to-end across the center of the cell. How does this happen? Hairlike fibers pull and push the chromosomes to the middle of the cell.

**Anaphase** In the third stage, **anaphase**, the sister chromatids of each replicated chromosome begin to separate. The hairlike fibers extend from each end of a cell and attach to the centromere of the sister chromatids. These fibers pull the centromere apart and chromatids move away from each other, toward opposite ends of the cell. Now, the chromatids are called chromosomes.

**Telophase** The final phase of mitosis is **telophase.** During telophase, a new membrane forms around each set of chromosomes. The chromosomes also become less tightly coiled. These two events are nearly the reverse of what happens in prophase. At the end of telophase, there are two new nuclei that are identical to each other and the original nucleus. However, the cell has not divided.

 What are the four phases of mitosis?

**Figure 6** The cell cycle of most eukaryotic cells, like the fish cell shown below, includes mitosis. It is difficult to determine when one phase of mitosis begins and another ends. However, each phase has certain characteristics. At the end of mitosis, two new, genetically identical nuclei form. The original nucleus no longer exists.

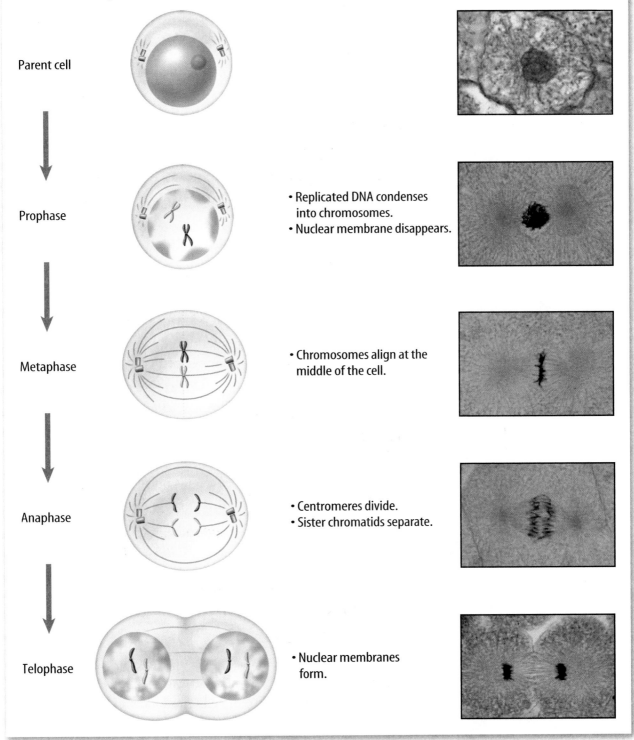

Parent cell

Prophase
- Replicated DNA condenses into chromosomes.
- Nuclear membrane disappears.

Metaphase
- Chromosomes align at the middle of the cell.

Anaphase
- Centromeres divide.
- Sister chromatids separate.

Telophase
- Nuclear membranes form.

**Figure 7** The flexible membrane cell pinches in during cytokinesis. The rigid cell wall of plant cells cannot pinch in.

**Identify** the stage of cell division shown here.

Color-enhanced SEM Magnification: 125×

Stained LM Magnification: 1,500×

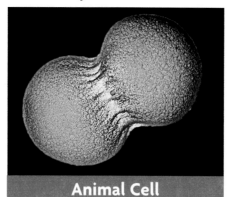

**Animal Cell**

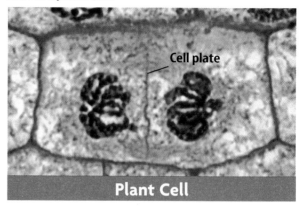

Cell plate

**Plant Cell**

**WORD ORIGIN**·············

cytokinesis
*cyto–* from Greek *kytos;* means
*a hollow receptacle*
*–kinesis* from Greek; means
*movement, motion*

## Dividing the Cell's Components

Cytokinesis is the final stage of cell division. During cytokinesis, the cytoplasm and its components divide to form two identical cells called **daughter cells.** A sign that cytokinesis has begun is when the cell membrane squeezes inward, as shown in **Figure 7.** This is similar to squeezing the middle of a balloon.

During cytokinesis, the appearance of a cell with a cell wall, such as a plant cell also in **Figure 7,** is different from an animal cell that does not have a cell wall. In a cell with a cell wall, a **cell plate** forms between the two new nuclei. The cell plate eventually becomes the cell membrane. The new cell walls of the plant daughter cells are built from molecules released by the cell membrane.

The process of mitosis divides a cell's nucleus. However, the nucleus is just one of many organelles inside a cell. How do daughter cells get organelles? Recall that organelles and other structures are suspended in the cytoplasm of a cell. During cytokinesis, each daughter cell receives half the cytoplasm with organelles that were replicated during G2 of interphase.

 **Reading Check** What is the first sign that cytokinesis has begun?

## Results of Cell Division

It is important to realize that after mitosis and cell division, the original cell—called the parent cell—no longer exists. However, daughter cells' chromosomes are identical to those of the parent cell, both in number and type. In other words, the daughter cells are genetically identical to each other and to the original parent cell. All the cells in your body, except sperm and egg cells, have identical chromosomes because of mitosis and cytokinesis.

# What have you learned about the cell cycle and cell division?

Cells have periods of growth and reproduction called cell cycles. The cell cycles of different cell types differ in the time that they last. A cell's nucleus divides in a process called mitosis. During mitosis, the DNA that makes up a replicated chromosome is packaged into tight coils. The membrane around the nucleus breaks apart, enabling the chromosomes to move around in the cytoplasm. The replicated chromosomes move to the middle of the cell and the chromatids line up in the center. The sister chromatids in each pair begin to separate and move toward opposite sides of the cell. At the end of mitosis, there are two identical nuclei. Following cytokinesis, two new genetically identical cells form, and the original cell no longer exists.

# LESSON 1 Review

## Summarize

Create your own lesson summary as you design a **study web**.

1. **Write** the lesson title, number, and page numbers at the top of a sheet of paper.

2. **Scan** the lesson to find the **red** main headings.

3. **Organize** these headings clockwise on branches around the lesson title.

4. **Review** the information under each **red** heading to design a branch for each **blue** subheading.

5. **List** 2–3 details, key terms, and definitions from each **blue** subheading on branches extending from the main heading branches.

 ELA7: W 2.5

## Standards Check

### Using Vocabulary

1. In your own words, write a definition of the cell cycle. **1.e**

2. Use the word *centromere* in a sentence. **1.e**

### Understanding Main Ideas

3. **Compare** interphase and the mitotic phase. **1.e**

4. Which are copies of a chromosome made during S-phase of the cell cycle? **1.c**
   A. centromeres
   B. parent cells
   C. daughter cells
   D. sister chromatids

5. **State** the results of mitosis and cell division. **1.e**

6. **Distinguish** between mitosis and cytokinesis. **1.e**

### Applying Science

7. **Predict** what would happen if a cell completed mitosis, but not cytokinesis. **1.e**

8. **Decide** What criteria would you use to decide which phase a cell is in? **1.e**

9. **Sequence** Draw a graphic organizer similar to the one below about the phases of mitosis. Begin with the phase that follows interphase and end with the phase that comes before cytokinesis. **1.e**

For more practice, visit **Standards Check** at ca7.msscience.com.

# DataLab

# How does your garden grow?

One of the most common tissues used for observing mitosis and cell division is onion root-tip tissue.

## Data Collection

1. Read and complete a lab safety form.

2. Create a data table to record your observations.

3. Use a **microscope** as instructed by your teacher to observe a **prepared slide of stained onion root-tip tissue.** Select the highest magnification to observe the slide.

4. Identify the stage of mitosis and cell division for each cell in your field of view. Record the number of cells in each stage of the cell cycle on your table.

5. Change the field of view twice and repeat step 4 each time.

## Data Analysis

1. **Determine** the percentage of cells in each stage of mitosis and cell division.

2. **Construct** a pie chart of your data.

| Sample Data Table | | | |
|---|---|---|---|
| | View 1 | View 2 | View 3 |
| Interphase | | | |
| Prophase | | | |
| Metaphase | | | |
| Anaphase | | | |
| Telophase | | | |
| Cytokinesis | | | |
| Total Cells | | | |

 **Science Content Standards**

**1.c** Students know the nucleus is the repository for genetic information in plant and animal cells.
**7.a** Select and use appropriate tools and technology (including calculators, computers, balances, spring scales, microscopes, and binoculars) to perform tests, collect data, and display data.

# Applying Math

## Probability and the Cell Cycle

Using microscopes, several science classes observed plant cells in different stages of the cell cycle. The table shows how many students in each class observed each cell stages.

| Stages of the Cell Cycle | | | | | |
|---|---|---|---|---|---|
| Class Period | Interphase | Prophase | Metaphase | Anaphase | Telophase |
| 1 | 22 | 4 | 2 | 1 | 1 |
| 2 | 20 | 5 | 1 | 2 | 2 |
| 3 | 24 | 2 | 1 | 1 | 2 |
| 4 | 22 | 3 | 3 | 1 | 1 |
| 5 | 23 | 3 | 2 | 1 | 1 |

### Example

What is the probability that a first-period student observed a cell in metaphase?

**What you know:**
- Number of cells observed in metaphase first period: 2
- Total number of cells observed first period: 30

**What you need to find:**
- Probability of observing a cell in metaphase to total number of cells observed

**1** The probability of observing a cell in metaphase to the total number of cells observed is:

$$\frac{\text{Number of cells observed in metaphase}}{\text{Total number of cells observed}} = \frac{2}{30}$$

**2** Reduce this fraction to get: $\frac{1}{15}$

**Answer:** The probability of a first-period student observing a cell in metaphase is 1 out of 15.

### Practice Problems

1. What is the probability of a second-period student observing a cell in anaphase?
2. What is the probability of a fifth-period student observing a cell in interphase?

**Science** nline
For more math practice, visit **Math Practice** at ca7.msscience.com.

### Science Content Standards

**1.f** Students know that as multicellular organisms develop, their cells differentiate.

**5.a** Students know plants and animals have levels of organization for structure and function, including cells, tissues, organs, organ systems, and the whole organism.

**7.d** Construct scale models, maps, and appropriately labeled diagrams to communicate scientific knowledge (e.g., motion of Earth's plates and cell structure).

**7.e** Communicate the steps and results from an investigation in written reports and oral presentations.

## Reading Guide

### What *You'll Learn*

▶ **Compare and contrast** a protist to a human skin cell.

▶ **Distinguish** between differentiation of a plant cell and an animal cell.

▶ **Sequence** the levels of organization from cell to organism.

### Why *It's Important*

Learning how all living things are organized will help you understand how organisms have organized structures and functions.

### Vocabulary

cell differentiation
stem cell
tissue
organ
organ system

### Review Vocabulary

**prokaryotic cell:** a cell without a nucleus and other organelles (p. 64)

# Levels of Organization

**( Main Idea )** From single-celled to multicellular organisms, all living things are organized.

**Real-World Reading Connection** How do people organize their belongings? They usually place things with similar functions together. For example, things used to cook food are probably in the kitchen. Pots and pans might be in a cabinet and silverware in a drawer. In a similar way, cells and organisms are organized. They have structures that have specialized functions.

## Single-Celled Organisms

Why would something that is one cell—a single-celled organism—need to be organized? A single-celled organism carries out all the functions needed for its survival, including obtaining nutrients, waste removal, movement, protection, and reproduction.

### Prokaryotes

Recall from Chapter 1 that prokaryotes are single-celled organisms that do not have membrane-bound organelles. For example, bacteria are prokaryotes without nuclei or other organelles. However, bacteria still have structures with specific functions. Some processes that occur in organelles of eukaryotes happen in bacteria along specialized membranes, such as those shown in **Figure 8.**

**Figure 8** This cyanobacterium, *Spirulina plantesis,* can perform photosynthesis, making its own food.
**Infer** how this organism obtains energy.

Photosynthetic membranes

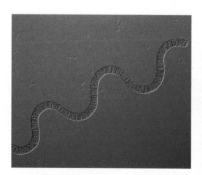

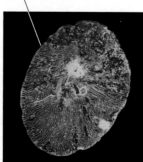

LM  Magnification: 160×

Cross-section Color-enhanced  TEM
Magnification: 6600×

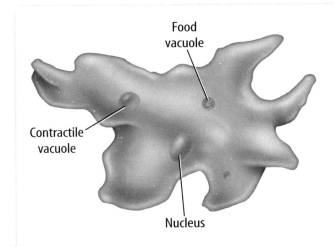

Food
vacuole

Contractile
vacuole

Nucleus

Stained  LM  Magnification: 160×

**Figure 9** An amoeba, such as this one, lives alone in freshwater.

## Eukaryotes

Single-celled eukaryotes include protists, such as the amoeba shown in **Figure 9,** and some fungi. They are more complex than bacteria. Each single-celled eukaryote has a nucleus and other membrane-bound organelles. Membranes seperate organelles and their specialized functions from each other. They also enable organelles to transport substances into and out of a cell.

Single-celled eukaryotes are also more complex than cells in multicellular eukaryotes. They usually exist alone and obtain by themselves all the things that they need to survive. Cells in multi-cellular organisms, however, rely on one another to provide their needs, and cannot survive alone.

Some single-celled eukaryotes, however, live and function together in groups or colonies. After cell division, the daughter cells stay together. The protist colony *Volvox*, as shown in **Figure 10,** is made of specialized eukaryotic green algal cells. Some scientists propose that colonies of single-celled organisms might have led to the development of multicellular organisms.

 How do cells of a protist colony differ from a single-celled protist?

Darkfield  LM  Magnification: 100×

**Figure 10** Small bridges of cytoplasm connect single-celled organisms in a *Volvox* colony. The flagella on each cell beat in unison with flagella on other cells, propelling the colony through water.

**ACADEMIC VOCABULARY**

assign (uh SINE)

*(verb)* to appoint to a duty or task

*The play's casting director will assign parts to the actors.*

# Multicellular Organisms

When doing a group project, someone must organize the group and **assign** tasks. Someone must also make sure everyone does his or her task. The project requires organization to be completed successfully. In a similar way, multicellular organisms require organization. Multicellular organisms have many cells and usually have more than one type of cell. Therefore, they have more complex organization than single-celled organisms.

## Cell Differentiation

You started as one fertilized egg. You grew by mitosis and cell division and developed into an organism with many types of cells. How did this happen? It occurred by a process called **cell differentiation** (dih fuh ren chee AY shun) in which cells become different types of cells.

You read in the previous lesson that nearly all the cells of an organism have identical sets of chromosomes. Also, recall that chromosomes contain the instructions of a cell. How can cells be different if they have the identical sets of instructions? Part of the answer is that different cell types use different parts of the instructions on the chromosomes. It's like the actors in a play who only need to memorize the lines in the script for their roles, not the entire script of the play.

Differentiated cells often have specialized structures and shapes for specific functions that are different from other cells. For example, liver cells, like those shown in **Figure 11,** have a greater amount of smooth ER than some other cells. Filtering blood is the main function of liver cells. Recall from Chapter 1 that smooth ER modifies poisons, making them easier to remove from a cell.

Brain cells, also shown in **Figure 11,** are another type of differentiated cell. Brain cells often are highly branched. Branching enables a brain cell to send and receive signals from many directions and over long distances. There are many other differentiated cells in humans, such as the ones shown in **Figure 12.**

**Figure 11** Liver cells and brain cells have different structures and functions.

**Infer** why brain cells are long and branched.

Color-enhanced TEM Magnification: 1240×

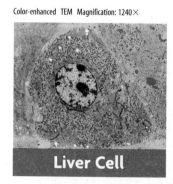

**Liver Cell**

Color-enhanced SEM Magnification: 1,700×

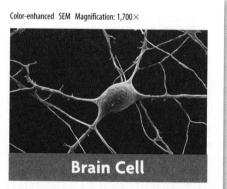

**Brain Cell**

# Visualizing Differentiated Human Cells

**Figure 12** Throughout your body, differentiated cells carry out the complex processes that keep you alive and functioning at your best.

▶ **BLOOD CELLS** Red blood cells carry oxygen to your tissues and remove carbon dioxide. White blood cells protect your body from harmful, foreign substances or organisms. Platelets help form blood clots.

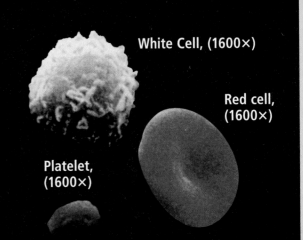

White Cell, (1600×)

Red cell, (1600×)

Platelet, (1600×)

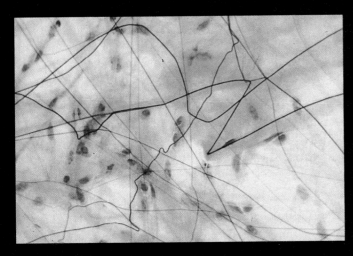

Connective Tissue, (80×)

◀ **CONNECTIVE TISSUE CELLS** Like the cells in blood, some connective tissue cells move about. These connective tissue cells can protect, repair, and transport. Other connective tissue cells are fixed, like those in the photo to the left. These cells can insulate, maintain, store, support, or produce substances.

▼ **MUSCLE CELLS** Skeletal muscle cells move body parts such as arms and legs. Smooth muscle cells move substances within or through internal organs and vessels. Cardiac muscle cells are found only in the heart.

Skeletal Muscle, (6000×)   Smooth Muscle, (100×)   Cardiac Muscle, (225×)

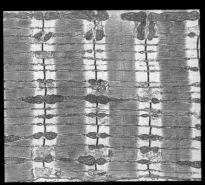

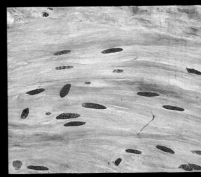

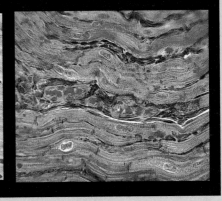

*Contributed by National Geographic*

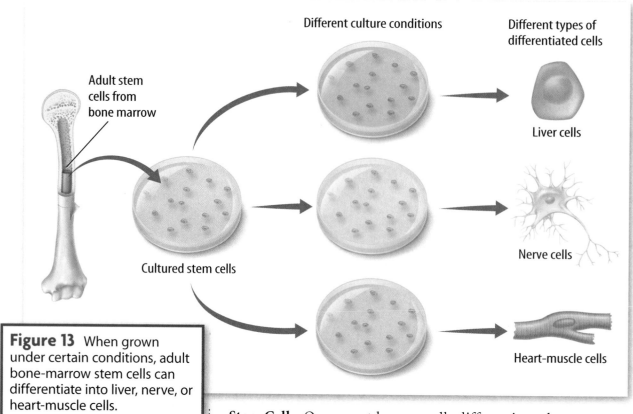

Different culture conditions

Different types of differentiated cells

Adult stem cells from bone marrow

Cultured stem cells

Liver cells

Nerve cells

Heart-muscle cells

**Figure 13** When grown under certain conditions, adult bone-marrow stem cells can differentiate into liver, nerve, or heart-muscle cells.

**Infer** how stem cells could be important for treating diseases.

**Stem Cells** Once most human cells differentiate, they cannot become any other type of cell. However, some cells in your body are undifferentiated. These cells, called **stem cells,** can become different types of cells. For example, there are stem cells in the middle of some of your bones. Under the right conditions, these stem cells can become many different types of cells, as shown in **Figure 13.**

**Plant Cells** Some plant cells can differentiate into another type of cell after they have differentiated into a specific type of cell. For example, the leaf of a begonia plant, as shown in **Figure 14,** contains differentiated cells with specialized functions. However, if you correctly cut a leaf from a begonia plant, place it on soil, and give it proper growing conditions, it can produce new plants.

**Figure 14** This begonia leaf has differentiated cells. However, the cells can differentiate again into other cell types and produce new begonia plants.

## Tissues

The cast of a play is made of different actors. Each actor must recite his or her lines to tell the play's story. Similarly, most multicellular organisms have groups of similar cells that work together and perform a function. A group of cells that work together and perform a function is a **tissue.** For example, skeletal muscle tissue in your body is made of cells called muscle fibers, as shown in **Figure 15.** The muscle fibers contract and relax and allow your body to move. Plants also have tissues, as also shown in **Figure 15.**

 **Reading Check** What is an example of a tissue?

**Figure 15** Tissues are similar cells that work together to perform one or more functions.

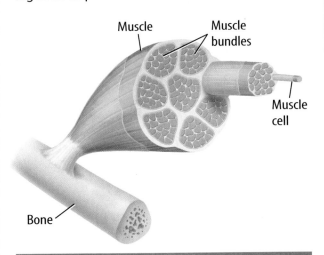

Muscle

Muscle bundles

Muscle cell

Bone

**Animal Tissue**

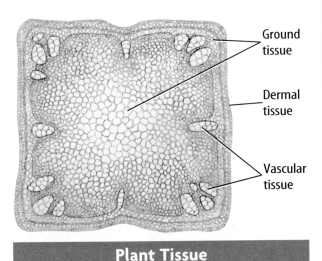

Ground tissue

Dermal tissue

Vascular tissue

**Plant Tissue**

 **MiniLab**  00:20 minutes

## What's in a tissue?

You read that different cell types make up tissues. Each cell type in a tissue has a specific function and contributes to the tissue's function.

### Procedure

1. Using the **drawings in your text** and the **information provided by your teacher,** organize a tissue that will absorb nutrients.

### Analysis

1. **Deduce** whether or not your tissue design is the only possible one. How did other students organize their tissue?

2. **Predict** where in a human body such a tissue might be found.

 5.a, 7.d

**SCIENCE USE V. COMMON USE**

tissue

*Science Use* a group of cells that work together and perform a function.
*Blood is a tissue that contains red blood cells, white blood cells, and platelets.*

*Common Use* a disposable, paper handkerchief.
*Please use a tissue to cover your mouth when you sneeze.*

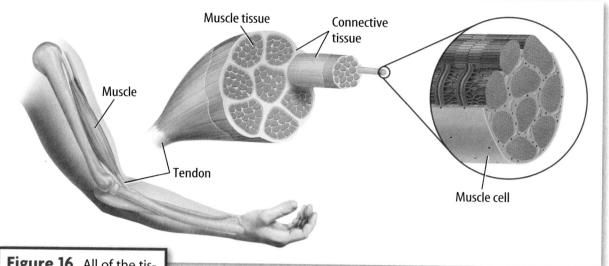

Muscle tissue

Connective tissue

Muscle

Tendon

Muscle cell

**Figure 16** All of the tissues of an organ must work together so that the organ can function. If one of the tissues is not functioning as it should, the organ cannot function.

## Organs

A play's stage crew might include carpenters and electricians. Both groups have specific functions, but work together to create a setting where the actors can perform. In a similar way, an **organ** is a group of similar tissues that work together to perform a function. Each tissue must function properly for the organ to function.

**Human Organs** Your heart, lungs, brain, stomach, and muscles are some of the organs in your body. A muscle, such as the bicep in your upper arm, is made of different tissues, as shown in **Figure 16.** Besides muscle tissue, a muscle also includes tissues that surround and protect muscle cells and other tissues that connect muscle tissues.

**Plant Organs** Plants also have organs that perform functions such as storing nutrients, exchanging gases, transporting water or nutrients, or performing photosynthesis. A leaf, as shown in **Figure 17,** is an example of a plant organ. Leaves have tissues that transport substances, provide protection, or are specialized for photosynthesis.

**Figure 17** The dark-green tissue is like the skin of a leaf. It has pores that allow gases to enter and exit the leaf. The tissue that looks like blobs is made of cells that perform photosynthesis.

**Infer** where chlorophyll would be found in this leaf.

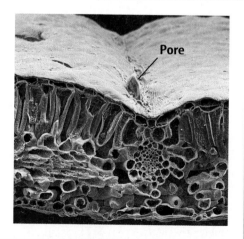

Pore

## Organ Systems

The cast of actors in a play work with makeup and wardrobe specialists, the director, and others in order to perform on stage. In a similar way, some organs in an organism work together. An **organ system** is one or more organs that work together and perform one or more functions. The muscles in your body work together with the bones of your skeleton to allow your body to move. The muscles and bones in your body make up your musculoskeletal system. Your heart, lungs, and digestive system work together to supply your muscles and bones with what they need to work together. Your brain receives and sends signals that coordinate all the organ systems in your body, as listed in **Table 2.**

 Which organ systems work together to supply the needs of your musculoskeletal system?

| Table 2 Human Organ Systems | | |
|---|---|---|
| **System Name** | **Organs** | **Function** |
| Integumentary (ihn teg yuh MEN tuh ree) | skin | protection and homeostasis |
| Skeletal | bones, cartilage, ligaments, and joints | protection and support; mineral storage |
| Muscular | muscles | movement |
| Nervous | brain, spinal cord, nerves, and sensory receptors | response and regulation |
| Endocrine (EN duh krun) | pituitary, thyroid, parathyroids, adrenals, thymus, pancreas, pineal, ovaries (females), and testes (male) | produces hormones that control body functions |
| Cardiovascular (kar dee oh VAS kyuh lur) | heart, blood vessels | transports blood that carries oxygen, nutrients, and wastes |
| Lymphatic (lihm FA tihk) | lymph nodes, tonsils, spleen, lymphatic vessels | returns fluid to blood and filters blood |
| Respiratory | nasal passages, pharynx, larynx, trachea, bronchi, and lungs | delivers oxygen to and removes carbon dioxide from blood |
| Digestive | mouth, esophagus, stomach, small and large intestines, rectum, anus | breakdown food and deliver nutrients and water to the blood |
| Urinary | kidneys, ureters, bladder, urethra | maintains homeostasis; removes nitrogen-containing substances from blood |
| Reproductive | • female—fallopian tubes, uterus, vagina, ovaries<br>• male—scrotum, penis, accessory glands, testes | produce offspring |

**Concepts In Motion**
Interactive Table To explore more about human organ systems, visit Tables at ca7.msscience.com.

## Organism

The most complex unit of living things is a multicellular organism. Multicellular organisms, such as the dog shown in **Figure 18,** usually have many organ systems. Each organ system has its own function but is dependent on other organ systems. For example, your circulatory system transports nutrients throughout your body. The nutrients come from the breakdown of food in your digestive system. Your organ systems depend on your nervous system. You would not be able to breathe, move, reproduce, or eat without your nervous system. Without all these levels of organization, your body would be like a jumble of food, wastes, gases, and cells.

**Figure 18** An organism is made of organ systems, organs, tissues, and cells that all function together and enable the organism's survival.

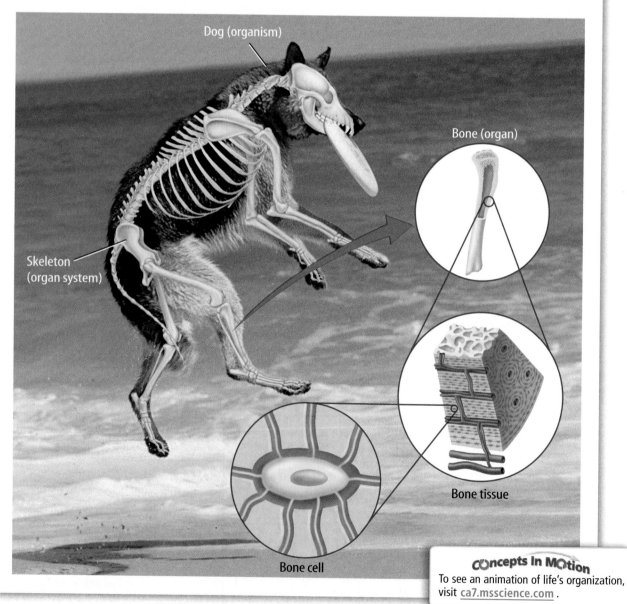

Dog (organism)

Bone (organ)

Skeleton (organ system)

Bone tissue

Bone cell

**Concepts in Motion**
To see an animation of life's organization, visit ca7.msscience.com .

# What have you learned about levels of organization?

Even the simplest single-celled organisms are organized. Most single-celled organisms perform all the functions they need for life inside one cell. Multicellular organisms have many types of specialized cells. Different types of differentiated cells have different functions.

Multicellular organisms have many levels of organization. They have groups of different cells called tissues that function together. Groups of tissues form an organ that performs a function. Two or more organs that perform a function are an organ system.

## LESSON 2 Review

### Summarize

Create your own lesson summary as you write a script for a **television news report.**

1. **Review** the text after the **red** main headings and write one sentence about each. These are the headlines of your broadcast.

2. **Review** the text and write 2–3 sentences about each **blue** subheading. These sentences should tell *who, what, when, where,* and *why* information about each **red** heading.

3. **Include** descriptive details in your report, such as names of reporters and local places and events.

4. **Present** your news report to other classmates alone or with a team.

 **ELA7: LS 2.2**

### Standards Check

#### Using Vocabulary

1. Distinguish between stem cells and differentiated cells. **1.f**

2. In your own words, write a definition of an organ system. **5.a**

#### Understanding Main Ideas

3. Which is a group of similar tissues that work together to perform a function? **5.a**

   A. organism
   B. organ
   C. prokaryote
   D. organ system

4. **Compare** the organization of a single-celled organism to a multicellular organism. **5.a**

5. **Give an example** of a differentiated cell and **state** how it is specialized. **1.f**

6. **Sequence** the levels of organization from a cell to an organism. **5.a**

7. **Compare and Contrast** Copy and fill in the graphic organizer below to compare and contrast a protist and a human skin cell. **5.a**

|  | Similarities | Differences |
|---|---|---|
| Protist/ human skin cell |  |  |

#### Applying Science

8. **Predict** why multicellular organisms need levels of organization. **5.a**

9. **Assess** What criteria would you use to assess the developmental potential of a cell? **1.f**

**Science** nline

For more practice, visit **Standards Check** at ca7.msscience.com.

# Model and Invent:
# Design an Organ

## Materials

colored pencils
paper
reference materials

### Science Content Standards

**5.a** Students know plants and animals have levels of organization for structure and function, including cells, tissues, organs, organ systems, and the whole organism.

**7.d** Construct scale models, maps, and appropriately labeled diagrams to communicate scientific knowledge (e.g., motion of Earth's plates and cell structure).

**7.e** Communicate the steps and results from an investigation in written reports and oral presentations.

## Problem

Organs are made up of tissues. Even organs that appear to be made up of only one type of tissue include cardiovascular tissue for oxygen supply and waste removal. Some organs have more than one function, although those functions are related.

## Form a Hypothesis

When an organ has more than one function, do the cells and tissues interact differently than in a tissue?

## Collect Data and Make Observations

1. Obtain reference materials from your teacher.
2. Using at least two types of tissue, design an organ that will move nutritive substances and absorb nutrients. Remember that the absorbed nutrients have to travel to the rest of the body.
3. Use colored pencils to draw the organ. Include cross sections and label the different tissues.

# Analyze and Conclude—Interpret Your Data

1. **Outline** the process you used to design the organ. What types of cells are included in your design?
2. **Describe** the types of tissue you included in your organ design. What is the purpose of each tissue?
3. **Explain** how each tissue supports the organ's function.
4. **Formulate models** for each tissue type that could be combined to model the organ you have designed.
5. **Compare and contrast** the two functions of the organ you have designed. How do the two functions interact?
6. **Summarize** how the tissues in your organ design interact. How did the cells of the tissue you designed in the previous lab interact? Is there a difference between how the tissues interact and how the different tissues interact?

## Communicate—Share Your Design

Share your design with your classmates. Explain the different tissues you used and how they interact to support the function of the organ.

# Real World Science

## David Burgess, PhD

David Burgess is a research scientist and biology professor. His research includes studying the role of a cell's cytoskeleton during cytokinesis—the division of the cytoplasm during cell division. The cytoskeleton plays an important role when the cell membrane pinches in or forms a contractile ring during cytokinesis. A focus of his research is how the formation of the contractile ring is related the timing of the mitotic cycle of cell division.

Write lyrics to a song about mitosis. Include relevant facts about what is occurring to the cell in your song. Visit **Careers** at **ca7.msscience.com** for additional references.

## Healing Burns with Artificial Skin

Serious burns require skin grafts—uninjured pieces of skin collected from the patient's body and transferred to the burned area. What if there isn't enough uninjured skin to provide a graft? Doctors can use artificial skin to temporarily cover the injured skin and promote healing. In the meantime, samples of the patient's healthy skin are removed and grown in the lab. When the new skin has grown large enough to cover the injured area, the artificial skin is surgically removed and replaced with the new skin.

Visit **Technology** at **ca7.msscience.com** to research treatment options for burns. Use the information to compare and contrast traditional skin grafts with those using artificial and cultured skin.

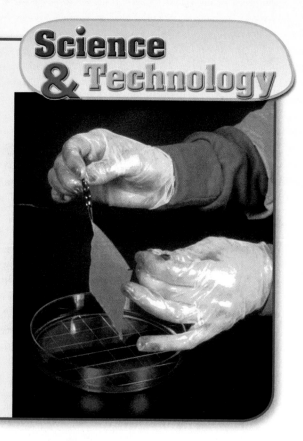

# Walther Flemming

Walther Flemming was the founder of cytology, the study of chromosomes. In the late 1800s, he used specific dyes to observe cell division. Flemming saw threadlike structures in a cells' nucleus separate and move into new cells. He called the thread-like structures chromatin and later they were named chromosomes. Flemming was the first person to use the term *mitosis* for the division of a cell's nucleus.

Draw the four stages of mitosis—prophase, metaphase, anaphase and telophase—and present your drawing to the class. Describe what is happening to the cell at each stage.

## SIGN UP, SAVE LIVES

Over 90,000 people in the United States wait for organ donations each year, and one in three will die before organs become available. One person can give organs to eight people and his or her tissues can help 50 individuals. Organ donations cannot be made if a person's wishes are not known. Most states, including California, now have state registries of people who are willing to donate their organs at the time of their death. In California, a pink sticker like the one to the left is placed on the driver's license of an organ donor.

Visit **Society** at **ca7.msscience.com** to find information about organ donation. Debate the pros and cons of having a national organ donation registry.

**ELA7:** LS 2.4

DONATE LIFE ®
*California*
**ORGAN & TISSUE DONOR REGISTRY**

DONOR

**The BIG Idea** Nearly all the cells in an organism are genetically identical and are organized to work together.

## Lesson 1 The Cell Cycle and Cell Division    1.c, 1.e, 7.a

**Main Idea** **The life of a cell usually includes a period of growth and reproduction.**

- The cell cycle is a eukaryotic cell's period of growth and development and reproduction.

- Different cell types have different cell cycle lengths.

- A cell's nucleus divides in a process called mitosis.

- Mitosis and cell division result in identical daughter cells.

- **anaphase** (p. 92)
- **cell cycle** (p. 88)
- **cell plate** (p. 94)
- **centromere** (p. 90)
- **cytokinesis** (p. 91)
- **daughter cell** (p. 94)
- **homologous chromosome** (p. 89)
- **interphase** (p. 88)
- **metaphase** (p. 92)
- **mitosis** (p. 91)
- **prophase** (p. 92)
- **sister chromatid** (p. 90)
- **telophase** (p. 92)

## Lesson 2 Levels of Organization    1.f, 5.a, 7.d, 7.e

**Main Idea** **From single-celled to multicellular organisms, all living things are organized.**

- Even the simplest single-celled organisms are organized.

- Single-celled organisms perform all the functions needed for life in one cell.

- Multicellular organisms have many types of specialized cells.

- Different types of differentiated cells have different functions.

- Multicellular organisms may have many levels of organization.

- **cell differentiation** (p. 100)
- **organ** (p. 104)
- **organ system** (p. 105)
- **stem cell** (p. 102)
- **tissue** (p. 103)

**STUDY TO GO** Download quizzes, key terms, and flash cards from ca7.msscience.com.

# Linking Vocabulary and Main Ideas

Use the vocabulary terms from page 112 to complete this concept map.

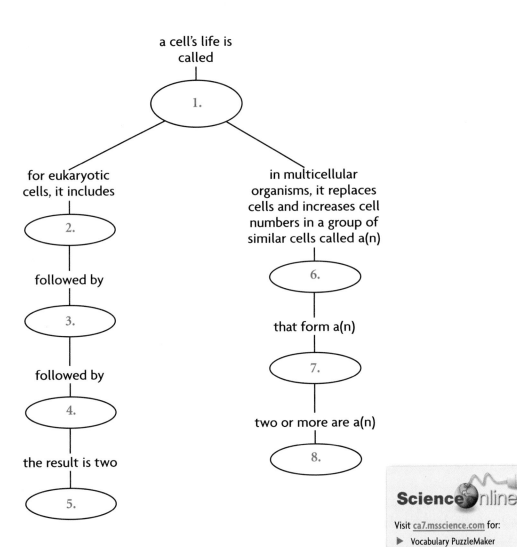

a cell's life is called

1.

for eukaryotic cells, it includes

2.

followed by

3.

followed by

4.

the result is two

5.

in multicellular organisms, it replaces cells and increases cell numbers in a group of similar cells called a(n)

6.

that form a(n)

7.

two or more are a(n)

8.

## Using Vocabulary

**Fill in the blanks with the correct vocabulary words. Then read the paragraph to a partner.**

New eukaryotic cells are produced by ____9.____ followed by ____10.____ . Pairs of replicated ____11.____ consist of two ____12.____ attached at a region called a(n) ____13.____ and become visible during ____14.____ . They move to the center of the cell during ____15.____ , and separate and move in opposite directions during ____16.____ . Two new nuclei form during ____17.____ . In plant cells, a(n) ____18.____ forms from the cell membranes of newly formed cells.

## Understanding Main Ideas

*Choose the word or phrase that best answers the question.*

1. Which phase of the cell cycle is shown below?

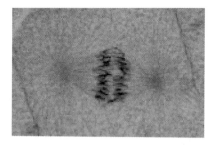

   A. telophase     **1.e**
   B. anaphase
   C. metaphase
   D. prophase

2. What is usually the longest phase of the cell cycle?
   A. interphase     **1.e**
   B. mitosis
   C. cytokinesis
   D. prophase

3. When are chromosomes replicated?
   A. mitosis     **1.e**
   B. G1 phase
   C. G2 phase
   D. S phase

4. Chromosomes line up in the middle of the cell during which phase of mitosis?
   A. telophase     **1.e**
   B. prophase
   C. metaphase
   D. anaphase

5. When does the cytoplasm divide?
   A. interphase     **1.e**
   B. mitosis
   C. telophase
   D. cytokinesis

6. Which term best describes a muscle fiber?
   A. organ     **5.a**
   B. cell
   C. organ system
   D. tissue

7. Which cells might be used in laboratory to make heart cells?
   A. liver cells     **1.f**
   B. bone marrow cells
   C. brain cells
   D. leaf cells

8. Which is the most complex level of organization?
   A. organ system     **5.a**
   B. organ
   C. cell
   D. tissue

9. How would you best describe the structure at the end of the arrow?

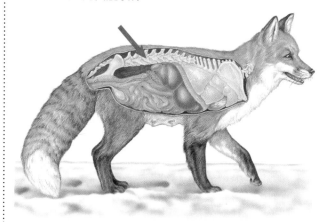

   A. cell     **5.a**
   B. organ
   C. tissue
   D. organ system

10. What level of organization does a leaf represent?
   A. cell     **5.a**
   B. organ
   C. tissue
   D. organ system

Science Online Standards Review ca7.msscience.com

## Applying Science

11. **Give an example** of a cell type that has a short cell cycle. `1.e`

12. **Predict** what would happen if your skin cells were unable to perform mitosis. `1.e`

13. **Hypothesize** why the length of the cell cycle is usually short during development from a fertilized egg. `1.e`

14. **Compare** the daughter cells formed in mitosis to the original cell that divided to produce them. `1.e`

15. **Give an example** of a cell that can make different types of cells. `1.f`

16. **Compare** the levels of organization in this textbook to the levels of organization in a multicellular organism. `5.a`

| Textbook | Organism |
|---|---|
|  |  |
|  |  |
|  |  |
|  |  |

17. **Infer** why some single-celled eukaryotes might form a colony. `5.a`

18. **Rearrange** the following events that happen during mitosis and cell division in the order that they happen: *chromosomes line up at the center of the cell, nuclear membrane breaks apart, plasma membrane pinches inward, sister chromatids separate.* `1.e`

### WRITING in Science

19. **Write** a paragraph to explain the following sentence: *It is easier for a begonia leaf to become a new begonia plant than it is for an animal's skin to become a new animal.*

## Cumulative Review

20. **Summarize** the phases of mitosis in your own words. `1.e`

21. **Explain** why the nucleus is sometimes called the brain of a cell. `1.c`

22. **Describe** how a prokaryote is organized. `1.a`

## Applying Math

**Use the table below to answer questions 23–26.**

| Two Phases of Mitosis | | |
|---|---|---|
| **Class Period** | **Prophase** | **Telophase** |
| 1 | 4 | 1 |
| 2 | 5 | 2 |
| 3 | 2 | 2 |
| 4 | 3 | 1 |
| 5 | 3 | 1 |

Students in five classes observed cells and identified phases of mitosis. Each class observed 30 cells. The table above lists the number of cells observed in prophase and telophase.

23. What is the probability of a first-period student observing a cell in prophase? **MA7:** NS 1.0, SP 1.0

24. What is the probability of a second-period student observing a cell in prophase? **MA7:** NS 1.0, SP 1.0

25. What is the probability of a third-period student observing a cell in telophase? **MA7:** NS 1.0, SP 1.0

26. What is the probability of a fifth-period student observing a cell in telophase? **MA7:** NS 1.0, SP 1.0

**1** **Groups of cells that all do the same sort of work are called**

  **A** organs.

  **B** organelles.

  **C** tissues.

  **D** nerves.    `5.a`

**2** **The diagram below shows replication of DNA.**

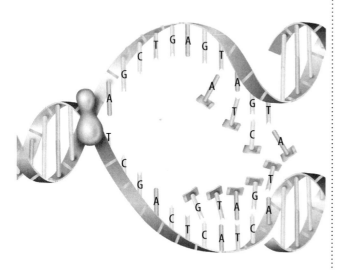

**When does this occur in the cell cycle?**

  **A** prophase

  **B** metaphase

  **C** interphase

  **D** anaphase    `1.c, 1.e`

**3** **Following cell division, each new cell's nucleus has**

  **A** half the number of chromosomes as the parent cell.

  **B** identical chromosomes to the parent cell.

  **C** an assortment of the chromosomes from the parent cell.

  **D** all different chromosomes than the parent cell.    `1.c, 1.e`

**4** **Which describes homologous chromosomes in G₁?**

  **A** paired

  **B** duplicated

  **C** tightly coiled as sister chromatids

  **D** in a row at the cell's center    `1.e`

**5** **The photo below shows a plant cell.**

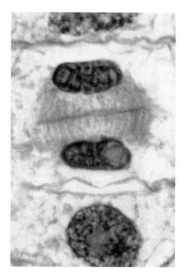

**Which phase of this plant's cell cycle is shown?**

  **A** cytokinesis

  **B** metaphase

  **C** interphase

  **D** prophase    `1.e`

**6** **What is the main purpose of mitosis?**

  **A** to produce different cells

  **B** to pair up the chromosomes in a cell

  **C** to reduce the number of chromosomes in a cell in half

  **D** to make a copy of the genetic material in a cell's nucleus    `1.e`

**7** **The figure below shows a cell reproducing.**

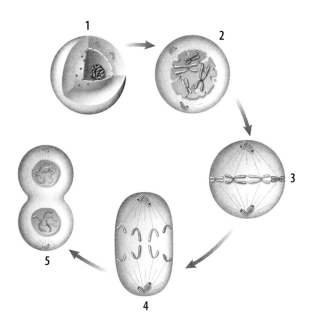

**Which best describes what happens during step 4?**

**A** Each duplicated chromosome pair moves to one end of the cell.

**B** The genetic material in the cell is duplicated.

**C** The sister chromatids separate.

**D** Membranes form around identical nuclei. **1.e**

**8** **Sister chromatids are shown to the right. What does the arrow point to?**

**A** Golgi apparatus

**B** centromere

**C** ribosome

**D** cytoplasm **1.c**

**Use the table below to answer questions 9–11.**

| Mitosis Phase | Description of Chromosomes |
|---|---|
| 1 | Chromosomes have moved to opposite ends of the cell |
| 2 | Chromosomes are clustered near center the cell's center |
| 3 | Chromosomes are in a line across the center of the cell |
| 4 | Chromosomes are enclosed in two new nuclei |

**9** **Which phase is number 1?**

**A** anaphase

**B** metaphase

**C** prophase

**D** telophase **1.e**

**10** **Which phase is number 2?**

**A** anaphase

**B** metaphase

**C** prophase

**D** telophase **1.e**

**11** **Which phase is number 3?**

**A** anaphase

**B** metaphase

**C** prophase

**D** telophase **1.e**

**From the Recommended Literature for Science and Math**

Are you interested in learning more about cells and multicellular organisms? If so, check out these great books.

## Nonfiction

**There's a Zoo on You,** by Kathy Darling, focuses on symbiotic organisms that live together and share food. The book has numerous color photographs of microorganisms including bacteria, E. coli, dust mites, eyelash mites, staphylococcus aureus, and papoviruses. *The content of this book is related to Science Standard 7.1.*

## Historical Fiction

**Fever, 1793,** by Laurie Anderson, describes the Yellow Fever epidemic in Philadelphia in 1793 through the eyes of Mattie, a teenage girl. The cause of the disease and possible cures were unknown. The book realistically describes how the citizens responded to the illness. *The content of this book is related to Science Standard 7.1.*

## Essay

**101 Things You Don't Know About Science and No One Else Does Either,** by James Trefil, contains easy-to-read essays that make science real. This book explores the top ten problems in science. *The content of this book is related to Science Standard 7.2.*

## Nonfiction

**Blood, Bones, and Body Bits,** by Nick Arnold, provides scientific information about the human body in a humorous way. This book explains the science of things that some would consider gross and disgusting. Cartoonlike drawings help explain the science. *The content of this book is related to Science Standard 7.5.*
*This book should be reviewed by an adult to determine appropriateness for specific readers.*

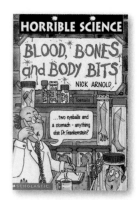

*Choose the word or phrase that best answers the question.*

1. Which term would not be used when describing a bacterium?
   A. cell membrane
   B. mitosis
   C. prokaryote
   D. single-celled                                    `1.a`

2. Which product of cellular respiration is used in photosynthesis?
   A. carbon dioxide
   B. glucose
   C. lactic acid
   D. oxygen                                           `1.d`

3. The table below includes some cell organelles and their functions.

| Organelle | Function |
|---|---|
| X | Directs all cellular activities |
| Mitochondrion | Releases energy from molecules following glycolysis |
| Y | Captures light energy and makes glucose |
| Ribosome | Makes proteins from amino acids |

   Which organelle is X?
   A. central vacuole
   B. endoplasmic reticulum
   C. lysosome
   D. nucleus                                          `1.c`

4. Which organelle is Y?
   A. chloroplast
   B. Golgi apparatus
   C. nucleolus
   D. vesicle                                          `1.b`

*Write your responses on a sheet of paper.*

5. **Compare and contrast** a cell wall and a cell membrane.                                             `1.b`

6. The table below shows data from an experiment about the rate of photosynthesis.

| Container | Distance from light (cm) | Bubbles per min |
|---|---|---|
| 1 | 10 | 45 |
| 2 | 30 | 30 |
| 3 | 50 | 19 |
| 4 | 70 | 6 |
| 5 | 100 | 1 |

   **Conclude** Water plants were placed at different distances from a light source. For 5 min, students counted the bubbles that formed on the plants. What conclusion can be made from this experiment?                                    `1.d`

7. **Describe** what occurs in a cell's cycle that results in genetically identical cells forming after cytokinesis.                                  `1.e, 2.e`

8. **Explain** what might be the result of damage to cells during the early development of organism.                                           `1.f, 5.a`

9. The photo below shows cytokinesis in a cell.

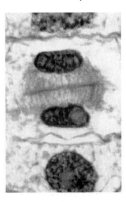

   **Determine** if this is cytokinesis of a plant cell or an animal. Explain.                          `1.b`

# UNIT 2
# Reproduction and Genetics

**Code of Life** This is a computer-generated model of DNA, the material that carries genetic information. This type of image helps to accurately display the chemistry of molecules in the body.

**West-Coast Events**

**10,000–9,000 Years Ago**
People in Mexico and southward plant food crops using seeds and shoots from parent plants.

**1870–1890**
Luther Burbank works in Santa Rosa, California, developing more than 800 new strains of plants to improve the quality of food; he is known as the father of plant breeding.

**A.D. 1 / 1700 / 1800 / 190**

**World Events**

**2,700 Years Ago**
Greeks develop different varieties of plants by grafting (splicing part of one plant with part of another).

**1791**
James Weatherby publishes book of pedigrees of race horses in England, which becomes basis for recording pedigrees of other animals.

**1890s**
The invention of better microscopes allows several scientists to discover the basic facts of sexual reproduction.

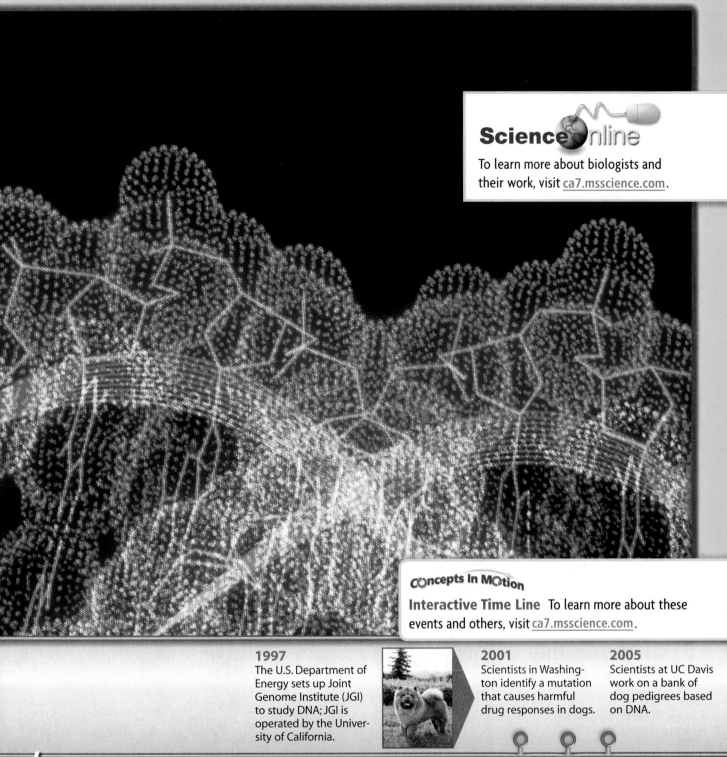

**Science Online**

To learn more about biologists and their work, visit ca7.msscience.com.

**Concepts In Motion**

**Interactive Time Line** To learn more about these events and others, visit ca7.msscience.com.

**1997**
The U.S. Department of Energy sets up Joint Genome Institute (JGI) to study DNA; JGI is operated by the University of California.

**2001**
Scientists in Washington identify a mutation that causes harmful drug responses in dogs.

**2005**
Scientists at UC Davis work on a bank of dog pedigrees based on DNA.

1950    1960    1970    1980    1990    2000    2010

**1951, 1952, 1953**
Rosalind Franklin has a photograph of DNA; Martha Chase and Alfred Hershey prove that DNA is the molecule of heredity; Francis Crick and James Watson model DNA.

**1997**
Scientists in Scotland announce the cloning of a sheep named Dolly.

**February 2001**
Scientists from around the world successfully map the human genome (all the genes of the human body).

### CHAPTER 3

# Reproduction of Organisms

## The BIG Idea

Different types of reproduction ensure the survival of different species.

### LESSON 1 · 2.b, 7.b
### Sexual Reproduction and Meiosis

**Main Idea** Meiosis maintains the chromosome number of a species from one generation to the next.

### LESSON 2 · 2.a, 5.f, 7.b
### Plant Reproduction

**Main Idea** A plant's life cycle includes a diploid generation that produces spores and a haploid generation that produces eggs and sperm.

### LESSON 3 · 2.a, 2.b, 7.c
### Animal Reproduction

**Main Idea** Animals have specialized structures for sexual reproduction.

### LESSON 4
### 2.a, 7.a, 7.c, 7.d, 7.e
### Asexual Reproduction

**Main Idea** Asexual reproduction produces offspring that are identical to the parent.

### Who planted all of these flowers?

Some of these yellow poppies and purple lupines might have grown from seeds produced in flowers that bloomed here the previous year. Or, an animal passing by might have deposited some seeds in its wastes. Still other plants might have grown from parts of existing plant roots or stems.

**Science *Journal*** List four plants you familiar with that grow from seeds. List other ways you know of that plants can be grown.

## How does reproduction happen?

When a photograph is reproduced, a copy is made. Does the same thing happen when an organism reproduces?

### Procedure

1. Create a spider concept map about what you know about reproduction.

2. Write the word *reproduction* in the center circle and add examples of reproduction around it.

### Think About This

- **Infer** Art and photographs can be reproduced. Does the same thing happen when an organism reproduces?

- **Compare** List ways that puppies are like their parents and ways they could be different from their parents.

- **Predict** Do plants have parents? Do bacteria have parents?

- **Analyze** Some organisms look like their parents, but others do not. How might this happen?

 2.a, 7.d

Visit ca7.msscience.com to:

- ▶ view **Concepts in Motion**
- ▶ explore Virtual Labs
- ▶ access content-related Web links
- ▶ take the Standards Check

 **Plant Reproduction**
Make the following Foldable about sexual and asexual reproduction in flowering plants.

▷ **STEP 1 Fold** a sheet of paper in half lengthwise. **Fold** the top down about 3 cm from the top.

▷ **STEP 2 Unfold** and draw lines along the folds as shown. **Label** the top and each column.

**Reading** *Skill*

**Clarifying**
As you read Lesson 2, list in the appropriate column the flowering-plant structures involved in each type of reproduction.

# Get Ready to Read

## New Vocabulary

**① Learn It!**  What should you do if you find a word you don't know or understand? Here are some suggested strategies:

1. Use context clues (from the sentence or the paragraph) to help you define it.
2. Look for prefixes, suffixes, or root words that you already know.
3. Write it down and ask for help with the meaning.
4. Guess at its meaning.
5. Look it up in the glossary or a dictionary.

**② Practice It!**  Look at the word *conifer* in the following passage. See how context clues can help you understand its meaning.

**Context Clue**

Examples of conifers are pines, firs, cypresses, red-woods, and yews.

**Context Clue**

Conifers are trees and shrubs with needlelike or scale-like leaves.

**Context Clue**

Most conifers are evergreen and can live for many years.

The most common gymnosperms are conifers. Conifers, such as **pines, firs, cypresses, red-woods, and yews,** are **trees and shrubs with needlelike or scalelike leaves.** Most conifers are **evergreen and can live for many years.** Bristlecone pines, shown in **Figure 11,** are among the oldest living trees on Earth.

—*from page 137*

**③ Apply It!**  Make a vocabulary bookmark with a strip of paper. As you read, keep track of words you do not know or want to learn more about.

# Target Your Reading

**Use this to focus on the main ideas as you read the chapter.**

**Reading Tip**

Read a paragraph containing a vocabulary word from beginning to end. Then, go back to determine the meaning of the word.

**1** **Before you read** the chapter, respond to the statements below on your worksheet or on a numbered sheet of paper.

- Write an **A** if you **agree** with the statement.
- Write a **D** if you **disagree** with the statement.

**2** **After you read** the chapter, look back to this page to see if you've changed your mind about any of the statements.

- If any of your answers changed, explain why.
- Change any false statements into true statements.
- Use your revised statements as a study guide.

| Before You Read<br>A or D | Statement | After You Read<br>A or D |
|---|---|---|
| | **1** All living organisms have two parents. | |
| | **2** Parents always pass their genetic material to their offspring. | |
| | **3** Not all reproduction involves a sperm cell and an egg cell. | |
| | **4** Meiosis is a type of cell division. | |
| | **5** All plants reproduce by forming flowers. | |
| | **6** All plants reproduce by forming seeds. | |
| | **7** Some animal embryos develop inside the body of the mother. | |
| | **8** All animal embryos develop inside eggs. | |
| | **9** Some organisms have only one parent. | |
| | **10** Plants can be cloned, but animals cannot. | |

**Science Online**

Print a worksheet of this page at ca7.msscience.com.

### Science Content Standards

**2.b** Students know that sexual reproduction produces offspring that inherit half their genes from each parent.
**7.d** Construct scale models, maps, and appropriately labeled diagrams to communicate scientific knowledge (e.g., motion of Earth's plates and cell structure).

## Reading Guide

### What *You'll Learn*

▶ **Compare** a sexually produced offspring to its parents.

▶ **Explain** the importance of meiosis in sexual reproduction.

▶ **Sequence** meiosis.

▶ **Describe** the results of meiosis.

### Why *It's Important*

If you know how cells divide for reproduction, it's easier to understand why offspring resemble their parents.

### Vocabulary

sexual reproduction
egg
sperm
fertilization
zygote
meiosis
diploid
haploid

### Review Vocabulary

**eukaryote:** an organism made of cells; each cell has a membrane-bound nucleus (p. 64)

# Sexual Reproduction and Meiosis

**Main Idea** Meiosis maintains the chromosome number of a species from one generation to the next.

**Real-World Reading Connection** You have a better chance of seeing a wild California condor than your parents did when they were your age. In the 1980s, fewer than 20 of these birds were in the wild. Naturalists captured condors and helped them produce offspring. Some of these condor offspring now live in the wild, and the condor population is increasing.

## What is sexual reproduction?

Many young organisms resemble their parents, such as the guinea pig pups shown in **Figure 1.** Like most animals, each guinea pig pup has two parents—a mother and a father. The genetic material that an organism receives from its parents determines what it looks like and how it functions.

Reproduction in organisms produces new offspring. **Sexual reproduction** is the production of an offspring that results when the genetic materials from two different cells combine. Half of the genetic material is contained in an **egg** cell. The other half is contained in a **sperm** cell. A process called **fertilization** (fur tuh luh ZAY shun) is the fusing together of a sperm cell and an egg cell. The new cell that forms is called a **zygote** (ZI goht). A zygote develops into a new organism.

**Figure 1** These guinea pig pups are not identical because each one inherited a different mix of genetic material from its parents.

## Advantages of Sexual Reproduction

Sexual reproduction is the most common form of reproduction in eukaryotes. As you just read, offspring from sexual reproduction receive genetic material from two cells. Each guinea pig pup in **Figure 1** inherited genetic material from the same two parents. Each pup inherited a different mix of genetic material. In a population of guinea pigs, or any other species that reproduces sexually, no two individuals, except identical twins, have the same mix of genetic material. This means that each individual has a different set of traits. The variety of genetic traits in a population of the same species is known as genetic variation.

 How does genetic variation affect the survival of a species?

**Genetic Variation** When environmental conditions change, genetic variation can help a species survive. Imagine a population of California poppies, like those shown in **Figure 2.** During a drought, poppy plants with traits that enable them to grow in dry conditions are more likely to survive and produce seeds. Plants without these traits might not survive. Because their genetic makeups **vary,** the population of poppies would include a few plants that could survive a drought.

A lack of genetic variation can cause problems for a species. Suppose every plant in the poppy population had the same genetic traits. If none of those traits enabled the plants to survive hot, dry weather, the entire population might die out.

**Selective Breeding** Plant breeders and animal breeders often select a male organism and a female organism with certain preferred traits to be the parents of offspring. This method of sexual reproduction is called selective breeding. It produces groups of organisms with similar traits, such as the dogs shown in **Figure 3,** but reduces genetic variation. Offspring produced by selective breeding can also inherit health problems.

 **Figure 3** Why do these puppies resemble each other more than the guinea pig pups resemble each other?

**Figure 2** Each California poppy plant in this population has a unique set of genetic information, making the population genetically varied.

**ACADEMIC VOCABULARY**
vary (VAYR ee)
*(verb)* to make different
*Musicians vary the tempo as directed by the conductor.*

**Figure 3** The golden retriever is one of many dog breeds created by mating dogs that have similar genetic material.

**Figure 4** Male sea urchins release sperm into the water at the same time that female sea urchins release millions of eggs. Male elephant seals might attack each other to become the dominant male that mates with female elephant seals.

## Disadvantages of Sexual Reproduction

Because males produce sperm and females produce eggs, one of the disadvantages of sexual reproduction is getting egg and sperm together for fertilization. Some species, such as the sea urchin shown in **Figure 4,** produce millions of egg cells or sperm cells and release them into water. This increases the chances that a sperm will find an egg. Other organisms have specific methods that ensure fertilization.

Another disadvantage of sexual reproduction is the time needed for organisms to grow and develop until they can reproduce. For example, male elephant seals, as shown in **Figure 4,** do not mate until they are about 9–10 years of age. Humans are even older. Later in this chapter, you will read about types of reproduction that can happen before organisms grow and develop enough to reproduce sexually and do not require fertilization.

# Why is meiosis important?

You read in Chapter 1 that genetic material is part of the chromosomes in the nucleus of each eukaryotic cell. Sexual reproduction includes fertilization, which is the combining of the genetic material in a sperm cell and the genetic material in an egg cell. **Meiosis** (mi OH sus) is cell division that produces sperm or eggs from certain reproductive cells in an organism. Meiosis takes place only in eukaryotes that reproduce sexually.

 What kinds of cells does meiosis produce?

Meiosis is important because it ensures that a species' offspring inherit the correct chromosome number. For example, tomatoes inherit 24 chromosomes, humans inherit 46 chromosomes, and chickens inherit 78 chromosomes. Without meiosis, the chromosome number would double with each generation. Instead of inheriting 46 chromosomes, children would inherit 92 chromosomes, their children would inherit 184, and so on.

## Maintaining Diploid Cells

Recall from Chapter 2 that homologous (huh MAH luh gus) chromosomes are similar in size, shape, and genetic material. A **diploid** cell in an organism contains pairs of chromosomes that equal the chromosome number of that organism's species. A diploid human cell has 23 pairs of homologous chromosomes. The chromosome number for humans is 46.

Homologous chromosomes are similar, but not identical. For example, each human chromosome in a homologous pair might contain genetic material for eye color. However, one chromosome might have blue eye-color information and the other brown eye-color information.

## Creating Haploid Cells

Sperm and egg cells have half the chromosome number of the species. For example, a human sperm cell contains 23 chromosomes—one chromosome from each homologous pair of chromosomes. Similarly, a human egg cell contains 23 chromosomes. A cell that contains one chromosome from each homologous pair is called a **haploid** cell.

It's important for offspring to inherit the correct number of chromosomes for their species. Because an egg and a sperm are haploid, the chromosome number of offspring does not double, as described on the previous page. Meiosis ensures that fertilization creates a zygote with the correct number of chromosomes, as shown in **Figure 5.**

**WORD ORIGIN** · · · · · · · · · · · ·
haploid
from Greek *haploeides*; means *single*

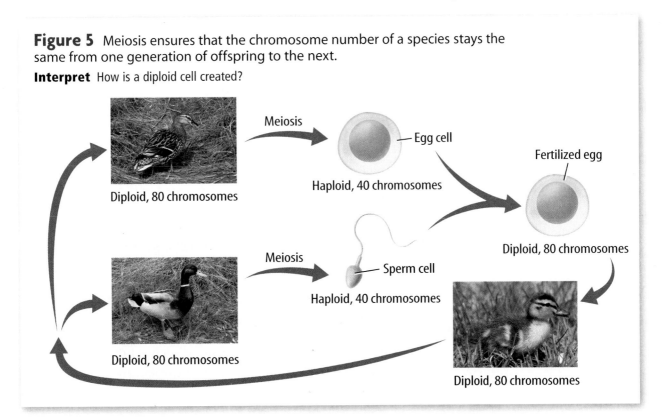

**Figure 5** Meiosis ensures that the chromosome number of a species stays the same from one generation of offspring to the next.

**Interpret** How is a diploid cell created?

Diploid, 80 chromosomes

Meiosis

Egg cell
Haploid, 40 chromosomes

Fertilized egg

Diploid, 80 chromosomes

Meiosis

Sperm cell
Haploid, 40 chromosomes

Diploid, 80 chromosomes

Diploid, 80 chromosomes

# What are the phases of meiosis?

In Chapter 2, you read about the stages of mitosis—the division of a cell nucleus. Meiosis happens in a similar way. For example, before meiosis begins, a cell's chromosomes replicate, just as they do before mitosis. Recall that each replicated chromosome consists of two identical sister chromatids that are held together near their middles.

In mitosis, division of the nucleus and cytokinesis happen once. In meiosis, division of the nucleus and cytokinesis happen twice. These two processes are called meiosis I and meiosis II. Like mitosis, the phases of each process are called prophase, metaphase, anaphase, and telophase. Diagrams of the phases of meiosis I and meiosis II are shown in **Figure 6.**

## Phases of Meiosis I

**Prophase I** The membrane surrounding the nucleus breaks apart. The replicated chromosomes condense and thicken. Then, unlike mitosis, homologous chromosomes line up close to each other.

**Metaphase I** The pairs of replicated homologous chromosomes form a line along the middle of the cell. Fibers of the cytoskeleton attach to each pair of sister chromatids.

**Anaphase I** Cytoskeleton fibers pull each pair of sister chromatids to opposite ends of the cell. Notice that the pairs of replicated homologous chromosomes separate, but not the sister chromatids. Sister chromatids stay together.

**Telophase I** A membrane forms around each group of replicated chromosomes. Then, the cytoplasm divides to form two daughter cells. Sister chromatids still are together.

## Phases of Meiosis II

During meiosis II, the nucleus of each daughter cell formed during meiosis I divides. Then, each daughter cell divides.

**Prophase II** Chromosomes do not replicate before prophase II. They remain condensed and thickened.

**Metaphase II** The cytoskeleton fibers move the replicated chromosomes to the middle of the cell.

**Anaphase II** The sister chromatids of each replicated chromosome separate and move toward opposite ends of the cell.

**Telophase II** A membrane forms around each set of chromatids, which now are called chromosomes. The cytoplasm divides, and meiosis II is complete.

**Figure 6** Meiosis produces four haploid daughter cells from one diploid parent cell. Meiosis I separates homologous chromosome pairs. Meiosis II separates sister chromatids.

**Identify** other differences between meiosis I and meiosis II.

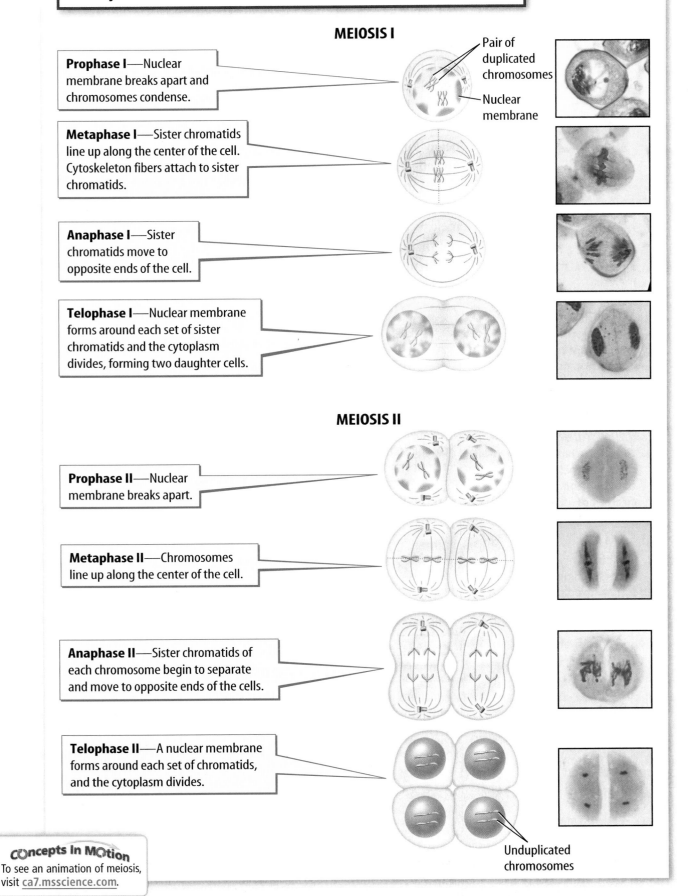

**MEIOSIS I**

**Prophase I**—Nuclear membrane breaks apart and chromosomes condense.

Pair of duplicated chromosomes

Nuclear membrane

**Metaphase I**—Sister chromatids line up along the center of the cell. Cytoskeleton fibers attach to sister chromatids.

**Anaphase I**—Sister chromatids move to opposite ends of the cell.

**Telophase I**—Nuclear membrane forms around each set of sister chromatids and the cytoplasm divides, forming two daughter cells.

**MEIOSIS II**

**Prophase II**—Nuclear membrane breaks apart.

**Metaphase II**—Chromosomes line up along the center of the cell.

**Anaphase II**—Sister chromatids of each chromosome begin to separate and move to opposite ends of the cells.

**Telophase II**—A nuclear membrane forms around each set of chromatids, and the cytoplasm divides.

Unduplicated chromosomes

**CONcepts In MOtion**
To see an animation of meiosis, visit ca7.msscience.com.

## What does meiosis look like?

How do chromosomes move during meiosis? Try this lab to model meiosis.

### Procedure

1. Complete a lab safety form.
2. Use **Figure 6** for reference as you model meiosis.
3. Model each phase of meiosis I and meiosis II using **colored yarn** to represent chromosomes.
4. Use **scissors** to cut the lengths of yarn to create homologous chromosomes.
5. **Glue** your yarn chromosomes to **construction paper circles** provided by your teacher.

### Analysis

1. **Explain** how your understanding of meiosis improved after you completed this lab.
2. **Evaluate** Is yarn a good material to use for modeling chromosomes during meiosis?
3. **Describe** ways in which this model worked well. List ways you could improve it.

2.b, 7.d

# What are the results of meiosis?

As you read earlier, meiosis is similar to mitosis, but there are important differences. Some of the similarities and differences are listed in **Table 1.**

Both meiosis and mitosis begin with one diploid parent cell. Both meiosis and mitosis take place only in eukaryotic cells. Recall that eukaryotic cells are cells that contain a nucleus surrounded by a membrane.

In meiosis, the nucleus of the parent cell divides, then the two newly formed nuclei divide. Mitosis has only one division of a nucleus. Also, mitosis is usually followed by cytokinesis that results in two daughter cells of equal size. Sometimes when meiosis occurs for egg production, the cytoplasm divides unequally during meiosis I. This results in a small cell that breaks down and a large cell that undergoes meiosis II. In meiosis II, the cytoplasm divides unequally again. The larger cell becomes the egg and the smaller cell breaks down.

**Visual Check** **Table 1** What process produces genetically different daughter cells?

| Table 1 Comparison of Meiosis and Mitosis | | |
|---|---|---|
| **Characteristic** | **Meiosis** | **Mitosis** |
| Number of chromosomes in parent cell | diploid | diploid |
| Type of parent cell | only certain reproductive cells in eukaryotic organisms | nearly all eukaryotic cells |
| Number of divisions of nucleus | 2 | 1 |
| Number of daughter cells produced | 4 | 2 |
| Chromosome number in daughter cells | haploid | diploid |
| Functions in the organism | • produces sperm and egg cells<br>• maintains chromosome number for the species | • daughter cells genetically identical to each other and to the parent cell<br>• growth, cell repair, some types of reproduction |

# Meiosis Summary

In this lesson, you learned that sexual reproduction includes fertilization—the fusion of a sperm cell with an egg cell. You also learned that fertilization produces a cell called a zygote. The zygote is a diploid cell, and an egg and a sperm are called haploid cells.

Sperm and egg cells are produced by meiosis. It is important to remember that all the eggs or sperm produced by an organism are different. Therefore, each zygote produced by sexual reproduction from the same parents will inherit different genetic material. This genetic variation can be important to the survival of a species. You will learn more about how meiosis promotes genetic diversity when you study genetics in Chapter 4.

## LESSON 1  Review

### Summarize

Create your own lesson summary as you organize an **outline.**

1. **Scan** the lesson. Find and list the first **red** main heading.

2. **Review** the text after the heading and list 2–3 details about the heading.

3. **Find** and list each **blue** subheading that follows the **red** main heading.

4. **List** 2–3 details, key terms, and definitions under each **blue** subheading.

5. **Review** additional **red** main headings and their supporting **blue** subheadings. List 2–3 details about each.

 ELA7: W 2.5

### Using Vocabulary

1. Distinguish *haploid* from *diploid*.  `2.b`

2. In your own words, write the definition for *meiosis*.  `2.b`

### Understanding Main Ideas

3. Why is meiosis important in sexual reproduction?  `2.b`
   A. It produces haploid daughter cells.
   B. It produces diploid daughter cells.
   C. It replicates chromosomes.
   D. It produces four daughter cells.

4. How many chromosomes are in a sperm cell compared to a skin cell?
   A. same number  `2.b`
   B. half as many
   C. three times as many
   D. twice as many

5. **List** the phases of meiosis in the order they occur.  `2.b`

 ## Standards Check

6. **Give an example** of how sexual reproduction increases genetic diversity.  `2.b`

7. **Simplify** meiosis into its basic events.  `2.b`

### Applying Science

8. **Analyze** why meiosis is not the type of cell division that produces new skin cells.  `2.b`

9. **Suggest** why brothers who have the same parents are not identical.  `2.b`

10. **Organize Information**  Copy the graphic organizer below and fill it in with details about meiosis I and meiosis II.  `2.b`

| Meiosis I | |
|-----------|---|
| Meiosis II | |

**Science** nline
For more practice, visit **Standards Check** at ca7.msscience.com.

### Science Content Standards

**2.a** Students know the differences between the life cycles and reproduction methods of sexual and asexual organisms.
**5.f** Students know the structures and processes by which flowering plants generate pollen, ovules, seeds, and fruit.
**7.d** Construct scale models, maps, and appropriately labeled diagrams to communicate scientific knowledge (e.g., motion of Earth's plates and cell structure).

### Reading Guide

#### What *You'll Learn*

▶ **Explain** alternation of generations.

▶ **Summarize** reproduction in seedless plants.

▶ **Distinguish** between reproduction in flowerless and flowering plants.

▶ **Identify** the reproductive structures in a flower and **state** their functions.

#### Why *It's Important*

Learning how plants reproduce helps you understand important differences between plants and animals.

#### Vocabulary

| | |
|---|---|
| spore | filament |
| pollen grain | pistil |
| ovule | stigma |
| seed | style |
| angiosperm | ovary |
| stamen | pollen tube |
| anther | fruit |

#### Review Vocabulary

**mitosis:** a process in which the nucleus of the cell divides (p. 91)

# Plant Reproduction

**Main Idea** A plant's life cycle includes a diploid generation that produces spores and a haploid generation that produces eggs and sperm.

**Real-World Reading Connection** In early spring, you might see cars or sidewalks covered with something that looks like yellow dust. Where did it come from? It came from some plants that are reproducing. As in all living things, reproduction is part of the life cycles of plants.

## What is alternation of generations?

The human body is made primarily of diploid cells. The only human haploid cells are sperm or eggs. As a result, you will live your entire life as a diploid organism. To put it another way, your life cycle includes only a diploid stage.

That isn't true for all organisms. Some organisms, including plants, have two life stages called generations. One generation has primarily diploid cells. The other generation has only haploid cells. Organisms that alternate between diploid and haploid generations have an alternation of generations as shown in **Figure 7.**

**Visual Check** **Figure 7** Why does the haploid generation begin with meiosis?

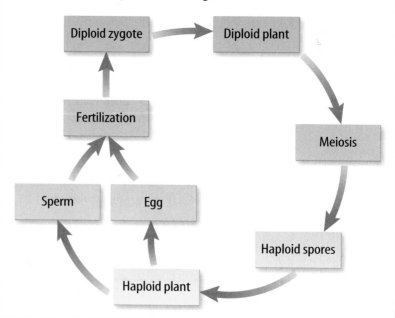

**Figure 7** The life cycles of all plants include an alternation of generations. The diploid generation begins with fertilization. The haploid generation begins with meiosis.

### The Diploid Generation

When you look at a tree or a flower, you're seeing part of the diploid generation of a plant. Meiosis occurs in certain cells in the reproductive structures of a diploid plant. The daughter cells produced from haploid structures are called **spores.** Spores grow by mitosis and cell division to form the haploid generation of a plant.

### The Haploid Generation

In most plants, the haploid generation is tiny and lives surrounded by **specific** tissues of the diploid plant. In other plants, the haploid generation lives on its own. Certain reproductive cells of the haploid generation produce haploid sperm and/or eggs by mitosis and cell division. Fertilization takes place when a sperm and an egg fuse to form a diploid zygote. Through mitosis and cell division, the zygote grows into the diploid generation of the plant.

 How are the sperm and eggs produced by the haploid generation of a plant formed?

---

### The Diploid Generation

When you look at a tree or a flower, you're seeing part of the diploid generation of a plant. Meiosis occurs in certain cells in the reproductive structures of a diploid plant. The daughter cells produced from haploid structures are called **spores.** Spores grow by mitosis and cell division to form the haploid generation of a plant.

### The Haploid Generation

In most plants, the haploid generation is tiny and lives surrounded by **specific** tissues of the diploid plant. In other plants, the haploid generation lives on its own. Certain reproductive cells of the haploid generation produce haploid sperm and/or eggs by mitosis and cell division. Fertilization takes place when a sperm and an egg fuse to form a diploid zygote. Through mitosis and cell division, the zygote grows into the diploid generation of the plant.

 How are the sperm and eggs produced by the haploid generation of a plant formed?

## How do seedless plants reproduce?

You've probably planted seeds and watched them grow into new plants. But, not all plants grow from seeds. The first land plants to inhabit Earth probably were seedless plants—plants that grow from haploid spores, not from seeds. The mosses and ferns in **Figure 8** are examples of seedless plants found on Earth today.

The life cycle of a moss is typical for some seedless plants. It begins with haploid spores that grow by mitosis and cell division into haploid plants. The tiny, green moss plants that carpet rocks, bark, and soil in moist areas are haploid plants. They have male structures that produce sperm and female structures that produce eggs. Fertilization results in a diploid zygote that grows by mitosis and cell division into the diploid generation. The diploid generation of mosses is tiny and not easily seen. It produces haploid spores by meiosis, and the cycle repeats.

**ACADEMIC VOCABULARY**

specific (spih SIHF ihk)

**(adj)** relating to or being an example of a certain kind of thing

*The race car needs a specific type of fuel.*

**Figure 8** Mosses and ferns usually grow in moist environments. Sperm must swim through a film of water to reach an egg.

**Diploid Moss Generation**

**Figure 9** Pollen grains of one type of plant are different from those of any other type of plant.

**Infer** how scientists might use this characteristic of pollen grains.

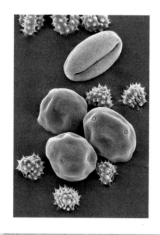

# How do seed plants reproduce?

Most of the land plants that cover Earth grew from seeds. Plants that grow from seeds are called seed plants. There are two groups of seed plants—flowerless seed plants and flowering seed plants.

Unlike seedless plants, the haploid generation of a seed plant is within diploid tissue. Separate diploid male and diploid female reproductive structures produce haploid sperm and haploid eggs that join during fertilization.

## The Role of Pollen Grains

A **pollen** (PAH lun) **grain** forms from tissue in a male reproductive structure of a seed plant. Each pollen grain contains nutrients and has a hard, protective outer covering, as shown in **Figure 9.** Sperm cells form inside pollen grains. Wind, animals, gravity, or water currents can carry pollen grains to female reproductive structures. Plants cannot move to find a mate like most animals can. Recall reading about the yellow dust at the beginning of this chapter. That dust was pollen grains. Male reproductive structures produce a vast number of pollen grains. When pollen grains land on a female reproductive structure of a plant that is the same species as the pollen grains, **pollination** (pah luh NAY shun) occurs.

## The Role of Ovules and Seeds

The female reproductive structure of a seed plant contains one or more **ovules.** A haploid egg develops inside each ovule. Following pollination, sperm enter the ovule and fertilization occurs.

A **seed,** as shown in **Figure 10,** develops from an ovule after fertilization. It consists of an embryo, a food supply, and a protective covering. The **embryo** (EM bree oh) is an immature diploid plant that developed from the zygote. A seed's food supply provides the embryo with nourishment for its early growth.

**Figure 10** A seed contains a diploid plant embryo and a food supply protected by a hard outer covering.

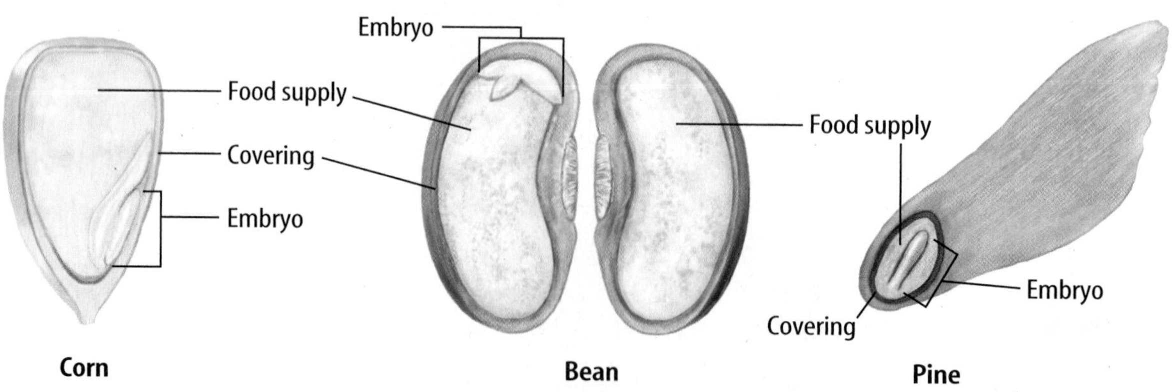

Embryo

Food supply

Covering

Embryo

**Corn**

Embryo

Food supply

**Bean**

Food supply

Covering

Embryo

**Pine**

**Female cones**

**Male cones**

**Male cones**

**Female cone**

**Western Bristlecone Pine**
**Inyo National Forest, CA**

**Macnab Cypress**
**Colusa County, CA**

**Figure 11** Pollen-producing male cones usually are smaller than female cones. Seeds form at the base of each scale on a female cone.

**Concepts in Motion**
To see an animation of gymnosperm reproduction, visit ca7.msscience.com.

# How do flowerless seed plants reproduce?

Flowerless seed plants are also known as gymnosperms (JIHM nuh spurmz). The word *gymnosperm* means "naked seed" and gymnosperm seeds are not surrounded by a fruit. The most common gymnosperms are conifers. Conifers, such as pines, firs, cypresses, redwoods, and yews, are trees and shrubs with needle-like or scalelike leaves. Most conifers are evergreen and can live for many years. Bristlecone pines, such as the one shown in **Figure 11,** are among the oldest living trees on Earth.

Cones are the male and female reproductive structures of conifers. They contain the haploid generation. Male cones are papery and produce pollen grains. Female cones are woody, berry-like, or soft and produce eggs. Seeds form as part of the female cone.

# MiniLab

## 00:20 minutes What's in a flower?

Sexual reproduction in flowering plants involves male and female parts of flowers. Can you discover which parts are which?

### Procedure

1. Complete a lab safety form.
2. Obtain a **flower** from your teacher.
3. Examine it with a partner. Make a sketch. Label your sketch according to **Figure 12.**
4. Using a **scalpel**, carefully cut the flower in half lengthwise.

5. Repeat steps 2–4 with **another type of flower.**

### Analysis

1. **Compare and contrast** the structures in the two flowers.
2. **Predict** the function of each structure.

5.f, 7.d

# How do flowering seed plants reproduce?

Do you enjoy the fragrance of roses or the bold colors of lilies? These are examples of flowering seed plants, also known as **angiosperms** (AN jee uh spurmz). Most of the plants you see around you are angiosperms. Fruits and vegetables come from angiosperms. Many animals depend on angiosperms for food.

## Reproduction and the Flower

Reproduction of an angiosperm begins in a flower. A typical flower has male and female reproductive organs surrounded by petals, as shown in **Figure 12.** Most flowers have several male reproductive organs but only one female reproductive organ. Some flowers have only male or only female organs.

The male reproductive organ of a flower is the **stamen.** Pollen grains form at the tip of the stamen, in a structure called the **anther.** The **filament** is a long stalk that supports the anther and connects it to the base of the flower.

The female reproductive organ of a flower is the **pistil.** At the tip of the pistil is the **stigma,** where pollen can land. The stigma is at the top of a long tube called the **style.** At the base of the style is the **ovary.** Inside the ovary is usually one or more ovules. As you read earlier in this lesson, each ovule eventually will contain a haploid egg.

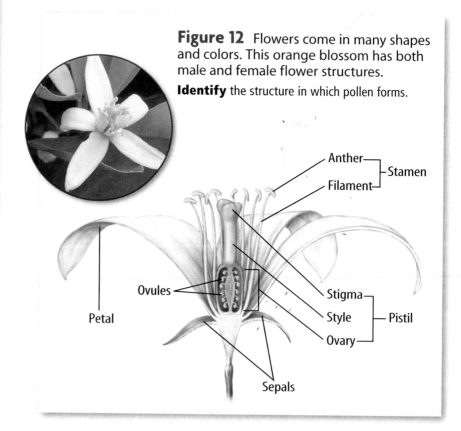

**Figure 12** Flowers come in many shapes and colors. This orange blossom has both male and female flower structures.

**Identify** the structure in which pollen forms.

Anther — Stamen
Filament —
Petal
Ovules
Stigma — Pistil
Style —
Ovary —
Sepals

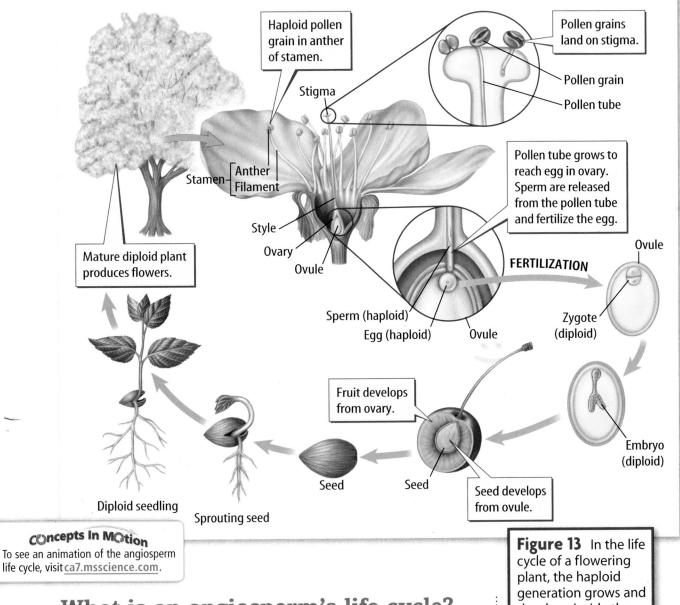

Haploid pollen grain in anther of stamen.

Pollen grains land on stigma.

Stigma

Pollen grain

Pollen tube

Stamen — Anther Filament

Pollen tube grows to reach egg in ovary. Sperm are released from the pollen tube and fertilize the egg.

Style

Ovary

Ovule

Sperm (haploid)

Egg (haploid)

Ovule

FERTILIZATION

Ovule

Zygote (diploid)

Embryo (diploid)

Mature diploid plant produces flowers.

Fruit develops from ovary.

Seed develops from ovule.

Diploid seedling

Sprouting seed

Seed

Seed

To see an animation of the angiosperm life cycle, visit ca7.msscience.com.

**Figure 13** In the life cycle of a flowering plant, the haploid generation grows and develops inside the diploid plant.

# What is an angiosperm's life cycle?

A typical life cycle for an angiosperm is shown in **Figure 13.** Pollen grains travel by wind, gravity, water, or an animal from the anther to the stigma, where pollination occurs. A **pollen tube** grows from the pollen grain into the stigma, down the style, to the ovary at the base of the pistil. Sperm develop from a haploid cell in the pollen tube. When the pollen tube enters an ovule, the sperm are released and fertilization takes place.

**Reading Check** Do sperm develop before or after pollination?

As you read earlier, the zygote that results from fertilization develops into an embryo. Each ovule and its embryo will become a seed. The ovary, and sometimes other parts of the flower, will develop into a **fruit** that contains one or more seeds. The seeds can grow into new, genetically related plants that produce flowers, and the cycle repeats.

**WORD ORIGIN**
angiosperm
*angio-* from Greek *angeion*, means a *vessel*; and
*-sperm* from Greek *sperma*, means *seed*

## Table 2 Flowers, Fruits, and Seeds of Common Plants

| Plant | Flower | Fruit | Seed |
|---|---|---|---|
| Pea | | | |
| Corn | | | |
| Strawberry | | | |
| Dandelion | | | |

 **Table 2** Which of the fruits has seeds on the outside?

## Fruit and Seed Dispersal

Fruits and seeds, including the peas, corn, and strawberries shown in **Table 2,** are important sources of food for people and animals. In most cases, seeds of flowering plants are contained inside fruits. Green pods are the fruits of a pea plant. The peas nestled inside a peapod are the seeds. A cob is the fruit of a corn plant. The kernels on a cob are the seeds. Strawberries have tiny seeds on the outside of the fruit. We usually think of fruits as juicy and edible, like an orange or a watermelon. However, some fruits are hard and dry, and not particularly edible. Each parachutelike structure of a dandelion is a dry fruit.

Fruits help protect seeds and help scatter or disperse them. For example, some fruits, like that of a dandelion, are light enough to float on air currents. When an animal eats a fruit, the fruit's seeds can pass through the animal's digestive system with little or no damage. Imagine what happens when an animal, such as the mouse shown in **Figure 14,** eats blackberries. The animal digests the juicy fruit, but deposits the seeds on the soil with its wastes. By the time that this happens, the animal might have traveled some distance away from the blackberry bush. This means that the animal helped to disperse the seed away from the blackberry bush.

# Visualizing Seed Dispersal

**Figure 14** Wind, water, gravity, and animals help disperse plant seeds.

▲ Some seeds are inside of dry fruits that have tiny hooks. These hooks can attach to fur, feathers, or clothing and as a result, the seeds inside the fruit move to new locations.

▲ Some animals, such as this squirrel, bury or hide fruits and seeds far from the parent plant. If not found and eaten, the seed can sprout.

Pressure ▶ builds within the seedpods of a jewelweed plant until the pod explodes. This propels the seeds far from the parent plant.

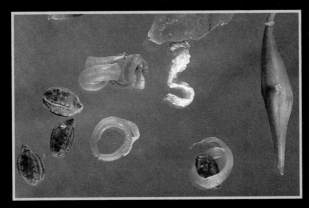

◀ A coconut is a type of seed that can float. Floating seeds are often carried many kilometers from the parent plant.

▲ The seeds of fruits usually are not damaged when they pass through an animal's digestive tract. When the animal excretes the seeds with its wastes, the seeds are usually moved to a location far from the parent plant.

# Plant Reproduction Summary

In this lesson, you learned that plants reproduce sexually. All plant life cycles include an alternation of generations—they alternate between a haploid generation and a diploid generation. Most of the plants you see around you, including trees, flowers, and grasses, are the diploid generation.

Familiar mosses are haploid plants that grew from a haploid spore. The diploid stage is small and often overlooked. Ferns are diploid plants. The haploid stage is small and rarely seen. Conifers and flowering plants are diploid seed plants. The haploid stage of seed plants is surrounded by diploid tissue. Seed plants reproduce by forming seeds. In conifers, seeds form as part of a female cone. In flowering plants, seeds form as part of a flower.

# LESSON 2  Review

## Summarize

Create your own lesson summary as you write a **newsletter.**

1. **Write** this lesson title, number, and page numbers at the top of a sheet of paper.

2. **Review** the text after the **red** main headings and write one sentence about each. These will be the headlines of your newsletter.

3. **Review** the text and write 2–3 sentences about each **blue** subheading. These sentences should tell *who, what, when, where,* and *why* information about each headline.

4. **Illustrate** your newsletter with diagrams of important structures and processes next to each headline.

 **ELA7:** W 2.5

## Standards Check

### Using Vocabulary

*Complete the sentences using the correct term.*

fruit        anther        spores

1. The diploid generation of a plant produces haploid _____ that grow to become the haploid generation. **5.f**

2. The flower part in which pollen grains form is the _____. **5.f**

3. Angiosperm seeds are part of a(n) _____. **5.f**

### Understanding Main Ideas

4. Which is NOT used to define alternation of generations?
   A. chromosome **2.a**
   B. diploid
   C. haploid
   D. spore

5. **State** the functions of a flower's reproductive structures. **5.f**

6. **Compare** the life cycles of flowerless seed plants and flowering seed plants. **2.a**

### Applying Science

7. **Assess** What criteria would you use to assess the reproductive success of a plant? **2.a**

8. **Organize Information** Draw a graphic organizer similar to the one below to list the female parts of a flower. Write "female flower parts" in the center oval. **5.f**

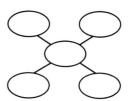

**Science**nline
For more practice, visit **Standards Check** at ca7.msscience.com.

## Science Content Standards

**2.a** Students know the differences between the life cycles and reproduction methods of sexual and asexual organisms.
**2.b** Students know that sexual reproduction produces offspring that inherit half their genes from each parent.
**7.c** Communicate the logical connection among hypotheses, science concepts, tests conducted, data collected, and conclusions drawn from the scientific evidence.

## Reading Guide

### What *You'll Learn*

▶ **Explain** the role of male and female reproductive organs.

▶ **Differentiate** between internal and external fertilization.

▶ **Compare and contrast** embryo development in animals.

### Why *It's Important*
Learning how animals reproduce will help you understand human reproduction.

### Vocabulary
gonad
testes
ovary
metamorphosis

### Review Vocabulary
**organ:** structure of an organism made of different types of tissues that work together (p. 104)

# Animal Reproduction

**Main Idea** Animals have specialized structures for sexual reproduction.

**Real-World Reading Connection** Have you ever found a cluster of tiny, beadlike things on the underside of a leaf? What could they be? They might be eggs laid by a butterfly, a ladybug, or some other insect. Eggs are an important part of the life cycle of all animals.

## What are animal reproductive organs called?

Animals often have external physical characteristics that distinguish males from females. For example, it's fairly easy to tell the difference between the male and female animals shown in **Figure 15.** In mammals and birds, males are often larger or more colorful than females.

**Lions**

**Peacocks**

**Figure 15** Male and female animals often have different physical characteristics. A lion has a ruff of fur around his neck and is larger than the lioness. A peacock has larger and more colorful tail feathers than a peahen.

**Compare** Which of these animals are male and which are female? How do you know?

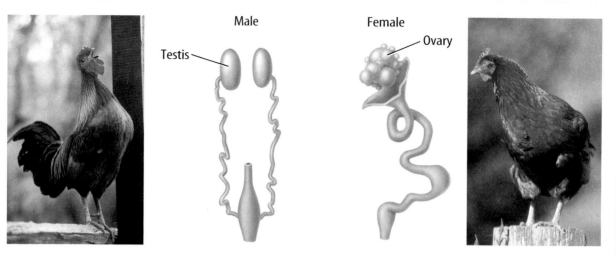

**Figure 16** Sperm cells are produced by meiosis in the testes of male animals. Meiosis in one or two ovaries of female animals produces egg cells.

**ACADEMIC VOCABULARY** · · ·

**network** (NET wurk)
*(noun)* a system of lines or channels that connect with each other. *The capillaries, veins, and arteries form a network for moving blood.*

## Male Reproductive Organs

The reproductive systems of animals include specialized reproductive organs called **gonads** that produce sperm or eggs. **Figure 16** shows the reproductive systems of male and female chickens. Male animals have gonads called **testes** that produce sperm. Testes contain a **network** of coiled tubes in which sperm cells form. Sperm have tails that enable them to swim through fluid to reach an egg cell. Most male animals have two testes located inside the body cavity.

 What type of cell forms in the testes?

Vertebrate animals—animals with backbones—have an additional adaptation that contributes to successful sexual reproduction. Glands near the testes produce fluid that nourishes sperm and helps them travel from the testes to the eggs of a female.

## Female Reproductive Organs

Female animals have gonads called **ovaries.** Most female animals have two ovaries except female birds, which have only one ovary. Ovaries produce egg cells. Eggs are larger than sperm and cannot move on their own. Many female mammals are born with all the eggs they will ever have. You will read more about the testes and ovaries of humans in Chapter 13.

# How does animal fertilization occur?

As you read earlier in this chapter, sexual reproduction requires fertilization—the fusion of a haploid egg cell and a haploid sperm cell that forms a diploid zygote. The way in which a sperm reaches the egg differs among animal species.

## Internal Fertilization

When fertilization happens inside the body of an organism, it is called internal fertilization. For many animals, the male has a specialized structure that can deposit sperm in or near a female's reproductive system. The sperm swim to the egg or eggs. Earthworms, spiders, insects, reptiles, birds, and mammals have internal fertilization.

Internal fertilization ensures that an embryo, which develops from a fertilized egg, is protected and nourished until it leaves the female's body. This protection increases the chance that the embryo will survive, develop into an adult, and reproduce.

## External Fertilization

A female toad, like the one shown in **Figure 17,** deposits unfertilized eggs under water. A male toad releases his sperm above the eggs as she lays them. Fertilization that occurs in the environment, outside of an animal's body, is called external fertilization. In most cases, the female animal releases eggs into water at about the same time a nearby male animal releases sperm into the water. When a sperm reaches an egg, fertilization takes place. Animals that reproduce using external fertilization include jellyfishes, clams, sea urchins, sea stars, many species of fish, and amphibians.

Most animals that reproduce using external fertilization do not care for the fertilized eggs or for the newly hatched young. As a result, eggs and young are exposed to predators and other dangers in the environment, reducing their chances of surviving. Successful reproduction of animals with external fertilization requires that a large numbers of eggs be produced. This helps to ensure that at least a few offspring will survive to become adults that reproduce. For example, a female California red abalone, a species of sea snail, produces about 2.5 million eggs in one breeding season.

**Figure 17** For organisms that have external fertilization, mating behaviors, such as that of the toads shown here, help make certain that eggs are fertilized as soon as possible after they leave the body of the female.

**Infer** why a female toad releases large numbers of eggs into the water.

**Figure 18** In most mammals, the embryo develops inside the body of the mother. The duck-billed platypus is an exception. Each duck-billed platypus embryo develops inside an egg laid in a nest. It hatches and is cared for by the mother.

**Compare** How does the size of a duck-billed platypus egg compare with the size of a chicken egg?

Duck-billed platypus egg

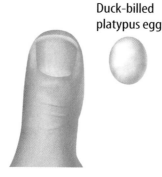

## How do animal embryos develop?

The zygote produced by fertilization is only the beginning of an animal's life. The zygote grows by mitosis and cell divisions and becomes an embryo—the next stage in an animal's life. A growing embryo needs nourishment and protection from predators and other dangers in the environment. Different animals have different ways of supplying the needs of an embryo. In some animals, the embryo develops outside the body of the mother. In others, the embryo develops inside the mother.

### External Development

The duck-billed platypus, as shown in **Figure 18,** is an example of an animal whose embryos develop outside the mother. Animals that develop outside the mother usually are protected inside an egg. In most instances, one embryo develops inside each egg. Most eggs contain a yolk that provides food for the developing embryo. Some kind of covering surrounds the egg. The covering protects the embryo, helps keep it moist, and discourages predators. Eggs laid by lizards, snakes, and other reptiles have a tough, leathery covering. A tough, jellylike substance usually surrounds eggs laid under water. As shown in **Figure 19,** bird eggs, like those of a robin, have a hard covering called a shell.

**Figure 19** A female robin usually lays four eggs in a nest. Each egg contains an embryo and a yolk that supplies food for the growing embryo.

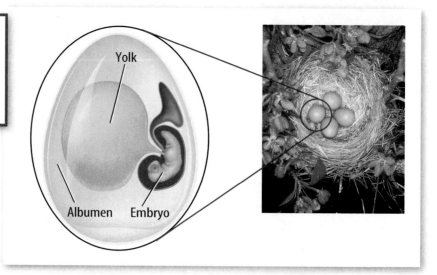

Yolk

Albumen     Embryo

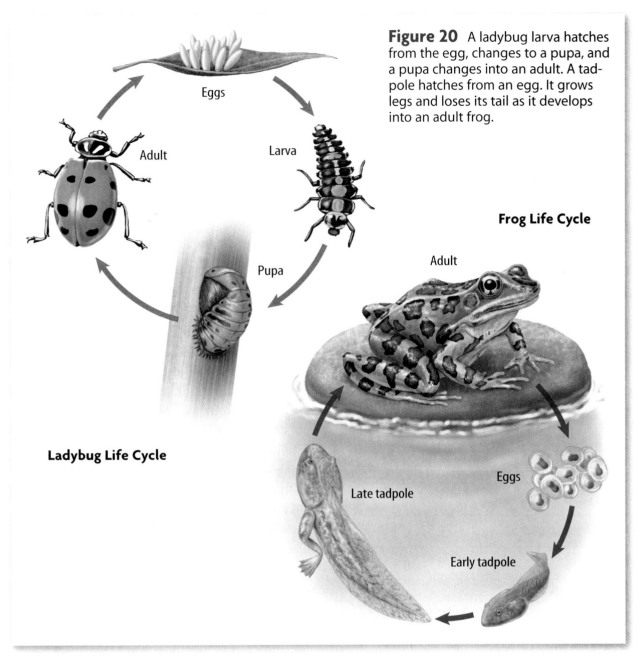

**Figure 20** A ladybug larva hatches from the egg, changes to a pupa, and a pupa changes into an adult. A tadpole hatches from an egg. It grows legs and loses its tail as it develops into an adult frog.

Eggs

Adult

Larva

Pupa

**Ladybug Life Cycle**

**Frog Life Cycle**

Adult

Late tadpole

Eggs

Early tadpole

**Metamorphosis** Some animals—including amphibians and many animals without backbones—go through more than one phase of development. **Metamorphosis** is a developmental process in which the form of the body changes as an animal grows from the egg to an adult.

The metamorphosis of a ladybug beetle and the metamorphosis of a frog are shown in **Figure 20.** A ladybug beetle goes through four stages during its development—egg, larva, pupa, and adult. The tadpole is the larval stage of a frog. Larva and adult forms often have different lifestyles. The larva of the frog lives only in the water. The adult frog can live on land or water.

**WORD ORIGIN**············
metamorphosis
from *meta-* (Greek, means *change*) and *morphe* (Greek, means *form*)

 **Reading Check** What developmental process does a tadpole go through as it becomes a frog?

# How fast do they grow?

A human fetus develops for nine months inside its mother. Most human babies weigh less than ten pounds at birth. How fast does a baby grow before it's born?

## Data

Examine the table below. It shows data about how the mass of a human fetus increases as it grows inside its mother.

| Increase in Mass of a Human Fetus | |
|---|---|
| **Age of Fetus** | **Mass of Fetus** |
| 16 weeks | 180 g |
| 20 weeks | 300 g |
| 24 weeks | 680 g |
| 28 weeks | 1,135 g |
| 32 weeks | 1,680 g |
| 36 weeks | 2,500 g |
| 40 weeks | 3,360 g |

*Source: http://www.dcdoctor.com/pages/rightpages_
wellnesscenter/pregnancy/fetaldevelopment.html*

## Data Analysis

1. **Graph** the growth of the fetus.

2. **Describe** your graph. Did the fetus grow the same rate for each four-week period?

3. **Estimate** the mass of the fetus at 8 weeks, at 18 weeks, and at 38 weeks.

4. **Evaluate** Could you estimate other points on the graph by looking at the graph line? Explain why or why not.

 Try at Home

## Internal Development

The embryos of some animals, including most mammals, develop inside the mother. These embryos get nourishment from the mother. An organ or tissue transfers nourishment from the mother to the embryo. Other embryos, such as those of some snakes, insects, and fishes, develop in an egg with a yolk while it is inside the mother. For these animals, the yolk, not the mother, provides nourishment for the developing young. The young hatch from the eggs while they are inside the mother and then leave the mother's body.

**Reading Check** Where does an embryo that develops in an egg inside the mother get its nourishment?

## Gestation

The length of time between fertilization and birth of an animal is called gestation. Gestation varies from species to species and usually relates to the size of the animal at birth—the smaller the animal, the shorter its gestation. For example, gestation for a mouse is about 21 days; a dog, about 60 days; humans, about 266 days; and an elephant, about 600 days. A kangaroo is an exception. Gestation for a kangaroo is 35 days. A kangaroo is only about 2.5 cm long at birth, as shown in **Figure 21.**

**Figure 21** A newborn kangaroo crawls into a pouch on the mother's body. It feeds and grows inside the pouch until it is large enough to live on its own.

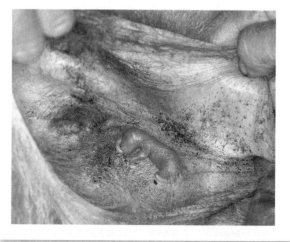

 2.a, 7.c

 00:30 minutes

# Animal Reproduction Summary

In this lesson, you learned how animals reproduce sexually. Males produce sperm in organs called testes. Females produce eggs in organs called ovaries. Internal fertilization takes place inside the female's reproductive system. External fertilization takes place outside the female, in the environment. Embryos that develop inside the body of the female are nourished and protected until they leave the female's body at birth. Embryos that develop outside the body of the female most often develop inside an egg. An egg has a protective covering and a yolk that provides nourishment to the developing embryo.

# LESSON 3  Review

## Summarize

Create your own lesson summary as you design a **visual aid.**

1. **Write** the lesson title, number, and page numbers at the top of your poster.

2. **Scan** the lesson to find the **red** main headings. Organize these headings on your poster, leaving space between each.

3. **Design** an information box beneath each **red** heading. In the box, list 2–3 details, key terms, and definitions from each **blue** subheading.

4. **Illustrate** your poster with diagrams of important structures or processes next to each information box.

ELA7: W 2.5

## Using Vocabulary

1. **Distinguish** between *testes* and *ovaries.*  2.a

2. In your own words, write the definition for *metamorphosis.*  2.a

## Understanding Main Ideas

**Use the image below to answer question 3.**

Testes
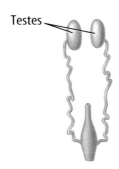

3. How would you describe the organ system above?

   **A.** asexual   **C.** female   2.a
   **B.** embryo    **D.** male

## Standards Check

4. What are the haploid cells that form in female animals?  2.b

   **A.** testes    **C.** eggs
   **B.** ovaries   **D.** sperm

## Applying Science

5. **Hypothesize** why snake eggs have leathery shells.  2.a

6. **Predict** whether an animal that reproduces by external fertilization is more likely to live in water or on land. Explain your reasoning.  2.a

7. **Organize Information** Copy the graphic organizer below and list types of animal development mentioned in this lesson.  2.a

|  |  |
|---|---|
|  |  |

**Science Online**
For more practice, visit **Standards Check** at ca7.msscience.com.

# Applying Math

## Life Span Conversions

Life spans vary greatly among species of insects. Insect life spans are sometimes given in days, weeks, months, and years. In order to make a comparison of life spans among insects, the average life spans must be in the same unit.

### Example

How many times longer does the green lacewing live than the housefly?

**What you know:**
- Life span of the green lacewing: 30 days
- Life span of the housefly: 1 week

**What you need to find:**
- How many times longer does the green lacewing live than the housefly?

**1** First convert both life spans to the same unit.
- The green lacewing life span is measured in days. The housefly life span is measured in weeks.
- Choose to convert the larger unit, weeks, into the smaller unit, days. Now find how many days are in 1 week. There are 7 days in 1 week.

**2** Now you have both insect life spans measured in the same units to compare. The green lacewing life span is 30 days, and the housefly life span is 7 days. To find how many times greater the green lacewing life span is than the housefly life span, divide 30 by 7.

30 ÷ 7 is about 4.3.

**Answer:** The green lacewing lives about 4.3 times longer than the housefly.

| Insect Life Spans | |
|---|---|
| **Species** | **Average Life Span** |
| Housefly | 1 week |
| Green lacewing | 30 days |
| Mountain pine beetle | 1 year |
| Angular-winged katydid | 360 days |
| Australian walking stick | 8 months |
| Common earwig | 355 days |
| Darkling beetle | 11 years |
| Honey bee queen | 4 years |
| Honey bee drone | 5 weeks |
| Madagascar hissing cockroach | 2 years (in captivity) |
| Oregon silverspot butterfly | 3 months |
| Vietnamese walking stick | 6 months |

### Practice Problems

1. How many times longer does the honey bee queen live than the honey bee drone?

2. How many times longer does the Australian walking stick live than the Vietnamese walking stick?

**Science** Online

For more math practice, visit Math Practice at ca7.msscience.com.

## Science Content Standards

**2.a** Students know the differences between the life cycles and reproduction methods of sexual and asexual organisms.
**Also covers:** 7.a, 7.c, 7.d, 7.e

## Reading Guide

### What You'll Learn

▶ **Define** asexual reproduction.

▶ **Differentiate** between regeneration and cloning.

▶ **Compare** an asexually produced offspring to its parent.

### Why It's Important

Learning about asexual reproduction will help you understand how cloning and other techniques determine genetic traits of organisms.

### Vocabulary

asexual reproduction
fission
budding
regeneration
cloning

### Review Vocabulary

**prokaryote:** organism made of a cell that does not have a membrane-bound nucleus (p. 64)

# Asexual Reproduction

**Main Idea** Asexual reproduction produces offspring that are identical to the parent.

**Real-World Reading Connection** Have you ever joked about wanting to clone yourself? That way, you could enjoy time with your friends while your clone does chores and homework. Do any organisms reproduce by making exact copies of themselves?

## What is asexual reproduction?

When we think of reproduction, we usually think of sexual reproduction. Recall that sexual reproduction occurs when a sperm and egg fuse, and it usually requires two parents. However, many organisms have only one parent. **Asexual reproduction** is the production of offspring by one parent without a sperm and an egg joining. Asexual reproduction results in offspring that are genetically identical to the parent organism. The poinsettias shown in **Figure 22** were produced by asexual reproduction.

### Advantages of Asexual Reproduction

Unlike sexual reproduction, asexual reproduction does not require a mate. Therefore, an asexually reproducing organism does not have to spend time and energy finding a mate. Also, to reproduce a number of offspring asexually takes less time than to reproduce the same number of offspring sexually. Since parent and offspring are genetically identical, both are equally well adapted to the same environmental conditions.

**Figure 22** Asexual reproduction makes it possible for a grower to produce hundreds of genetically identical poinsettias for the holiday season.

## Disadvantages of Asexual Reproduction

The major disadvantage of asexual reproduction is the lack of genetic variation. Recall that genetic variation in a population increases the chances that a few individuals will survive a change in the environment. Imagine a population of poinsettia plants growing in a greenhouse, like those shown in **Figure 22.** Suppose a greenhouse worker unknowingly plants the poinsettias in soil contaminated with disease-causing bacteria. Because the poinsettias are genetically identical, the disease might affect all of them. The entire poinsettia population might be destroyed.

Another disadvantage of asexual reproduction involves genetic changes, or mutations, that can occur. A harmful mutation in cells of an organism will be passed to asexually reproduced offspring. This could affect the offspring's ability to survive.

 **Reading Check** What are two disadvantages of asexual reproduction?

## What are the types of asexual reproduction?

There are many types of asexual reproduction. However, each type involves cell division. Prokaryotes, or bacteria, reproduce asexually by cell division that does not involve mitosis. Eukaryotes reproduce asexually by mitosis and cell division.

### Fission

A bacterium has a small, circular DNA chromosome but no nucleus. Bacteria reproduce asexually by a process called **fission,** as shown in **Figure 23.** Fission produces two genetically identical cells. Asexual reproduction by fission can occur rapidly. *E. coli,* a species of bacteria found in human intestines, can reproduce asexually every twenty minutes.

**WORD ORIGIN**

fission
from Latin *fissionem;* means *a breaking up, cleaving*

**Figure 23** During fission, a bacterium grows while its DNA is replicated. When the DNA has replicated and the cell is about twice its original size, the two DNA copies separate. The cell membrane grows inward and the cell divides in half to produce two identical daughter cells.

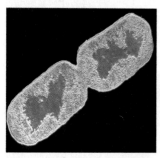

Color-enhanced TEM Magnification: 17,650×

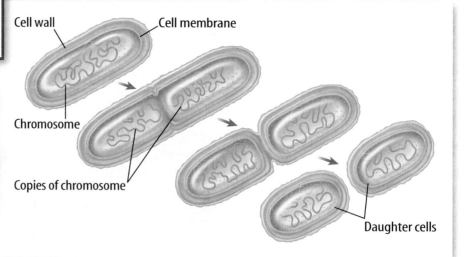

Cell wall · Cell membrane · Chromosome · Copies of chromosome · Daughter cells

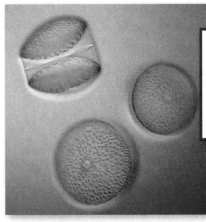

**Figure 24** Diatoms belong to a group of single-celled, eukaryotic organisms called protists. They live in water and make their own food through photosynthesis.

## Mitotic Cell Division

Some single-celled eukaryotes, such as the diatom in **Figure 24,** reproduce asexually by mitotic cell division—mitosis followed by cell division. Recall from Chapter 2 that mitosis and cell division produce two genetically identical cells from one cell. Asexual reproduction in a single-celled eukaryote also produces two identical cells, except that each cell is an individual organism.

## Budding

Yeasts are single-celled eukaryotes that are related to mushrooms and other fungi. As shown in **Figure 25,** yeast cells reproduce by **budding**—a type of asexual reproduction in which a new organism forms on the parent organism. The new organism is called a bud and forms by mitosis and cell division. It is genetically identical to the parent and eventually separates from the parent to live on its own.

Some multicellular animals, such as freshwater hydra also shown in **Figure 25,** can reproduce by budding. Notice how the bud grows from the stalk of the parent hydra. Like many multicellular eukaryotes, including plants, hydras can reproduce both sexually and asexually.

Bud

Hydra

LM  Magnification: 10×

**Figure 25** This yeast cell is budding. The bud of the hydra looks like a smaller version of the parent.

**Compare** the genetic makeup of the hydra bud to the hydra parent.

Bud

Yeast Cells

Color-enhanced  SEM  Magnification: 10,000×

(tl)Wim van Egmond/Visuals Unlimited, (tr)Horizons Companies, (bl)Ed Reschke/Peter Arnold, Inc., (br)Dr. Richard Kessel & Dr. C. Y. Shih/Visuals Unlimited

# MiniLab

⏱ 00:25 minutes

## How do yeast reproduce?

What happens when you add sugar and warm water to dried yeast?

### Procedure

1. Complete a lab safety form.
2. Pour 125 mL of **34°C water** into a cup or beaker.
3. Add 5 g of **sugar** and 5 g of **yeast** to the water. Stir slightly. Record your observations after 5 min.
4. Using an **eyedropper**, put a drop of yeast solution on a **microscope slide**. Place a **coverslip** over the drop.
5. View the yeast solution under a **microscope**. Draw what you see.

### Analysis

1. **Describe** evidence of yeast reproduction.
2. **Identify** the process you observed under the microscope.

 2.a, 7.a, 7.c, 7.d

**Figure 26** New, genetically identical plants grow from the horizontal stems, or runners, of strawberry plants. A kalanchoe plant forms so many plantlets that it is known as the maternity plant.

**Strawberry Plants**

**Kalanchoe Plantlets**

**ACADEMIC VOCABULARY**
differentiate (dih fuh REN chee ayt)
*(verb)* to show a difference between two or more things. *Students must be able to differentiate meiosis from mitosis.*

**Figure 27** Sea stars can reproduce asexually by regeneration.

**Identify** the kind of cell division that takes place when a sea star regrows missing body parts.

## Plant Cuttings

In Lesson 3, you read how plants reproduce sexually. Many plants can also reproduce asexually. If you cut a green stem from a houseplant and place it in water, roots and leaves can grow, producing a new plant. A new plant grown from a stem cutting is genetically identical to the parent plant. Poinsettias, like those in **Figure 22,** can be grown from stem cuttings. Depending on the type of plant, leaf cuttings or root cuttings can also be used to grow a new plant.

Some plants propagate themselves asexually. The kalanchoe plant shown in **Figure 26** has produced tiny plantlets at the edges of its leaves. These plantlets can fall to the ground, take root, and produce new plants. A strawberry plant, as shown in **Figure 26,** produces new plants along horizontal stems that grow on the surface of the ground.

## Animal Regeneration

Recall from Chapter 2 that the process in which cells in an embryo become different types of cells is called cell differentiation. But as you just read, some plant cells can dedifferentiate—change from a differentiated cell type and grow into other cell types. You also read in Chapter 2 that **differentiated** human cells cannot change and grow into other cell types. However, some animals have cells that can change into other cell types.

**Producing New Animals** Asexual reproduction that produces new animals from pieces of an animal's body is called **regeneration.** The sea star shown in **Figure 27** can asexually reproduce by regeneration. If it is broken into pieces, each piece can grow the missing parts. The new organisms are genetically identical.

**Producing Body Parts** Sometimes, the term *regeneration* is used to describe growth that replaces a missing part of an animal. For example, if a sea star just loses part of an arm, it can regrow that lost part. The regrowth of a body part is not an example of asexual reproduction, because a new individual is not created.

**WORD ORIGIN**

regeneration
from Latin *regeneratus;* means *make over*

# What is cloning?

Fission, budding, and regeneration are all types of asexual reproduction that produce genetically identical offspring in nature. In the past, the term *cloning* described any process that produced genetically identical offspring. Today, however, **cloning** usually refers to a method of asexual reproduction developed by scientists and performed in laboratories. Cloning produces identical individuals from a cell or from a cluster of cells taken from a multicellular organism.

 Give two different meanings for *cloning*.

## Plant Cloning

Plant tissue culture is a cloning technique that enables scientists to produce genetically identical plants from a few plant cells grown in a test tube, as shown in **Figure 28.** Plant tissue culture can be used to produce thousands of identical plants from a plant that has desirable genetic traits, such as high nutritional value or rapid growth.

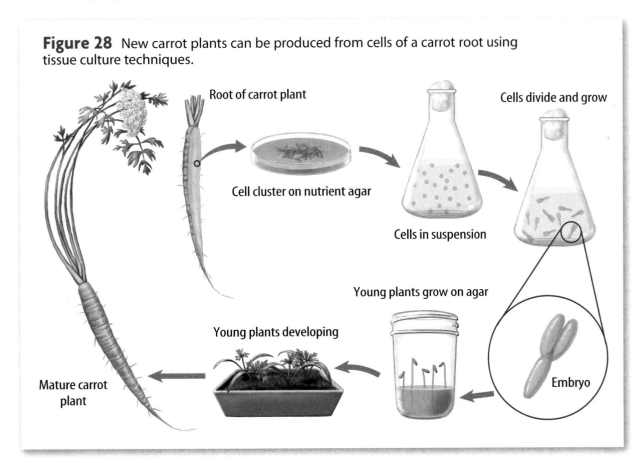

**Figure 28** New carrot plants can be produced from cells of a carrot root using tissue culture techniques.

Root of carrot plant

Cells divide and grow

Cell cluster on nutrient agar

Cells in suspension

Young plants grow on agar

Embryo

Young plants developing

Mature carrot plant

## Animal Cloning

The first animal to be successfully cloned from an adult cell was a sheep. In 1996, scientists in Scotland cloned a female sheep that they named Dolly. **Figure 29** illustrates the reproductive methods used to make Dolly. Since then, scientists have cloned other animals, including mice, cows, and a horse.

Although several cloned animals have been produced successfully, they often are not as healthy as animals produced by sexual reproduction. Some animal clones, including Dolly, have had a much shorter life span than animals produced by sexual reproduction. Animal cloning raises ethical issues that people are concerned about. For example, many people think the cloning of humans should never be allowed. You might be asked to consider issues like this during your lifetime.

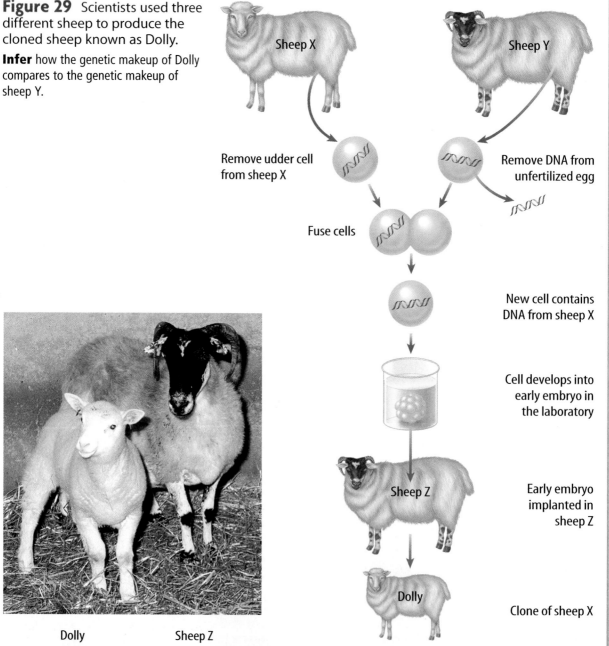

**Figure 29** Scientists used three different sheep to produce the cloned sheep known as Dolly.

**Infer** how the genetic makeup of Dolly compares to the genetic makeup of sheep Y.

Sheep X

Sheep Y

Remove udder cell from sheep X

Remove DNA from unfertilized egg

Fuse cells

New cell contains DNA from sheep X

Cell develops into early embryo in the laboratory

Sheep Z

Early embryo implanted in sheep Z

Dolly

Clone of sheep X

Dolly          Sheep Z

# Asexual Reproduction Summary

In this lesson, you read that many organisms reproduce asexually, which means they have only one parent. Offspring from asexual reproduction have genetic material that is identical to the genetic material of the parent. Bacteria reproduce asexually by fission, which is a type of cell division. Some eukaryotes, including yeast, reproduce asexually by budding. Other eukaryotes reproduce asexually by mitosis and cell division. Parts of plants, such as stem cuttings or root cuttings, can grow into new plants. In some animals, a body part can regenerate and form a new individual. Cloning is a scientific process that produces offspring genetically identical to one parent organism.

# LESSON 4  Review

## Summarize

Create your own lesson summary as you design a **study web.**

1. **Write** the lesson title, number, and page numbers at the top of a sheet of paper.

2. **Scan** the lesson to find the **red** main headings.

3. **Organize** these headings clockwise on branches around the lesson title.

4. **Review** the information under each **red** heading to design a branch for each **blue** subheading.

5. **List** 2–3 details, key terms, and definitions from each **blue** subheading on branches extending from the main heading branches.

 ELA7: W 2.5

## Standards Check

### Using Vocabulary

*Match these terms with the correct definition.*

cloning
regeneration

1. the growth of a new individual from a broken-off portion of another animal's body  `2.a`

2. a method of asexual reproduction developed by scientists and performed in laboratories  `2.a`

### Understanding Main Ideas

3. Which term does not apply to asexual reproduction?

   **A.** budding  **C.** cloning  `2.a`
   **B.** fission  **D.** fertilization

4. How do prokaryotes reproduce?

   **A.** budding  **C.** fission  `2.a`
   **B.** cloning  **D.** regeneration

5. **Discuss** advantages and disadvantages of asexual reproduction.  `2.a`

6. **Distinguish** between fission and budding.  `2.a`

### Applying Science

7. **Debate** how the use of animal cloning might affect the food industry.  `2.a`

8. **Organize Information** Draw a graphic organizer similar to the one below to list the types of asexual reproduction. Write *Asexual Reproduction* in the center oval.  `2.a`

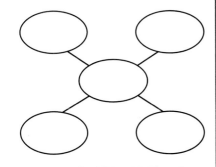

For more practice, visit **Standards Check** at ca7.msscience.com.

# Plant Propagation

00:45
minutes

## Materials

coleus seeds
coleus plants
packaged potting soil
containers
clear plastic wrap
room-temperature
  water

## Safety Precautions

## Science Content Standards

**2.a** Students know the differences between the life cycles and reproduction methods of sexual and asexual organisms.
**7.a** Select and use appropriate tools and technology (including calculators, computers, balances, spring scales, microscopes, and binoculars) to perform tests, collect data, and display data.
**7.c** Communicate the logical connection among hypotheses, science concepts, tests conducted, data collected, and conclusions drawn from the scientific evidence.
**7.e** Communicate the steps and results from an investigation in written reports and oral presentations.

## Problem

You know that plants can reproduce both sexually and asexually. Coleus plants are easy to reproduce both ways: from seeds and from stem cuttings. In this lab, you will get a chance to try both methods.

## Form a Hypothesis

Which method of propagating plants do you think will be the most successful? Which one will grow faster? Which one will have a lower rate of failure? Write two hypotheses.

## Collect Data and Make Observations

1. Read and complete a lab safety form before you begin.
2. Design and construct a data table to record your daily observations and the measured height of the seedlings and cuttings.

### Part A

3. Obtain three seeds from your teacher.
4. Plant the seeds in a container of damp potting soil, as directed by your teacher.
5. Loosely cover the top of the container with a piece of clear plastic wrap. Place the containers in a bright location, away from cold or hot drafts of air and away from direct sun.
6. Each day, remove the plastic wrap so that you can sprinkle the top of soil with room-temperature water, and then replace the plastic wrap.
7. Every other day, measure the height of the seedlings and record this data and other observations in your data table.

## Part B

8. Cut a stem of the plant just below the third set of leaves, as shown in the photo to the right.

9. Remove the bottom set of leaves.

10. Place the cutting into a container of damp potting soil. The spot on the stem where the leaves were attached must be below the soil's surface.

11. Repeat steps 1–3 twice.

12. Sprinkle the top of the soil daily with room-temperature water.

13. Every other day, measure the height of the cuttings and record this data and other observations in your data table.

## Analyze and Conclude

1. **Identify** which trial was sexual reproduction and which one was asexual.

2. **Describe** the growth of the seedlings and cuttings.

3. **Graph** the average growth of the three seedlings over the observation period.

4. **Graph** the average growth of the three cuttings over the observation period.

5. **Evaluate** your hypotheses. Were they correct? Explain why or why not. How would you adjust your hypotheses if you were going to do another experiment?

6. **Error Analysis** Which of your trials worked better? Use scientific explanations to explain your results.

## Communicate

**WRITING in** Science

Take your plants from this experiment and plant them in a public garden, near a retirement home, or in an outdoor space that needs cheering up. Remember to water them regularly. Putting some bark or leaf mulch around your plants will help keep them moist. Create a sign that explains how the plants were produced. With permission, post your sign near your plants.

# Real World Science

## Lions and Tigers and Bears, Oh My!

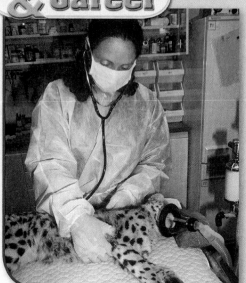

Animals can have infections, sprain joints, or need medicines and vaccines. Instead of a physician, a veterinarian cares for animals. Veterinarians often help female animals with the delivery of their young. Some veterinarians take care of small domestic animals, like cats or dogs, but large animals need care too. Large-animal vets spend time caring for farm animals, like horses and cows, or zoos animals, such as lions, tigers, and bears.

Work in pairs. Pretend you're a news reporter interviewing a large-animal veterinarian. Ask about his or her day on the job, including the kinds of problems he or she encountered, and how he or she fixed them.

## Producing Disease-Free Plants

Plant tissue culture is used to produce disease-free plants. When a virus enters a plant, it usually infects the entire plant. However, scientists have learned that the rapidly reproducing cells at the tips of stems remain disease-free in a virus-infected plant. Using tissue culture techniques, scientists can reproduce virus-infected plants without transferring the virus to the new plants.

Visit **Technology** at ca7.msscience.com to research plant tissue culture. Write a paragraph about how tissue culture technology helps farmers and other plant growers.

**ELA7: W 1.2**

# Ernest Everett Just and Parthenogenesis

Ernest Everett Just was an African-American scientist who became well-known for his research into cell fertilization and embryology at the beginning of the twentieth century. Just was interested in learning about the structure of healthy cells as a means of curing disease. He also studied parthenogenesis (par thuh noh JEH nuh sus)—how some embryos can develop without fertilization.

How can an organism develop from an unfertilized egg? Visit **History** at **ca7.msscience.com** to research parthenogenesis. Compile a class list of organisms that undergo parthenogenesis.

## ANIMAL CLONING—Yes or No?

Since 1996, several types of mammals have been cloned using the process that created Dolly, the sheep. The process uses genetic material from adult cells, which allows animal breeders to create clones that have traits observed in the adult animal. These calves—Dot and Ditto—are clones of an adult cow.

Animal cloning is controversial. Write an editorial for or against animal cloning. Use scientific evidence to support your position.

 **ELA7:** W 2.4

**The BIG Idea** Different types of reproduction ensure the survival of different species.

## Lesson 1 Sexual Reproduction and Meiosis
`2.b, 7.b`

**Main Idea** Meiosis maintains the chromosome number of a species from one generation to the next.

- Sexual reproduction includes the fusion of a sperm cell with an egg cell to produce a new organism.
- Meiosis is cell division that produces sperm and egg cells.
- Meiosis maintains a constant number of chromosomes from one generation of sexually produced offspring to the next.

- **diploid** (p. 129)
- **egg** (p. 126)
- **fertilization** (p. 126)
- **haploid** (p. 129)
- **meiosis** (p. 128)
- **sexual reproduction** (p. 126)
- **sperm** (p. 126)
- **zygote** (p. 126)

## Lesson 2 Plant Reproduction
`2.a, 5.f, 7.b`

**Main Idea** A plant's life cycle includes a diploid generation that produces spores and a haploid generation that produces eggs and sperm.

- The life cycle of all plants includes an alternation of generations.
- Angiosperms are flowering plants that produce seeds enclosed in a fruit.

- **angiosperm** (p. 138)
- **anther** (p. 138)
- **embryo** (p. 137)
- **filament** (p. 138)
- **fruit** (p. 139)
- **ovary** (p. 138)
- **ovule** (p. 137)
- **pistil** (p. 138)
- **pollen grain** (p. 136)
- **pollen tube** (p. 139)
- **pollination** (p. 137)
- **seed** (p. 137)
- **spore** (p. 135)
- **stamen** (p. 138)
- **stigma** (p. 138)
- **style** (p. 138)

## Lesson 3 Animal Reproduction
`2.a, 2.b, 7.c`

**Main Idea** Animals have specialized structures for sexual reproduction.

- Animals have specialized organs, called gonads, for sexual reproduction.
- In some animal species, fertilization happens outside the body; in other species, fertilization happens inside the body.
- In some animal species, embryos develop outside the mother; in other species, embryos develop inside the mother.

- **gonad** (p. 144)
- **metamorphosis** (p. 147)
- **ovary** (p. 144)
- **testes** (p. 144)

## Lesson 4 Asexual Reproduction
`2.a, 7.a, 7.c, 7.d, 7.e`

**Main Idea** Asexual reproduction produces offspring that are identical to the parent.

- Asexual reproduction requires only one parent.
- Types of asexual reproduction include fission, budding, mitosis, and cloning.

- **asexual reproduction** (p. 151)
- **budding** (p. 153)
- **cloning** (p. 155)
- **fission** (p. 152)
- **regeneration** (p. 154)

 **STUDY TO GO** Download quizzes, key terms, and flash cards from ca7.msscience.com.

# Linking Vocabulary and Main Ideas

Use vocabulary terms from page 162 to complete this concept map.

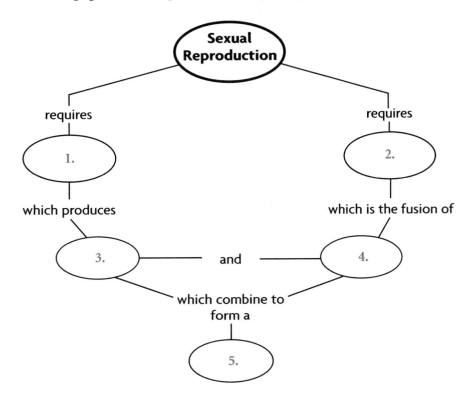

Visit ca7.msscience.com for:
► Vocabulary PuzzleMaker
► Vocabulary eFlashcards
► Multilingual Glossary

## Using Vocabulary

**Write the vocabulary term that best matches each phrase.**

6. process that produces haploid cells from a diploid cell

7. process that produces a diploid cell from two haploid cells

8. cells that have two of each chromosome

9. generation of a plant that produces eggs and sperm

10. part of the flower that will become a fruit

11. produces sperm

12. asexual reproduction used by prokaryotes

13. produces a new individual from a part of an animal or plant

14. method scientists use to make identical offspring from adult cells

## Understanding Main Ideas

**Use the image below to answer question 1.**

1. What phase of meiosis is pictured above?
   A. anaphase I     `2.a`
   B. anaphase II
   C. metaphase I
   D. metaphase II

2. Which organism can reproduce asexually by dedifferentiation of cells?
   A. diatom     `2.b`
   B. bacterium
   C. plant
   D. yeast

3. Which term describes the daughter cells produced by meiosis?
   A. identical     `2.a`
   B. diploid
   C. homologous
   D. haploid

4. Which reproductive structure grows into the haploid generation of a plant?
   A. cone     `5.f`
   B. seed
   C. sperm
   D. spore

5. What type of plant produces fruit?
   A. conifer     `5.f`
   B. seedless
   C. gymnosperm
   D. angiosperm

6. Which term describes the development of a tadpole into an adult frog?
   A. alternation of generations     `2.b`
   B. fertilization
   C. meiosis
   D. metamorphosis

7. What method of asexual reproduction involves the regrowth of missing body parts from part of an organism?
   A. budding     `2.b`
   B. fission
   C. cloning
   D. regeneration

**Use the image below to answer questions 8–10.**

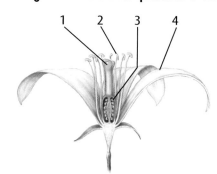

8. What is the name of structure number 1?
   A. anther     `5.f`
   B. filament
   C. stigma
   D. style

9. Where is pollen produced?
   A. 1     `5.f`
   B. 2
   C. 3
   D. 4

10. Which part of the flower becomes a seed?
   A. 1     `5.f`
   B. 2
   C. 3
   D. 4

# Applying Science

**11. Distinguish between** mitosis and meiosis. **2.a**

**Use the image below to answer question 12.**

**12. Predict** how many chromosomes each daughter cell of the cell above will have at the end of meiosis. **2.a**

**13. Compare** gymnosperms and angiosperms. **5.f**

**14. Compare** external fertilization and internal fertilization. **2.a**

**15. Predict** why most frog species enter water to reproduce. **2.a**

**16. Suggest** why animals that reproduce by external fertilization produce more eggs than animals that reproduce by internal fertilization. **2.a**

**17. Predict** how the success of plants in a particular environment would be affected if the plants could not reproduce asexually. **2.a**

**18. Hypothesize** why bacteria are able to reproduce much more quickly than humans and other multicellular eukaryotic organisms. **2.a**

**19. Defend** Some lizards can grow a new tail if theirs breaks off. Is this asexual reproduction? Defend your answer. **2.a**

**20. Evaluate** Yeasts are commonly used to make bread. How might the bread-making process be affected if yeast could reproduce only sexually? **2.a**

**21. Infer** why seedless plants depend on water for fertilization, but seed plants do not. **2.a**

**22. Develop** a concept map to identify if a plant is a gymnosperm, an angiosperm, or a seedless plant. **2.a**

## WRITING in Science

**23. Write** one paragraph describing the similarities and differences of sexual reproduction and asexual reproduction. **ELA7: W 1.2**

# Applying Math

**Use the table below to answer questions 24–27.**

| Insect Life Spans | |
|---|---|
| **Species** | **Average Life Span** |
| Mountain pine beetle | 1 year |
| Angular-winged katydid | 360 days |
| Common earwig | 355 days |
| Darkling beetle | 11 years |
| Madagascar hissing cockroach | 2 years (in captivity) |
| Oregon silverspot butterfly | 3 months |

**24.** How much longer does the darkling beetle live than the mountain pine beetle? **MA7: NS 1.0, MG 1.1**

**25.** How much longer does the Madagascar hissing cockroach live than the angular-winged katydid? **MA7: NS 1.0, MG 1.1**

**26.** How much longer does the common earwig live than the Oregon silverspot butterfly? **MA7: NS 1.0, MG 1.1**

**27.** How much longer does the mountain pine beetle live than the Oregon silverspot butterfly? **MA7: NS 1.0, MG 1.1**

**1** A new plant can grow from a white potato, as shown below.

How does the genetic material of the new plant above compare to that of the potato?

A  identical

B  different

C  greater

D  less    **2.a**

**2** Which term describes this type of reproduction?

A  fission

B  budding

C  regeneration

D  cloning    **2.a**

**3** Which is the correct sequence for sexual reproduction?

A  sex cells, zygote, fertilization, meiosis

B  zygote, sex cells, meiosis, fertilization

C  fertilization, meiosis, zygote, sex cells

D  meiosis, sex cells, fertilization, zygote    **2.a**

**4** Which describes what happens to chromosomes during meiosis?

A  Homologous chromosomes separate, then they replicate in meiosis II.

B  Replicated homologous chromosome pairs separate in meiosis I, then sister chromatids separate during meiosis II.

C  Sister chromosomes separate during meiosis I.

D  Homologous chromosomes stay together during meiosis I and meiosis II.    **2.b**

**5** Bacteria reproduce by asexual reproduction, as shown below.

What is the term used for this type of asexual reproduction?

A  fission

B  budding

C  regeneration

D  cloning    **2.a**

**6** Which term means the joining of a sperm and an egg?

A  pollination

B  mitosis

C  fertilization

D  meiosis    **2.b**

Science Online  Standards Assessment ca7.msscience.com

Use the diagram below to answer questions 7 and 8.

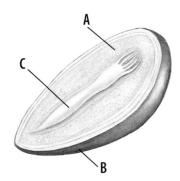

**7** What does structure C represent?

A stored food

B embryo

C ovary

D seed covering    **5.f**

**8** Which part(s) of this seed will grow into the new plant?

A A

B C

C A and C

D C and B    **5.f**

**9** What is the term used to describe the process of when a plant's sperm-producing structure lands on the female reproductive structure of the same type of plant?

A pollination

B mitosis

C fertilization

D meiosis    **5.f**

**10** Which is the correct sequence in the life cycle of a beetle?

A larva, adult, egg, pupa

B egg, larva, pupa, adult

C pupa, egg, adult, larva

D adult, pupa, larva, egg    **2.a**

Use the diagram below to answer questions 11 and 12.

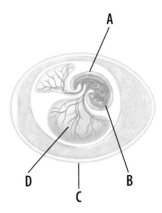

**11** Which letter represents the yolk?

A A

B B

C C

D D    **2.a**

**12** Which letter represents the developing organism?

A A

B B

C C

D D    **2.a**

# Genetics

## The BIG Idea

Inherited genes determine an organism's traits.

### LESSON 1 · 2.b, 2.d
**Foundations of Genetics**

**Main Idea** Gregor Mendel discovered the basic principles of genetics.

### LESSON 2
**2.c, 2.d, 7.a, 7.b, 7.c, 7.e**

**Understanding Inheritance**

**Main Idea** The interactions among alleles, genes, and the environment determine an organism's traits.

### It's all in the genes!

These dogs are purebred boxers, but they are not identical. Purebred dogs inherited similar sets of genes. However, the differences in each set of genes result in dogs with distinct appearances.

**Science Journal** List the differences and similarities that you observe among this dog and her puppies.

## How well can you predict?

Probability describes the likelihood that something will happen. For example, if you had a penny, a nickel, a dime, and a quarter in your pocket, the probability that you would pull out the quarter is 1 in 4.

### Procedure

1. Your teacher will give you **marbles** in a **paper bag.**

2. Open the bag and examine its contents.

3. Create a data table to record the contents.

### Think About This

- **Examine** your data table. How many marbles are in the bag? How many of each color are included?

- **Predict** If you pulled out a marble, what is the probability of choosing one particular color?

**2.d, 7.c**

Visit ca7.msscience.com to:

▶ view **Concepts in Motion**

▶ explore Virtual Labs

▶ access content-related Web links

▶ take the Standards Check

---

**FOLDABLES** Study Organizer

**Patterns of Inheritance**
Make the following Foldable to organize information about patterns of inheritance.

▷ **STEP 1 Collect** three sheets of paper and layer them about 2 cm apart vertically. Keep the left edges even.

▷ **STEP 2 Fold** up the bottom edges of the paper to form 5 equal tabs. Crease the fold to hold the tabs in place.

▷ **STEP 3 Staple** along the fold. **Label** as shown.

Maternal
X-Linked
Polygenic
Multiple Alleles
Codominance
Dominant-Recessive
Patterns of Inheritance

**Reading Skill**

### Reviewing

As you read Lesson 2, add information about each type of pattern of inheritance under the appropriate tab.

# Get Ready to Read

## Monitor

**1 Learn It!** An important strategy to help you improve your reading is monitoring, or finding your reading strengths and weaknesses. As you read, monitor yourself to make sure the text makes sense. Discover different monitoring techniques you can use at different times, depending on the type of test and situation.

**2 Practice It!** The paragraph below appears in Lesson 1. Read the passage and answer the questions that follow. Discuss your answers with other students to see how they monitor their reading.

> After analyzing the results of his experiments, Mendel concluded that two factors control each inherited trait. He also proposed that when organisms reproduce, each gamete contributes one factor for each trait.
>
> —from page 175

- What questions do you still have after reading?
- Do you understand all of the words in the passage?
- Did you have to stop reading often? Is the reading level appropriate for you?

**3 Apply It!** Identify one paragraph that is difficult to understand. Discuss it with a partner to improve your understanding.

# Target Your Reading

Use this to focus on the main ideas as you read the chapter.

**Reading Tip**

Monitor your reading by slowing down or speeding up depending on your understanding of the text.

**1** **Before you read** the chapter, respond to the statements below on your worksheet or on a numbered sheet of paper.
  - Write an **A** if you **agree** with the statement.
  - Write a **D** if you **disagree** with the statement.

**2** **After you read** the chapter, look back to this page to see if you've changed your mind about any of the statements.
  - If any of your answers changed, explain why.
  - Change any false statements into true statements.
  - Use your revised statements as a study guide.

| Before You Read A or D | Statement | After You Read A or D |
|---|---|---|
| | **1** A gene is a section of RNA that has information about a specific trait. | |
| | **2** Only the genotype determines the phenotype. | |
| | **3** The movement of chromosomes during meiosis supports Mendel's law of independent assortment. | |
| | **4** Mendel's ideas about inheritance remain true today. | |
| | **5** Plant breeders do not need to use tools to predict traits. | |
| | **6** For accurate genetic studies, a few offspring are just as good as many offspring. | |
| | **7** All inherited traits follow Mendel's patterns of inheritance. | |
| | **8** Every trait is determined by just one gene. | |
| | **9** Humans inherit mitochondrial genes from both parents. | |

**Science Online**

Print a worksheet of this page at ca7.msscience.com.

## Science Content Standards

**2.b** Students know sexual reproduction produces offspring that inherit half their genes from each parent.

**2.d** Students know plant and animal cells contain many thousands of different genes and typically have two copies of every gene. The two copies (or alleles) of the gene may or may not be identical, and one may be dominant in determining the phenotype while the other is recessive.

## Reading Guide

### What *You'll Learn*

▶ **Model** Mendel's pea plant experiments.

▶ **State** Mendel's two laws of heredity.

▶ **Define** dominant and recessive alleles.

▶ **Distinguish** between the phenotype and genotype of a trait.

### Why *It's Important*

Genetics helps to explain how traits are passed from parents to offspring.

### Vocabulary

| | |
|---|---|
| heredity | allele |
| genetics | phenotype |
| dominant | genotype |
| recessive | homozygous |
| gene | heterozygous |
| law of segregation | |
| law of independent assortment | |

### Review Vocabulary

**chromosome:** a structure in a nucleus made of coiled, long chains of DNA; contains genetic material (p. 60)

# Foundations of Genetics

(**Main Idea**) Gregor Mendel discovered the basic principles of genetics.

**Real-World Reading Connection** Why are all dogs of the same breed similar? Why do some disorders run in families? Why do grapevines produce only one type of grape? People have asked questions like these for many years, but scientists have found the answers only recently.

## Early Ideas About Heredity

In Chapter 3, you read that a sperm and an egg contain genetic material that combines at fertilization. The combined genetic material determines the traits or features of an offspring. The passing of traits from parents to offspring is called **heredity** (huh REH duh tee).

Have you ever mixed two paint colors to get a new paint color? People used to believe that the genetic material from a sperm cell and an egg cell mixed like colors of paint. They believed that because offspring resembled both parents, the genetic material mixed or blended. Blending inheritance is the idea that offspring are a blend of genetic material from both parents. Supporters of this idea proclaimed that, over many generations, populations would eventually look alike because of blending inheritance. This does not happen. Blending inheritance also cannot explain why some traits appear to skip generations, such as eye color, as shown in **Figure 1.** Because of the work of Gregor Mendel, these questions have new answers.

**Figure 1** Some traits seem to skip generations. Brown-eyed parents might have blue-eyed children.

**Infer** why eye color of the children does not support the idea of blending inheritance.

# Gregor Mendel and His Experiments

The first person known to record evidence that traits of organisms are determined by factors passed from parents to offspring was Gregor Mendel. He was born in 1822 in a part of Europe that is now the Czech Republic. Mendel made his discoveries during the 1850s at a monastery, as shown in **Figure 2.** The monks at the monastery were dedicated to teaching science and scientific research.

Mendel experimented with garden pea plants in the monastery's gardens. After carefully analyzing the results of his experiments, Mendel established the basic laws of heredity. Because of his scientific research, Mendel is known as the father of genetics. **Genetics** (juh NE tihks) is the study of how traits of organisms are passed from parents to offspring.

## Mendel's Experimental Methods

Mendel studied genetics by conducting breeding experiments with pea plants. He chose pea plants because they are easy to grow, they flower and reproduce quickly, they come in many varieties, and the peas are edible. Mendel studied seven different traits of pea plants, as shown in **Table 1.** Each trait had only two variations. For example, flower color was either purple or white and seeds were either round or wrinkled.

 **Reading Check** Why did Mendel use pea plants for his experiments?

**Figure 2** Mendel experimented in a garden at this monastery in Brno, Czech Republic.

**WORD ORIGIN**
genetics
from Greek *genesis;* means *origin*

**Concepts In Motion**
**Interactive Table** To organize information about pea traits, visit Tables at ca7.msscience.com.

| \ | \ | \ | \ | \ | \ | \ |
|---|---|---|---|---|---|---|
| **Table 1 Pea Traits Studied by Mendel** | | | | | | |
| **Flower Color** | **Flower Position** | **Seed Color** | **Seed Shape** | **Pod Shape** | **Pod Color** | **Stem Length** |
| Purple | Axial | Yellow | Round | Inflated | Green | Long |
| White | Terminal | Green | Wrinkled | Constricted | Yellow | Short |

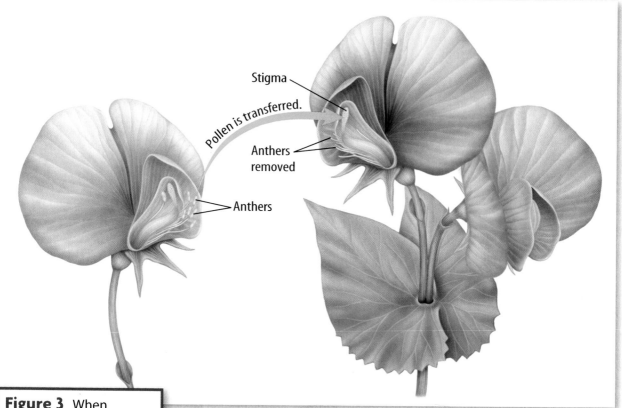

Stigma

Pollen is transferred.

Anthers
removed

Anthers

**Figure 3** When performing cross-pollination of the pea flowers, Mendel removed the anthers from the flower receiving pollen to prevent self-fertilization.

**ACADEMIC VOCABULARY**

method (MEH thud)
*(noun)* a way of doing something
*Juan's method of reviewing for the science test helped him remember the important information.*

**Controlled Exeriments** Recall from Chapter 3 that a flower contains male reproductive organs (stamens) and/or female reproductive organs (pistils). The flowers of pea plants have both stamens and pistils. Mendel controlled fertilization in the experimental pea plants. He allowed some of the flowers to self-fertilize as they usually do in nature. Mendel also performed cross-fertilization by transferring pollen from the stamen of one pea flower to the stigma of a pistil in another pea flower, as shown in **Figure 3.** This allowed him to record the parents of the offspring produced from the cross, and observe how traits pass from one generation to the next.

**Mendel's Unique Methods** Mendel was not the first person to breed plants. So, what made his experimental **methods** unique? First, Mendel used true-breeding plants for each trait. When true-breeding plants for a trait self-pollinate, they always produce offspring with that trait. For example, when pea plants that are true-breeding for wrinkled seeds self-pollinate, they only produce offspring with wrinkled seeds. Second, Mendel recorded the inheritance of traits for several generations. Last, and most importantly, Mendel used a mathematical approach. He was careful to breed large numbers of plants and count the number of each kind of offspring, generation after generation. He collected and recorded large amounts of numerical data.

 How were Mendel's plant-breeding methods unique?

**Figure 4** Mendel observed that the color of a pea plant's flowers was the result of dominant and recessive genetic factors.

## Mendel's Experimental Results

After analyzing the results of his experiments, Mendel concluded that two factors control each inherited trait. He also proposed that when organisms reproduce, each gamete—sperm or egg—contributes one factor for each trait.

 **Figure 4** Explain to a classmate which color factor is dominant and which factor is recessive.

**Dominant Factors** Mendel often crossed true-breeding plants to create hybrids. A hybrid inherits a different form of a specific trait from each parent. For example, when Mendel crossed a true-breeding, purple-flowered plant with a true-breeding, white-flowered plant, the hybrid offspring had purple flowers, as shown in **Figure 4.** Why were there no white flowers? Mendel hypothesized that the offspring had one genetic factor for purple flowers and one genetic factor for white flowers, but only the purple factor is observed because it blocks the white factor. A genetic factor that blocks another genetic factor is called **dominant** (DAH muh nunt). A dominant trait, such as purple flower color in pea plants, is observed when offspring have one or two dominant factors.

**Recessive Factors** A genetic factor that is blocked by the presence of a dominant factor is called **recessive** (rih SE sihv). A recessive trait, such as white flower color in pea plants, can be observed only when two recessive genetic factors are present in offspring.

**SCIENCE USE V. COMMON USE**

**cross**

*Science Use* to cause animals or plants to breed. *Ivan plans to cross two different roses to produce a new variety of roses.*

*Common Use* move or pass from one side to another side. *Always cross a street at a traffic light.*

## Peas, Anyone?

One of Mendel's fellow monks supposedly said, "Brother Mendel, we grow tired of peas." Mendel's records show that he had counted at least 300,000 peas!

**Data Collection**

| Mendel's Data | | | |
|---|---|---|---|
| | **Round Peas** | **Wrinkled Peas** | **Total Peas** |
| Trial 1 | 5,474 | 1,850 | 7,324 |
| | **Yellow Peas** | **Green Peas** | **Total Peas** |
| Trial 2 | 6,022 | 2,001 | 7,324 |

**Source:** Henig, Robin Marantz. *The Monk in the Garden: The Lost and Found Genius of Gregor Mendel, the Father of Genetics*. New York: Houghton Mifflin, 2000.

**Data Analysis**

1. **Calculate** these ratios: round peas to wrinkled peas, and yellow peas to green peas.

2. **Infer** which traits are dominant and which are recessive.

**MA7: NS 1.0**

Try at Home

# Mendel's Laws of Heredity

Because Mendel did many experiments and carefully recorded the results, he was able to form two important hypotheses that allowed him to predict how traits are inherited. His hypotheses have been supported by other scientists and are called Mendel's laws of heredity—the law of segregation and the law of independent assortment.

According to the **law of segregation,** the two factors for each trait segregate or separate from each other during meiosis when gametes form. You can review meiosis in Chapter 3.

Mendel's **law of independent assortment** states that the factors for one trait separate independently of how factors for other traits separate, and gametes have all possible combinations of traits. For example, the separation of the two factors for seed color does not affect how the two factors for seed shape separate. The independent separation of the factors for these two traits makes four possible combinations of traits, as shown in **Figure 5.**

# Modern Definitions of Mendel's Ideas

Mendel did not know about DNA or how cells reproduce, yet his ideas about inheritance remain true today. However, the terms used to describe his ideas have changed over time.

**Figure 5** Mendel found that the inheritance of one trait, such as pea color, does not influence the inheritance of another trait, such as pea shape.

**Explain** why yellow peas can be round or wrinkled.

Yellow, round

Yellow, wrinkled

Green, round

Green, wrinkled

## Genes and Alleles

Recall that a chromosome is made up of DNA and proteins. A section of DNA that has information about a specific trait of an organism is called a **gene** (JEEN). However, the gene's information about a trait can vary among the same kind of organisms.

Recall that Mendel used pea plants with purple or white flowers. Each pea plant had a gene for flower color, but each plant's gene for flower color had either purple or white information. In a similar way, we all have genes for eye color, but we all do not have the same information about the color of our eyes. Each form of a gene with different information is called an **allele** (uh LEEL). Mendel called these *factors* instead of alleles. As shown in **Figure 6,** scientists now know that the alleles of a gene are at the same locations on a pair of homologous chromosomes.

 How many alleles were there for flower color in Mendel's experiments?

## Phenotype and Genotype

How would you describe the dog in **Figure 7?** You might say the dog has a lot of hair, short legs, and a wrinkled face. These observable traits and all characteristics of an organism make up the organism's **phenotype** (FEE nuh tipe). You read in Chapter 2 that an organism can have different levels of organization—organ system, organ, tissue, and cell. Each level of organization has a phenotype. A dog's phenotype includes not only its physical appearance, but also how its organs function, how it reproduces, and many other characteristics.

An organism's phenotype results from the interactions among its alleles and genes. In the next lesson, you will read that the environment can influence phenotype, too. The alleles of all the genes on an organism's chromosomes make up the organism's **genotype** (JEE nuh tipe). An organism's genotype can refer to one or more genes. The alleles of a particular gene are that gene's genotype.

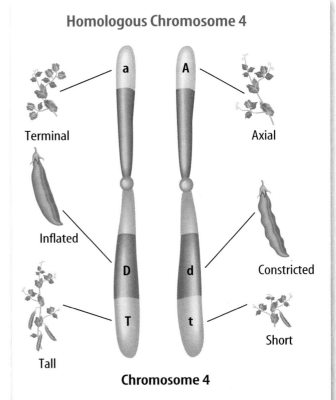

**Homologous Chromosome 4**

Terminal
Inflated
Tall

Axial
Constricted
Short

**Chromosome 4**

**Figure 6** Homologous chromosomes have genes for the same traits. A gene's alleles are in the same location on homologous chromosomes.

**Figure 7** The phenotype of this chow chow distinguishes it from other dog breeds.

**Figure 8** Peas can show the phenotype smooth or wrinkled. A homozygous genotype for pea shape consists of two of the same alleles, but a heterozygote genotype consists of two different alleles.

**Explain** why the heterozygous pea is smooth.

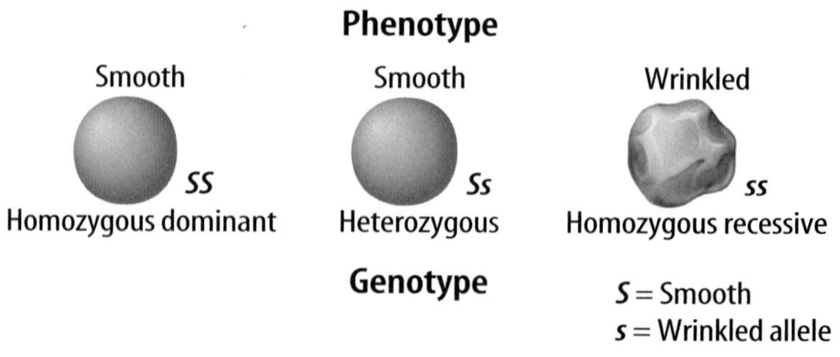

**Phenotype**

Smooth
*SS*
Homozygous dominant

Smooth
*Ss*
Heterozygous

Wrinkled
*ss*
Homozygous recessive

**Genotype**

*S* = Smooth
*s* = Wrinkled allele

**WORD ORIGIN**

homozygous
heterozygous
**homo–** from Greek *homos;*
means *one and the same*
**hetero–** from Greek *heteros;*
means *the other, different*
**–zygous** from Greek *zygotos;*
means *yoked*

**Homozygous and Heterozygous Genotypes** Because eukaryotic organisms have pairs of chromosomes, a genotype for a gene has two alleles. If the two alleles have the same information, their genotype is called **homozygous** (hoh muh ZI gus), as shown in **Figure 8.** If the two alleles for a gene have different information, their genotype is called **heterozygous** (he tuh roh ZI gus).

**Representing Genotypes** Also shown in **Figure 8** are the possible genotypes for the smooth-pea phenotype—*SS* and *Ss.* Uppercase letters represent dominant alleles, and lowercase letters represent recessive alleles. Both of these genotypes result in a smooth phenotype because the *S* allele is dominant over the *s* allele. The wrinkled phenotype is possible only if the two recessive alleles—*ss*—are present.

## Law of Segregation Explained

The movement of chromosomes during meiosis explains Mendel's law of segregation. Recall that in meiosis I, replicated homologous-chromosome pairs separate from each other. Then, each set of sister chromatids separates into different gametes during meiosis II, as shown in **Figure 9.** Each gamete only receives one allele.

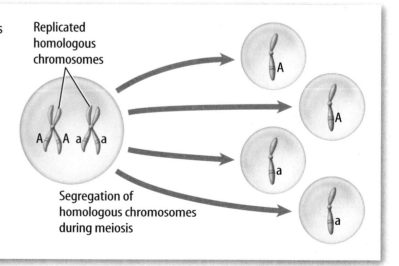

**Figure 9** Homologous chromosomes separate into different daughter cells during meiosis.

Replicated homologous chromosomes

Segregation of homologous chromosomes during meiosis

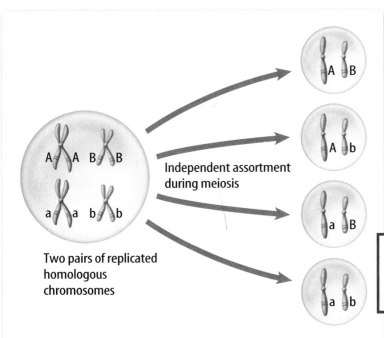

**Figure 10** The separation of one pair of homologous chromosomes is independent of the separation of other homologous pairs.

### Law of Independent Assortment Explained

In Mendel's law of independent assortment, he hypothesized that the separation and movement of two factors for a trait is independent of the separation and movement of the factors for other traits. This can also be explained by the movement of chromosomes during meiosis. The daughter cells produced by meiosis receive only one chromosome from each pair of homologous chromosomes. As shown in **Figure 10,** a daughter cell might receive a chromosome with an **A** allele from one pair and a chromosome with a **B** allele from the other pair. On the other hand, a daughter cell might receive a chromosome with an **a** allele from one pair and a chromosome with a **b** allele from the other pair. This results in four possible allele combinations for two homologous pairs of chromosomes.

## Importance of Mendel's Genetic Studies

You might be surprised to learn that Mendel's discoveries were unnoticed for about 35 years. In the 1860s, no one knew about the existence of chromosomes or about the process of meiosis. Therefore, it might have been hard for others to understand Mendel's discoveries. However, scientists doing background research for their genetic studies rediscovered Mendel's work early in the 1900s. All the research of modern genetics is based on Mendel's conclusions from his work with pea plants.

 **Reading Check** Why were Mendel's studies important?

# Mendel's Studies: A Summary

Mendel's discoveries about how traits are inherited paved the way for future genetic scientists. Below are Mendel's principles about genetics that are true today for many characteristics.

- An individual has two sets of factors (alleles) for each trait—one from each parent.
- A factor (allele) might not be observed in one generation if it is recessive and masked by a dominant allele.
- The two factors (alleles) for each trait can be the same (homozygous) or be different (heterozygous).
- The two factors (alleles) for each trait segregate or separate from each other during meiosis—the law of segregation.
- The separation and movement of the two factors (alleles) for a trait during meiosis is independent of the separation of the factors for other traits—the law of independent assortment.

# LESSON 1 Review

## Summarize

Create your own lesson summary as you write a script for a **television news report.**

1. **Review** the text after the **red** main headings and write one sentence about each. These are the headlines of your broadcast.

2. **Review** the text and write 2–3 sentences about each **blue** subheading. These sentences should tell *who, what, when, where,* and *why* information about each **red** heading.

3. **Include** descriptive details in your report, such as names of reporters and local places and events.

4. **Present** your news report to other classmates alone or with a team.

 ELA7: LS 2.2

## Standards Check

### Using Vocabulary

1. **Define** the terms *dominant* and *recessive*. **2.d**

2. **Distinguish** between an allele and a gene. **2.d**

3. **Relate** the terms *phenotype* and *genotype*. **2.d**

### Understanding Main Ideas

4. Which helps to explain Mendel's laws of heredity? **2.b**

    A. meiosis   C. mitosis
    B. proteins   D. phenotypes

5. **Describe** the methods Mendel used in his experiments. **2.d**

6. **Summarize** Mendel's two basic laws of heredity. **2.d**

### Applying Science

7. **Design an experiment** to test for true-breeding plants. **2.d**

8. **Examine** how Mendel's conclusions disprove the blending theory of inheritance. **2.d**

9. **Organize Information** Copy and fill in the graphic organizer below to identify three things that made Mendel's experiments unique. **2.d**

Mendel's Experimental Methods

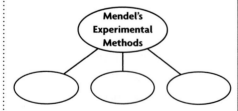

**Science** Online

For more practice, visit **Standards Check** at ca7.msscience.com.

# Applying Math

## Probabilities in Inheritance

MA7: NS 1.2, NS 1.3, MR 2.4

2.c

Probabilities can be used to predict the likelihood of a particular outcome. The probability, P, of an event can be written as either a percentage or a fraction. For example, for every birth there is a 50 percent probability that the baby will be a boy and a 50 percent probability that the baby will be a girl. The probability of each event can be written as $\frac{1}{2}$. To find the probability of two events both occurring, the two probabilities, written as fractions, are multiplied.

### Example

If the probability of having one girl is 50 percent, what is the probability that a woman will have two girls? What is the probability that a woman will have two girls and then a boy?

**1** **This is what you know:**

The probability of having a girl is 50 percent. This can be written as $\frac{1}{2}$.

**2** **This is what you need to find:**

- the probability that a woman will have two girls: P(G, G)

- the probability that a woman will have two girls and then a boy P(G, G, B)

**3** **Multiply the probabilities of individual events.**

- $P(G, G) = \frac{1}{2} \times \frac{1}{2} = \frac{1}{4}$

  The probability of having two girls in a family is $\frac{1}{4}$ = 25 percent.

- $P(G,G,B) = \frac{1}{2} \times \frac{1}{2} \times \frac{1}{2} = \frac{1}{8}$

  The probability of having two girls and then a boy is $\frac{1}{8}$ = 12.5 percent.

---

### Practice Problems

1. Find the probability of a woman having four boys.

2. Find the probability of a woman having two girls, a boy, and then two girls.

**Science** nline

For more math practice, visit Math Practice at ca7.msscience.com.

---

**Science Content Standards**

**2.c** Students know an inherited trait can be determined by one or more genes.

**2.d** Students know plant and animal cells contain many thousands of different genes and typically have two copies of every gene. The two copies (or alleles) of the gene may or may not be identical, and one may be dominant in determining the phenotype while the other is recessive.

**Also covers:** 7.a, 7.b, 7.c, 7.e

### Reading Guide

**What** *You'll Learn*

▶ **Interpret** a Punnett square and a pedigree.

▶ **Distinguish** between multiple alleles and polygenic inheritance.

▶ **Explain** how the environment influences inherited traits.

▶ **Describe** three human genetic disorders.

**Why** *It's Important*
Genetics helps to explain why each person is unique.

**Vocabulary**
Punnett square
pedigree
incomplete dominance
codominance
multiple alleles
sex chromosome
polygenic inheritance
genetic disorder

**Review Vocabulary**
**soil:** a mixture of weathered rock, minerals, and organic matter on Earth's surface (Grade 6)

# Understanding Inheritance

**Main Idea** The interactions among alleles, genes, and the environment determine an organism's traits.

**Real-World Reading Connection** Have you ever wondered why your nose or lips are shaped the way they are? How can scientists determine if you are at risk for carrying alleles for any genetic disorders, such as sickle cell disease? Scientists now have tools to answer these questions and study patterns of human inheritance over many generations.

## Modeling Inheritance

Plant breeders and animal breeders need a way to predict how traits will appear in offspring. Two tools—a Punnett square and a pedigree—can be used to identify and predict traits among genetically related individuals, such as the family shown in **Figure 11.**

### Punnett Squares

If the genotypes of the parents are known, then the different genotypes and phenotypes of the offspring can be predicted. A **Punnett square** is a model used to predict possible genotypes and phenotypes of offspring.

**Figure 11** Offspring of the same parents resemble each other because they carry some of the same gene combinations.

**One-Trait Model** **Figure 12** shows a Punnett square of the possible offspring of two parents—a true-breeding pea plant for yellow seeds and a true-breeding pea plant for green seeds. *Y* represents the dominant allele for yellow seeds, and *y* represents the recessive allele for green seeds. The Punnett square shows that the only possible genotype for hybrid offspring is heterozygous—*Yy*. The true-breeding pea plant for yellow seeds only can contribute gametes that have a *Y* allele. The true-breeding pea plant for green seeds can only contribute gametes that have a *y* allele. All, or 100 percent, of the offspring will have the genotype *Yy*. The phenotype of the genotype *Yy* is yellow seeds because *Y* is dominant to *y*.

 **Figure 12** Use the top Punnett square to explain to a classmate why all offspring are heterozygous.

**Hybrid-Cross Model** What would a Punnett square look like if two of these hybrid offspring were crossed? The second Punnett square, also shown in **Figure 12,** is the cross between two organisms with heterozygous genotypes—*Yy* and *Yy*. The possible offspring from this cross includes three different genotypes but only two phenotypes. We expect that three-fourths, or 75 percent, of the offspring from this cross will have yellow seeds and one-fourth, or 25 percent, will have green seeds. In other words, the probability is that for every four seeds, three should be yellow, and one should be green. This can be stated as a 3:1 ratio. However, you cannot expect that every group of four seeds will consist of three yellow seeds and one green. When studying genetics, a large number of offspring need to be counted in order to get accurate results, as Mendel determined during his experiments. The more individuals counted, the closer the actual numbers will be to the predictions.

 Why are a large number of offspring needed to get accurate results in genetic experiments?

**Figure 12** In the top cross, all the offspring have the same phenotype and genotype. In the bottom cross, they are not the same.

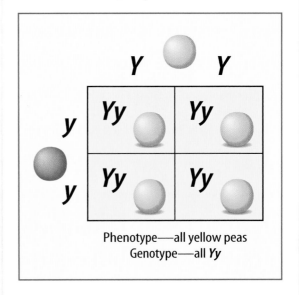

Phenotype—all yellow peas
Genotype—all *Yy*

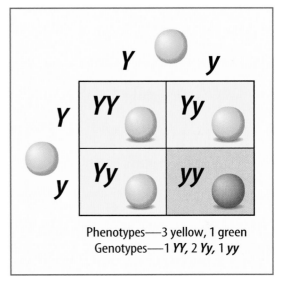

Phenotypes—3 yellow, 1 green
Genotypes—1 *YY*, 2 *Yy*, 1 *yy*

The ratio of phenotypes is 3:1, yellow:green. The ratios of genotypes are 1:2:1, *YY:Yy:yy*.

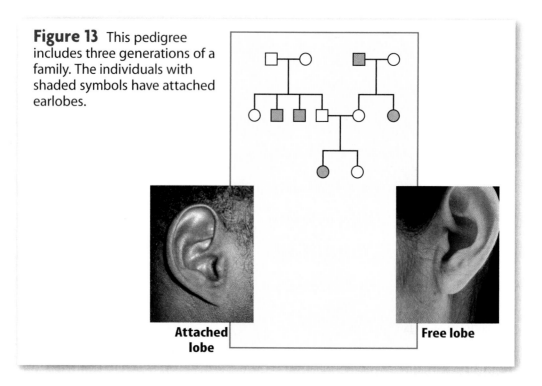

**Figure 13** This pedigree includes three generations of a family. The individuals with shaded symbols have attached earlobes.

**Attached lobe**

**Free lobe**

## Pedigrees

All genetically related members of a family are part of a family tree. A **pedigree** shows genetic traits that were inherited by members of a family tree, as illustrated in **Figure 13.** A pedigree usually only indicates the phenotype of individuals. The genotypes of the individuals in a pedigree might not be known but can often be determined. In a pedigree, circles represent females, and squares represent males. Connecting lines indicate relationships among members of the family tree. A line connects a set of parents. Branching lines below a set of parents indicate their offspring. The inheritance of attached and free earlobes in two generations of a family is shown in **Figure 13.** Besides tracking common inherited traits, pedigrees are important tools to track **complex** patterns of inheritance and genetic disorders in families.

# Complex Patterns of Inheritance

By chance, Mendel studied traits only influenced by one gene with two alleles. However, we know now that some inherited traits have complex patterns of inheritance.

## Types of Dominance

You read in Lesson 1 about dominant alleles and recessive alleles. Recall that for pea plants, the presence of one dominant allele results in a dominant phenotype. Not all allele pairs, however, have a dominant-recessive interaction.

**ACADEMIC VOCABULARY**

**complex** (kuhm PLEKS)
*(adjective)* complicated or intricate
*Eva deciphered the complex code left by the spies and solved the mystery.*

 ×  →

Figure 14 The interaction of alleles with incomplete dominance determines the color of camellia flowers.

**Incomplete Dominance** Sometimes traits appear to be blends of alleles. Alleles show **incomplete dominance** when they produce a phenotype that is a blend of the parents' phenotypes. For example, a pink camellia, as shown in **Figure 14,** results from incomplete dominance. A cross between a white camellia flower and a red camellia flower only produces camellia plants with pink flowers.

**Codominance** The human blood type AB is an example of another type of interaction between two alleles. When both alleles can be observed in a phenotype, this type of interaction is called **codominance.** If an individual inherits the B allele from one parent and an A allele from the other parent, he or she will have type AB blood, not type A blood or type B blood.

**WORD ORIGIN**
dominance
from Latin *dominari*; means *to rule, have dominion over*

## Multiple Alleles

Some genes only have two alleles. However, there are genes that have more than two alleles, or **multiple alleles.** Besides codominance, the human ABO blood group also is an example of a trait that is determined by multiple alleles. There are three different alleles for the ABO blood type—$I^A$, $I^B$, and $i$. The $I^A$ and $I^B$ alleles are codominant to each other, but both are dominant to the $i$ allele. Even though there are multiple alleles, a person can only inherit two of these alleles—one from each parent, as shown in **Table 2.**

 **Table 2** Which blood types have only one genotype?

| Table 2 Human ABO Blood Types | |
|---|---|
| **Phenotype** | **Possible Genotypes** |
| Type A | $I^A I^A$ or $I^A i$ |
| Type B | $I^B I^B$ or $I^B i$ |
| Type O | $ii$ |
| Type AB | $I^A I^B$ |

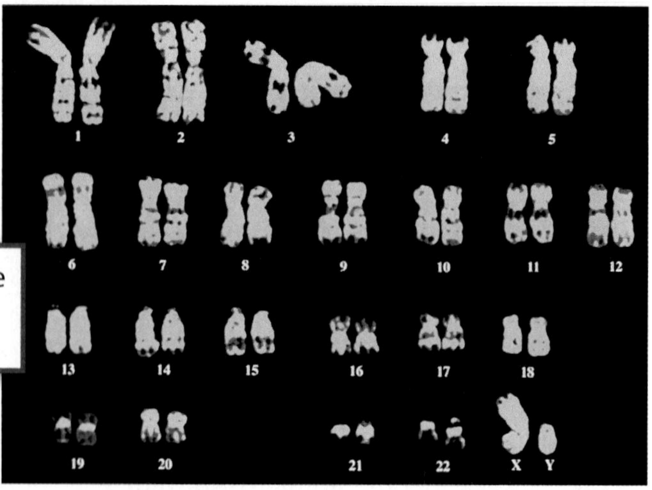

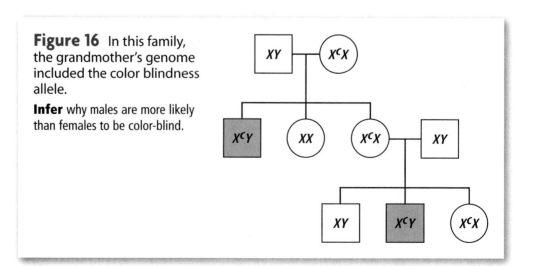

**Figure 15** This chart of chromosome pairs of a human male shows the X and Y sex chromosomes.

## Sex-Linked Inheritance

Recall that we have 23 pairs of homologous chromosomes in the cells of our bodies, except for sperm and egg cells that have only one chromosome from each chromosome pair. Most pairs of homologous chromosomes are of equal size with one exception—the long X and short Y pair, as shown in **Figure 15.** Chromosomes X and Y are the **sex chromosomes** because they contain the genes that determine a person's gender or sex. With the exception of sperm and eggs, each cell in a male has an X chromosome and a Y chromosome, and each cell in a female has two X chromosomes.

Because the Y chromosome is shorter than the X chromosome, many genes on the X chromosome are not on the Y chromosome. Therefore, each of those genes has only one allele, not two. It is the allele on the X chromosome. Recall that a recessive phenotype usually is observed only if the genotype is homozygous. However, a recessive phenotype is observed in a male when a one-allele gene on his X chromosome has a recessive allele. That's why males are more likely than females to have X-linked recessive conditions, as shown in **Figure 16.**

**Figure 16** In this family, the grandmother's genome included the color blindness allele.

**Infer** why males are more likely than females to be color-blind.

**Figure 17** At least seven different genes determine the coat color of horses. However, a horse with just one dominant allele for the inability to form pigment in skin and hair, will lack color regardless of the information in the other six genes.

## Polygenic Inheritance

Some traits are determined by only one gene, but one gene can affect more than one trait in an organism. In fact, many traits result from the interactions of more than one gene. **Polygenic inheritance** is when multiple genes determine the phenotype of a trait. When several genes determine a trait, many alleles affect the phenotype even though each gene has only two alleles. Therefore, many phenotypes are possible when polygenic inheritance determines a trait, such as the color of horses, as shown in **Figure 17.** Height, weight, and skin color in humans are examples of characteristics that are determined by polygenic inheritance.

## Maternal Inheritance

When discussing human heredity, we usually only talk about the DNA that makes up the chromosomes in the nucleus in each of our cells. But, you read in Chapter 1 that mitochondria contain DNA too. Mitochondria are scattered throughout the cytoplasm of cells, including an egg cell, but a sperm cell only has mitochondria in its tail. A sperm's tail does not enter the egg during fertilization. As a result, humans inherit mitochondrial genes, such as the genes involved in making ATP during cellular respiration, only from their mothers. This means that the inheritance of traits related to mitochondria can be traced from a grandmother to her children and then to her grandchildren.

 **Reading Check** Why do humans inherit mitochondrial genes only from their mothers?

# Human Genetic Disorders

Imagine that you are putting a bicycle together. You have all the right parts, but the directions say to put the handlebars on the seat post. If you did this, your bicycle could not function the way it should. A similar thing can happen if a mutation, or a change to a gene, occurs. The organism with the mutation cannot function as it should.

An inherited mutation can result in a phenotype called a **genetic disorder.** A genetic disorder can result in minor or major health problems and sometimes shorten a person's life. A common genetic disorder among Caucasians is a recessive disorder called cystic fibrosis. People with cystic fibrosis have tissues that produce abnormally thick mucus. This thick mucus can affect the functions of the respiratory, digestive, and reproductive systems. Other human genetic disorders are listed in **Table 3.**

 **Table 3** Which human genetic disorders affect the blood?

# Genes and the Environment

You read earlier in the chapter that the genotype determines the phenotype. Scientists have determined that genes are not the only factors that can affect phenotypes. An organism's environment can also affect its phenotype.

Many genes affect a person's chances of having heart disease. However, what a person eats and the amount of exercise he or she gets can influence whether heart disease will develop. Also, your genotype for skin color determines the amount of pigment in your skin. But, long exposures to sunlight can temporarily change your skin color. Other examples of how environmental factors can affect phenotype are shown in **Figure 18.**

 What factors affect phenotype?

| Table 3 Some Human Genetic Disorders | | |
|---|---|---|
| **Genetic Disorder** | **Type of Disorder** | **Health Problems** |
| Huntington's disease | Dominant | Breakdown of brain tissue; shortened life span |
| Sickle-cell disease | Codominant | Red blood cell destruction; clogged blood vessels |
| Hemophilia | X-linked recessive | Excessive bleeding due to blood clotting problems |
| Down syndrome | Trisomy—extra chromosome # 21 | Mental retardation; heart defects |

# Visualizing the Interactions of Genes and the Environment

**Figure 18**

Environmental factors, such as temperature, soil conditions, and the number of hours of light, can affect the phenotypes of genotypes.

◄ These hydrangea plants are genetically identical. The acidic condition of the soil in which they grow determines flower color— more acidic produces blue flowers and less acidic produces pink flowers.

Siamese cats have alleles that produce a dark ▶ pigment only in cooler areas of the body. That's why a Siamese cat's ear tips, nose, paws, and the end of its tail are darker than warmer areas of its body.

◄ The wing patterns of the map butterfly, *Araschnia levana,* depend on when the adult develops. Adults that develop in the spring have more orange in their wing patterns than those that develop in summer.

Pond water crowfoot, *Ranunculus peltatus,* ▶ is an aquatic plant that has two leaf types. Submerged leaves are threadlike and those that float are flat.

*Contributed by National Geographic*

# Inheritance: A Summary

The relationship between a phenotype and a genotype can be complex. Each gene's alleles interact, and genes interact with each other and the environment to produce a phenotype. Here is a summary of what you have read:

- Traits may show intermediate phenotypes.
- Traits may show two phenotypes at the same time.
- Traits may be influenced by more than one allele.
- Traits may be influenced by more than one gene.
- Traits may be sex-specific.
- Traits might be influenced by the environment.
- Gene and chromosomal mutations associated with human genetic disorders might lead to abnormal traits.

# LESSON 2  Review

## Summarize

Create your own lesson summary as you organize an **outline.**

1. **Scan** the lesson. Find and list the first **red** main heading.

2. **Review** the text after the heading and list 2–3 details about the heading.

3. **Find** and list each **blue** subheading that follows the **red** main heading.

4. **List** 2–3 details, key terms, and definitions under each **blue** subheading.

5. **Review** additional **red** main headings and their supporting **blue** subheadings. List 2–3 details about each.

**ELA7:** W 2.5

##  Standards Check

### Using Vocabulary

1. **Define** *incomplete dominance* in your own words. **2.c**

2. **Distinguish** between multiple alleles and polygenic inheritance. **2.c**

### Understanding Main Ideas

3. **State** what squares and circles represent on a pedigree. **2.c**

4. **Predict** the possible blood genotypes of a child, using **Table 2,** if one parent is Type O and the other parent is Type AB. **2.d**

5. **Explain** the relationship between the environment and genes. **2.c**

6. **Summarize** the symptoms associated with three genetic disorders. **2.c**

### Applying Science

7. **Organize Information** Draw a graphic organizer similar to the one below to list complex patterns of inheritance. **2.c**

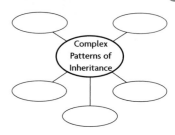

8. **Interpret** this pedigree showing the inheritance of Huntington's disease. **2.c**

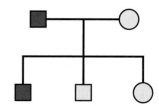

**Science** nline

For more practice, visit **Standards Check** at ca7.msscience.com.

Brain POP

# Data Lab

**00:25**
minutes

**Try at Home**

# Can you see a genotype?

The terms genotype and phenotype can be confusing. A Punnett square shows the genotypes of a specific cross. By knowing the genotype, the phenotype can be determined.

## Data

Pea plant crosses (*P* = purple flowers, *p* = white flowers, *Y* = yellow peas, *y* = green peas)

| 1st Generation Punnett Square | | |
| --- | --- | --- |
| | *PY* | *PY* |
| *py* | *PpYy* | *PpYy* |
| *py* | *PpYy* | *PpYy* |

| 2nd Generation Punnett Square | | | | |
| --- | --- | --- | --- | --- |
| | *PY* | *Py* | *pY* | *py* |
| *PY* | *PPYY* | *PPYy* | *PpYY* | *PpYy* |
| *Py* | *PPYy* | *PPyy* | *PpYy* | *Ppyy* |
| *pY* | *PpYY* | *PpYy* | *ppYY* | *ppYy* |
| *py* | *PpYy* | *Ppyy* | *ppYy* | *ppyy* |

## Data Analysis

1. **Analyze** Which phenotypes are represented in the 1st generation pea plant crosses? In the 2nd generation? How many of each phenotype are there?

2. **Calculate** the percentage of offspring in the 1st generation that will have a dominant phenotype and the percentage that will have a recessive phenotype.

3. **Determine** the percentage of the 2nd generation that will have a homozygous recessive phenotype.

 **Science Content Standards**

**2.d** Students know plant and animal cells contain many thousands of different genes and typically have two copies of every gene. The two copies (or alleles) of the gene may or may not be identical, and one may be dominant in determining the phenotype while the other is recessive.

**MA7: NS 1.3**

**00:45**
minutes

# Use the Internet:
# What makes you unique?

**Materials**

human traits table
computer with
    internet access

**Science Content
Standards**

**2.d** Students know plant and animal cells contain many thousands of different genes and typically have two copies of every gene. The two copies (or alleles) of the gene may or may not be identical, and one may be dominant in determining the phenotype while the other is recessive.

**7.a** Select and use appropriate tools and technology (including calculators, computers, balances, spring scales, microscopes, and binoculars) to perform tests, collect data, and display data.

**7.b** Use a variety of print and electronic resources (including the World Wide Web) to collect information and evidence as part of a research project.

**7.c** Communicate the logical connection among hypotheses, science concepts, tests conducted, data collected, and conclusions drawn from the scientific evidence.

**7.e** Communicate the steps and results from an investigation in written reports and oral presentations.

## Problem

Unless you have an identical twin, you are the only person with your specific set of genes. No one else looks quite like you, but many people probably have the same eye color or hair color.

## Form a Hypothesis

What phenotypes do you think are most common in your class-room? In your school?

## Collect Data and Make Observations

1. Read and complete a lab safety form.
2. Choose three traits to study from the list below.
3. Make a data table to collect information about the number of your classmates who express each trait. Record the total number of students included in your survey.
4. Collect trait information from each student.

| Human Traits | | |
|---|---|---|
| **Trait** | **Phenotype 1** | **Phenotype 2** |
| Earlobes | free | attached |
| Forelock | white | not white |
| Dimples | present | not present |
| Thumbs | curved | straight |
| Pinkies | straight | bent |
| Mid-digit hair | present | not present |

## Analyze and Conclude

1. **Calculate** what percentage of people had phenotypes you studied.

2. **Graph** the data you collected using a bar graph for each trait you studied.

3. **Compare and contrast** the frequency of each trait. Did any of your findings surprise you?

4. **Infer** from your data the traits that are recessive and those that are dominant.

5. **Error Analysis** Would surveying a larger group of people change your results? Do you think that results from the group you surveyed are scientifically valid? Why or why not?

6. Visit ca7.msscience.com and combine your data with that of other students. Calculate the percentage of the total number of students that express the traits you studied.

## Communicate

 **Science**  **ELA7: W 2.2**

Write a brief report, including your graphs, and post it at ca7.msscience.com.

# Real World Science

## Making New Plant Breeds

New plant species with bigger blossoms, better nutritional value, better taste, or plants with more pest resistance are often needed by plant growers or demanded by consumers. Plant breeders identify plants with such traits and breed them to produce new plants that have the trait as part of their genomes. Methods used by plant breeders include tissue culture, breeding through mutation, and genetic engineering.

Visit **Careers** at **ca7.msscience.com** and find out what plants are being researched by plant breeders and the methods used. Make a table of your results.

## Genetic Engineering

Scientists use a molecule called restriction endonuclease to cut DNA at specific gene sequences. This enables a scientist to insert new DNA with genes that modify an organism's genotype and phenotype. For example, a gene that codes for insect resistance might be inserted into a virus. Then, the virus could be made to infect a plant. The new genetic code carried by the virus would become part of the plant's genome.

Imagine that you're a salesman, trying to sell a new plant that is genetically engineered for some trait, such as insect resistance. Create a promotional brochure to sell this plant to your classmates.

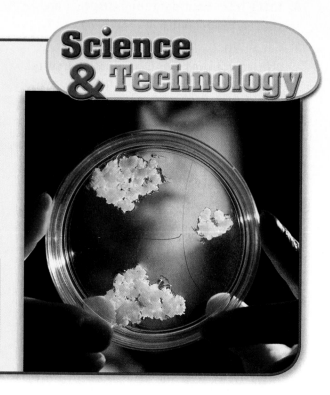

# Luther Burbank's Legacy

In the mid-nineteenth century, botanist Luther Burbank began breeding plants. He created over 800 new plant varieties including new types of blackberries, strawberries, peaches, potatoes, and almonds. It was common for Burbank to have thousands of breeding experiments in progress at the same time in gardens in Santa Rosa and Sebastopol, California. In 1930, the U.S. Congress passed an act enabling botanists to patent their new plant breeds.

Imagine that you're Luther Burbank and have created a new plant breed. Create an advertisement for the plant.

# GENETICALLY-MODIFIED PLANTS

Geneticists have developed techniques to transfer genes from one plant species to another plant species. These genetic modifications can increase a plant's nutritional value, make it disease resistant, or enable it to grow under different conditions than it normally would grow. Many edible, genetically modified plants are available to consumers.

Research and then debate whether genetically modified plants help or harm humans and the environment.

# CHAPTER 4 — Standards Study Guide

**The BIG Idea** Inherited genes determine an organism's traits.

## Lesson 1 Foundations of Genetics

*2.b, 2.d*

**Main Idea** Gregor Mendel discovered the basic principles of genetics.

- Early ideas about inheritance could not explain why traits are not present in every generation.

- Gregor Mendel determined the basic laws of genetics.

- Some alleles can be dominant and others can be recessive.

- The movement of chromosomes during meiosis explains Mendel's laws of segregation and independent assortment.

- An organism's phenotype results from the interactions of its alleles and genes.

- Modern genetics research is based on Mendel's conclusions.

- Mendel's principles of genetics still hold true today for many characteristics.

- **allele** (p. 177)
- **dominant** (p. 175)
- **gene** (p. 177)
- **genetics** (p. 173)
- **genotype** (p. 177)
- **heredity** (p. 172)
- **heterozygous** (p. 178)
- **homozygous** (p. 178)
- **law of independent assortment** (p. 176)
- **law of segregation** (p. 176)
- **phenotype** (p. 177)
- **recessive** (p. 175)

## Lesson 2 Understanding Inheritance

*2.c, 2.d, 7.a, 7.b, 7.c, 7.e*

**Main Idea** The interactions among alleles, genes, and the environment determine an organism's traits.

- A Punnett square is used to predict the genotypes and phenotypes of offspring.

- A pedigree traces an inherited trait in a family.

- Inheritance patterns studied since Mendel include incomplete dominance, codominance, multiple alleles, polygenic inheritance, sex-linked inheritance, and maternal inheritance.

- The human ABO blood group is an example of a trait that shows codominance and multiple alleles.

- Genes are not the only factors that affect phenotype.

- The environment can affect an organism's phenotype.

- Genetic disorders can result in minor or major health problems or can even lead to death.

- Human genetics disorders include Huntington's disease, sickle-cell disease, cystic fibrosis, hemophilia, and Down syndrome.

- The relationship between a phenotype and a genotype can be complex.

- **codominance** (p. 185)
- **genetic disorder** (p. 188)
- **incomplete dominance** (p. 185)
- **multiple alleles** (p. 185)
- **pedigree** (p. 184)
- **polygenic inheritance** (p. 187)
- **Punnett square** (p. 182)
- **sex chromosome** (p. 186)

**STUDY TO GO** ▸ Download quizzes, key terms, and flash cards from ca7.msscience.com.

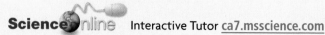

**Science Online** Interactive Tutor ca7.msscience.com

# Linking Vocabulary and Main Ideas

Copy this concept map and then use vocabulary terms from page 196 to complete it.

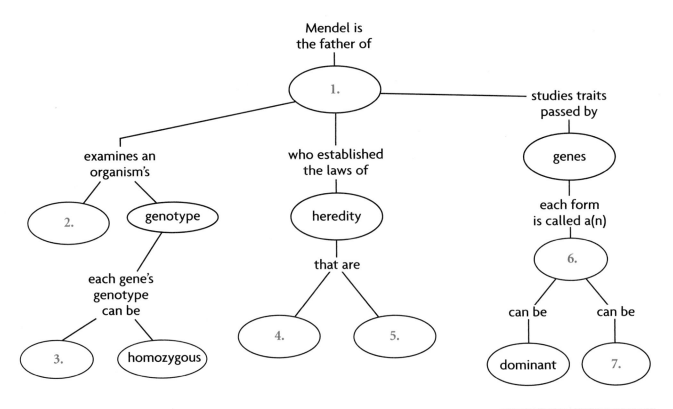

Mendel is
the father of

1.

studies traits
passed by

examines an
organism's

who established
the laws of

genes

genotype

heredity

each form
is called a(n)

2.

6.

each gene's
genotype
can be

that are

can be    can be

3.    homozygous

4.    5.

dominant    7.

**Science**nline

Visit ca7.msscience.com for:
▶ Vocabulary PuzzleMaker
▶ Vocabulary eFlashcards
▶ Multilingual Glossary

## Using Vocabulary

**Fill in the blanks with the correct vocabulary word.**

8. The idea that chromosomes separate independently of one another is part of the law of _____.

9. The idea that alleles separate when gametes are produced is part of the law of _____.

10. A(n) _____ chromosome has two different alleles for the same gene.

11. A dominant allele blocks the effects of a(n) _____ allele.

12. A(n) _____ is a family tree that shows a heritable trait.

13. Human height, weight, and skin color are examples of characteristics determined by _____ .

14. A(n) _____ is a helpful device for predicting the ratios of possible genotypes.

15. _____ is a type of interaction between alleles in which both alleles can be observed in a phenotype.

# Understanding Main Ideas

1. The process shown below was used by Mendel during his experiments.

   What is the process called?
   **A.** blending inheritance `2.c`
   **B.** asexual reproduction
   **C.** cross-fertilization
   **D.** segregation

2. Which describes Mendel's experiments?
   **A.** Mendel used plants that gave different off-spring with every cross. `2.d`
   **B.** Mendel counted large numbers of offspring.
   **C.** Mendel observed only one generation.
   **D.** Mendel used plants that reproduced slowly.

3. Which describes how people believed traits were inherited before Mendel's discoveries?
   **A.** Parental traits blend like colors of paint to produce offspring. `2.c`
   **B.** Parental traits blend like oil and water to produce offspring.
   **C.** Parental traits sort to produce offspring.
   **D.** Parental traits segregate to produce offspring.

4. Which characteristic did Mendel study?
   **A.** flower size `2.c`
   **B.** stem shape
   **C.** pod color
   **D.** root type

5. What term is used for each form of a gene?
   **A.** allele `2.c`
   **B.** chromosome
   **C.** pedigree
   **D.** Punnett square

6. Which genetic disorder is also known as trisomy 21?
   **A.** sickle-cell disease `2.c`
   **B.** Down syndrome
   **C.** Huntington's disease
   **D.** cystic fibrosis

7. When were Mendel's discoveries noticed?
   **A.** Never; Mendel's discoveries are not important to science. `2.d`
   **B.** immediately after he published his results
   **C.** decades after he performed his experiments
   **D.** Before he published his work; other scientists made the same discoveries before Mendel

8. The Punnett square below is of a cross between two pea plants with round seeds.

|     | R   | r   |
| --- | --- | --- |
| **R** | RR | Rr |
| **r** | Rr | rr |

   If mating produces eight offspring, how many will have round seeds?
   **A.** 1 `2.d`
   **B.** 3
   **C.** 6
   **D.** 8

9. Which is multiple genes affecting the phenotype of one trait?
   **A.** codominance `2.d`
   **B.** blending inheritance
   **C.** multiple alleles
   **D.** polygenic inheritance

## Applying Science

10. **Restate** the law of segregation and the law of independent assortment. **2.c**

11. **Compare** heterozygous genotype and homozygous genotype. **2.d**

12. **Distinguish** between multiple alleles and polygenic inheritance. **2.d**

13. **Give an example** of how the environment can affect an organism's phenotype. **2.d**

14. **Predict** In pea plants, the allele for inflated pods is dominant to the allele for constricted pods. Predict the genotype of a plant with constricted pods. Can you predict the genotype of a plant with inflated pods? Explain. **2.d**

15. In tomato plants, red fruit (*R*) is dominant to yellow fruit (*r*).

|   | R | r |
|---|---|---|
| **r** | Rr | rr |
| **r** | Rr | rr |

**Interpret** the Punnett square between a heterozygous red plant and a yellow plant. Include all the genotypes and corresponding phenotypes. **2.d**

### WRITING in ▶ Science

16. **Write** a paragraph comparing the blending theory of inheritance to the current theory of inheritance.

17. **Write** an essay about how life might be different if Mendel had not made his discoveries. **ELA7: W 2.4**

## Cumulative Review

18. **Compare** regeneration of a body part to regeneration as a type of asexual reproduction. **2.a**

19. **Evaluate** the importance of sexual reproduction to genetic variation. **2.b**

## Applying Math

20. A dresser drawer contains five pairs of socks of different colors. Each pair is folded together. Without looking, you reach into the drawer and pull out a pair but they are not the color you wanted. You put them back and choose a second pair without looking. What is the probability that you will pull out the first pair of socks again? **MA7: MR 1.2**

21. You flip a coin and then roll a six-sided number cube. Find the probability of the coin landing head side up and the number 3 being on top of the number cube. **MA7: MR 1.2**

22. To decide who will be first in a game, you place four equal-sized pieces of paper into a paper bag. One piece has an X on it. Without looking, you pull out a piece of paper but it is not marked with an X. What is the probability that the next person will pull out the paper with the X? **MA7: MR 1.2**

23. A jar contains three red, five green, two blue, and six yellow marbles. You randomly choose a marble from the jar. After replacing it, you choose another marble. What is the probability of choosing a green marble and then a yellow marble? **MA7: MR 1.2**

24. A school survey found that nine out of ten students like pizza. If you randomly ask three students if they like pizza, what is the probability that all three students like pizza? **MA7: MR 1.2**

**1** In fruit flies, the allele for red eyes (*R*) is dominant over the allele for white eyes (*r*). The diagram below shows the eye-color alleles of two fruit flies.

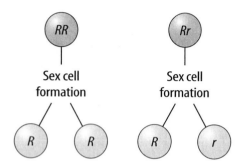

When the sex cells from these two fruit flies join, what is the percent chance that the offspring will have red eyes?

**A** 25 percent

**B** 50 percent

**C** 75 percent

**D** 100 percent          2.b

**2** Which is not part of heredity?

**A** traits

**B** chromosomes

**C** nutrients

**D** phenotype          2.d

**3** The gender of offspring from sexual reproduction is determined by

**A** the mother only, because she has two X chromosomes.

**B** the father only, because he has one X and one Y chromosome.

**C** environmental factors.

**D** polygenetic inheritance.          2.b

**4** In rabbits, the allele for black fur is dominant over the allele for brown fur. What are the phenotypes of four offspring that have parents with brown fur?

**A** all brown

**B** all black

**C** three black, one brown

**D** two black, two brown          2.c, 2.d

**5** The illustration below shows a chromosome.

What is represented in the small circle?

**A** a cell

**B** an egg

**C** a gene

**D** a sperm          2.d

**6** Which is when two alleles are observed in an individual?

**A** incomplete dominance

**B** recessive

**C** codominance

**D** multiple dominance          2.d

Science online Standards Assessment ca7.msscience.com

Huntington disease has a dominant (DD or Dd) inheritance pattern. Use the pedigree below to answer questions 7–9.

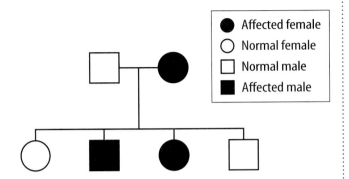

Legend:
- ● Affected female
- ○ Normal female
- □ Normal male
- ■ Affected male

**7** What is the genotype of the father?

A  DD

B  Dd

C  dd

D  D                                                    `2.b, 2.c`

**8** What is the genotype of the mother?

A  DD

B  Dd

C  dd

D  D                                                    `2.b, 2.c`

**9** What is the genotype of the unaffected children?

A  DD

B  Dd

C  dd

D  D                                                    `2.b, 2.c`

**10** If a pea plant that has two dominant alleles for wrinkled seeds is crossed with a pea plant that has one dominant allele for wrinkled seeds and one recessive allele for round seeds, what is the probability that an offspring will have wrinkled seeds?

A  25 percent

B  50 percent

C  75 percent

D  100 percent                                          `2.d`

**11** The Punnett square below shows the possible phenotypes of offspring from parents with blood types $A$ ($I^A i$) and $AB$ ($I^A I^B$).

|         | $I^A$      | $i$      |
|---------|------------|----------|
| $I^A$   | $I^A I^A$  | $I^A i$  |
| $I^B$   | $I^A I^B$  | $I^B i$  |

How many phenotypes are possible for these offspring?

A  1

B  2

C  3

D  4                                                    `2.b, 2.d`

**12** The fur colors seen in a Siamese cat are determined by body temperature. This is an example of

A  environmental influences on phenotype.

B  maternal influences on phenotype.

C  recessive influences on phenotype.

D  sex-linked influences on phenotype.                  `2.d`

Are you interested in learning more about cells reproduction and genetics? If so, check out these great books.

## Fiction

**Neanderthal: Their Time Has Come,** by John Darnton, describes what happens after a team of researchers discovers a tribe of primitive people. The researchers explore whether they could be the "missing link." *The content of this book is related to Science Standard 7.2.*

## Narrative Nonfiction

**The Double Helix: A Personal Account of the Discovery of the Structure of DNA,** by James Watson, describes the discovery of the structure of DNA by James Watson and Francis Crick. This book describes the process of science, classic scientific method, and the detailed structure of the DNA molecule. *The content of this book is related to Science Standard 7.2.*

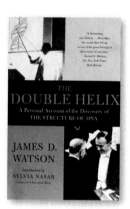

## Narrative Nonfiction

**The Egg,** by Shelley Gill, examines the mythology, legends, evolution, and biology of eggs through short facts and large, colorful illustrations. The book also introduces egg-laying animals and the adaptations they have made to protect their eggs. *The content of this book is related to Science Standard 7.2.*

## Nonfiction

**Darwin and the Beagle,** by Alan Moorehead, tells the story of Charles Darwin's journey on the HMS Beagle. Darwin collected and observed the plants and animals of the ecosystems he visited. This book details the shaping of modern-day genetics and the theory of evolution. *The content of this book is related to Science Standard 7.5.*

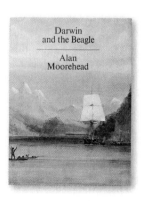

*Choose the word or phrase that best answers the question.*

**Use the concept map below about a typical plant's life cycle to answer questions 1 and 2.**

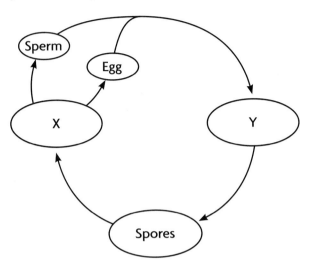

**1.** What term best replaces X?
  **A.** diploid
  **B.** fission
  **C.** haploid
  **D.** mitosis                                    **2.a**

**2.** What term best replaces Y?
  **A.** diploid
  **B.** fission
  **C.** haploid
  **D.** mitosis                                    **2.a**

**3.** Which is not an example of asexual reproduction?
  **A.** a new plant growing from a leaf cutting
  **B.** a sea star regenerating a lost arm
  **C.** a population of bacteria increasing in number
  **D.** yeast cells budding                         **2.a**

**4.** Which results in a range of phenotypes, such as skin color in humans?
  **A.** codominance
  **B.** multiple alleles
  **C.** polygenic inheritance
  **D.** sex-linked inheritance                      **2.c**

*Write your responses on a sheet of paper.*

**5.** **Explain** how a zygote might have an extra chromosome.                             **2.b**

**6.** **Explain** how someone with cystic fibrosis can have parents who do not have the disease.
                                                     **2.b, 2.d**

**Use the image below to answer questions 7 and 8.**

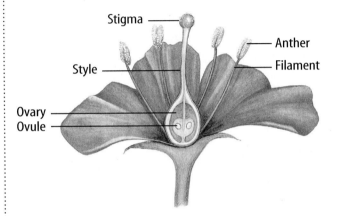

**7.** **Identify** which structures are part of the male reproductive system of the flower and which are part of the female reproductive system.   **5.f**

**8.** **Describe** how a seed would be produced in this flower.                                 **5.f**

**9.** The Punnett square below is for a cross between two fruit flies. In fruit flies, the long-wing trait (*L*) is dominant to the short-wing trait (*l*).

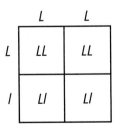

**Classify** each offspring as homozygous or heterozygous for the trait. Describe the phenotypes of the offspring.                          **2.b, 2.d**

# Evolution— Change over Time

**Lonesome Tortoises** These tortoises are found nowhere else on Earth, except the Galápagos Islands. These islands are well known for their species that exist here alone. The islands are being threatened by introduced species and other human activities.

**West-Coast Events**

**10,000–9,000 Years Ago**
Horses migrate over the land bridge between North America and Asia; horses in the western hemisphere then became extinct.

**1500s**
The Spanish reintroduce horses to the western hemisphere (to California in the late 1700s); these modern horses evolved from those that migrated to Asia thousands of years before.

**A.D. 1    1500    1600    1700    1800    1900**

**World Events**

**2,300 Years Ago**
Aristotle, a Greek scientist, observes nature and classifies organisms as belonging to one of two kingdoms—plant or animal—based on the way they move, eat, and grow.

**1831–1836**
Charles Darwin, a naturalist, studies rock formations, fossils, life-forms, and how the life-forms varied; he then proposes the idea of natural selection, published in 1859.

**Science Online**

To learn more about naturalists and their work, visit ca7.msscience.com.

**Concepts In Motion**

**Interactive Time Line** To learn more about these events and others, visit ca7.msscience.com.

**1987**
The last wild California condor is added to 26 others being raised in captivity to increase the population; as the condors are ready, they are released and can be seen flying over California's Central Coast.

**1997–2001**
Scientists from UC Berkeley find jawbone and teeth fossils in Ethiopia, dating around 5.5 million years ago; in 2004 this human ancestor is named as a species, *Ar. Kadabba*.

**1970**     **1980**     **1990**     **2000**     **2010**

**1977**
Carl Woese discovers single-celled organisms without a nucleus that are not bacteria; Kingdom Archaebacteria is added to classification system in the mid-1980s.

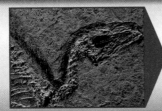

**1996–1997**
Three dinosaurs, the first ones found with feather impressions, are discovered in China; scientists say these dinosaurs provide a definite link to the evolution of birds from dinosaurs.

**March 2005**
Scientists in Montana discover T. rex fossil that includes soft tissue, cells, and blood vessels; the dinosaur was female and more closely related to modern birds than to crocodiles.

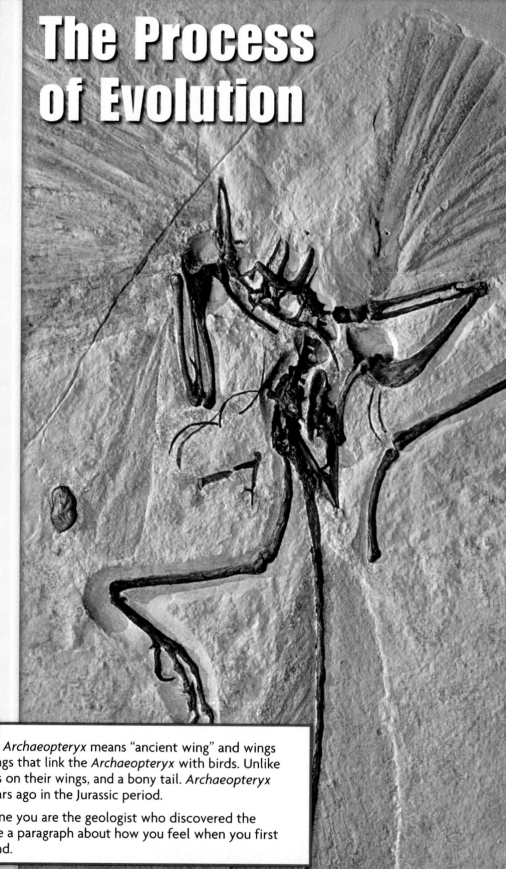

# 5

# The Process of Evolution

**The BIG Idea**

Genetic changes occurring in populations can result in new species, the extinction of species, and organisms suited for different environments.

**LESSON 1** `3.a, 3.b, 7.c`
## Natural Selection

**Main Idea** Charles Darwin developed a theory of how organisms with the same ancestors can look and behave differently over time.

**LESSON 2**
`3.a, 3.e, 7.a, 7.b, 7.c`

## Adaptation and Extinction

**Main Idea** Adaptations are traits that help an organism survive and reproduce in a particular environment, and the inability to adapt can lead to extinction.

### Major Fossil Find

*Archaeopteryx* means "ancient wing" and wings and feathers are a few things that link the *Archaeopteryx* with birds. Unlike birds they had teeth, claws on their wings, and a bony tail. *Archaeopteryx* lived about 150 million years ago in the Jurassic period.

**Science *Journal*** Imagine you are the geologist who discovered the *Archaeopteryx* fossil. Write a paragraph about how you feel when you first realize what you have found.

### What attracts insects to certain flowers?

An insect might be attracted to a specific flower by its color, or it might be attracted to many kinds of flowers.

**Procedure**

1. Read the **description of the flower** you have been assigned. Look at the **photo.**

2. Select a **pollinator** you think would be attracted to the flower.

3. Draw the pollinator on a **small card.**

4. Attach your flower and its pollinator to the board under the proper heading.

**Think About This**

- **Explain** why flowers have a variety of traits to attract pollinators.

- **Infer** why some insects prefer a specific flower.

**Science Online**

Visit ca7.msscience.com to:

▶ view **Concepts in Motion**

▶ explore Virtual Labs

▶ access content-related Web links

▶ take the Standards Check

**Process of Evolution**
Make the following Foldable to classify the outcomes of evolution.

▷ **STEP 1 Fold** a sheet of paper in half lengthwise. **Fold** the top down about 3 cm from the top.

▷ **STEP 2 Unfold** and draw lines along all folds. **Label** as shown.

**Reading Skill**

**Interpreting**
As you read this chapter, identify each outcome of evolution and classify it by placing it in the correct column.

# Get Ready to Read

## Visualize

**① Learn It!** Visualize by forming mental images of the text as you read. Imagine how the text descriptions look, sound, feel, smell, or taste. Look for any pictures or diagrams on the page that may help you add to your understanding.

**② Practice It!** Read the following paragraph. As you read, use the underlined details to form a picture in your mind.

> … notice the unique shape of the shells found in the two different tortoises. Darwin found that tortoises had <u>dome-shaped shells and short necks</u> in places where they primarily ate <u>low-growing plants.</u> But, tortoises that fed on <u>high-growing cacti</u> had <u>saddle-shaped shells</u> that seemed to allow their <u>longer necks to reach the cactus pads.</u>
>
> —*from page 212*

Based on the description above, try to visualize the two different tortoises. Now look at the photos on page 212.

- How closely does it match your mental picture?
- Reread the passage and look at the picture again. Did your ideas change?
- Compare your image with what others in your class visualized.

**③ Apply It!** Read the chapter and list three subjects you were able to visualize. Make a rough sketch showing what you visualized.

# Target Your Reading

Use this to focus on the main ideas as you read the chapter.

**Reading Tip**

Forming your own mental images will help you remember what you read.

**1** **Before you read** the chapter, respond to the statements below on your worksheet or on a numbered sheet of paper.

- Write an **A** if you **agree** with the statement.
- Write a **D** if you **disagree** with the statement.

**2** **After you read** the chapter, look back to this page to see if you've changed your mind about any of the statements.

- If any of your answers changed, explain why.
- Change any false statements into true statements.
- Use your revised statements as a study guide.

| Before You Read A or D | Statement | After You Read A or D |
|---|---|---|
| | **1** Organisms can change to occupy a new environment during their lifetime. | |
| | **2** A naturalist studies plants, animals, and rocks. | |
| | **3** Every continent has different kinds of plants and animals from those on other continents. | |
| | **4** Offspring of animals and plants vary in size and color. | |
| | **5** Darwin believed that Earth was only 4,000 years old. | |
| | **6** Changes in species can be caused by mutations. | |
| | **7** The way a bird builds its nest may help it to survive and reproduce. | |
| | **8** There are species of organisms alive on Earth that have always existed. | |
| | **9** Most of the species that have gone extinct did so when a catastrophe happened. | |
| | **10** Species that have lots of genetic variations are more likely to survive. | |

**Science Online**

Print a worksheet of this page at ca7.msscience.com.

## Reading Guide

### What *You'll Learn*

▶ **Infer** how Darwin developed his theory of natural selection.

▶ **Identify** the ways organisms adapt to their environments or perish.

### Why *It's Important*

Many observations of life on Earth can be explained by the theory of evolution.

### Vocabulary

evolution
naturalist
natural selection
adaptation

### Review vocabulary

**population:** the number of organisms of one species that occupy an area (Grade 6)

# Natural Selection

**Main Idea** Charles Darwin developed a theory of how organisms with the same ancestors can look and behave differently over time.

**Real-World Reading Connection** Did you know that there are more species of insects on Earth than any other type of organism? Did you ever wonder why there are so many different species? Charles Darwin thought about this very question as he explored some of life's most remarkable diversity around the world. It was Darwin who would uncover an important process that accounts for the great variety of species seen today.

## Charles Darwin

**Evolution** is change over time. Modern scientists refer to evolution as genetic change in a population over time. Charles Darwin was not the first person to talk about evolution, but he was the first person to write the most thorough collection of evidence supporting evolution.

Charles Darwin was a **naturalist,** a person who studies the natural world, including plants, rock formations, and animals. During his extensive traveling and research on the HMS *Beagle,* shown in **Figure 1,** he developed an important theory about how organisms evolve. His revolutionary theory, which is described in more detail later in this lesson, helps explain the unity and diversity of life. Darwin's theory also transformed the natural sciences and serves as the basis of much biological research today.

**Figure 1** Charles Darwin spent five years as a naturalist on the HMS *Beagle.*

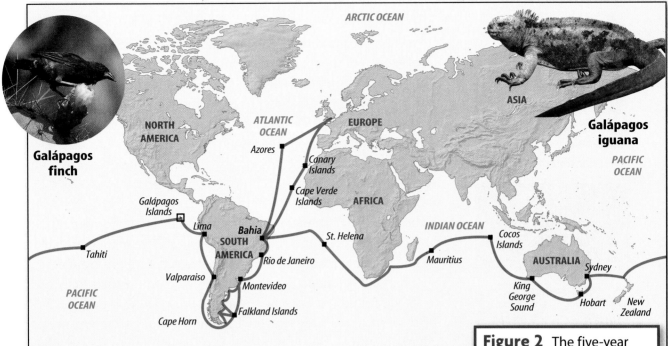

**Galápagos finch**

**Galápagos iguana**

**Figure 2** The five-year voyage of the HMS *Beagle* took Darwin around the world. His visit to the Galápagos Islands would change the world view on life.

**Examine** Where did the *Beagle* stop before reaching the Galápagos Islands?

## Voyage of the *Beagle*

In December 1831, Charles Darwin was 22 when he accepted an invitation to serve as a naturalist on the British naval ship called the HMS *Beagle*. The *Beagle* sailed from England to South America and other parts of the world to make navigational maps. The voyage of the *Beagle* would last for almost five years. Examine **Figure 2** and follow the route the *Beagle* traveled.

Darwin spent time exploring South America and its remote islands, such as the Galápagos (guh LAH puh gohs) Islands. The Galápagos Islands are located about 1000 km off the coast of South America, as shown in **Figure 2.** Darwin spent most of his time observing nature, collecting samples of new plants and animals, and writing about places and organisms few had ever seen.

## Darwin's Observations

Darwin made extensive observations and detailed notes of the biology and geology of the locations he visited. Collecting numerous samples, some of his most interesting findings were of the **diversity** and uniqueness of the organisms he saw, especially on the Galápagos Islands. He noticed many new animals and plants that had not been recorded prior to this trip. He became particularly fascinated in comparing the similarities and differences among the animals and fossils of animals from the different islands.

When he compared them, many of the turtles, birds, and lizards on the Galápagos were similar, but not the same as organisms that he found in the South American mainland. Darwin reasoned from these observations that perhaps some of the animals and plants on the Galápagos originally came from South America, and over time, they evolved to be different.

**ACADEMIC VOCABULARY**
diversity (duh VER suh tee)
*(noun)* being different from others, variety
*There was a great diversity of ice cream flavors.*

**Saddle-shaped**

**Dome-shaped**

**Figure 3** The saddle-shaped shell allows the tortoise's neck to reach higher.

**Explain** Why does the longer-necked tortoise need to reach up?

**Tortoises** During his travels, Charles Darwin made interesting observations of the giant Galápagos tortoises, or land turtles. He found tortoises on all of the Galápagos Islands and nowhere else that he visited. The tortoises were enormous in size. What was most interesting to Darwin was that the tortoises varied from island to island in the Galápagos. Darwin wondered why all the tortoises were different from each other even though they lived on islands only 80 km apart.

Look at **Figure 3** and notice the unique shape of the shells found in the two different tortoises. Darwin found that tortoises had dome-shaped shells and short necks in places where they primarily ate low-growing plants. But, tortoises that fed on high-growing cacti had saddle-shaped shells that seemed to allow their longer necks to reach the cactus pads. Darwin reasoned that perhaps the different tortoises "descended with modification" from an ancestral population in South America. Each generation of the population would change genetically until a trait for long necks evolved.

 **Reading Check** Why might one tortoise population evolve long necks?

**Finches** Darwin also made important observations of birds called finches on the Galápagos Islands. These birds were not the same as the birds he observed in other parts of the world. He described 13 finch species, although at the time he thought they were all the same species.

Like the tortoises, Darwin was impressed by the diversity of finches on the different islands, as shown in **Figure 4.** He was most fascinated by the diversity of beak size and shape in the finches, as shown in **Figure 4** and **Figure 5.** Beaks ranged from small to large and each beak type was well-suited for eating a particular food. For example, the large ground finch shown in **Figure 4** has a large beak that was well-suited for cracking open large seeds on the ground. The small tree finch in **Figure 5** has a long and narrow beak that was compatible for catching insects in the trees. Darwin would later explain that if individuals from an ancestral species in South America were separated for a long enough period of time, the future generations or descendants on the different islands might look and behave differently. Thus, in a similar way to the tortoises, the finches became different because genetically, they fit the different habitats on the islands. **Figure 5** indicates the differences in beak size and shape in all of Darwin's finches. Notice how the beak size and shape is related to the kind of food the finch eats and where it must go to get the food. Ground finches need a large beak to break and eat seeds on or near the ground. Small tree finches have smaller beaks to catch insects in the air.

**Finches**

**Large Ground**

**Cactus**

**Small Ground**

**Figure 4** Each of these finches has a unique beak shape.

# Visualizing Natural Selection

**Figure 5**
British naturalist Charles Darwin hypothesized that the 13 species of finches he found on the Galápagos Islands evolved from a common ancestor through a process of natural selection. "Darwin's Finches," as they became known, probably evolved their different beak structures and feeding habits over time, as a result of the specific environment on each of the islands.

◄ **LARGE GROUND FINCH** Ground finches have short, stout "crushing" beaks, useful for breaking seeds. They spend much of their time foraging on the ground.

▼ **SMALL TREE FINCH** The beak of this tree-dwelling finch is sharper than that of the ground finch and better suited to the tree finch's plant and insect diet.

▼ **CACTUS FINCH** The long beak of the cactus finch allows it to eat the fruit of the prickly pear cactus.

▼ **WARBLER FINCH** The smallest of Darwin's finches, the warbler finch, has a long, narrow beak for eating insects.

▲ **WOODPECKER FINCH** This finch uses twigs or cactus spines to pry insects or their larvae out of small holes in cacti or from beneath bark.

*Contributed by National Geographic*

## How does the shape of a bird's beak determine what it eats?

All living organisms have structures that enable them to survive, grow, and reproduce. Birds have different sizes and shapes of beaks. Some birds eat seeds; others eat only insects or worms. Darwin's finches are a good example of how a species has adaptations for feeding in different ecological environments.

### Procedure

1. Complete a lab safety form.

2. Study the **diagram of the beaks of Darwin's finches** and what they eat.

3. Your teacher will assign a beak style to you. Pick a **tool** that most closely matches your beak style.

4. Use your tool to try to pick up a **variety of foods** in the feeding box. See how many pieces of food you can pick up in 30 s.

5. Chart the number of each kind of food each tool was able to pick up. How did your "beak" compare to the others?

### Analysis

1. **Explain** What might happen to a finch that had a mutation that made its beak a different shape from that of the parent birds?

2. **Conclude** What will happen if the finch cannot find anything to eat with its beak shape?

7.c

## Selective Breeding

For thousands of years humans have been breeding plants and animals. In plants the goal might be to get the largest fruit, the best taste, the tallest plant, or the prettiest flower. In animals farmers want the cow with the most milk, the largest hog, or the fastest horse. You can probably think of other traits you might want in dogs or cats. When a plant or an animal is bred to get these characteristics, it is known as selective breeding. Selective breeding does not lead to a new species. The organism is still able to breed with other members of its species. Dogs have been bred for many special features, such as size and fur length. Even so, crosses between breeds still produce animals with doglike characteristics. **Figure 6** shows some pigeons that have been selectively bred. The original species of these pigeons is the rock dove.

**Figure 6** The fantailed pigeon and the frill-backed pigeon were selectively bred from rock doves.

**Rock Dove**

**Fantailed Pigeon**

**Frill Backed Pigeon**

# Darwin's Theory of Natural Selection

Darwin and other scientists realized that organisms with a trait that allowed them to survive under particular environmental conditions produced more offspring than those organisms without this trait. Eventually, these traits would become very common in a species.

## Genetic Variation

Recall from Chapters 3 and 4 that traits are passed on to the offspring from father and mother. Traits are sorted during the process of gamete formation. Sometimes changes occur in the genes and new traits are created. **Figure 7** shows the genetic variation of some common flowers. If a trait is harmful, the organism might die, but if it is beneficial, the organism is more likely to survive and reproduce. That trait will then be passed on to the next generation. With time, it will become common in many populations of the species. Genetic variation is necessary for evolution to occur. But, survival depends on other factors as well.

 How does a trait become more predominant in a population?

## The Struggle to Survive

One influence on Darwin's ideas was an essay by Thomas Malthus, which presented the argument that if the human population were to continue to grow unchecked, eventually humans would run out of food and space. There would be a "struggle to survive."

**Population Growth** Darwin too had noticed that animals often produced more offspring than could survive. Limited resources, such as food, water, and habitat, allowed for only some individuals to survive. Darwin decided that this was a natural process that selected which organisms could survive. Darwin's next step was to find out how the organism was selected. He reasoned that an organism that was better prepared to get food or protect its space would be better able to survive. You have read about niches and the competition within those niches. **Figure 8** shows competition between two animals. The animal that is best suited to the environment will ultimately win the competition.

**Environmental Factors** Different habitats can put pressure on animals to survive as well. Darwin suggested that those organisms best prepared for living in specific habitats would survive and be most able to reproduce. Their offspring would also be able to survive in the specific habitat.

**Figure 7** Color is just one trait that varies among organisms.

**Infer** what other traits might vary in snapdragons.

**Figure 8** Competition between these two males is for the best territory and to acquire a mate.

**WORD ORIGIN**·············

adaptation

*ad–* from Latin, means *to* or *toward*

*–aptare* from Latin, means *to fit*

·············

## Natural Selection

Darwin defined **natural selection** as a process by which individuals with traits that better suit the environment are more likely to survive longer and reproduce more successfully than those individuals without these traits. Inherited traits that increase an organism's chance of surviving and reproducing in a particular environment are called **adaptations.** Adaptations spread through a population in future generations if natural selection favors them.

Darwin spent a great amount of time working out how natural selection can lead to adaptation within a species and to the evolution of a new species. He proposed that if groups of organisms with common ancestors are isolated from other organisms of the same species, natural selection can cause them to become different over generations. The isolated groups adapt to different environmental conditions and this process can develop a new species. With enough time, this could explain the large number of species on Earth today.

Darwin's theory of evolution by natural selection can be best explained by the following four steps or requirements.

**1** **Overproduction** Organisms produce more offspring than can be supported by the available food, water, and shelter in an environment. Many will die due to natural events such as predation, competition, and starvation.

**2** **Variation** Offspring vary in traits such as color and size, as shown in a hypothetical fish population in **Figure 9.**

**Figure 9** Darwin proposed the idea of natural selection to explain how species change over time.

**3** **Inherited Variation** Recall from Chapter 4 that some of the variation in populations is genetic and such traits can be passed from parents to offspring. Sources of genetic variation include mutations, formation of the gametes, and sexual reproduction. Genetic variation is necessary for evolution by natural selection to occur.

**4** **Natural Selection** Individuals with inherited variations that are better able to survive and reproduce in a particular environment will have more offspring, and thus pass on these favorable traits, than individuals without those features.

Populations will change over time in particular environments. They will evolve, and come to look different and behave differently from their ancestors as favorable traits spread through a population. If the environment changes again, different heritable traits may be favored and the population can evolve again.

 **Visual Check** **Figure 9** How are the offspring different from their ancestors?

## Evolution and Diversity

Charles Darwin spent years developing his ideas on natural selection. Darwin finally published his revolutionary and controversial book called *The Origin of Species by Natural Selection*. In his book, he built a strong case for evolution by natural selection. He also developed the idea that all organisms have "descended with modification" from common ancestors over a long period of time. Thus, all species have changed through time and are related by descent from a common ancestor.

Considering the geological evidence that Earth is millions of years old, Darwin proposed there had been enough time for organisms to change and for new species to develop from ancestral species.

# LESSON 1 Review

## Summarize

Create your own lesson summary as you design a **visual aid.**

1. **Write** the lesson title, number, and page numbers at the top of your poster.

2. **Scan** the lesson to find the **red** main headings. Organize these headings on your poster, leaving space between each.

3. **Design** an information box beneath each **red** heading. In the box, list 2–3 details, key terms, and definitions from each **blue** subheading.

4. **Illustrate** your poster with diagrams of important structures or processes next to each information box.

**ELA7:** W 2.5

## Using Vocabulary

1. Using your own words, define *evolution.* **3.b**

2. Traits that enable organisms to survive in a specific environment are called _____. **3.a**

## Understanding Main Ideas

3. **Explain** why Darwin's comparison of organisms from the South American mainland to those on the islands was significant. **3.b**

4. Which factor listed below is not important in determining an organism's chances of survival? **3.a**

   A. ability to get food
   B. size of the individual
   C. whether it is male or female
   D. ability to protect space

5. **Explain** the relationship between population growth and potential for survival. **3.a**

## Standards Check

6. **Sequencing** Draw a diagram to show the changes that the ancestral tortoise might have gone through to result in those that Darwin observed. Include relevant plants. **3.b**

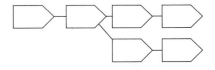

7. **List** the steps of natural selection. **3.b**

## Applying Science

8. **Infer** why you have not directly observed the appearance of a new species. **3.a**

9. **Summarize** the changes that might occur in a population of squirrels if acorn shells became harder. **3.a**

**Science**Online

For more practice, visit **Standards Check** at ca7.msscience.com.

# Applying Math

## The Accommodations of the HMS Beagle

Charles Darwin traveled to the Galápagos Islands in the HMS *Beagle* in 1835. In the five-year journey of the ship, Darwin lived in small quarters in the chart room. The mizzenmast came up through the floor, and most of the room was taken by a chart table and book-shelves. The chart room was about 3.0 m × 1.7 m of living space shown in the diagram.

### Example

Find the area of the chart room including storage, living space, and bookshelves.

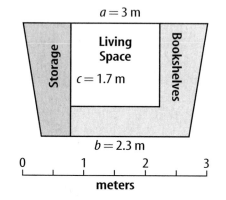

| What you know: | The room is shaped like a trapezoid.<br>The longer width of the, *a*, room is 3.0 meters.<br>The shorter width of the room, *b*, is 2.3 meters.<br>The length of the room, *c*, is 1.7 meters. |
|---|---|
| **What you need to find:** | Area of a trapezoid |
| **Use the formula:**<br>$\dfrac{(a + b)}{2} \times c$ = area of a trapezoid | Substitute for *a*, *b* and *c* in the formula:<br>$a = 3.0$ m, $b = 2.3$ m, $c = 1.7$ m<br>$\dfrac{(a + b)}{2} \times c = \dfrac{(3.0 + 2.3)}{2} \times 1.7 =$<br>$\dfrac{9.0}{2} = 4.5$ m$^2$<br>The area of the trapezoid is 4.5 m$^2$. |

### Practice Problems

1. What is the approximate area of the storage area?
2. What is the approximate area of the book shelves? (**hint:** draw a line to divide the area into a trapezoid and a rectangle)

**Science** nline
For more math practice, visit **Math Practice** at ca7.msscience.com.

**Science Content Standards**

**3.a** Students know both genetic variation and environmental factors are causes of evolution and diversity of organisms.
**3.e** Students know that extinction of a species occurs when the environment changes and the adaptive characteristics of a species are insufficient for its survival.
**Also covers:** 7.a, 7.b, 7.c

## Reading Guide

### What *You'll Learn*

▶ **Identify** the importance of adaptations.

▶ **Compare** two kinds of adaptations.

▶ **Describe** three of the causes of extinction.

### Why *It's Important*

Understanding how organisms adapt to environmental change and the causes of extinction may help us preserve species that are threatened.

### Vocabulary

structural adaptation
camouflage
mimicry
behavioral adaptation
extinct

### Review Vocabulary

**habitat:** a place an organism lives (Grade 6)

# Adaptation and Extinction

**Main Idea** Adaptations are traits that help an organism survive and reproduce in a particular environment, and the inability to adapt can lead to extinction.

**Real-World Reading Connection** Have you ever thought about why giraffes have such long necks? It makes sense if you consider that giraffes are the only plant eaters in Africa that can reach the top of the tallest trees. Such adaptive traits can be explained by Darwin's theory of natural selection.

## Adaptations

Humans are very skilled at changing their environment. We have buildings, heaters, and air conditioners to make our environment more comfortable. Other organisms are not able to change their environment to meet their needs. Plants cannot walk into a greenhouse when the weather gets cold. Organisms that do have unique characteristics, or adaptations, to live in their specific environments have evolved them over time by the process of natural selection.

### Understanding Adaptations

Recall that adaptations are inherited traits that increase an organism's chance of surviving and reproducing in a particular environment. The night-dwelling tarsier shown in **Figure 10** has large eyes that are adapted for seeing in dim light.

**Figure 10** An adaptation of some nocturnal animals is larger eyes. This improves their ability to see at night.

## Natural Selection in Action

Sometimes things change. A prey species might be devastated by disease. A natural disaster like a hurricane or a tsunami might affect a local area, or a volcano spewing ash into the atmosphere might affect the whole Earth. These changes may kill off some individuals, but the survivors can repopulate the species. But what about longer lasting changes in climate, or physical features? These will require organisms to adapt to match the changes. Can we see natural selection happening? No, but we can see the results. Natural selection leads to adaptations in organisms.

**How do organisms adapt?** Many people misunderstand Darwin's theory of natural selection because they **misinterpret** the word *adaptation*. Adaptations are the final products of the long process of natural selection. Adaptations occur in groups of organisms when a trait is passed from one generation to another. The organisms receiving the trait are better suited to survive and reproduce.

Not all traits are adaptations. Recall from Chapter 4 that a chromosome has many genes that code for traits. In this way, some traits can be passed down because they are linked with other traits, whether they are beneficial to the organism or not. So, an undesirable trait might stay in the population because it is somehow linked to another more beneficial trait. Some traits might help an organism survive, while other traits might cause it to die off. Remember, adaptations are naturally selected, not intentionally chosen.

**One Example of Adaptation** There is an abundance of examples of adaptation in the natural world. For example, the desert rabbits in **Figure 11** have blotchy, brown coats that help them blend in with their environment. Desert rabbits also have long ears that help them stay cool as heat is released through the extensive system of blood vessels in the ears.

How might natural selection have shaped the ears of a rabbit? The population may have initially been made of rabbits with different-sized ears. Those rabbits with long ears would be better able to survive in higher temperatures than rabbits with small ears. So, rabbits with big ears would be more likely to live long enough to have offspring than those with smaller ears. Their offspring would probably have big ears, too. After many generations of rabbits, if it remains hot, it will be hard to find rabbits with small ears. This is because the small-eared rabbits will not have thrived and thus left fewer offspring. When the population shifts to mostly large-eared rabbits, the rabbit population has adapted to the environment, and thus evolved by natural selection.

**Figure 11** What other feature besides color helps the jackrabbit to escape predators?

**Figure 11** Notice how the mottled coat of the jackrabbit helps it blend in with the desert.

# Types of Adaptations

There are many kinds of adaptations. Scientists divide adaptations into two main categories—structural and behavioral.

## Structural Adaptations

**Structural Adaptations** are inherited physical traits of a species that make its members better suited to their environment. You have already read about the desert rabbit's ears. The ears have lots of blood vessels and the blood carries body heat to the ears. The heat is given off to the air and helps the rabbit stay cool. An added advantage of large ears is that they help the rabbit hear any predator that might be sneaking up on it.

Other structural adaptations of the desert rabbit are its long back legs for running and jumping fast, its high-placed eyes that allow it to see almost 360° around, and its mottled appearance. The mottled fur color helps it blend in with its surroundings.

**Camouflage** Another type of structural adaptation is **camouflage,** or blending in with the surrounding environment. Some lizards have a coloration that matches their primary surrounding area, such as the lava lizards on the Galápagos Islands shown in **Figure 12.** Darwin probably observed many lava lizards. Those living on islands with black lava are difficult to see because they are of the same blackish color as the volcanic rocks on which they sunbathe. Other lava lizards match the color of the sandy beaches.

Darwin probably also saw Sally Lightfoot crabs on the Galápagos Islands. The adult crabs are not well camouflaged. They are very bright and colorful. However, their young are a dull-grey color and are well camouflaged among the volcanic rocks. This coloration helps protect vulnerable young crabs from being captured by predators.

 How does the color of the young Sally Lightfoot crab help it survive?

**Figure 12** Lava lizards blend in with the color of the rocks.

**Figure 13** The snake eel has an adaptation that mimics the venomous sea snake. Predators stay away from both. The frogfish has an adaptation that may look like a piece of food to another fish.

**Banded Sea Snake**

**Snake Eel**

**Frogfish**

 **Figure 13** What feature of the snake eel tells you it is a fish?

**Mimicry** Another structural adaptation is **mimicry,** in which one species (the mimic) looks like another species (the model) so that a third species is deceived or fooled. There are several types of mimicry.

**Batesian Mimicry** In one type of mimicry, Batesian mimicry, the model organism is dangerous or venemous, and the mimic is not dangerous. For example, the harmless snake eel looks like the venomous black and white banded sea snake. Because the snake eel looks like the banded sea snake, predators stay away from both organisms. Notice the similarities between the two in **Figure 13.**

**Mullerian Mimicry** In a second type of mimicry, called Mullerian mimicry, two different species that are either venomous or distasteful have evolved to look like one another. Unlike Batesian mimicry, in which only the mimic species benefits from the mimicry, Mullerian mimicry is beneficial to both the mimic species and the model species. An example of a Mullerian mimic and model pair is the monarch and viceroy butterflies. Both butterflies have an orange and black color pattern, and both species are distasteful to birds. However, a bird needs to eat only one member of either species to learn to avoid orange and black butterflies. More members of both species will ultimately survive.

 How is Mullerian mimicry beneficial to a species?

**Self Mimicry** In another type of mimicry, self mimicry, a species fools its prey by looking inviting or familiar. As shown in **Figure 13,** frogfish display this type of mimicry by using a small body part like a lure. This attracts other smaller fish looking for food. Unfortunately for the deceived animals, when they get close, the frogfish eats them.

**Figure 14** On the left is a clapper rail in its marshland habitat. At the right a male bower bird decorates its nest to attract females.

Clapper rail

Male bower bird

## Behavioral Adaptations

In addition to natural selection of physical traits, natural selection of inherited behaviors can also occur. **Behavioral adaptations** are inherited behaviors of a species that make its members better suited to their environment.

Scientists sometimes call them instinctive or inborn behaviors. These adaptations enhance survivorship and reproduction. For example, as shown in **Figure 14,** an endangered bird called the clapper rail lives in muddy, brackish, salt marshes. Twice a day, high tides cover this habitat with water and the low tides leave it exposed. As an adaptive trait, the clapper rail builds its nest in tall, grassy marsh plants. Thus, when the water rises, the nests float up, but the plants keep the nest from drifting away. When the tide is low, the nests slide back onto the wetland mud.

 **Reading Check** What behavior has the clapper rail adapted to nesting?

Many behavioral adaptations are designed to attract mates. The satin bower bird in **Figure 14** uses berries, saliva, and blue scraps to decorate its nest. This technique attracts females for mating, which makes it possible for him to pass along his genes to the next generation.

**Herding Instinct** You might have gone for a ride in the country and driven by a farm where you saw a herd of cows. If you go to a national park you will likely see a herd of bison or elk. Many grass-eating mammals live in large groups or herds. They instinctively know that a group is less likely to be attacked by a predator than one animal alone. The herding instinct is a behavioral adaptation. Prey animals can band together to frighten or chase away a group of predators.

# Extinction

When all the individuals of a particular species die off, that species becomes **extinct.** Natural selection can lead to extinction if the conditions of the environment change in a way that none of the organisms of a species can survive. Climate change, volcanoes, and earthquakes are some of the environmental factors associated with extinction.

There have been several major extinction events in the history of Earth. For example, some scientists have proposed that a meteorite collided with Earth about 65 million years ago causing the extinction of the dinosaurs. It has been suggested that when this large meteorite hit Earth, it caused so much dust in the atmosphere that the plants did not receive enough sunlight to grow. Thus, the dinosaurs all starved. You will read more about extinctions in a later chapter.

 **Reading Check** What is one theory for dinosaur extinction?

## Causes of Extinction

There are many causes for extinction. They include habitat destruction, loss of genetic diversity, and the introduction of exotic species. Most species are not able to withstand these factors as well as other severe environmental changes.

**Loss of Habitat** Extinction rates for individual species are on the rise. One important reason is that habitats for plants and animals are shrinking in size as humans develop and occupy more space and use more resources. **Figure 15** shows some effects human activities may have on natural habitats. With diminishing natural habitat, fewer organisms can survive.

**Figure 15** Clear cutting a forest changes the habitat from forest to grassland.
**Think Critically** What happens to the forest dependent organisms?

**Loss of Genetic Diversity** The fewer the number of individuals left of a species, the less genetic variability there is in the population. Species need genetic variability to increase the likelihood that some individuals will have the right gene combinations to survive different environmental conditions and for evolution to occur. If there are only a few individuals or if the individuals have limited genetic variability, it is much easier for a change in environmental conditions to lead to extinction.

We designate some species as threatened if they are likely to become endangered in the near future within much of its range. Cheetahs are threatened because they have little genetic diversity. In fact, related individuals share 99 percent of the same genes. This has led to low survivorship, low fertility, and disease in the remaining cheetah populations.

**Competition with Exotic Species** Sometimes competition between organisms is caused by the introduction of a new species to the habitat, known as an exotic species. Humans are constantly introducing new species of plants to their environment because of their uniqueness or beauty. If there is no known consumer of a species in the new environment, it may be able to outcompete the native species and push them toward extinction. Introduction of natural consumers or disease-causing agents may reduce the numbers of the invading species.

The kudzu plant was introduced in the southern United States in the 1930s to help prevent erosion. The vine grows so well there that it can grow up to 30 cm per day. However, it shades out forests and kills the trees that are its climbing base. The plant grows naturally in Japan where cool weather, diseases, and consumers help keep it under control. **Figure 16** shows some kudzu taking over a tree line.

**Figure 16** Kudzu grows so rapidly it can outcompete the native species.

## Table 1 Causes of Slow Extinction

| Organism | Cause | Details |
|---|---|---|
| | Loss of habitat | One of the first insects placed on the endangered species list, this rare Schaus butterfly depends on the semi-shade of tropical hardwood trees. As these forests were cleared in southern Florida, the butterfly populations were pushed back into the Florida Keys. Hurricane Andrew in 1992 left only 70 individuals, but captive breeding allowed reintroduction to help the population survive. |
| | Loss of genetic diversity | Cheetahs have an unusually low genetic diversity. Their original range was from India to Saudi Arabia and the grassland areas of Africa. Today there are only small pockets of cheetahs in Iran and eastern, sub-Saharan Africa. There are as few as 50 cheetahs in Iran, and the African animals are on preserves. The remainder of the species is in captivity in zoos. |
| | Exotic species competition | Found mainly in Eurasia, the purple loosestrife has been introduced into the United States. Purple loosestrife adapts readily to natural and disturbed wetlands. It outcompetes and replaces the native grasses, sedges, and other flowering plants that provide a higher quality nutrition source for wildlife. It also reduces habitat for waterfowl. |

**Inability to Adapt** Another possible reason that species become extinct is their inability to adapt. If a climate changes suddenly, a species might not have any individuals with genetic traits that will allow them to adapt. Over time the population becomes smaller and the individuals become less able to reproduce. For example, there are so few cheetahs on Earth that inbreeding is resulting in the appearance of recessive traits that are harmful to the species. Inbreeding is mating between closely related individuals and occurs in small populations. Should a rapid environmental change occur, the species could become extinct. The potential causes of slow extinction are summarized in **Table 1.**

# Darwin's Conclusions Today

Just as extinction does not always happen at the same rate or in the same way, new species formation occurs at different rates, too. Because the environment is always changing natural selection is always acting on organisms. Most of the environmental changes are small and localized, leading to very slow changes among populations over many generations. Think about a large environmental change that would affect many species at the same time. Whether the species lives or becomes extinct depends on whether it has adapted to the change. In the next chapter you will read about evidence that has helped to reinforce Darwin's ideas.

# LESSON 2  Review

## Summarize

Create your own lesson summary as you design a **study web**.

1. **Write** the lesson title, number, and page numbers at the top of a sheet of paper.

2. **Scan** the lesson to find the **red** main headings.

3. **Organize** these headings clockwise on branches around the lesson title.

4. **Review** the information under each **red** heading to design a branch for each **blue** subheading.

5. **List** 2–3 details, key terms, and definitions from each **blue** subheading on branches extending from the main heading branches.

 ELA7: W 2.5

## Standards Check

### Using Vocabulary

1. Using your own words, define *structural adaptation*. **3.e**

2. **Explain** what it means when a species becomes *extinct*. **3.e**

3. **Compare and contrast** *mimicry* and *camouflage*. **3.a**

### Understanding Main Ideas

4. Use the graphic organizer to diagram how loss of genetic diversity can lead to extinction. Use as many arrows as you need. **3.e**

5. **Explain** the statement: Not all traits are adaptations. **3.e**

6. **Describe** how kudzu became a pest species in the United States. **3.a**

7. Which of the following is not a physical adaptation? **3.e**

   A. long necks for reaching food in high places

   B. grasping tails to aid in climbing

   C. large ears to aid in cooling body temperatures

   D. creative nest construction to attract mates

### Applying Science

8. **Develop** a plan to limit the possibility of habitat destruction in the building of a large apartment complex. **3.a**

9. **Evaluate** the effects of small, common changes in the environment versus the effects of large, rare changes on the same population in terms of species adaptation. **3.e**

**Science** nline
For more practice, visit **Standards Check** at ca7.msscience.com.

# MiniLab

## How can your species have the strongest, longest-lasting survivors?

00:30 minutes

When a species survives through several generations, it has traits that allow it to live and grow, avoid its predators, and reproduce in the environment in which it lives. Use the principles of natural selection to help assemble a model population.

### Procedure

1. Read and complete a lab safety form.
2. With your lab group, use items such as **small craft sticks, toothpicks, clay, cotton balls,** and **markers** to assemble as many members of a population in the time allotted to you.
3. Use **twine** to mark a habitat on the grass approximately 5 m × 5 m. Place your population throughout the habitat.
4. Select two students from each group to be predators. For 30 s let them pick up prey from the other student groups.
5. Count the remainder of your population.

### Analysis

1. **Use the number** of your original population and the number of the remainder to record your survivors as a ratio.
2. **Evaluate** Did your organisms meet natural selection criteria?
   - simple part combinations = large numbers of organisms
   - combinations that camouflage the organism
   - non-eaten organisms pass on their traits
   - passed on traits increase survivor numbers

### Science Content Standards

**3.a** Students know both genetic variation and environmental factors are causes of evolution and diversity of organisms.

**7.a** Select and use appropriate tools and technology (including calculators, computers, balances, spring scales, microscopes, and binoculars) to perform tests, collect data, and display data.

# How many bird species live near you?

Every winter there is a national bird counting event. Volunteers from every state count the number of bird species they see on one day in their neighborhood. The data below are from a recent bird count from locations in California.

## Data

| Bird Species Counted in California | | |
|---|---|---|
| **Area Name** | **Number of Volunteers** | **Number of Bird Species Counted** |
| Big Sur | 13 | 136 |
| China Lake | 15 | 84 |
| Death Valley | 7 | 59 |
| Redding | 18 | 108 |
| Yosemite | 23 | 58 |
| Yreka | 9 | 120 |

*California Audubon Society*

## Data Analysis

1. **Calculate** the average number of species counted per volunteer.

2. **Calculate** the number of species counted per volunteer for each area. Which area had the highest number of species counted per volunteer?

3. **Infer** which area might have the greatest diversity of bird species. Assume that all volunteers counted for equal numbers of hours during the same time of day and had equivalent observation skills. Explain your inference.

 **Science Content Standards**     MA7: NS 1.3

**7.c** Communicate the logical connection among hypotheses, science concepts, tests conducted, data collected, and conclusions drawn from the scientific evidence.

## Use the Internet:
# Can you apply the principles of natural selection to island species?

There are five islands off the coast of southern California that are known as the Channel Islands. These islands include San Miguel Island, Santa Barbara Island, Santa Rosa Island, Santa Cruz Island, and East Anacapa Island. These islands have animals and plants that live on one or more of them, but not anywhere else. The species are diverse and include reptiles, birds, plants, mammals, and others.

## Form a Hypothesis

You will be given the name of one species that lives on one or more of the Channel Islands. How can you explain why this species survives there and if it will continue to survive?

## Collect Data and Make Observations

1. **Research** your assigned species at ca7.msscience.com, keeping the following data in mind: appearance, where it lives, how it moves, what it eats, how it eats, and other data.

2. **Draw** a picture of your species and describe its habitat.

3. **List** characteristics of your species and identify any known adaptations.

4. **Apply** each principle of natural selection to prove that your species is able to fulfill all the principles.

## Analyze and Conclude

1. **Explain** Did you discover if the species you researched is extinct or endangered? Explain.
2. **Conclude** After you evaluated your species according to the principles of natural selection, what conclusions can you make in relation to its survival?
3. **Determine** Was your species native to the island habitat you studied, or did humans bring the animal onto the island?
4. **Decide** What is the impact of animals that are introduced into island ecosystems?
5. **Explain** Is your species a possible cause for extinction of another species on your island?
6. **Infer** If you moved your species to the continent, could it survive? Explain.
7. **Evaluate** How can you evaluate the future of your species when you consider how it reproduces?

## Communicate

**WRITING in Science**  **ELA7: LS 2.3**

Make a power point presentation of your findings that includes all the characteristics; color pictures of the species; adaptations, habitat, and your outline of proof that the species has what it needs to survive as an individual and as a species.

# Real World Science

## You can be an evolutionary biologist!

Evolutionary biology is the study of the origin and descent of species, as well as their changes over time. Evolutionary biology includes many different fields, such as ornithology, the study of birds, or herpetology, the study of reptiles. Scientists use those organisms as systems to answer general questions about evolution. It also includes paleontologists who use fossils to answer questions about when and over how long a period evolution occurred.

The biologists in the photo have their hands full weighing a black caiman, a species of crocodile found in South America. Visit **ca7.msscience.com** to learn more about biology and evolution careers. Write a 500-word paper describing another area of biology and how it relates to evolutionary biology.

**ELA7: W 2.3**

## A MOLECULAR CLOCK

Mutations, changes in DNA, can be harmful, lead to adaptations, or have no effect on the organism. Scientists can sequence sections of DNA to see whether or not a mutation has occurred. Molecular clocks are a way to compare DNA sequences from different species. Scientists compare mutation locations to estimate how long the species have been evolving since they shared a common ancestor. The figure on the right shows three species that have some mutations in common and some mutations that are unique to that species. Scientists consider these data and the fossil record to estimate how long species have been evolving apart from each other.

Some scientists think that a clock is not a good analogy for the model described above. Visit **Technology** at **ca7.msscience.com** to learn more about how scientists calibrate molecular clocks. Discuss some other analogies for the model that might be more accurate.

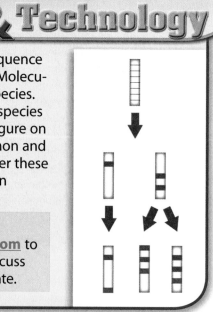

# Counting Coprolites

When you think of paleontologists, you might think of someone who studies bones and rocks. Karen Chin is a paleontologist who studies dung. That's right—she is one of the world's experts on fossilized dinosaur dung, called a coprolite (KAH pruh lyt). When a suspected coprolite is found, chemical tests are performed to confirm its identity. Other clues, such as other fossils found with it, the presence or lack of bones, and the size of the coprolite, help Chin to determine which dinosaur species made it. One of Chin's most famous coprolites belonged to a Tyrannosaurus rex. Coprolites provide information about what dinosaurs ate and how they interacted with their environment.

Visit **History** at **ca7.msscience.com** to learn more about paleontology. With a partner, create a time line highlighting major events in paleontology in the past 100 years.

# Habitat Degradation and Extinction

Extinction is a natural phenomenon, and it is estimated that more than 99 percent of all species that have ever lived are now extinct. However, many people are concerned about species extinction due to habitat destruction caused by humans. Many scientists are searching for ways to combat human-induced extinction. For example, the desert tortoise population is declining. This is an indicator that the health of California's desert habitat is also declining. Conservationists and the government are investigating the causes of this decline and are working towards its recovery.

To find out more about extinction and habitat degradation, visit **Society** at **ca7.msscience.com**. What are some human factors that influence habitat degradation? Write a short article on one factor and a California habitat that it affects. Make sure to use proper spelling, punctuation, grammar, and capitalization.

**The BIG Idea** Genetic changes occurring in populations can result in new species, the extinction of species, and organisms suited for different environments.

## Lesson 1 Natural Selection

3.a, 3.b, 7.c

**Main Idea** Charles Darwin developed a theory of how organisms with the same ancestors can look and behave differently over time.

- Naturalist Charles Darwin developed his theory of evolution by natural selection based on a voyage of the HMS *Beagle*.

- Darwin first saw evidence of natural selection while collecting specimens in the Galapagos Islands off the coast of South America.

- Selective breeding of many animals brings out different characteristics, but does not lead to a new species.

- Darwin didn't know about genetic variation, so his observations were confusing to him.

- The steps of natural selection are overproduction of offspring to ensure survival; variation of characteristics and passing the inherited characteristics on to the next generation; and the survivability of those organisms with the traits.

- Diversity is the key to survival of a species.

- **adaptation** (p. 216)
- **evolution** (p. 210)
- **naturalist** (p. 210)
- **natural selection** (p. 216)

## Lesson 2 Adaptation and Exinction

3.a, 3.e, 7.a, 7.b, 7.c

**Main Idea** Adaptations are traits that help an organism survive and reproduce in a particular environment, and the inability to adapt can lead to extinction.

- Traits that help an organism within a species to survive are adaptations.

- Adaptations start out as changes in the DNA that create some advantage to the organism in the environment.

- Adaptations may be structural (long ears in desert rabbits) or behavioral (building nests that float).

- Camouflage is a structural adaptation that lets the organism blend into the surroundings.

- Mimicry helps avoid predation or helps the predator to attract its prey.

- Organisms that cannot adapt may become extinct.

- The causes of extinction hinge on loss of habitat, lack of genetic diversity, competition with other species including exotic species, and the inability to adapt.

- **behavioral adaptation** (p. 223)
- **camouflage** (p. 221)
- **extinct** (p. 224)
- **mimicry** (p. 222)
- **structural adaptation** (p. 221)

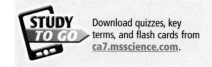

STUDY TO GO Download quizzes, key terms, and flash cards from ca7.msscience.com.

# Linking Vocabulary and Main Ideas

Use the vocabulary terms on page 234 to complete the concept map.

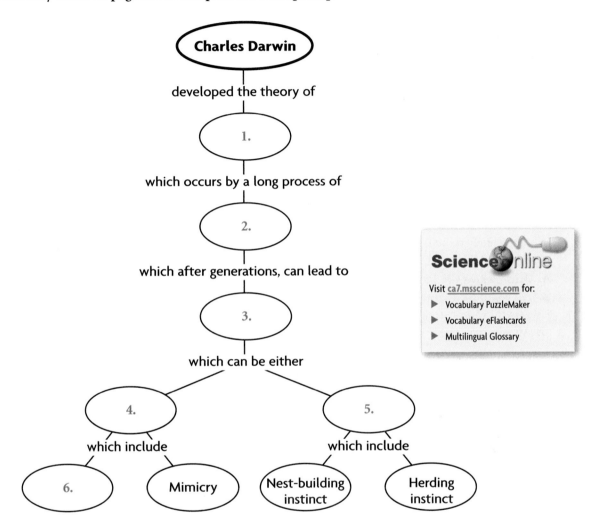

Charles Darwin

developed the theory of

**1.**

which occurs by a long process of

**2.**

which after generations, can lead to

**3.**

which can be either

**4.**

**5.**

which include

which include

**6.**

Mimicry

Nest-building instinct

Herding instinct

## Using Vocabulary

**Fill in each blank with the correct vocabulary term.**

7. An octopus uses _____ to hide in its surroundings.

8. _____ adaptations include nesting habits and courting.

9. Isolation on the Galápagos Islands allowed _____ by natural selection to develop 13 finch species.

10. A frogfish exhibits one kind of _____ to catch food.

11. A(n) _____ is a person who studies rocks, plants, and animals.

12. A(n) _____ is a trait that helps an organism survive in its habitat.

13. The long process of _____ has created the diversity of life we see on Earth today.

14. Organisms that are unable to adapt to a changing environment might become _____.

# Understanding Main Ideas

**Use the image below to answer questions 1 and 2.**

1. Which is likely to be true of the offspring of this pigeon, according to Darwin's theory?
   A. All will look the same.
   B. All will have a fantail.
   C. All will survive to adulthood.
   D. All will have the best traits. **3.b**

2. Which is the human influenced process by which this pigeon developed a fantail?
   A. evolution
   B. overproduction
   C. selective breeding
   D. natural selection **3.b**

3. Which was true of Darwin's experiences while in the Galápagos?
   A. Darwin realized that the birds were all new species.
   B. Darwin noticed that the mockingbirds varied.
   C. Darwin understood how species could change over time.
   D. Darwin saw that the tortoises showed variation of characteristics. **3.b**

4. Which is a requirement of the process of evolution by natural selection?
   A. genetic variation
   B. environmental variation
   C. species remain unchanged
   D. all offspring survive **3.b**

5. What is likely to happen to a tree species that cannot adapt to frequent fires?
   A. mutation
   B. overproduction
   C. extinction
   D. variation **3.e**

6. Which would NOT be an adaptation to cold weather?
   A. long hair
   B. hibernation
   C. migration
   D. brown fur **3.a**

7. Which is not available to a single-celled, asexual organism as a way to respond to environmental change?
   A. natural selection
   B. genes from two parents
   C. beneficial mutations
   D. changes in DNA **3.a**

8. What is the end result of species change over time?

   A. overproduction
   B. diversity of a species
   C. inherited variation
   D. natural selection **3.a**

Science online Standards Review ca7.msscience.com

## Applying Science

9. **Discuss** how unlimited food would affect the process of natural selection. `3.b`

10. **Infer** Discuss why an individual organism does not evolve by natural selection. `3.b`

11. **Predict** Choose a species alive today and predict how it might evolve through natural selection. Be sure to explain how the traits that increase are advantageous. `3.b`

12. **Hypothesize** what would be the result of natural selection if organisms of a species did not vary. `3.e`

13. **Describe** how the snapdragons in the photo below use color variation to avoid extinction. `3.a`

14. **Infer** how a population of mammals that fed on fruit on the ground and on the trees might change as the trees evolved to be increasingly tall. `3.e`

15. **Predict** how the extinction of a predator would affect the other species in the environment. Consider the prey of the predator and the things that the prey eats. `3.e`

## WRITING in Science

16. **Write** the inside details for a pamphlet on natural selection in the Galápagos Islands. Pick your topic from tortoises, finches, or iguanas.

## Applying Math

**Use the formula below to answer questions 17–21.**

$$\frac{(a + b)}{2} \times c = \text{area of a trapezoid}$$

17. A corner hutch has shelves shaped like a trapezoid. The front of the shelf is 64 cm wide, while the back of the shelf is 50 cm. The depth is 60 cm. What is the area of each shelf?

18. The top shelf of the hutch is ornamental and measures 20 cm across the back and 34 cm across the front. The depth is 45 cm. What is its area?

19. Find the area of a trapezoid whose bases are 25 cm and 35 cm and whose length is 4 cm.

20. Find the area of a pair of trapezoids that have the same depth (24 cm) and one base length (24 cm). The other bases are different. One trapezoid has a short base of 12 cm, and the other one has a short base of 16 cm.

21. Find the area of a stop sign that is 60 cm tall. Each edge of the stop sign is 24.8 cm. (Hint: Divide the sign into a rectangle and two trapezoids. The height of each trapezoid is 17.5 cm)

**1** What is an example of adaptation?

A a fossil

B gradualism

C camouflage

D embryo    3.e

**Use this diagram to answer questions 2 and 3.**

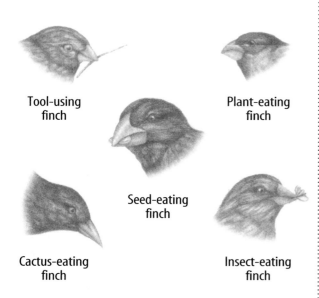

Tool-using
finch

Plant-eating
finch

Seed-eating
finch

Cactus-eating
finch

Insect-eating
finch

**2** A series of helpful variations in a species result in

A adaptation.

B fossils.

C embryology.

D climate change.    3.e

**3** What, besides competition for food, contributed to the evolution of the species of Darwin's finches?

A predation

B natural disaster

C DNA

D variation in beak shapes    3.a

**4** Some harmless species imitate a poisonous species as a means for increased survival. This an example of what?

A camouflage

B mimicry

C variation

D geographic isolation    3.e

**5** Which is NOT a way that humans influence the rate of species extinction?

A mining

B farming

C volcanic eruptions

D construction    3.e

**6** What explains all the different breeds of dogs and cats?

A phenotype

B genes and the environment

C dominant alleles

D selective breeding    3.a

**7** Having a body part that looks like food to another organism is an example of what?

A camouflage

B mimicry

C behavioral adaptation

D exotic species    3.b

Science online Standards Assessment ca7.msscience.com

**8** Which is the process by which adaptations are more likely to be inherited while traits that are not advantageous are less likely to be inherited?

**A** selective breeding

**B** natural selection

**C** behavioral adaptation

**D** natural adaptation   3.b

**9** Which is an expected outcome of natural selection?

**A** extinction

**B** common ancestors

**C** diversity of life

**D** mutations   3.b

**10** Which is a behavioral adaptation?

**A** mimicry of coloration

**B** camouflage

**C** analogous structures

**D** building specialized nests   3.e

**11** How would environmental conditions have to change to give this albino lemur a chance for survival?

**A** Volcanic ash covers the forest.

**B.** The climate gets cold enough to snow.

**C.** A city dump moves nearby.

**D.** An earthquake lifts the land 2 meters.   3.e

**12** What do we call an organism on the brink of extinction?

**A** threatened

**B** selected

**C** exotic

**D** adapted   3.e

**13** Which is an example of a structural adaptation?

**A** long ears of a desert rabbit

**B** tool use of finches

**C** herd of elk

**D** nest-building of a clapper rail   3.b

**14** A population of lizards has been studied for the last 50 years.

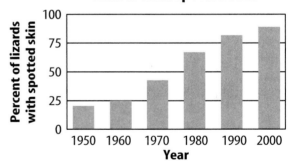

**Lizards with Spotted Skin**

Which conclusion can be drawn from the graph?

**A** Spotted skin is increasing in the population.

**B** Loss of habitat is occurring.   3.b

**C** Exotic species are outcompeting the lizards.

**D** Spotted skin is declining in the population.

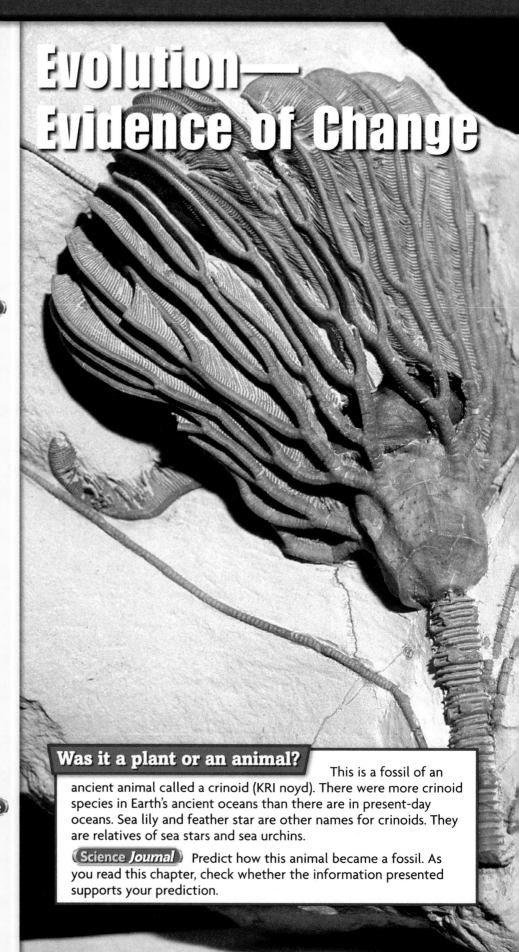

# Evolution— Evidence of Change

(The BIG Idea)

Evidence from biology and paleontology is best explained by the theory of evolution.

**LESSON 1** (3.c, 4.c, 4.e, 7.d)
## Fossils and Evolution

(Main Idea) Fossils provide evidence of changes to species and the environment over time.

**LESSON 2** (3.c)
## Biological Evidence

(Main Idea) Evidence from comparative anatomy and molecular biology are best explained by the theory of evolution by natural selection.

**LESSON 3** (3.a, 4.f)
## Evolution and Plate Tectonics

(Main Idea) Over time, the movement of lithospheric plates has changed environments that led to changes in species.

**LESSON 4** (3.d, 7.c, 7.d, 7.e)
## Classifying Organisms

(Main Idea) Scientists use traits and evolutionary history to classify species.

### Was it a plant or an animal?

This is a fossil of an ancient animal called a crinoid (KRI noyd). There were more crinoid species in Earth's ancient oceans than there are in present-day oceans. Sea lily and feather star are other names for crinoids. They are relatives of sea stars and sea urchins.

(Science *Journal*) Predict how this animal became a fossil. As you read this chapter, check whether the information presented supports your prediction.

 00:20 minutes

## Can you make an animal evolve?

Animals and plants living on Earth today evolved from simpler animals and plants. In fact, species on Earth are still evolving.

### Procedure

1. Complete a lab safety form.

2. Create a primitive animal that evolves into a more complex animal over time. Make models from **materials provided** showing your animal at four different stages of its evolution.

3. Record descriptions of the changes your animal has gone through at each stage.

### Think About This

• **List** specific adaptations that your animal has evolved to ensure its survival.

• **Describe** how these adaptations would help your animal survive through the process of natural selection.

 3.a, 7.d

### Science Online

Visit ca7.msscience.com to:

▶ view **Concepts in Motion**

▶ explore Virtual Labs

▶ access content-related Web links

▶ take the Standards Check

## Evidence of Evolution

Make the following Foldable to organize the evidence of evolution.

**STEP 1** **Fold** a sheet of paper in half lengthwise. Make the back about 3 cm longer than the front.

**STEP 2** **Fold** into thirds.

**STEP 3** **Unfold** and **cut** along the folds of the front flap to make three flaps.

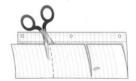

**STEP 4** **Label** the flaps as shown.

Evidence of Evolution — Fossils | Biology | Plate Tectonics

### Reading Skill

**Analyzing**
As you read this chapter, you will learn about the evidence that supports evolution. List the evidence under the appropriate flap.

# Get Ready to Read

## Questioning

**①Learn It!** Asking questions helps you to understand what you read. As you read, think about the questions you'd like answered. Often you can find the answer in the next paragraph or lesson. Learn to ask good questions by asking *who, what, when, where, why,* and *how.*

**②Practice It!** Read the following passage from Lesson 1.

> Did you see the movie in which an entire organism was preserved in amber—the fossilized sap of an ancient gymnosperm? A preserved organism in amber is a type of fossil called original material. Another example of original material is the head from a frozen woolly mammoth shown in **Figure 6.** An original material fossil is unique because none of the hard and soft structures of the original organism have been replaced or altered. The organism is preserved in its original form. It is rare to find original material, but when it happens, it provides much information to paleontologists. Most original material fossils are more recent than other fossil types.
>
> —*from page 248*

Here are some questions you might ask about this paragraph:

- What is an original material fossil?
- Where can original material fossils be found?
- How often are original material fossils discovered?

**③Apply It!** As you read the chapter, look for answers to lesson headings that are in the form of questions.

# Target Your Reading

**Reading Tip**

Test yourself. Create questions and then read to find answers to your own questions.

Use this to focus on the main ideas as you read the chapter.

**1** **Before you read** the chapter, respond to the statements below on your worksheet or on a numbered sheet of paper.

- Write an **A** if you **agree** with the statement.
- Write a **D** if you **disagree** with the statement.

**2** **After you read** the chapter, look back to this page to see if you've changed your mind about any of the statements.

- If any of your answers changed, explain why.
- Change any false statements into true statements.
- Use your revised statements as a study guide.

**Science** Online

Print a worksheet of this page at ca7.msscience.com.

| Before You Read A or D | Statement | After You Read A or D |
|---|---|---|
| | **1** Fossils are the naturally preserved remains of ancient organisms. | |
| | **2** Paleontologists study organisms living on Earth to learn more about fossils. | |
| | **3** The fossil record is the only evidence for evolution by natural selection. | |
| | **4** Some organisms have structures that have no function now but had a function in an ancient ancestor. | |
| | **5** The moving lithospheric plates had no influence on the evolution of plants and animals. | |
| | **6** Changes in landforms and in climate can result in the evolution of new species. | |
| | **7** Present-day classification is based on the idea of common ancestors. | |
| | **8** The classification of an organism remains the same even when scientists learn new information that contradicts its current classification. | |

## Reading Guide

### What *You'll Learn*

▶ **Describe** the work of a paleontologist.

▶ **Compare and contrast** the processes that form different fossil types.

▶ **Explain** how fossils support evolution by natural selection.

### Why *It's Important*

Learning how fossils form helps you understand how Earth and organisms change over time.

### Vocabulary
fossil
paleontologist
permineralization
mold
cast
fossil record

# Fossils and Evolution

**Main Idea** Fossils provide evidence of changes to species and the environment over time.

**Real-World Reading Connection** Do you watch television shows about forensic science? A show usually includes one or more forensic scientists who search for and analyze evidence to solve a mystery. Studying evolution is similar to solving a mystery. What evidence do scientists look for to determine the types of organisms that lived on Earth in the past?

## What are fossils?

Organisms leave evidence of their existence on Earth. Much of this evidence lasts for only a short time, but occasionally it is preserved for a long time. **Fossils** are the naturally preserved remains, imprints, or traces of organisms that lived long ago. Fossils, as shown in **Figure 1,** can include bones, shells, and footprints of ancient life.

A **paleontologist** (pay lee ahn TAH luh just) is a scientist who studies fossils. Paleontologists study fossils to determine the relationships among organisms, the approximate times when life first appeared, when different organisms first lived on Earth, and when organisms became extinct. Some paleontologists work outside to discover and then carefully uncover fossils. Other paleontologists work in laboratories analyzing and learning about fossils.

**Figure 1** Some fossils, called microfossils, can only be seen under a microscope. Other fossils are larger than humans.

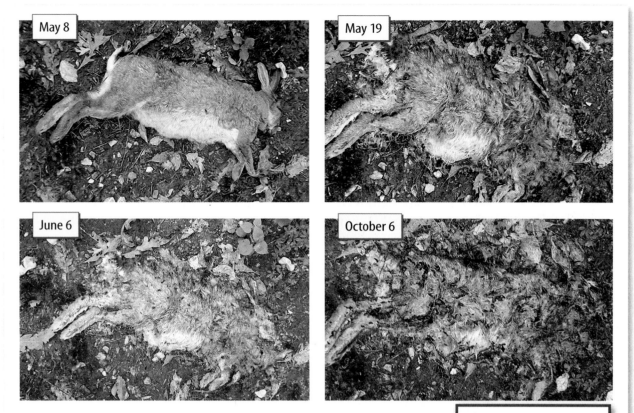

May 8

May 19

June 6

October 6

**Figure 2** As an organism decomposes, only hard body structures remain.

# When do fossils form?

Have you ever forgotten about a fruit in the refrigerator? When you discover it, the fruit might be soft and have mold growing on it. The fruit is decomposing—breaking down into substances that can be used by other organisms. The process of decomposition, as shown in **Figure 2,** is part of an organism's life cycle. In nature, organisms, such as insects, worms, bacteria, fungi, and others, consume and help break down dead organisms. These organisms are decomposers and help the decomposition process. Scavengers might eat part of a dead organism and then scatter the parts they cannot eat. What keeps decomposers and scavengers from destroying the remains of an organism before it is preserved as a fossil? What conditions provide for fossil formation?

 **Reading Check** What term describes the breakdown of a dead organism?

For a dead organism to become a fossil, it must be well protected from decomposers, scavengers, and environmental factors, such as heavy rains or acidic soils. Also, if a dead organism has hard structures such as teeth, bones, or a shell, it has a better chance of becoming a fossil than if it does not have hard structures. Hard structures decay more slowly than softer structures do, also shown in **Figure 2,** and scavengers are less likely to eat hard structures.

**WORD ORIGIN**

paleontology
from Greek *palaios* (means *old, ancient)* and *–ology* (means *study of)*

# How are fossils formed?

When the word *fossil* was first used, no one knew that fossils were from ancient organisms. In fact, some scholars argued that fossils could not be from ancient animals. They thought that the only way for fossils to have originated from once-living animals was for the bones and teeth to change magically to stone, which was impossible. It was not until the seventeenth century that scientists began to figure out how fossils form.

Fossils only form under certain conditions. This means that fossils are not commonly found in most rocks or in most locations. Usually, when we find a fossil, it is only part of a once-living organism. The most frequently found fossils are preserved hard **structures,** but occasionally soft structures are preserved. In rare instances, entire organisms are preserved. There are several different methods of preservation.

## Permineralization

A living organism's hard structures usually contain tiny spaces filled with air, blood, or other substances. After the organism dies, the substances inside the tiny spaces decompose leaving the spaces empty. If the hard structure is buried, layers of sediment slowly begin to compact and cement to form rock. During this process, **permineralization** (pur mihn ur ul i ZAY shun) can occur if water in the ground seeps into the tiny empty spaces and deposits minerals. Usually silica, calcite, or a similar mineral is left in the tiny spaces. This forms a strong, rocklike fossil. The details of the organism's original hard structure are often preserved. Most bones and trees become fossilized through permineralization, as shown in **Figure 3.** They have hard structures with small spaces where minerals can be deposited. When trees are fossilized through this process, they are often referred to as petrified wood.

**ACADEMIC VOCABULARY**

structure (STRUHK cher)
*(noun)* any part of an organism *A plant has structures called roots that hold it in the ground.*

**Figure 3** This part of a dinosaur's leg bone and these tree trunks were preserved by permineralization.

**Infer** what hard structures of the original tree are preserved.

**Figure 4** Mineral deposits have replaced the shells and filled the insides of these ancient snails. All that remains of this ancient fish is the carbon from the molecules that made up its body.

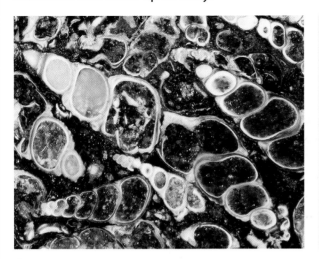

## Replacement

There are similarities between permineralization and replacement. Minerals such as silica, iron, and pyrite are critical for fossilization in both processes. However, in replacement, the hard structures of the organism dissolve and are replaced with minerals. During replacement, the original microscopic details, such as the inside of a bone, are partially or totally destroyed. Only the shape of the original organism remains. For example, a solution of water and dissolved silica might flow into and through the shell of a dead organism. If the water is acidic, it might dissolve the shell. Simultaneously, the dissolved silica in the water crystallizes and fills in the places where the shell had been and replaces the original shell. **Figure 4** shows an example of replacement.

 What remains of the organism after replacement has occured?

## Carbonization

If a dead organism is quickly buried under conditions without oxygen, elements that are normally found in the living tissue of the organism, such as hydrogen, oxygen, and nitrogen, are removed. A thin film of carbon is all that is left when these elements leave the organism's remains. As pressure from built-up sediment compresses the buried organism, a carbon film forms that preserves an image or shape of the original organism on a rock. Also, soft materials of animals, such as skin, fur, and feathers, can be preserved as carbon films, as shown in **Figure 4.** Countless plant fossils are preserved as carbon films and are the bases of present-day coalfields.

**SCIENCE USE V. COMMON USE**
film
**Science Use** a thin coating or layer. *The oil formed a film on the water's surface.*
**Common Use** a motion picture. *The film about penguins received rave reviews.*

**Figure 5** This is a mold of the interior of an ancient snail shell. The shell was dissolved long ago. These casts are of ancient squidlike animals called ammonites.

Mold

Cast

## Molds and Casts

Preservation of an impression or indentation of an organism is a mold or cast, as shown in **Figure 5.** In these fossils, there are no remaining parts of the original organism. For example, **molds** can be the imprints from a shell or the skin of an animal. There are molds of bite marks, footprints, and eggs in a nest. If the mold is filled in with sediment that hardens into rock, a **cast** fossil forms.

## Original Material

Did you see the movie in which an entire organism was preserved in amber—the fossilized sap of an ancient gymnosperm? A preserved organism in amber is a type of fossil called original material. Another example of original material is the head from a frozen woolly mammoth shown in **Figure 6.** An original material fossil is unique because none of the hard and soft structures of the original organism have been replaced or altered. The organism is preserved in its original form. It is rare to find original material, but when it happens it provides much information to paleontologists. Most original-material fossils are more recent than other fossil types.

**Figure 6** Scientists discovered a wooly mammoth preserved in thick ice in Siberia. It still had hair on its head.

Visual Check

**Figure 6** What other body structures might have been preserved by freezing?

# What do fossils tell us?

Much of the evidence for the pattern of evolution and evolutionary relationships comes from fossils. Scientists also study fossils in order to understand some processes and rates of evolution. Recall from Chapter 5 that natural selection is the survival and reproduction of species with traits that enable them to survive under particular conditions. Over generations, species change due to the loss of organisms that did not have those traits that enabled them to survive. Fossils provide a record of different species that lived in the past.

## Relative Fossil Ages

Generally, the older the rock layer, the deeper it is in Earth. If a paleontologist finds fossils in a fairly shallow sedimentary rock layer and then finds others in a deeper sedimentary rock layer, the older fossils are usually those in the deeper sedimentary rock layer, as illustrated in **Figure 7.** This is true unless there has been an unusual disturbance to the area that has rearranged the rock layers. In this way, ages of the fossils can be compared by the relative ages of the rocks.

 **Reading Check** How can sedimentary rock layers indicate the relative age of fossils?

**Figure 7** Fossil-filled sedimentary rocks usually form horizontal layers. If undisturbed, sedimentary rock layers can provide evidence of the approximate ages of the fossils in them.

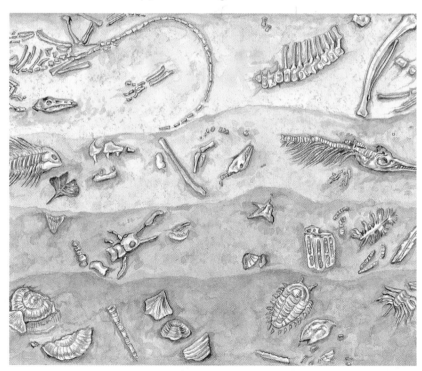

## How do fossils form?

Fossils form over time in several ways. Can you create a fossil?

### Procedure

1. Complete a lab safety form.
2. Choose an **object** provided by your teacher to fossilize.
3. Make two **clay** pancakes. Rub **petroleum jelly** over one side of each pancake.
4. Press your object into the petroleum-covered side of one clay pancake. Cover the object with the other pancake (petroleum-jelly sides together). Press down lightly.
5. Carefully separate the two pancakes.

### Analysis

1. **Identify** the type of fossil you made.
2. **Compare and contrast** your fossil with a real fossil.
3. **Analyze** any problems you had with this lab activity. How do you think you could improve it?

 3.c, 7.d

## Species and Environmental Changes

The **fossil record** is made of all known fossils and their placements in the formation of rocks and positions in time. It is evidence that supports the evolution of organisms. However, the fossil record has gaps, much like a story in a book that has missing pages. The gaps exist because most organisms decay before fossilization happens, geological processes destroy fossils, or fossils are undiscovered. Even with the gaps, the fossil record is evidence that most of the species that ever lived on Earth are now extinct.

 Why are there gaps in the fossil record?

Fossils provide evidence of how life and environmental conditions have changed throughout time. By studying fossils, scientists have determined that during Earth's early history, life was not as complex as it is now. More complex organisms appeared later in Earth's history.

Scientists can use fossils to make models that show what an organism might have looked like, as shown in **Figure 8.** From fossils, scientists can sometimes determine whether an organism lived in family groups or alone, what types of food it ate, what kind of environment it lived in, and many other things about it.

**Figure 8** Paleontologists can reconstruct organisms from pieces of their fossilized remains. However, new evidence might require corrections to existing reconstructed organisms.

# How do fossils provide evidence of the past?

Most organisms decompose and leave no direct evidence of their existence. However, the parts of organisms that are preserved through permineralization, replacement, carbonization, or other methods can tell us much about when organisms lived, how they changed, and when they became extinct. Fossils provide clues that paleontologists can use to reconstruct extinct organisms.

The locations of fossils in sedimentary rock layers can indicate the relative ages of fossils. The pattern of when organisms appear in the fossil record and the structure of the organisms is best explained by the theory of evolution by natural selection.

# LESSON 1  Review

## Summarize

Create your own lesson summary as you design a **study web.**

1. **Write** the lesson title, number, and page numbers at the top of a sheet of paper.

2. **Scan** the lesson to find the **red** main headings.

3. **Organize** these headings clockwise on branches around the lesson title.

4. **Review** the information under each **red** heading to design a branch for each **blue** subheading.

5. **List** 2–3 details, key terms, and definitions from each **blue** subheading on branches extending from the main heading branches.

 **ELA7:** W 2.5

## Standards Check

### Using Vocabulary

Write the vocabulary term defined below.

1. scientists who specialize in studying fossils **3.c**

2. naturally preserved remains of organisms that lived long ago **3.c**

### Understanding Main Ideas

3. **Explain** why most plants and animals do not become fossils. **3.c**

4. **Give examples** of the types of fossils formed through permineralization and carbonization. **3.c**

5. **Describe** one method a paleontologist can use to approximate the age of fossils. **4.c**

### Applying Science

6. **Evaluate** how fossils support the theory of evolution by natural selection. **4.e**

7. **Create** a map to show where fossils of different ages would be found along a cliff. **4.c**

8. **Identify** Copy and fill in the graphic organizer below to identify three fossilization processes. **3.c**

Fossilization Processes

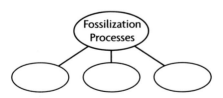

**Science** nline

For more practice, visit **Standards Check** at ca7.msscience.com.

**Science Content Standards**

**3.c** Students know how independent lines of evidence from geology, fossils, and comparative anatomy provide the bases for the theory of evolution.

## Reading Guide

### What *You'll Learn*

▶ **List** several sciences that have provided evidence for the theory of natural selection.

▶ **Describe** the study of embryology.

▶ **Summarize** how the study of DNA has affected the search for common ancestors.

▶ **Explain** how homologous structures provide evidence of evolution.

### Why *It's Important*

Knowing how biological evidence supports the theory of evolution by natural selection will add to your understanding of how some species are related.

### Vocabulary

comparative anatomy
homologous structure
embryology

### Review Vocabulary

**adaptation:** inheritance of traits that allow an organism to survive in a particular environment (p. 216)

# Biological Evidence

**Main Idea** Evidence from comparative anatomy and molecular biology are best explained by the theory of evolution by natural selection.

**Real-World Reading Connection** At the zoo, there might be animals that appear similar. For example, different bears might have different colors of fur but you can easily recognize that they are bears. Are these similar animals related? Is it coincidence that they are similar? Scientists have wondered about the same things.

## Comparative Anatomy

Another form of evidence that supports the theory of evolution by natural selection is comparative anatomy. **Comparative anatomy** is the study of similarities and differences in the structures of organisms. By using comparative anatomy, scientists have made important scientific discoveries.

Scientists who study insects have known for years that two groups of insects—true flies and scorpionflies—are similar. A true fly, shown in **Figure 9,** has a pair of large, thin wings and a pair of small, knoblike appendages behind them. A scorpionfly has two pairs of large, thin wings. Scientists predicted that if these groups of insects had a common ancestor, a fossil existed of an ancestor of true flies with two pairs of wings. In 1976, scientists found fossils of four-winged true flies that confirmed their prediction of a common ancestor. The anatomy of the tiny insect fossils provided much evidence to support evolution. The combination of studying and comparing the structures of fossils and living organisms has supported the pattern of evolution.

**Figure 9** Although present-day true flies and scorpionflies appear different, they have a common ancestor.

**True Fly**

**Scorpionfly**

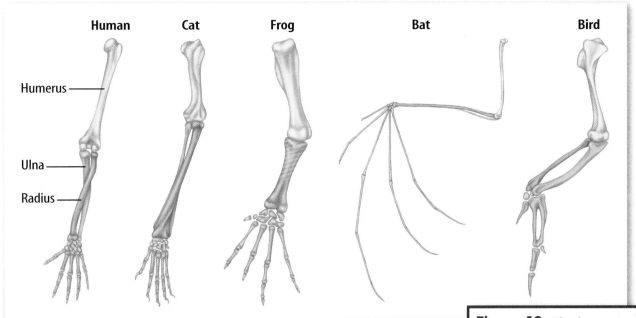

**Human**    **Cat**    **Frog**      **Bat**      **Bird**

Humerus

Ulna

Radius

**Figure 10** The bones in the upper limbs of these animals are homologous structures.

## Structures in Living Organisms

Humans, frogs, bats, birds, and cats all have a common set of three bones in their front or upper appendages, as shown in **Figure 10.** The sizes of the bones are different but their forms are similar. At some point in our past, we all shared a common ancestor, but some share more recent ancestors than others.

**Homologous Structures** In plants, many angiosperms have similar fruits. Recall from Chapter 3 that fruits develop mostly from flower ovaries and they protect the seeds. Angiosperms have a more recent common ancestor than gymnosperms—seed plants without fruits. Parts of organisms that are similar in origin and structure are called **homologous** (huh MAH luh gus) **structures.** Homologous structures are the result of evolution and can indicate how closely two or more species share common ancestors.

 What can homologous structures in organisms indicate?

**Analogous Structures** The wings of birds and insects are examples of **analogous** (uh NAH luh gus) structures. They appear similar but have different ancestral origins. They resulted from similar environmental conditions that produced similar natural selection outcomes over time, but on distantly related organisms.

Scientists do not observe two organisms and decide that because they look alike, they share an ancestor. Instead, scientists consider geography, environmental conditions, fossil records, structures and functions of the body parts, and genetics when possible, in order to understand evolutionary relationships. The accumulation of evidence from these different sources supports evolutionary lines.

**WORD ORIGIN**
homologous
from Greek *homologos;* means *agreeing, of one mind*

**ACADEMIC VOCABULARY**
analogous (uh NAHL uh gus)
*(adjective)* being or related to *Analogous animal behaviors include humans talking, frogs croaking, and birds singing.*

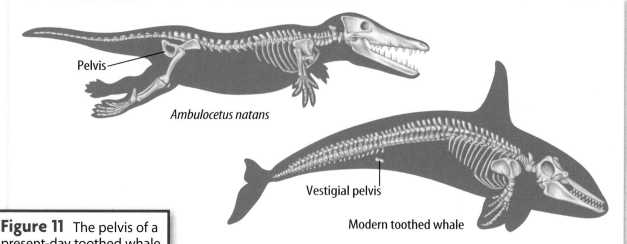

Pelvis

*Ambulocetus natans*

Vestigial pelvis

Modern toothed whale

**Figure 11** The pelvis of a present-day toothed whale is just two small bones. In its ancient ancestors, the pelvis was larger and supported hind legs.

**Propose** an explanation as to why a toothed whale's pelvis is smaller today.

**Vestigial Structures** Another source of evidence for evolution are vestigial (veh STIH jee ul) structures. These structures have no function in their present-day form. However, scientists hypothesize that vestigial structures once functioned in an ancestor. For example, most mammals have pelvic bones that support a pair of legs. Present-day whales have pelvic bones but do not have leg bones like their ancestors, as shown in **Figure 11.** Some people question why vestigial structures would remain through natural selection if they have no function. It is because vestigial structures are genetically related to an advantageous trait of the species or because their absence would have harmful effects for the survival of the species.

## Embryology

The science of the development of embryos from fertilization to birth is **embryology** (em bree AH luh jee). Scientists who study embryos of different animals often compare and contrast their patterns of development. Similar patterns can provide clues to the evolutionary relationships among organisms.

Embryos of different vertebrate animal species have similar early developmental stages during which they show common features. As the embryos grow and develop, those features become unique structures in different species. For example, embryos of vertebrate animals have bulges in the region of the neck called pharyngeal (fuh rihn JEE ul) pouches, as shown in **Figure 12.** They become facial and neck structures. In fish, they develop into structures called gill arches; in humans, one of the pharyngeal pouches develops into part of the ear.

It is important to remember that the more closely related species are, the more features they share during development. These shared similarities are best explained by the theory of common ancestors and evolution through natural selection. However, while developmental patterns indicate evolutionary history, they are not an historical journey through evolution.

**Figure 12** Similarities among vertebrate animal embryos provide evidence of evolution.

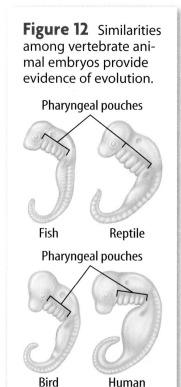

Pharyngeal pouches

Fish    Reptile

Pharyngeal pouches

Bird    Human

# Molecular Biology

What is known today about genetics, biochemistry, and molecular biology probably would have amazed Darwin. New technology provides the tools to continue making rapid discoveries in these areas. These molecular data also support the theory of evolution through natural selection.

The proteins in all organisms consist of countless arrangements of just 20 different molecules called amino acids. Recall from Chapter 1 that cellular respiration requires oxygen and releases energy. Organisms that use cellular respiration must have a protein called cytochrome *c* for this process to occur. Scientists have discovered slight differences in the cytochrome *c* molecules found in different organisms that use cellular respiration. It is unlikely that these differences developed independently from different ancestral lines. For example, this protein is more similar among mammals, such as a pig, a monkey, and a human, as shown in **Figure 13,** than are the forms of the protein found in other organisms. This supports the theory that different mammals have a more recent ancestor in common than do mammals and yeast.

Scientists also look at other proteins and at the sequences of DNA. Recent molecular data suggests that closest living relative of whales are hippopotamuses. This molecular evidence supports prior evidence from comparative anatomy about whales' relationships to even-toed hoofed animals, but offers specific information about the relationship than previously known.

 **Reading Check** What types of molecules provide evidence of evolution?

## DataLab

**00:15 minutes**

## What do proteins tell us about evolution?

**Data**

Use the graph in **Figure 13** to compare cytochrome *c* of different organisms.

**Data Analysis**

1. **Name** the organism whose cytochrome *c* is most like human cytochrome *c*.

2. **Determine** if a dog or a turtle has a more recent common ancestor with a frog.

3.c  **Try at Home**

**Figure 13** Analysis of the protein—cytochrome *c*—can indicate common ancestors among organisms.

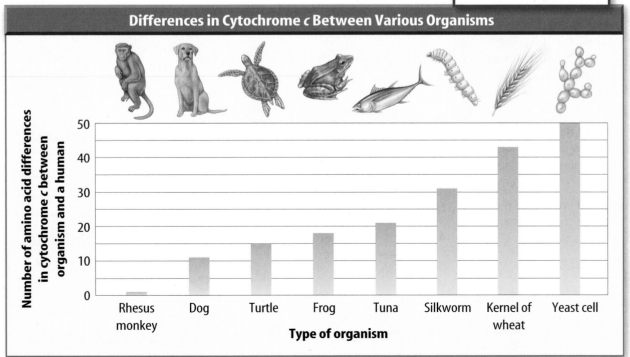

**Differences in Cytochrome *c* Between Various Organisms**

Number of amino acid differences in cytochrome *c* between organism and a human

Type of organism

Rhesus monkey, Dog, Turtle, Frog, Tuna, Silkworm, Kernel of wheat, Yeast cell

## How does biological evidence support the theory of evolution?

Evolution is also supported through different biological evidence. Scientists use homologous and analogous structures to determine possible relationships among modern organisms and their ancestors. Examining vestigial structures provides further understanding of the evolution of present-day organisms from ancient ancestors. Studying the embryology of different organisms provides supporting evidence for evolution from a common ancestor, but does not provide evidence of how evolution occured. Recent technologies have enabled scientists to use molecular biology to search for common ancestors. The data from different branches of science are compared and used to build a better understanding of evolution.

# LESSON 2 Review

## Summarize

Create your own lesson summary as you write a script for a **television news report.**

1. **Review** the text after the **red** main headings and write one sentence about each. These are the headlines of your broadcast.

2. **Review** the text and write 2–3 sentences about each **blue** subheading. These sentences should tell *who, what, when, where,* and *why* information about each **red** heading.

3. **Include** descriptive details in your report, such as names of reporters and local places and events.

4. **Present** your news report to other classmates alone or with a team.

 ELA7: LS 2.2

##  Standards Check

### Using Vocabulary

Complete each sentence using the correct term.

> comparative anatomy
> homologous structure
> embryology

1. The femur bone in the upper appendages of birds, humans, and frogs is an example of a(n) _____. **3.c**

2. _____ provides evidence of evolution using structures of organisms. **3.c**

3. Pharyngeal pouches are an example of evidence of evolution based on _____. **3.c**

### Understanding Main Ideas

4. **Explain** how DNA sequences can provide evidence of evolution. **3.c**

5. Which is most likely a vestigial structure?

   **A.** an ape's thumb    **3.c**
   **B.** a dolphin's flipper
   **C.** a whale's pelvis
   **D.** a rabbit's fluffy tail

### Applying Science

6. **Organize Information** Copy and fill in the graphic organizer below to describe the different examples of comparative anatomy as evidence of evolution. **3.c**

| Comparative Anatomy | |
|---|---|
| **Example** | **Description** |
|  |  |
|  |  |
|  |  |
|  |  |

For more practice, visit **Standards Check** at ca7.msscience.com .

## Reading Guide

### What *You'll Learn*

▶ **Explain** how plate tectonics changes landforms and environments.

▶ **Discuss** how changes in landscapes and environments can lead to new species.

▶ **Describe** how plate tectonics relates to biogeography.

### Why *It's Important*

Knowing that plate tectonics results in environmental and geological changes helps you understand how evolution can occur over time.

### Vocabulary

geographic isolation
convergent evolution

### Review Vocabulary

**lithospheric plate:** large, brittle pieces of Earth's outer shell composed of crust and uppermost mantle (Grade 6)

# Evolution and Plate Tectonics

**Main Idea** Over time, the movement of lithospheric plates has changed environments that led to changes in species.

**Real-World Reading Connection** If you quickly glance at a clock, you probably notice the movement of the second hand but not the movement of the hour hand. Like the hour hand, the ground below you is slowly moving. Over time, the slow movement of Earth's plates has led to changes in species.

## Continental Drift

Earth's surface slowly changed over time, and it is hard to recognize the changes. However, earthquakes are evidence that changes to Earth's lithospheric plates are still occurring.

Recall that Alfred Wegener proposed the continental drift hypothesis in 1912. The most obvious evidence for his hypothesis included the fit of shorelines of Africa and South America, as shown in **Figure 14.** As lithospheric plates move, environmental changes result for the species that live on and near them. Natural selection acts upon species when there are environmental changes. Only individuals that are well-suited to the new conditions will be able to survive and pass their genes to offspring. Environmental changes can also lead to species extinctions.

**Figure 14** Because present-day continents can fit together like a jigsaw puzzle, Wegner proposed that they once were one large landmass.

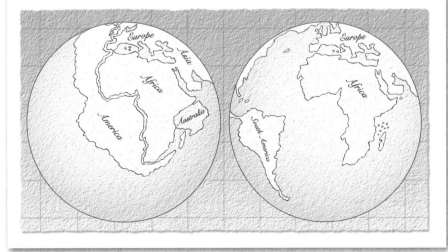

# Visualizing Geographic Isolation

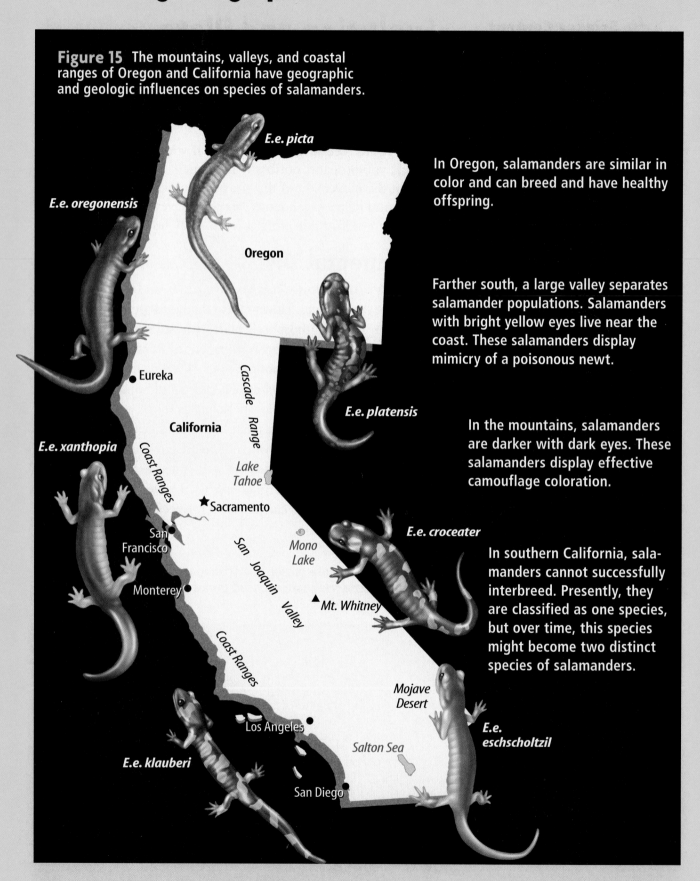

**Figure 15** The mountains, valleys, and coastal ranges of Oregon and California have geographic and geologic influences on species of salamanders.

*E.e. picta*

*E.e. oregonensis*

Oregon

In Oregon, salamanders are similar in color and can breed and have healthy offspring.

Eureka

Cascade Range

California

*E.e. platensis*

Farther south, a large valley separates salamander populations. Salamanders with bright yellow eyes live near the coast. These salamanders display mimicry of a poisonous newt.

*E.e. xanthopia*

Coast Ranges

Lake Tahoe

★ Sacramento

San Francisco

Mono Lake

Monterey

San Joaquin Valley

▲ Mt. Whitney

*E.e. croceater*

In the mountains, salamanders are darker with dark eyes. These salamanders display effective camouflage coloration.

In southern California, salamanders cannot successfully interbreed. Presently, they are classified as one species, but over time, this species might become two distinct species of salamanders.

Coast Ranges

Mojave Desert

Los Angeles

Salton Sea

*E.e. eschscholtzil*

*E.e. klauberi*

San Diego

# Geographic Isolation

Landforms are created when lithospheric plates move. Mountains and volcanoes form when lithospheric plates move together. Valleys form where lithospheric plates move apart. Sometimes, landforms become barriers between populations of species, and breeding between these populations is **prohibited.** When this happens, **geographic isolation** can occur. Once separated, the populations in different environments might follow different evolutionary paths over time. Other geographic features, such as rivers and large bodies of water, can lead to geographic isolation of species, also. **Figure 15** illustrates geographic isolation in California. The geography of a location plays an important role in how organisms evolve.

 How can geographic isolation occur?

## Darwin's Observations of Geographic Isolation

Geographic isolation was responsible for many of the organisms described in Darwin's journals. The results of geographic isolation puzzled Darwin and prompted much of his research. Imagine if you have two islands with very similar environmental conditions—island A and island B—but on different sides of Earth. Imagine that island A is near the mainland, but the environmental conditions on island A and those on the mainland are quite different. Obviously, you would expect the organisms on island A and island B to be more similar than those on island A and the mainland. In the Galápagos Islands and Ecuador, Darwin found just the opposite. Species on the Galápagos Islands were more similar to those on the Ecuador mainland even though the environments of the islands and the mainland were different. Yet, the similar organisms were clearly unique species. These observations led to the idea of evolution by natural selection.

## Geographic Isolation v. Convergent Evolution

Sometimes distant locations with similar environmental conditions have species with similar traits. These species have evolved independently but under similar conditions. This type of evolution is known as **convergent evolution** and results in structural and functional similarities. New research in genetics has supported the finding that although two species in similar environments can appear similar, they did not evolve from common ancestors. **Figure 16** shows two plant species that have undergone convergent evolution. They appear similar, but they are from different branches of the evolutionary tree. Geographic isolation leads to closely related species that appear different while convergent evolution results in very distantly related species that appear similar.

**ACADEMIC VOCABULARY**
prohibit (pro HIH bit)
*(verb)* to prevent from doing something
*An automobile accident can prohibit other vehicles from moving on the freeway.*

**Figure 16** Cacti and euphorbias evolved in desert-like environments. But cacti evolved in the Americas and euphorbias evolved in Africa.

**Cactus**

**Euphorbia**

# How are plate tectonics and evolution related?

The moving lithospheric plates result in changes to Earth's surface, such as the formations of mountains, valleys, and bodies of water. These geographic barriers can result in the evolution of new species when populations become separated. Some related species are now separated because of plate tectonics. Widely separated species can evolve similar traits that ensure survival in similar environments.

Changes in climate, whether from plate tectonics or for other reasons, resulted in the evolution of new species by natural selection. Recall from Chapter 5 that environmental changes can cause species adaptations or extinctions. Only members of the species with traits that enable them to survive the new environmental conditions will survive, reproduce, and pass their genetic material to offspring.

# LESSON 3  Review

## Summarize

Create your own lesson summary as you organize an **outline.**

1. **Scan** the lesson. Find and list the first **red** main heading.

2. **Review** the text after the heading and list 2–3 details about the heading.

3. **Find** and list each **blue** subheading that follows the **red** main heading.

4. **List** 2–3 details, key terms, and definitions under each **blue** subheading.

5. **Review** additional **red** main headings and their supporting **blue** subheadings. List 2–3 details about each.

 **ELA7:** W 2.5

##  Standards Check

### Using Vocabulary

1. Define *geographic isolation* in your own words.  **4.f**

2. Use *convergent evolution* correctly in a sentence.  **3.a**

### Understanding Main Ideas

3. **Describe** how the movement of lithospheric plates can lead to evolution in species.  **4.f**

4. **Explain** how hummingbirds from North America and unrelated sunbirds from Africa could both evolve long beaks for reaching into flowers.  **3.a**

5. **Show** how the formation of a valley could result in the evolution of new species.  **4.f**

### Applying Science

6. **Predict** what would happen to the plants in your neighborhood if Earth's climate cooled over the next century.  **3.a**

7. **Infer** what might have happened to the South American population of beech trees if South America had drifted south instead of west.  **4.f**

8. **Determine Cause and Effect**  Draw a graphic organizer like the one below to list two ways evolution can occur because of plate tectonics.  **4.f**

 **Science** nline

For more practice, visit **Standards Check** at ca7.msscience.com.

# Applying Math

## Converting Time Ranges of Fossils into Years

Fossil data span millions of years. These data are sometimes written in a decimal form of millions of years ago (mya). The data table for the time ranges of some fossil species is given below.

| Fossil Species | Time Range (mya) |
|---|---|
| *Homo erectus javanicus* | 1.6–0.6 |
| *Homo erectus pekinensis* | 0.7–0.5 |
| Neanderthal | 0.07–0.04 |
| *Homo sapiens* | 0.3–0.1 |
| *Homo erectus soloensis* | 0.8–0.46 |

## Example

Find how many years ago *Homo erectus soloensis* lived.

1. **Use the data to find the beginning of the range and the end of the range for *Homo erectus soloensis*:**

   beginning: 0.8, end: 0.46

2. **Multiply each number by 1,000,000 to find the range in years.**

   $0.8 \times 1{,}000{,}000 = 800{,}000$ years ago
   $0.46 \times 1{,}000{,}000 = 460{,}000$ years ago

**Answer:** *Homo erectus soloensis* lived between 800,000 and 460,000 years ago.

### Practice Problems

1. In years, when was the first appearance of *Homo erectus javanicus* on Earth?

2. In years, when was the latest appearance of *Homo erectus javanicus* on Earth?

3. What is the time range for the existence of *Homo erectus javanicus* on Earth?

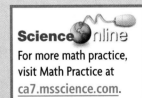

Science Online

For more math practice, visit Math Practice at ca7.msscience.com.

## Reading Guide

### What *You'll Learn*

▶ **Describe** how people in the past classified organisms.

▶ **List** the hierarchical order of classifications for our current system.

▶ **Explain** how the recent advances in biotechnology have supported the theory of evolution through natural selection.

### Why *It's Important*

Classification of organisms is a way to organize information about evolutionary relationships.

### Vocabulary

systematics

### Review Vocabulary

**species:** a group of organisms that share similar characteristics and can reproduce among themselves producing fertile offspring (Grade 6)

# Classifying Organisms

**Main Idea** Scientists use traits and evolutionary history to classify species.

**Real-World Reading Connection** How do you organize your clothes? Do you hang your T-shirts with your other shirts in your closet or put them in a drawer with other folded clothes? Do your friends organize their clothes in the same way? Scientists organize Earth's organisms into groups, but they do not always agree on the best system.

## Historic Classification Systems

The Greek philosopher Aristotle was one of the first people to classify organisms. He categorized things as animals, plants, or minerals. Aristotle also grouped living things by where they lived—in the air, on the land, or in the sea. Scholars used this system for hundreds of years. When Europeans began exploring new lands, they discovered many new plants and animals that could not be classified using Aristotle's system. A new classification system was needed.

In the mid-eighteenth century, Swedish botanist and explorer Carolus Linnaeus developed a classification system that grouped organisms based on similar physical structures. The Linnaeus classification system has many related levels. The largest group of organisms is a kingdom and the smallest group is a species. A species includes organisms that have the greatest number of traits in common and can breed and produce fertile offspring. Only species are subject to natural selection and evolution.

### Naming and Grouping Species

Linnaeus also developed a system for naming species that is still used. The two-word scientific name of an organism is its species name. For example, the species name for the California black oak is *Quercus kelloggii*.

Groups of similar living species belong to a genus (plural, genera). The first word of a species name identifies the genus to which the species belongs. All oaks have *Quercus* as the first word of their species name. Similar genera belong to a family, similar families belong to an order, similar orders belong to a class, similar classes belong to a phylum (plural, phyla), and similar phyla belong to a kingdom. **Table 1** shows these classifications levels for the western spotted skunk.

## Determining Kingdom

Cell type, the presence of a cell wall, or whether organisms are single-celled or multicellular, are used to define a kingdom. Scientists classify living organisms into one of six kingdoms—Kingdom Eubacteria, Kingdom Archeabacteria, Kingdom Protists, Kingdom Fungi, Kingdom Plantae, and Kingdom Animalia.

 What are some traits that scientists use to classify organisms?

**Concepts In Motion**
Interactive Table To organize levels of classification, visit Tables at ca7.msscience.com.

### Table 1 Classification of Living Things

| Level | Example | Representative Organism |
|-------|---------|-------------------------|
| Species | *Spilogale gracilis* | Western spotted skunk |
| Genus | *Spilogale* Spotted skunks (three species) | |
| Family | Mephitidae Skunks and stink badgers (four genera) | Hog-nosed skunk |
| Order | Carnivora All animals with large pointed teeth for tearing flesh (13 families) | Mountain Lion |
| Class | Mammalia Animals with mammary glands (26 orders) | Mule deer |
| Phylum | Chordata Animals with a spinal cord (11 classes) | Desert tortoise |
| Kingdom | Animalia Multicellular eukaryotes whose cells do not have cell walls (32 phyla) | Coral Reef at Anacapa Island, California |

## How can you create a dichotomous key?

In this lab, you'll create a dichotomous key to classify objects.

**Procedure**

1. Complete a lab safety form.

2. Obtain a **container of objects** from your teacher.

3. Examine the objects and then brainstorm a list of possible characteristics.

4. Choose a characteristic that separates the objects into two groups. Write a sentence to describe the characteristic. Write a sentence below it that has the word "not" in front of the characteristic. For example, if the characteristic is "round," then the second sentence would say "not round." At the end of the first sentence, write "Go to 1." At the end of the second sentence write "Go to 2."

5. Repeat step 4 for the two new groups. Sentences for new groups formed from the first group should have consecutive odd numbers. Sentences for groups formed from the second group should have consecutive even numbers. At the end of each new sentence, add the appropriate "Go to" directions.

6. Repeat steps 4 and 5 until there is one object in each group, then write the name of the object at the end of the sentence.

### Analysis

**Compare** your key with at least three of your classmates' keys. Record differences and similarities.

# Modern Methods of Classification

The modern study of classification is called **systematics.** In systematics, mostly DNA and molecular biology are used to identify relationships between organisms.

Scientists can now determine the order or sequence of the molecules in an organism's DNA. The more DNA sequences two species have in common, the more likely it is that they share a recent ancestor. Such DNA evidence has confirmed many existing classifications. However, scientists have found that species established as close relatives, do not share as many DNA sequences as expected. When this occurs, scientists review existing evidence of evolution such as fossils and comparative anatomy data, and often reclassify organisms.

**Reading Check** How can examining DNA sequences affect classification?

It is too expensive to find the complete DNA sequence for all organisms. However, scientists can determine the sequence of a sample of 1,000 molecule pairs in DNA called haplotype (HA ploh tipe). Scientists compare these small sequences of DNA between organisms to search for similarities. The more similar two haplotypes are, the more closely the organisms are related.

DNA hybridization is another tool used in systematics. Scientists do not learn the actual sequences of DNA that two organisms share using DNA hybridization, but they can determine the percentage of DNA that is the same.

A new level of classification that developed because of molecular biology is domain. Domain is now the highest level instead of kingdom. Based on differences in a particular DNA sequence, organisms are separated into three domains—Bacteria, Archaea, or Eukarya. The Eukarya includes organisms that have cells with a nucleus. As other molecular biology techniques are developed, classification systems might change.

# How are classification of organisms and evolution related?

Classification in based on the idea of common ancestors, from the theory of natural selection. Aristotle developed the first classification system. Linnaeus used similar physical structures to place organisms into groups and developed the species naming system. The first word of a species name identifies the genus of the species. Molecular systematics is part of the classification process now. The new hierarchy of classification is domain, kingdom, phylum, class, order, family, genus, species. Classification is very useful for understanding and communicating evolutionary relationships.

# LESSON 4  Review

## Summarize

Create your own lesson summary as you write a **newsletter.**

1. **Write** this lesson title, number, and page numbers at the top of a sheet of paper.

2. **Review** the text after the **red** main headings and write one sentence about each. These will be the headlines of your newsletter.

3. **Review** the text and write 2–3 sentences about each **blue** subheading. These sentences should tell *who, what, when, where,* and *why* information about each headline.

4. **Illustrate** your newsletter with diagrams of important structures and processes next to each headline.

 ELA7: W 2.5

## Standards Check

### Using Vocabulary

1. Define *systematics* in your own words. **3.d**

### Understanding Main Ideas

2. **Describe** how scientists use evolution to classify species. **3.d**

3. **Discuss** two advantages of the Linnean system over previous systems. **3.d**

4. **Sequence** the following classification categories from the one with the least number of organisms to the one with the greatest number of organisms: *family, domain, class, species, phylum,* and *order.* **3.d**

### Applying Science

5. **Classify** a species of your choice. List all of the taxa in which it belongs, starting with its species name. **3.d**

6. **Develop** a classification tree for desserts. Be sure the most similar desserts are on the branches with the fewest divisions between them. The desserts that are less similar should branch farther back on the tree. **3.d**

7. **Take Notes** Copy the graphic organizer below and list methods of analyzing DNA mentioned in this lesson, and describe how each might affect modern classification. **3.d**

| Method of DNA Analysis | Effect on Modern Classification |
|---|---|
|  |  |
|  |  |
|  |  |

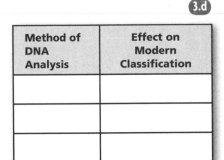

**Science**nline

For more practice, visit **Standards Check** at <u>ca7.msscience.com</u>.

# Lab

# Classifying the Students in Your Class

## Materials

paper and pencil

### Science Content Standards

**3.d** Students know how to construct a simple branching diagram to classify living groups of organisms by shared derived characteristics and how to expand the diagram to include fossil organisms.

**7.c** Communicate the logical connection among hypotheses, science concepts, tests conducted, data collected, and conclusions drawn from the scientific evidence.

**7.d** Construct scale models, maps, and appropriately labeled diagrams to communicate scientific knowledge (e.g., motion of Earth's plates and cell structure).

**7.e** Communicate the steps and results from an investigation in written reports and oral presentations.

## Problem

If you had a dog, a cat, a mouse, and a gecko, how would you classify them? You could place them in the same group because they're all possible pets. Or, you might put the gecko in a different group because it doesn't have fur like the others. For any group of objects, there are several possible ways to classify them. Scientists create diagrams, called cladograms, like the one shown on the next page, to group organisms based on certain characteristics. A cladogram shows common ancestry and helps scientists to better understand evolution. What other uses might a cladogram have?

## Form a Hypothesis

Before you gather the data, propose a way to classify students in your class. Write a hypothesis.

## Collect Data and Make Observations

1. With other students in your class, brainstorm a list of characteristics about yourselves. Examples of characteristics might include:
   - number of pets
   - number of siblings
   - number of aunts or uncles or total family members
   - length of hair
   - height
   - hobbies
   - favorite school subject

2. Make a questionnaire from the list of characteristics and distribute it to everyone in the class.

3. Complete your questionnaire as homework and bring it back to the class the next day. Do not put your name on your questionnaire.

4. Analyze the information about the characteristics of yourself and your classmates. How many different ways can you classify the members of your class?

5. Create a cladogram of your class using some or all of the characteristics from the questionnaire.

## Analyze and Conclude

1. **Explain** your choice of characteristic(s) used in making your cladogram.

2. **Describe** any difficulties you had in making your cladogram.

3. **Explain** what you like about this method of classification. Do you think it is useful?

4. **Identify** other sorting patterns you could use instead of producing a cladogram. What are the advantages and disadvantages of these other methods?

5. **Analyze** Is this a true cladogram? Explain.

6. **Infer** where a fossil of an ancient human might be on your cladogram.

7. **Error Analysis** Compare your cladogram to the cladograms of some of your other classmates. Write down advantages and disadvantages of each one. Would you do the activity differently next time? Explain.

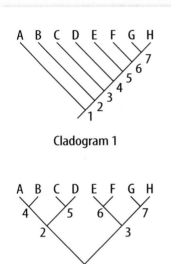

Cladogram 1

Cladogram 2

## Communicate

**WRITING in Science**

What did you learn from your experience of classifying a real set of data with multiple characteristics? Was it easy to identify individuals by their characteristics? Was this important? What might be the usefulness of the classifications? Summarize your findings in your Science Journal.

# Real World Science

## Studying Bacteria Evolution

Since some bacteria reproduce quickly, scientists called microbiologists can observe many generations of these organisms within a few weeks. Often during that time, these organisms change or evolve. Some scientists study bacteria as they evolve to look for ways to control diseases in crops and humans. Others study bacteria to learn about their genetics and how to apply that knowledge to humans. Still others study these organisms to answer evolutionary questions.

Visit **Careers** at **ca7.msscience.com** to learn more about microbiologists. Create a list of interview questions that you might ask a microbiologist, such as questions about his or her background, current research and how it applies to the real world, and what a typical day is like.

## Observe Evolution in Action

Scientists have created programs that can evolve digital organisms. These complex computer simulations can model real-life organisms, like ants, to study their behavior. Some programs allow the evolution of artificial brains to see if the animals can survive in specific environments. Other programs use artificial organisms only found within the computer world. This picture shows a digital form evolving.

Visit **Technology** at **ca7.msscience.com** to find out more. Write a short report describing one of the programs currently used.

ELA7: W 1.1

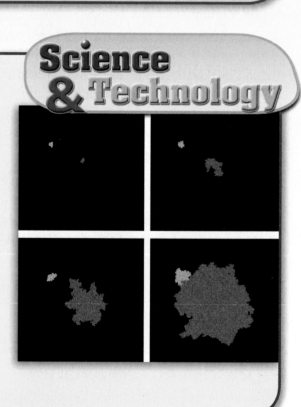

# Early Hypothesis of Evolution

In 1801, a French naturalist named Jean Baptiste Chevalier de Lamarck proposed that microscopic organisms appear spontaneously and then evolve into more complex life-forms. Eventually, perfection was reached when humans evolved. One of his ideas was that the long necks of giraffes evolved as giraffes stretched their necks to reach leaves on trees generation after generation. Today we know that his hypothesis about these processes was incorrect.

Visit **History** at **ca7.msscience.com** to find out more about Lamarck's ideas. Write a paragraph describing another of his incorrect hypotheses. **ELA7: W 1.1**

# The Galápagos Islands— An Evolution Museum

Until Darwin returned from his voyage, no one knew about these islands and their inhabitants. Today, the Galápagos Islands are known worldwide and recognized for their scientific importance. Visitors to the islands and the resident population are affecting native organisms, such as the Galápagos tortoises. However, conservation plans are underway to preserve this evolution museum.

Visit **Society** at **ca7.msscience.com** to learn about the plans to preserve life on the Galápagos Islands. Create a visual aid about one of the plans and share it with your class.

**The BIG Idea**   Evidence from biology and paleontology is best explained by the theory of evolution.

## Lesson 1 Fossils and Evolution    3.c, 4.c, 4.e, 7.d

**Main Idea** **Fossils provide evidence of changes to species and the environment over time.**

- Paleontologists study fossils—the naturally preserved remains of ancient organisms—to learn more about these organisms.

- Permineralization and replacement are processes that result in dissolved minerals hardening and forming fossils of the remains of organisms.

- Molds and casts are preserved imprints and indentations that leave no part of the original organism.

- The fossil record provides evidence for evolution by natural selection.

- **cast** (p. 248)
- **fossil** (p. 244)
- **fossil record** (p. 250)
- **mold** (p. 248)
- **paleontologist** (p. 244)
- **permineralization** (p. 246)

## Lesson 2 Biological Evidence    3.c

**Main Idea** **Evidence from comparative anatomy and molecular biology are best explained by the theory of evolution by natural selection.**

- Scientists use homologous, analogous, and vestigial structures to determine possible relationships among organisms and their ancestors.

- Similarities and differences in development of embryos provide evidence of evolutionary relationships among different organisms.

- Scientists use molecular biology to search for common ancestors of organisms.

- **comparative anatomy** (p. 252)
- **embryology** (p. 254)
- **homologous structure** (p. 253)

## Lesson 3 Evolution and Plate Tectonics    3.a, 4.f

**Main Idea** **Over time, the movement of lithospheric plates has changed environments that led to changes in species.**

- The moving lithospheric plates can isolate populations and result in the development of new species.

- Changes in climate can also result in new species.

- **convergent evolution** (p. 259)
- **geographic isloation** (p. 259)

## Lesson 4 Classifying Organisms    3.d, 7.c, 7.d, 7.e

**Main Idea** **Scientists use traits and evolutionary history to classify species.**

- Early classification systems were based on the physical characteristics and where the organisms lived.

- Present-day classification is based on the idea of common ancestors.

- Molecular systematics is used to improve established classification.

- **systematics** (p. 264)

 **STUDY TO GO** Download quizzes, key terms, and flash cards from ca7.msscience.com.

   Science Online   Interactive Tutor ca7.msscience.com

# Linking Vocabulary and Main Ideas

Use the vocabulary terms on page 270 to complete this concept map.

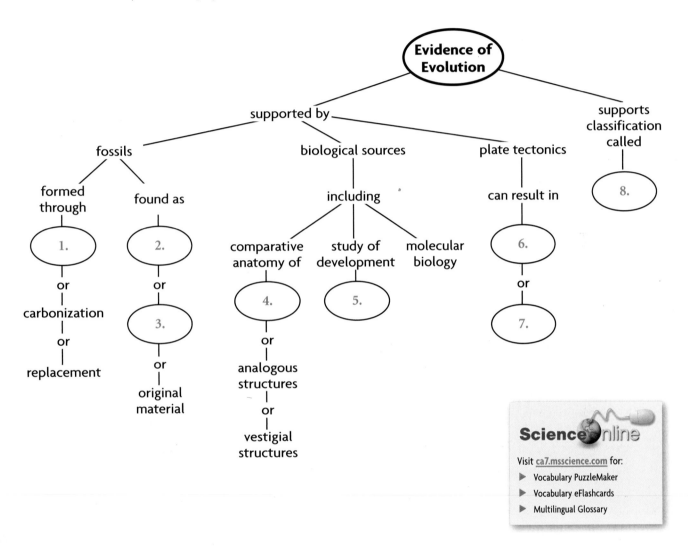

## Using Vocabulary

A(n) ____9.____ is a scientist that researches, gathers, and examines evidence of evolution from the ____10.____. It includes all known ____11.____ and their placements in the formation of rocks and positions in time. Through ____12.____, the remains of trees become petrified wood. Over time, the imprint of a shell can be preserved as a ____13.____. If the imprint fills with sediment that hardens into rock, then a(n) ____14.____ forms.

## Understanding Main Ideas

*Choose the word or phrase that best answers the question.*

1. Which fossil formation process would most likely produce an image of an ancient fern leaf on a rock?
   A. carbonization
   B. cast
   C. mold
   D. permineralization          `3.c`

2. The diagram below shows fossils in different, undisturbed rock layers.

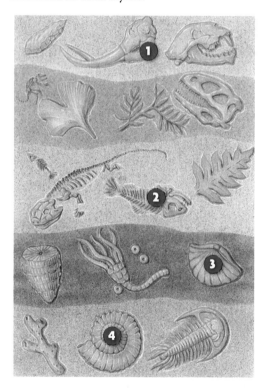

   Which fossil would scientists predict to be the oldest?
   A. 1
   B. 2
   C. 3
   D. 4          `4.c, 4.e`

3. What term describes a structure in an organism that has no function but might have had a function in an ancient ancestor?
   A. analogous
   B. convergent
   C. homologous
   D. vestigial          `3.c`

4. Which would be considered homologous structures?
   A. bones in a bird's arm and bones in a frog's arm
   B. the cytochrome *c* in yeast and cytochrome *c* in rhesus monkeys
   C. a permineralized bone of a wooly mammoth and original material of a wooly mammoth
   D. the wing of bat and the wing of an insect          `3.c`

5. Comparisons of these organisms provide evidence of evolution.

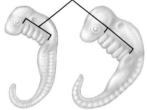

Pharyngeal pouches

Fish          Reptile

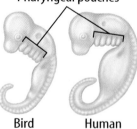

Pharyngeal pouches

Bird          Human

   What type of scientist studies these organisms?
   A. embryologist
   B. entolomologist
   C. microbiologist
   D. paleontologist          `3.c`

## Applying Science

**6. Explain** why the fossils shown in question 2 on the opposite page are in different layers. **4.c, 4.e**

**7. Compare and contrast** the processes of replacement and permineralization. **3.c**

**8. Evaluate** the benefits of DNA sequencing compared to DNA hybridization as a tool for classification. **3.d**

**9. Explain** why the classification of organisms can be diagrammed as shown below. **3.c**

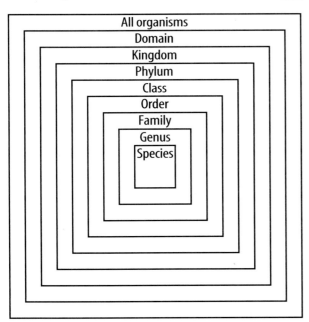

All organisms
Domain
Kingdom
Phylum
Class
Order
Family
Genus
Species

**10. Discuss** why the fossil record for life on Earth has gaps.

**WRITING in Science**

**11. Imagine** you are a paleontologist. A friend asks you, "How can finding a bunch of old bones support the theory of natural selection?" Write a response to explain the connections between fossils and the theory of evolution by natural selection. **ELA7: W 1.1**

## Cumulative Review

**12. Predict** Choose a present-day species and predict how it might leave fossil remains. Identify the type of fossil mostly likely to form from your species. Explain your choices. **3.c**

**13. Describe** the process of radioactive decay. Use the terms *isotope, nucleus,* and *half-life* in your answer. **3.c**

## Applying Math

**Use the data table below to answer questions 14–17.**

| Fossil Species | Time Range (mya) |
|---|---|
| *Homo erectus javanicus* | 1.6–0.6 |
| *Homo erectus pekinensis* | 0.7–0.5 |
| Neanderthal | 0.07–0.04 |
| *Homo sapiens* | 0.3–0.1 |
| *Homo erectus soloensis* | 0.8–0.46 |

**14.** In years, what was the first appearance of *Homo erectus pekinensis* on Earth? **MA7: NS 1.2**

**15.** In years, what was the last appearance of *Homo erectus pekinensis* on Earth? **MA7: NS 1.2**

**16.** In years, approximately how long did *Homo erectus pekinensis* exist on Earth? **MA7: NS 1.2**

**17.** Which species existed for the greatest number of years on Earth? **MA7: MR 1.1**

**1** What is the study of fossils?

A   embryology                    `3.c`

B   entolomology

C   microbiology

D   paleontology

**2** The table below shows some of the proteins in different species of organisms.

| Proteins | |
|---|---|
| Species 1 | A, G, T, C, L, E, S, H |
| Species 2 | A, G, T, C, L, D, H |
| Species 3 | A, G, T, C, L, D, P, U, S, R, I, V |
| Species 4 | A, G, T, C, L, D, H |

Which species are more closely related?

A   species 1 and species 2       `3.d`

B   species 3 and species 4

C   species 1 and species 3

D   species 2 and species 4

**3** Which structure of an ancient organism is least likely to be found as a fossil?

A   a clam shell                  `3.c`

B   a tree trunk

C   a shark tooth

D   a dinosaur muscle

**4** Which classification level includes the greatest number of species?

A   class                         `3.d`

B   family

C   genus

D   kingdom

**5** Below is an image of a type of fossil.

What type of fossil formation process created these tree fossils?

A   carbonization                 `3.c`

B   cast

C   mold

D   permineralization

**6** Which condition makes fossil formation of an organism's remains more likely?

A   attacked by scavengers        `3.c`

B   contains mostly hard structures

C   covered by acidic soils

D   decomposed by bacteria

**7** Which is true for an original material fossil?

A   Minerals replaced hard structures.   `3.c`

B   Only carbon from molecules that made up its body remains.

C   No hard or soft structures have been altered.

D   An imprint of the material has been filled with sediment that hardened as rock.

**8** The graph below shows the relationship between the rate at which an organism is buried in sediment and the potential for it to be preserved as a fossil.

**Relationship Between Sediment Burial Rate and Potential for Remains to Become Fossils**

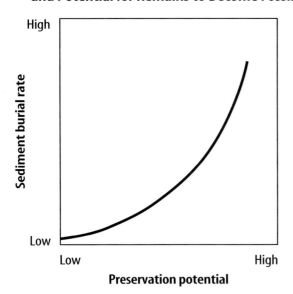

Which statement correctly describes the graph?

**A** The higher the rate of sediment burial, the lower the preservation potential.

**B** The higher the rate of sediment burial, the higher the preservation potential.

**C** The lower the rate of sediment burial, the higher the preservation potential.

**D** The rate of sediment burial has no effect on the preservation potential.                4.c, 4.e

**9** What are cavities left in rocks when shells or bones dissolve?

**A** casts                3.c

**B** molds

**C** original material

**D** carbon films

**10** These two plants evolved in similar environments but on two different continents.

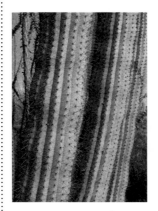

Which term describes this type of evolution?

**A** analogous                4.f

**B** convergent

**C** homologous

**D** vestigial

**11** Imagine that a river suddenly becomes wider and separates a population of a species of flightless birds. What is most likely to happen to the two populations of flightless birds over time?

**A** One population will learn to fly and abandon the other population.                3.a

**B** The two populations will become separate species because they cannot interbreed.

**C** Both populations will become extinct because they cannot get across the river.

**D** The two populations will remain unchanged.

# Reading on Your Own...

Are you interested in learning more about how species have changed over time? If so, check out these great books.

## Biography

**Dragon Bones and Dinosaur Eggs: A Photobiography of Explorer Roy Chapman Andrews,** by Ann Bausum, describes the life of explorer-adventurer Roy Chapman Andrews. He led five expeditions to the Gobi desert to study the ecosystem. This book contains photographs from his expeditions and quotations from his writings. *The content of this book is related to* Science Standard 7.3.

## Nonfiction

**Collision Course: Cosmic Impacts and Life on Earth,** by Fred Bortz, examines how comets or asteroids are formed and gives examples of the effects of asteroid impacts. Detailed photographs of the people, impacts, and equipment add interest. *The content of this book is related to* Science Standard 7.3.

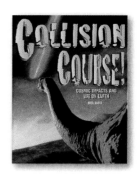

## Nonfiction

**Galapagos in 3-D,** by Mark Blum, presents up-close photos of and information about an amazing variety of animals found on Galapagos. This book is informative not only about the animals, but also about how our eyes see things. *The content of this book is related to* Science Standard 7.3.

## Nonfiction

**Dinosaur Mountain: Graveyard of the Past,** by Caroline Arnold, describes the discoveries made at the Dinosaur National Monument quarry in Utah. This book details the work of paleontologists and contains color photographs of the digs and the work of the scientists. *The content of this book is related to* Science Standard 7.4.

*Choose the word or phrase that best answers the question and write your response on a sheet of paper.*

1. The figure below shows finches with different types of beaks.

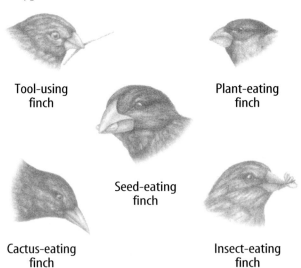

Tool-using finch

Plant-eating finch

Seed-eating finch

Cactus-eating finch

Insect-eating finch

Which, besides competition for food, contributed to the evolution of the species of Darwin's finches?
A. predation
B. DNA
C. camouflage
D. variation in beak shape  `3.a`

2. Some harmless species imitate or mimic a poisonous species which increases their survival. Which is this an example of?
A. acquired characteristics
B. adaptation
C. variation
D. geographic isolation  `3.e`

3. A series of helpful variations in a species results in which?
A. adaptation
B. fossils
C. gradualism
D. climate change  `3.a`

*Write your responses to the following on a sheet a paper.*

4. **Discuss** why trilobites are classified as index fossils.  `4.e`

5. **List** three examples of direct evidence for evolution.  `3.c`

6. **Describe** the typical conditions necessary for fossil formation.  `4.e`

7. The photo below shows an albino lemur.

**Describe** an environment in which this albino lemur might not be at a disadvantage.  `3.e`

8. **Explain** how camouflage might benefit a species?  `3.e`

9. **Compare** Lamarck's and Darwin's ideas about how evolution occurs.  `3.b`

10. **Design a flow chart** to show how natural selection might cause a species to change through time.  `3.b`

11. **Discuss** Fossil remains of plants and animals that lived millions of years ago have been found on more than one continent. How are the locations of these fossil remains evidence that Earth's continental and oceanic plates have moved?  `4.f`

# UNIT 4

# Earth and Life History

**Ancient Carvings**
These beautiful formations in Paria Canyon, along the boder of Arizona and Utah, were carved by the Paria River about 5.4 million years ago.

## West-Coast Events

**40,000–12,000 Years Ago**
Organisms are trapped in tar pits found at La Brea (Los Angeles, California).

**1875**
Henry Hancock discovers that a tooth more than 23 cm long and 9 cm wide may be from a saber-tooth cat; realizes the bones at La Brea could be ancient.

A.D. 1    1750              1800            1850            1900

**1795**
James Hutton proposes idea that natural processes forming rock layers occur uniformly throughout time.

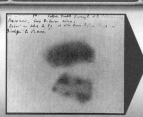

**1896**
Henri Becquerel discovers radioactivity of uranium salts not long after Wilhelm Conrad Roentgen discovers the X ray in 1895.

## World Events

**Science Online**

To learn more about geologists and paleontologists and their work, visit ca7.msscience.com.

**Concepts In Motion**

**Interactive Time Line** To learn more about these events and others, visit ca7.msscience.com.

**c. 1910–1915**
First scientific digs of the La Brea Tar Pits are made by scientists from the University of California; about 170,000 fossils found.

**1980**
Luis and Walter Alvarez from UC Berkeley propose that an asteroid crashed into Earth 65 million years ago, causing the sudden extinction of dinosaurs and many other living things.

**1990**
NASA researchers Kevin Pope, Adriana Ocampo, and Charles Duller, identify a huge crater in the Yucatan, Mexico, that they think is the site of the asteroid crash.

| 1900 | 1920 | 1940 | 1960 | 1980 | 2000 | 2020 |

**1913**
First numeric time scale of geologic ages is proposed by Arthur Holmes of Great Britain; he used radioactive means to measure the age of Earth (about 4 billion years old).

**1967**
Richard Leakey finds two skulls and uses new technology to date objects more accurately; one is 195,000 years old, the oldest for a fully modern human skull.

**November 2002**
The National Science Foundation launches a program, scientists from around the world will verify dates and class of old specimens and analyze new ones to find connections.

# The Age of Earth

## The BIG Idea

Geologists use a variety of methods to estimate and determine the age of Earth.

### LESSON 1  `4.a, 4.c, 7.d`
**Relative Ages of Rocks**

**Main Idea** Geologists can determine the relative ages of rocks by studying the order of rock layers, fossils, and geologic processes that are occurring today.

### LESSON 2  `4.d, 7.c, 7.d`
**Absolute Ages of Rocks**

**Main Idea** Unstable parent isotopes change to stable daughter isotopes at a constant rate. Geologists measure the amounts of these isotopes in minerals to determine how long ago the minerals formed.

## Which is older?

Imagine that you are a geologist and you want to know which is older—the mountain in the background or the rocks beneath your feet. What kinds of things do you suppose you could do to answer the question?

**Science Journal** Write two paragraphs explaining what a geologist might have to do to answer the question. In one paragraph, describe the tools you might need to use and the way you would gather data.

## Launch Lab

## What is Earth's surface like?

How did the soil under you form? You can answer this question by observing what the soil around you is like.

### Procedure

1. Walk through your neighborhood or through a nearby park. What natural land features do you see? Make simple sketches of your observations.

2. List your observations. Be sure to consider the Think About This questions when making your observations.

### Think About This

- **Describe** the soil type. Is it filled with clay, sandy, or black and filled with plant matter? What sizes are any rocks and grains?

- **Identify** clues that tell you what the area might have been like in the past. Explain the clues and describe any evidence of river or stream erosion.

 4.a, 7.e

## Science Online

Visit ca7.msscience.com to:

▶ view **C**oncepts in M**o**tion

▶ explore Virtual Labs

▶ access content-related Web links

▶ take the Standards Check

 **The Age of Earth** Make the following Foldable to summarize the ways the age of Earth can be determined.

▷ **STEP 1 Fold** a sheet of paper in half from top to bottom and then in half from side to side.

▷ **STEP 2 Unfold** the paper once. **Cut** along the fold of the top flap to make two flaps.

▷ **STEP 3 Label** the flaps as shown.

Relative Age Dating | Absolute Age Dating

### Reading *Skill*

**Comparing and Contrasting** As you read this chapter, record information to compare relative age dating to absolute age dating.

# Get Ready to Read

## Make Predictions

**1** **Learn It!** A prediction is an educated guess based on what you already know. One way to predict while reading is to guess what you believe the author will tell you next. As you are reading, each new topic should make sense because it is related to the previous paragraph or passage.

**2** **Practice It!** Read the excerpt below from Lesson 1. Based on what you have read, make predictions about what you will read in the rest of the lesson. After you read Lesson 1, go back to your predictions to see if they were correct.

Predict how rocks are broken into pieces.

Predict at which step the pieces are changed into rock again.

Predict how rock pieces are transported most often.

Sedimentary rocks form from **pieces** of preexisting rocks. There are four steps in the process that forms sedimentary rock: **weathering, transportation, deposition, and lithification.** These four steps occur simultaneously everywhere on Earth's surface.

*—from page 287*

**3** **Apply It!** Before you read, skim the questions in the Chapter Assessment. Choose three questions and predict the answers.

# Target Your Reading

Use this to focus on the main ideas as you read the chapter.

**Reading Tip** As you read, check the predictions you made to see if they were correct.

**1** **Before you read** the chapter, respond to the statements below on your worksheet or on a numbered sheet of paper.

- Write an **A** if you **agree** with the statement.
- Write a **D** if you **disagree** with the statement.

**2** **After you read** the chapter, look back to this page to see if you've changed your mind about any of the statements.

- If any of your answers changed, explain why.
- Change any false statements into true statements.
- Use your revised statements as a study guide.

| Before You Read A or D | Statement | After You Read A or D |
|---|---|---|
| | **1** The processes that are at work on Earth today work at a faster rate than they did a million years ago. | |
| | **2** Moving water is able to carry large rocks, sand, and soil downstream. | |
| | **3** Sand particles can be pressed by layers of sand above them and cemented by minerals in the groundwater to become sandstone. | |
| | **4** Layers of rock that are tilted at an angle because they have been eroded by glaciers. | |
| | **5** Unless they have been folded or turned over, rock layers on the bottom are older than rock layers above them. | |
| | **6** All the atoms of one kind of element are the same and never change. | |
| | **7** We can use the position of rock layers to determine exact dates for the history of Earth's geologic events. | |
| | **8** Igneous rocks are the best rocks to use for finding out how old Earth is. | |

**Science Online**

Print a worksheet of this page at ca7.msscience.com.

### Science Content Standards

**4.a** Students know Earth processes today are similar to those that occurred in the past and slow geologic processes have large cumulative effects over long periods of time.

**4.c** Students know that the rock cycle includes the formation of new sediment and rocks and that rocks are often found in layers, with the oldest generally on the bottom.

**Also covers:** 7.d

## Reading Guide

### What *You'll Learn*

▶ **Explain** how geologists identify past events by studying rocks.

▶ **Recognize** the geologic history of an area.

▶ **Describe** how early geologists estimated Earth's age.

### Why *It's Important*

Identifying the processes that have been at work on Earth will guide scientists in predicting what will happen on Earth in the future.

### Vocabulary

uniformitarianism
rock cycle
clast
lithification
stratum
superposition
relative age

### Review Vocabulary

**fossil:** remains, trace, or imprint of a plant or animal preserved in Earth's crust (p. 244)

# Relative Ages of Rocks

**Main Idea** Geologists can determine the relative ages of rocks by studying the order of rock layers, fossils, and geologic processes that are occurring today.

**Real-World Reading Connection** When detectives go to the scene of a crime, they look for clues. After recording their observations, they try to determine what happened. Geologists search for clues in the rocks that can provide information about events that occurred millions of years ago.

## The Beginning of Modern Geology

Before the late 1700's most scientists believed that rocks formed by evaporation of minerals dissolved in sea water. By observing rock features and the movement of sediments in streams, a Scotsman named James Hutton first realized there were two processes at work on Earth. One process formed rock and the other tore it down again. **Figure 1** shows one of these destructive processes.

**Figure 1** These rocks look different from when they first formed.

**Infer** What changes do you think the rock layers in the mountain experienced?

# The Principle of Uniformitarianism

Geologists, like all scientists, search for ideas to explain how Earth's processes work. Hutton had an idea that "the present is the key to the past." His principle of **uniformitarianism** states that the processes that are at work today are the same processes that have been at work in Earth's past. Another way to say this is that the same Earth processes have been at work for a very long time. Therefore, scientists can observe the processes that are active on Earth today, and use them to interpret what happened in the past. So when scientists observe soil layers being put down during annual flooding, they can compare that to how layering in rocks might have occurred. **Figure 2** shows what might have happened to a sand beach.

## Change is Slow

No one has ever directly observed a mountain forming or a steep river valley becoming wider and less steep. Yet we know these things happen. The process is so slow that direct observation is not possible. James Hutton realized this. He reasoned that if erosion occurred for a long time, it could greatly change Earth's surface. In fact, with enough time, erosion could wear down mountain ranges. **Figure 3** shows a young, rugged mountain range and an older, smoother range. How might time and erosion change the rugged mountains?

**Figure 2** The beach sand and the sand grains in the sandstone share similar characteristics. This suggests that the sandstone formed from the same processes that the beach sand is experiencing now.

**Sorted Sand**

**Layered Sandstone**

**Figure 3** Young mountains have not been exposed to the effects of erosion for very long. Their peaks are jagged and angular. Tops of older mountains that have been eroding for millions of years are more rounded.

**Younger Mountains**

**Older Mountains**

# The Rock Cycle

James Hutton had begun to recognize what geologists now call the rock cycle, shown in **Figure 4.** The **rock cycle** is the series of processes that make and change rocks through heating, melting, cooling, uplift, weathering, burial, and increasing pressure. You can trace the formation of the three major types of rocks—igneous, sedimentary, and metamorphic—on the figure.

## Igneous, Metamorphic, and Sedimentary

Geologists divide rocks into three groups determined by how a rock is formed. Igneous rocks are produced when magma solidifies. Different kinds of igneous rock are identified by the size of the crystals that they contain. Large crystals form when magma cools very slowly underground. Smaller crystals form in igneous rock that cools rapidly at the surface. Some igneous rocks have no crystals because they cool very rapidly, perhaps in the ocean water.

Metamorphic rock is any rock that is put under extreme pressure or heat short of melting. The rocks that are most affected are those that come in contact with hot fluids and magma moving through fractures toward the surface. Pressure may cause the mineral spaces to collapse and become more closely packed. Temperature may cause the minerals to recrystallize and form a new rock mineral.

Sedimentary rocks are those that form from sediments. Sediments are the tiny particles that come from the erosion of various types of rocks. The particles eventually become compacted and cemented into rocks.

Estimating the age of each type of rock is a challenge geologists encounter as they observe these rock formation processes. The most important ideas in determining the ages of rocks are related to sedimentary rock formation.

**Figure 4** The rock cycle traces the recycling pathways of Earth materials.

**Identify** Trace the complete path through the rock cycle of a mineral crystal formed from lava.

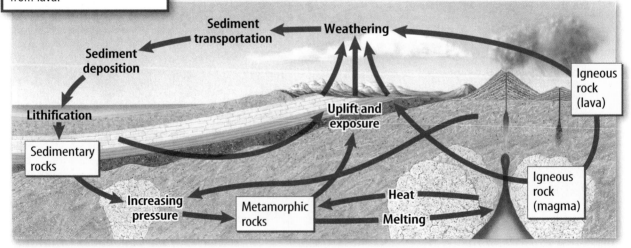

## Sediment Formation and Layering

Sedimentary rocks form from pieces of preexisting rocks. There are four steps in the process that forms sedimentary rock: weathering, transportation, deposition, and lithification. These four steps occur simultaneously everywhere on Earth's surface.

**Weathering** The first step in the formation of sedimentary rocks is weathering. Weathering is the physical or chemical breakdown of rocks into smaller pieces. Physical weathering breaks down rocks without changing the mineral composition. Frost wedging, the weathering process that occurs when water freezes and expands in cracks, can force rocks to break apart. This process is illustrated in the top photo of **Figure 5.**

Chemical weathering changes the mineral composition of rocks. When minerals that are holding a rock together change to new minerals, the rock often falls apart. This crumbling increases the surface area of the rock. As surface area increases, the rate of chemical weathering increases. Chemical weathering usually involves water. Rainwater can combine with carbon dioxide in the atmosphere to form carbonic acid. Acidic rainwater can dissolve limestone. The cave shown in **Figure 5** was formed when acidic rainwater dissolved limestone under Earth's surface.

 How does physical weathering change rocks?

**Transportation** The next step in sedimentary rock formation is transportation. It occurs when sediments move downhill to lower areas where they come to rest. Sediments are moved by running water, wind, moving ice, and gravity.

Sediments vary in size from large boulders to microscopic bits of rock. These different-sized pieces of rock are called **clasts.** Different amounts of force are needed to move them. The force is applied by gravity as the slope of the landscape changes. When the slope of the landscape is steep, more force can be applied to the clast. The more force that is applied to the clast, the larger the clast that can be moved.

Gravity pulling on water, air, and ice can also move the clasts. Fast-moving water can move larger clasts than slowly moving water. You can understand how wind might move large clasts during large storms while sand and smaller clasts are commonly blown across the landscape. Clasts of all sizes can be moved by glaciers because of the glacier's mass and size, but they move very slowly. During the process of being transported, clasts may change size and shape. They become rounded as they knock into each other and chips are broken off. This reduces their size at the same time.

**Physical Weathering**

**Chemical Weathering**

**Figure 5** Physical and chemical weathering result in formation of sediment that may eventually become a sedimentary rock.

**WORD ORIGIN**

clast
from Greek *klastos;* means *broken*

**Figure 6** This stack of sedimentary rock strata is in Utah. Slight differences in grain size and composition produce the distinct layering.

**Deposition** The third step in the formation of sedimentary rocks is depostion (deh puh ZIH shun). It occurs when sediment being transported by water, wind, or a glacier slows down or stops. This usually happens in low areas on the landscape called depositional environments. As the sediments are dropped, gravity causes them to form **parallel,** horizontal layers. Distinct layering is a common feature in sedimentary rocks, as shown in **Figure 6.** Another characteristic of deposition is sorting. As the carrier of the sediment slows down, heavier objects are dropped first. Lighter and lighter objects are carried farther and deposited later. **Figure 7** shows how different materials may be sorted.

 Why are river deposits well sorted?

**Lithification** The final step in the formation of sedimentary rock is **lithification** (lih thuh fuh KAY shun). As older sediment layers become buried beneath layers of younger sediments, the weight of the younger sediments squeezes the older sediments together. This is called compaction. Mineral-rich liquids are still able to seep into the pore spaces between the sediment grains. Evaporation of the water and the weight of the layers cause the minerals in the pore spaces to turn to cement. This compaction and cementation changes the sediments into rock. The sediments have become lithified.

**Figure 7** These diagrams illustrate the different grades of sediment sorting. Sediment that has been deposited by glacial ice or mass wasting is very poorly sorted. Beach sand is commonly very well sorted.

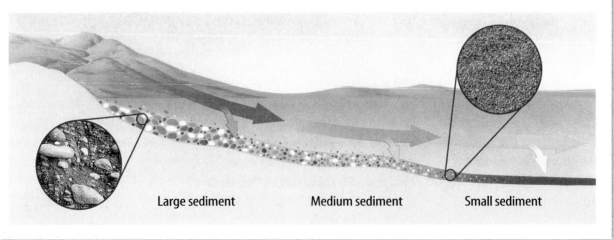

Large sediment     Medium sediment     Small sediment

# Superposition and the Fossil Record

Layers of rocks are called **strata** (singular, stratum). In 1669, Nicolas Steno, a Danish physician, presented four principles that helped geologists study strata and interpret the rocks' history. They are the principles of superposition, original horizontality, original lateral continuity, and cross-cutting relationships.

## Principle of Superposition

The principle of **superposition** states that in a stack of undisturbed sedimentary rock layers, the layers on the bottom were deposited before the layers on the top. This means that the rocks on the bottom are older than the rocks on the top. **Figure 8** shows this relationship. The exact ages of the rocks are not known, but their relative age is known. **Relative age** tells you how old something is when compared to something else. For example you know that the middle strata are younger than the bottom stratum, but are older than the top stratum.

The principle of superposition is perhaps the most important of Steno's four principles. Once the relationship between strata and age was understood, geologists could study the rock layers and determine the geologic events that resulted in their deposition.

The remaining three Steno's principles are:
- Rock layers are originally deposited in horizontal, or nearly horizontal, layers.
- These rock layers usually do not end suddenly.
- A rock layer or feature that cuts across other rock layers is younger than the layer(s) being cut.

**Table 1** on the next page more fully explains these three principles.

## Fossils and Relative Age

You have read that the fossil record provides information on changes in life throughout Earth's history. By keeping track of which fossils came from which strata, and by applying the principle of superposition, geologists use the fossil occurrences in layers to confirm or assign relative ages to rock strata. **Figure 9** show how the superposition has helped date the layers.

**Figure 8** Note the distinct layers in the Paria Canyon, Utah. The layers at the bottom were deposited first, so they are older than the layers on the top.

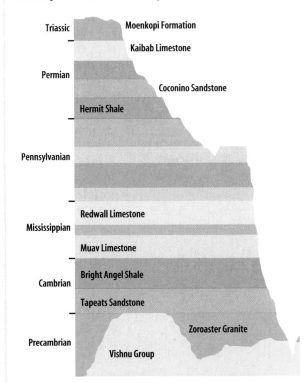

**Figure 9** The relative ages of these layers have been found using superposition.

**Interpret Data** Which layer is oldest?

Triassic — Moenkopi Formation

Kaibab Limestone

Permian — Coconino Sandstone

Hermit Shale

Pennsylvanian

Redwall Limestone

Mississippian

Muav Limestone

Bright Angel Shale

Cambrian — Tapeats Sandstone

Zoroaster Granite

Precambrian — Vishnu Group

## Table 1 Steno's Principles

| Principle | Definition | | |
|-----------|------------|---|---|
| **Principle of superposition** | **In a stack of undisturbed sedimentary rock layers, the layers on the bottom were deposited before the layers on the top.** They are the oldest in the sequence. Fossils in the rocks also follow this principle. They are oldest at the bottom and are younger toward the top. | | |
| **Principle of original horizontality** | **Rock layers are originally deposited in horizontal, or nearly horizontal, layers.** This principle explains that rock strata that are now at an angle must have been tilted after the rocks formed. | | |
| **Principle of original lateral continuity** | **Sedimentary rocks form layers that cover large areas.** Imagine a trench being cut in the ground to bury a wire. Now the ground is divided, with the once-continuous grass on either side. Rock strata are affected the same way. The river valley in the picture is like the trench and the strata are like the grass. | | |
| **Principle of cross-cutting relationships** | **A rock layer or feature that cuts across other rock layers is younger than the layers being cut.** Imagine magma getting injected into and across a sequence of strata and then cooling to granite. Because the strata had to be there in order for the granite to cut across them, the strata are necessarily older than the dike is. | | |

# Using Rocks to Determine Relative Age

**WORD ORIGIN** · · · · · · · ·
stratum
from Latin *stratere;* means *to spread out*

Estimating when a rock layer formed or the age of certain fossils in those layers is one of the tasks of a geologist. James Hutton explained the process of uniformitarianism. Scientists can use geologic processes observed today to interpret geologic events of the past. Nicolas Steno stated four principles that help scientists determine the order, or the relative ages, of these geologic events. The rock cycle outlines the formation processes of the three main types of rock. Following the four steps in the formation of sedimentary rocks helps scientists understand how Earth formed. Layering and fossils are common in sedimentary rocks. Fossils can also be used to determine or confirm the relative ages of rock strata.

# LESSON 1  Review

## Summarize

Create your own lesson summary as you design a **visual aid.**

1. **Write** the lesson title, number, and page numbers at the top of your poster.

2. **Scan** the lesson to find the **red** main headings. Organize these headings on your poster, leaving space between each.

3. **Design** an information box beneath each **red** heading. In the box, list 2–3 details, key terms, and definitions from each **blue** subheading.

4. **Illustrate** your poster with diagrams of important structures or processes next to each information box.

 **ELA7:** W 2.5

##  Standards Check

### Using Vocabulary

1. Explain the relationship between the following terms: *superposition, strata.* **4.a**

2. Using your own words, define *relative age.* **4.c**

3. Describe the principle of uniformitarianism. **4.a**

### Understanding Main Ideas

4. **List** the four processes involved in the formation of sedimentary rocks. **4.a**

5. **Complete** the graphic organizer to summarize how Hutton came to realize that Earth is old. Add more arrows if needed. **4.a**

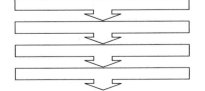

6. Which of Steno's principles is illustrated below? **4.a**

7. **Contrast** the formation of igneous rocks and the formation of metamorphic rocks. **4.a**

### Applying Science

8. **Explain** how scientists use fossils and rock strata to determine the relative age of rocks. **4.a**

9. **Summarize** Hutton's reasoning that allowed him to conclude that Earth's processes are cyclic. **4.c**

**Science** nline
For more practice, visit **Standards Check** at ca7.msscience.com.

# MiniLab

## How does Earth change over time?

Earth has changed over time by slow geologic processes, and by catastrophic events. Create a mini-world to show changes that are happening to a landscape over time.

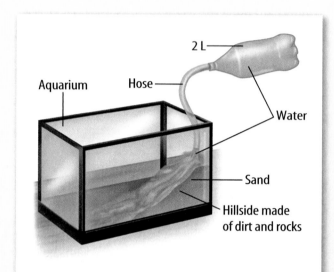

### Procedure

1. Read and complete the lab safety form.

2. Choose one of the following geologic environments to model: beach, mountains, glacier-covered mountains, or river valley.

3. Think about the geologic processes you have read about in this chapter. Make a list of the ways landscapes change over time and the forces and processes that cause the changes.

4. Create a model showing some of these processes. Materials you might use include **modeling clay, water, rocks, sand, dirt and rocks, an aquarium,** and any other materials you think will work well.

### Analysis

1. **Describe** the types of rock and the processes you have modeled. Be specific.

2. **Analyze** your model. How does your model compare to real life?

### Science Content Standards

**4.c** Students know that the rock cycle includes the formation of new sediment and rocks and that rocks are often found in layers, with the oldest generally on the bottom.

**7.d** Construct scale models, maps, and appropriately labeled diagrams to communicate scientific knowledge (e.g., motion of Earth's plates and cell structure).

## Science Content Standards

**4.d** Students know that evidence from geologic layers and radioactive dating indicates Earth is approximately 4.6 billion years old and that life on this planet has existed for more than 3 billion years.
**7.c** Communicate the logical connection among hypotheses, science concepts, tests conducted, data collected, and conclusions drawn from the scientific evidence.
**7.d** Construct scale models, maps, and appropriately labeled diagrams to communicate scientific knowledge (e.g., motion of Earth's plates and cell structure).

## Reading Guide

### What *You'll Learn*

▶ **Describe** the different types of radioactive decay.

▶ **Determine** the age of a mineral given the relative amounts of parent and daughter isotopes and the half-life of the parent.

▶ **Explain** how sedimentary rocks are dated.

### Why *It's Important*

Knowing the absolute age of Earth helps scientists predict how the universe formed and when.

### Vocabulary

isotope
radioactive decay
half-life

### Review Vocabulary

**radiation:** thermal energy transferred by electromagnetic waves (Grade 6)

# Absolute Ages of Rocks

**Main Idea** Unstable parent isotopes change to stable daughter isotopes at a constant rate. Geologists measure the amounts of these isotopes in minerals to determine how long ago the minerals formed.

**Real-World Reading Connection** Bog bodies are well-preserved human remains found in peat bogs. They range in age from hundreds to thousands of years old. Their clothes and hairstyles have allowed researchers to infer about when these people lived. What dating methods allow researchers to confirm their inferences and more closely pinpoint when these people lived?

## What is Earth's age?

How would you go about finding out how old Earth is? In the past, scientists have tried measuring rates of erosion to see how long it would take mountains to erode. They tried calculating the time it would take Earth to cool from a molten mass to its present temperature. Each attempt was unsuccessful at predicting Earth's age. Finally, scientists discovered a natural "clock" that ticked away with great accuracy. This new clock allowed geologists to date the age of Earth, meteorites, and the Moon. In this lesson, you will read about natural clocks and how they work. **Figure 10** shows a bog body. Since bog bodies are well preserved by the acid conditions of the bog, scientists used the natural clock to determine their age.

 Why was the discovery of a natural clock so important?

> **Figure 10** Found in peat bogs in Great Britain and Northern Europe, bog bodies are human remains preserved by the acidic bog conditions.

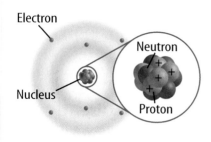

Carbon atom

**Figure 11** The carbon-12 atom has 6 protons, 6 neutrons, and 6 electrons.

**WORD ORIGIN**············

isotope
from Greek *iso–;* means *the same*
from Greek *–topos;* means *place*
·············

# Atoms and Isotopes

Atoms are the building blocks of all matter. Atoms are made of protons, neutrons, and electrons. Protons and neutrons are located in the center of an atom called the nucleus. Electrons are located outside the nucleus. **Figure 11** shows a representation of a carbon atom.

Carbon is one of more than 100 known chemical elements that exist on Earth. An element is defined by the number of protons in its atoms. For example, a carbon atom contains six protons while an oxygen atom contains eight protons. Although the number of protons in an atom of any given element is always the same, the number of neutrons in that element can vary. **Isotope** is the term for atoms of a given element that have the same number of protons, but a differing number of neutrons. Isotopes of carbon atoms can have six, seven, or eight neutrons. The isotopes are written as carbon-12, carbon-13 and carbon-14. The carbon isotope numbers are found by adding the number of protons and neutrons. Carbon-12 has six protons and six neutrons. Carbon-13 has six protons and seven neutrons. Carbon-14 has six protons and eight neutrons.

## Radioactive Decay

Isotopes of an element may be stable or unstable. Carbon has two stable isotopes and one unstable, or radioactive, isotope. An isotope that has an unstable nucleus emits particles and energy. A more stable nucleus is formed through a process called radioactive decay. **Radioactive decay** occurs when an unstable atomic nucleus changes into another nucleus by emitting particles and energy. A nucleus that is unstable and undergoes radioactive decay is called radioactive. This decay is the natural clock that scientists use to find the ages of Earth's rocks. **Figure 12** illustrates the radioactive decay process for the element polonium. Radioactive decay is useful for finding the age of objects that are very old. **Figure 13** shows a method for dating things only a few thousand years old.

**Figure 12** The nucleus of this polonium atom has lost two protons and two neutrons.

**Explain** Why does the atomic number change when polonium decays to bismuth?

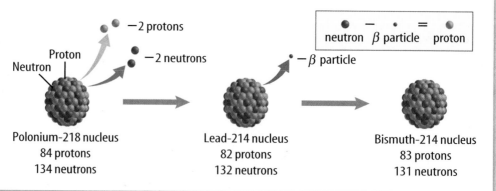

Polonium-218 nucleus
84 protons
134 neutrons

Lead-214 nucleus
82 protons
132 neutrons

Bismuth-214 nucleus
83 protons
131 neutrons

# Visualizing Accurate Dating with Tree Rings

**Figure 13** The science of dendrochronology compares annual tree-ring growth in trees to date events and changes in past environments.

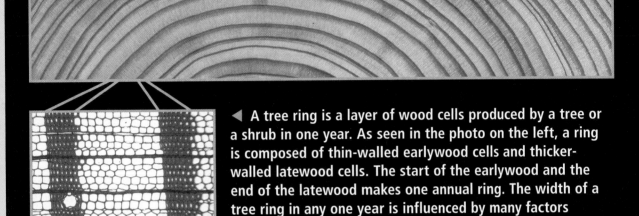

◀ A tree ring is a layer of wood cells produced by a tree or a shrub in one year. As seen in the photo on the left, a ring is composed of thin-walled earlywood cells and thicker-walled latewood cells. The start of the earlywood and the end of the latewood makes one annual ring. The width of a tree ring in any one year is influenced by many factors including rainfall, temperature, sunlight, and disease.

Use these steps to date the age of ▶ the Pueblo beams.

**1** Core samples are taken from living trees. This provides the common starting point for all the living trees in the area.

**2** Core samples are taken from dead trees that are still standing. There will be a point that will match in the living trees and in the standing, dead trees.

**3** Core samples are taken from the beams. A correlation between the beams and the dead trees will allow us to find the age of the tree the beam was made from. This will tell us the age of the building. The cores are all cross-dated by comparing patterns of rings in all the core samples.

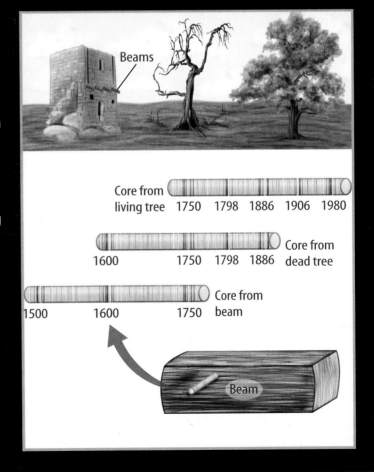

Core from living tree 1750 1798 1886 1906 1980

1600 1750 1798 1886 Core from dead tree

1500 1600 1750 Core from beam

Beam

*Contributed by National Geographic*

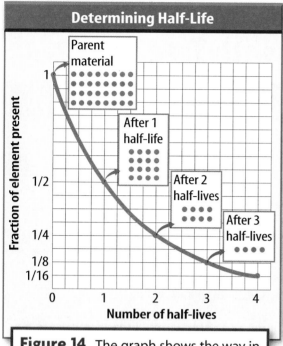

### Determining Half-Life

Parent material

After 1 half-life

After 2 half-lives

After 3 half-lives

**Figure 14** The graph shows the way in which all radioactive elements decay.

**Calculate** How many half-lives have elapsed if a sample has 25 percent of a parent isotope and 75 percent of the daughter isotope?

**Parent and Daughter Isotopes** Scientists call the isotope that undergoes radioactive decay the parent isotope. The stable form of the element that forms is called the daughter isotope. Recall that carbon has two stable isotopes and one radioactive isotope. Uranium-238 goes through fourteen steps as it decays to a stable isotope of lead. Uranium decay is the process behind nuclear fission and nuclear power.

### Half-Life

In 1902, Ernest Rutherford and Frederick Soddy discovered that parent isotopes decay into daughter isotopes at a constant rate. This rate is the decay rate. **Table 2** lists the decay rates of some common radioactive isotopes. To measure decay rates, scientists must compare the amount of parent and daughter isotopes in a material. They then measure the rate at which the radioactive element gives off energy and particles. The time it takes for a sample of a radioactive isotope to decay to half its original mass is called **half-life.** Geologists can determine the absolute age of a piece of the Earth's crust by calculating the absolute age of the minerals that compose it. They do this by measuring the parent-to-daughter ratio of an isotope in the minerals. The method for calculating half-lives and age is illustrated in **Figure 14.**

 What is the half-life of an isotope?

| Table 2 Half-Lives of Selected Radioactive Isotopes | | |
|---|---|---|
| **Radioactive Isotope** | **Approximate Half-Life** | **Decay Product** |
| Rubidium-87 | 48.6 billion years | strontium-87 |
| Thorium-232 | 14.0 billion years | lead-208 |
| Potassium-40 | 1.3 billion years | argon-40 |
| Uranium-238 | 4.5 billion years | lead-206 |
| Uranium-235 | 0.7 billion years | lead-207 |
| Carbon-14 | 5,730 years | nitrogen-14 |

# Determining Earth's Age

When scientists discovered that radioactive isotopes decay at a constant rate, they knew they had found a "natural clock." Then they turned their attention to the age of Earth. If they could find a way to use this "clock," would they be able determine the age of Earth's oldest rocks?

## Radiometric Dating

The procedure that scientists use to calculate absolute ages of rocks and minerals is called radiometric dating. By measuring the amount of parent material and comparing it to the daughter material in a rock, the number of half-lives the material has been through can be counted. Igneous rocks are the most common rocks used for radiometric dating. They usually contain only parent isotopes when they formed. Dates calculated from minerals in igneous rocks indicate when the mineral crystallized from magma.

Determining the age of metamorphic rocks can be difficult. The increase in temperature and pressure during metamorphism can cause a rock to partially melt. When rocks melt, they become igneous and their radiometric clock gets reset. Decay begins again. Geologists rarely use radiometric dating for sedimentary rocks. This is because the dates from sedimentary rocks indicate when the minerals in the rock formed, not when the sedimentary rock itself formed. The lab shown in **Figure 15** is one that does radiometric dating of rocks.

 Why are igneous rocks most often used in radiometric dating?

**SCIENCE USE V. COMMON USE**

dating

*Science Use* to determine the period of time to which something belongs. *Radioactive decay is used in dating rocks billions of years in age.*

*Common Use* an ongoing romantic social engagement between two people. *Kei and Mai Lin have been dating for two months.*

**Figure 15** Radiometric dating is done in a lab using sophisticated equipment.

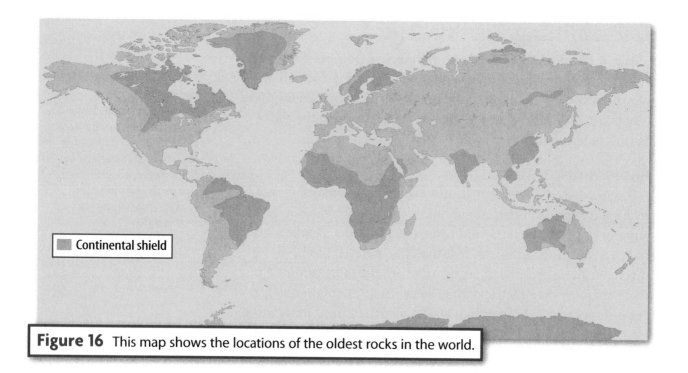

**Figure 16** This map shows the locations of the oldest rocks in the world.

**Figure 17** The Moon's surface is covered with broken rock and sediment.

**Infer** Why do you think the astronaut's footprints are so well preserved?

## The Absolute Age of Earth

As you have read, Earth's material constantly moves through the rock cycle. Geologists feared this recycling would have destroyed Earth's oldest rocks.

In 1989, scientists made an important discovery. **Figure 16** shows that the oldest rocks on Earth are part of areas called continental shields. Continental shields are areas where exposed rock dates back to Precambrian time—billions of years ago. Grains from sedimentary rock can be dated as if they are an igneous rock sample. The ages reported by different scientists using different isotope pairs ranged between 3.62 and 3.65 billion years. Until 1989, geologists doubted they would find any older rocks from Earth. Then researchers reported a 3.96-billion-year-old age for a zircon grain from a metamorphic rock in Canada.

New technology allowed scientists to date other zircon crystals from rocks in Canada in 1998 and Australia in 2001. The ages they reported were 4.0 and 4.4 billion years.

**Meteorites and the Moon** Scientists use radiometric dating to determine the age of meteorites and the Moon. The ages of stony meteorites collected in Antarctica have been calculated to be between 4.48 and 4.56 billion years old. As shown in **Figure 17,** the Moon's surface is covered with loose rock material. Rocks brought back from the Moon have been radiometrically dated to be approximately 4.6 billion years old. This closeness of the calculated ages of Earth, the Moon, and meteorites helps to **confirm** the idea that the entire solar system formed at the same time.

# Isotopes and Earth's Age

Scientists use radioactive isotopes to measure the percentage of parent to daughter material in a substance. This allows scientists to provide absolute, or numerical ages to the geologic layers and events. Unstable parent isotopes decay into stable daughter isotopes. Measuring the rate at which this occurs provides useful data that can be transformed into a unit called a half-life. Using half-life values of certain isotopes allows scientists to calculate the absolute ages of igneous rocks and some metamorphosed rocks. Earth's age has been calculated to be about 4.55 billion years, the age of its oldest rocks.

In the next chapter you will read how relative and absolute age dating have been used to help explore the history of Earth's life.

# LESSON 2 Review

## Summarize

Create your own lesson summary as you design a **study web.**

1. **Write** the lesson title, number, and page numbers at the top of a sheet of paper.

2. **Scan** the lesson to find the **red** main headings.

3. **Organize** these headings clockwise on branches around the lesson title.

4. **Review** the information under each **red** heading to design a branch for each **blue** subheading.

5. **List** 2–3 details, key terms, and definitions from each **blue** subheading on branches extending from the main heading branches.

ELA7: W 2.5

## Standards Check

### Using Vocabulary

1. What process results in the natural breakdown of unstable atoms? **4.d**

2. Explain how the terms *isotope* and *half-life* are related. **4.d**

### Understanding Main Ideas

3. **Determine** the age of a mineral that contains 25 percent of the parent, potassium-40, and 75 percent of the daughter, argon-40. The half-life of potassium-40 is 1.25 billion years. **4.d**

4. **Explain** the difference between carbon-12 and carbon-14. **4.d**

5. **Construct** a bar graph that demonstrates the decrease in the amount of parent isotope during the first five half-lives. **4.d**

6. **Predict** the age of the oldest rocks on Mars. **4.d**

7. Fill in the chart with the correct number of protons and neutrons. **4.d**

| Isotope | Protons | Neutrons |
|---------|---------|----------|
| Carbon-12 | | |
| Carbon-13 | | |
| Carbon-14 | | |

### Applying Science

8. **Decide** how to use relative dating and radiometric dating to find and date the oldest rock on a continent. **4.d**

9. **Evaluate** the possibility of using radiometric dating methods on a meteorite made of sedimentary rock. **4.d**

10. **Explain** how sedimentary rocks are dated. **4.d**

**Science** Online

For more practice, visit **Standards Check** at ca7.msscience.com.

# DataLab

# How long until it's all gone?

Geologists can determine the age of certain types of rock by calculating the amounts of certain radioactive elements in them. You will see how these calculations work as you complete this lab.

- The half-life of uranium-233 is 162,000 years.
- The half-life of plutonium-239 is 24,400 years.
- The half-life of radium-226 is 1,600 years.

## Data Collection

1. With a group of two or three classmates, collect 100 pennies. The pennies represent 100 g of one of the elements listed above. Choose one of the elements.

2. Make a data table like the one below.

3. Fill in the data table by repeating these two steps. Divide the amount of pennies in half. Write the number of years that has passed according to the half life of your chosen element.

4. Graph your data.

## Data Analysis

1. **Solve**  How many half-lives did it take to get to 1 g of your element?

2. **Describe** the shape of your graph.

3. **Interpret data**  How accurate can your calculations be once the amount of your element gets below 8 half-lives?

| Number of Half-Lives of Element | Number of Pennies Left (equal to mass in grams of substance left over) | Number of Years that Have Passed |
|---|---|---|
| 0 | 100 | 0 |
| 1 | | |
| 2 | | |
| 3 | | |

 **Science Content Standards**

**4.d** Students know that evidence from geologic layers and radioactive dating indicates Earth is approximately 4.6 billion years old and that life on this planet has existed for more than 3 billion years.

**MA7:** MR 2.5

Also covers: 7.c

# Applying Math

## Measuring Mineral Production in California

California produces about 8 percent of the minerals produced in the United States each year. The table shows some of the minerals produced in the years 1999, 2000, and 2001.

### Mineral Production in California

| Mineral | 1999 Quantity (short tons) | 2000 Quantity (short tons) | 2001 Quantity (short tons) |
|---|---|---|---|
| Asbestos | 7,900 | 5,800 | 5,800 |
| Boron minerals | 681,300 | 602,000 | 716,600 |
| Cement: masonry | 513,800 | 533,600 | 521,000 |
| Cement: Portland | 11,344,700 | 12,017,200 | 11,245,500 |
| Bentonite clay | 33,900 | 23,600 | 23,700 |
| Common clay | 1,017,900 | 1,067,800 | 1,068,300 |
| Gypsum | 3,561,800 | 3,534,600 | 3,197,200 |
| Construction sand and gravel | 159,505,300 | 163,170,000 | 163,170,000 |
| Industrial sand and gravel | 1,972,400 | 1,992,200 | 1,934,900 |
| Crushed stone | 66,452,100 | 65,819,200 | 65,047,500 |
| Dimension stone | 32,400 | 36,700 | 36,400 |

## Example

What is the total quantity of minerals produced in 2000?

**What you know:** Each quantity of minerals in the year 2000

**What you need to find:** The total produced

**Add the values in the year 2000 column.** 248,802,700 short tons

**Answer:** The total quantity of minerals produced in 2000 is 248,802,700 short tons.

### Practice Problems

1. What percent of the total minerals produced in 2000 is gypsum?

2. What percent of the total minerals produced in 2000 is construction sand and gravel?

Science online
For more math practice, visit **Math Practice** at ca7.msscience.com.

## Model and Invent:
# Erosion Stoppers

### Materials

stream table
textbooks or bricks
sand
gravel
water container
hose or tubing
clamps
bucket
plant matter
stone
water

### Safety Precautions

### Science Content Standards

**4.c** Students know that the rock cycle includes the formation of new sediment and rocks and that rocks are often found in layers, with the oldest generally on the bottom.
**7.c** Communicate the logical connection among hypotheses, science concepts, tests conducted, data collected, and conclusions drawn from the scientific evidence.
**7.d** Conduct scale models, maps, and appropriately labeled diagrams to communicate scientific knowledge (e.g., motion of Earth's plates and cell structure).

## Problem

You have learned that water erodes sandy soil. While there are places where the soil is clearly exposed, in most places, the landscape, such as trees and grass, holds the soil in place.

## Form a Hypothesis

What happens when landscape elements are added to a model hillside? Will the water follow a predictable path?

## Collect Data and Make Observations

1. Read and complete a lab safety form.
2. Decide how many textbooks or bricks you will use to prop up one end of the stream table. Record the final height.
3. Create a hill with the sand and gravel at one end of the stream table.
4. Record the size of the water container in your setup. Fill it with water and attach tubing.
5. Smooth out the slope. Cover the left half with rows of rocks or plant matter. Leave the other half bare.
6. Pour the water out first on one side, then refill the container and repeat on the other half. Be sure to pour with the same pressure and volume.
7. Draw or photograph the results.
8. Change the height of your stream table and repeat steps 5–7.

| Stream Table Results | | | | |
|---|---|---|---|---|
| | Trial | Height of Stream Table | Sketch of Covered— Before Water | Sketch of Uncovered— Before Water |
| First Height | 1 | | | |
| | 2 | | | |
| Second Height | 1 | | | |
| | 2 | | | |

## Analyze and Conclude

1. **Summarize** the differences and similarities between your results in step 6.

2. **Compare and contrast** your drawings or photographs with those from other students. Did everyone get the same results? Consider the other heights your classmates choose and the container volumes that were used.

3. **Describe** how different volumes of water affect erosion.

4. **Explain** how the height of the stream table affects erosion.

5. **Infer** from the data you have collected how landscape elements affect erosion.

6. **Think critically** about what you have learned about erosion. What places are most vulnerable to erosion? What could be done to protect such areas? What places would be least affected by erosion?

## Communicate

 Science

Write a brief report that explains how landscape affects erosion. Present your findings to your class.

# Real World Science

## Science & Career

## STUDYING THE ROCKS OF EARTH

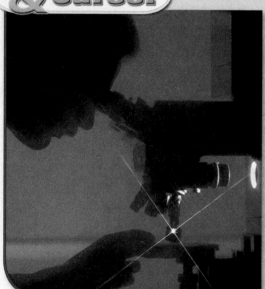

Some geologists examine rocks formed in or on Earth's crust, such as sedimentary rocks or metamorphic rocks, and igneous rocks from the Earth's interior. They might cut a very thin slice of rock in a laboratory and examine it with a microscope. They determine the mineralogical and chemical composition of rocks, then deduce the conditions of heat and pressure that caused them to be formed. These geologists are called petrologists and geophysicists.

Visit **Careers** at **ca7.msscience.com** to find out more about how to become a geologist. Why do you think geologists are eager to study the processes involved in creating and changing rock formations?

## It's looking at the small stuff and changing it.

## Science & Technology

To study rocks at the elemental level, scientists create thin sections. The rock is cut down until it is thin and small enough to see through a microscope. The individual minerals that make up the rock can be seen. Scanning electron microscopes, electron microprobes, and infrared spectrometers are used routinely for study of the experimental samples.

Visit **Technology** at **ca7.msscience.com** to find out more about spectrometers. Write two paragraphs about how they work and what they are used for.

# Carving Rocks Through History

Besides being used for building, foraging, and protection, rocks have been used for art through the years. Even before painting cave walls, early humans fashioned shapes from stone. Rocks of many different types have been used for sculpture, including fine marbles used by Michelangelo and compressed volcanic ash used by the ancient inhabitants of Easter Island in the South Pacific. They created these giant sculptures called moai.

Visit **History** at **ca7.msscience.com** to research several historic works. Select one work and create a brochure. Give the work's history, creator, material, and the material's origin. Use pictures of the work and creator, if possible.

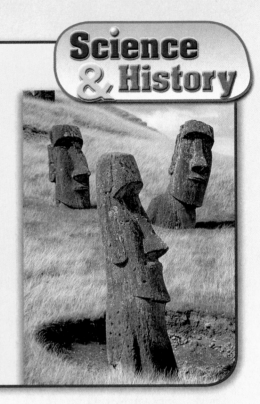

## Science & Society

### The State Mineral and its History

State legislation signed on April 23, 1965, designated native gold as California's official state mineral. California is ranked fourth in the nation for gold production. In the years 2000–2001 there were 16 significant active gold mines in operation, about half were located in the historic Mother Lode Belt. The California Gold Rush began in 1848 with discovery of gold at Sutter's Mill in Coloma. This started a bonanza that brought California fame and gave it the title of the "Golden State." The Gold Rush of 1849 and the subsequent influx of settlers led to California becoming the thirty-first state in 1850.

Go to **Society** at **ca7.msscience.com** for more information about the Gold Rush. Divide the class into two groups to represent the Anti-Debris Association (farmers) and the Miners Association. Research the legal activities of both associations and their evidence. Reenact a courtroom scene from the trial that ended with an injunction against the mining companies.

**The BIG Idea** Geologists use a variety of methods to estimate and determine the age of Earth.

## Lesson 1 Relative Ages of Rocks

4.a, 4.c, 7.d

**Main Idea** Geologists can determine the relative ages of rocks by studying the order of rock layers, fossils, and geologic processes that are occurring today.

- All of Earth's processes are related.

- Uniformitarianism allows scientists to use their observations today to interpret Earth's history.

- The cooling of molten rock forms igneous rocks. Crystal size indicates the rate of cooling.

- Metamorphic rocks form from an increase in temperature and pressure.

- Sedimentary rocks form from pieces of preexisting rock. They are often layered and may contain fossils.

- The processes of weathering, transportation, deposition, and lithification make sedimentary rocks.

- Four principles are used to assign relative ages to rock strata and geologic events. The principle of superposition states that strata at the bottom of a stack of sedimentary rocks are the oldest.

- The principles of original horizontality, original lateral continuity, and cross-cutting relationships are also used to interpret past geologic events.

- Fossils are used to assign relative ages of rocks.

- **clast** (p. 287)
- **lithification** (p. 288)
- **relative age** (p. 289)
- **rock cycle** (p. 286)
- **stratum** (p. 289)
- **superposition** (p. 289)
- **uniformitarianism** (p. 285)

## Lesson 2 Absolute Ages of Rocks

4.d, 7.c, 7.d

**Main Idea** Unstable parent isotopes change to stable daughter isotopes at a constant rate. Geologists measure the amounts of these isotopes in minerals to determine how long ago the minerals formed.

- Radioactive parent isotopes decay into stable daughter isotopes at a constant rate.

- The time it takes for half the amount of the parent isotope to decay into the daughter isotope is called the half-life.

- Using the half-life and the amounts of the parent and daughter isotopes, scientists can determine when a mineral formed.

- The oldest mineral discovered on Earth is 4.4 billion years old.

- The age of the Moon, meteorites, and Earth are calculated to be approximately 4.5 billion years old.

- **half-life** (p. 296)
- **isotope** (p. 294)
- **radioactive decay** (p. 294)

STUDY TO GO  Download quizzes, key terms, and flash cards from ca7.msscience.com.

# Linking Vocabulary and Main Ideas

Use the vocabulary terms on page 306 to complete the concept map.

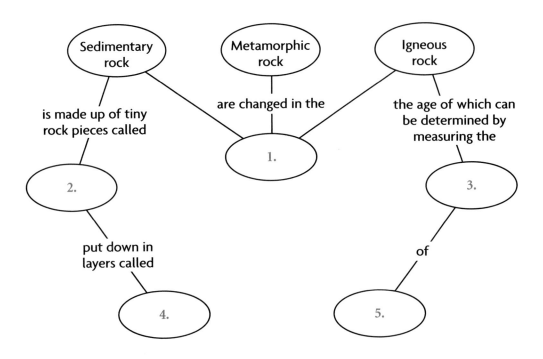

Sedimentary rock

Metamorphic rock

Igneous rock

are changed in the

is made up of tiny rock pieces called

the age of which can be determined by measuring the

1.

2.

3.

put down in layers called

of

4.

5.

## Using Vocabulary

Complete each statement using a term from the vocabulary list.

6. Different _____ of an element have different numbers of neutrons in their nuclei.

7. Layers of rock are called _____.

8. Individual grains of sediment are called _____.

9. The process during which a nucleus gains or loses protons or neutrons is called _____.

10. Watching waves sort sand on a beach and comparing the sand to sandstone is an example of _____.

11. The process that cements grains together to form a rock is called _____.

## Understanding Main Ideas

1. The phrase "the present is the key to the past" summarizes which principle? `4.a`
   A. original time
   B. superposition
   C. unconformities
   D. uniformitarianism

2. Why do geologists use the principle of superposition?
   A. to determine the best position to study rocks
   B. to measure the position of continents
   C. to determine the relative ages of rock layers
   D. to predict the position of the plates in the future `4.a`

3. What processes cause metamorphism?
   A. weathering, transportation, and deposition
   B. melting, cooling, and crystallization
   C. erosion, uplift, and nondeposition
   D. pressures, temperatures, and water `4.a`

4. What does the principle of original horizontality state?
   A. Sediments always remain horizontal.
   B. Sediments are always deposited horizontally.
   C. Any sediments that are deposited horizontally will eventually become tilted.
   D. All sediments are deposited in rows. `4.a`

5. Which of Steno's principles explains how we know these rocks were tilted after they were formed?

   A. principle of superposition `4.a`
   B. principle of original horizontality
   C. principle of original lateral continuity
   D. principle of cross-cutting relationships

6. What evidence did James Hutton use to explain that Earth was old?
   A. erosion `4.a`
   B. glaciers
   C. ocean tides
   D. volcanic eruptions

7. Which does not transport sediment?
   A. water `4.a`
   B. lava
   C. wind
   D. ice

8. Which is true about isotopes?
   A. They contain no neutrons. `4.d`
   B. They have varying numbers of neutrons.
   C. They have very heavy neutrons.
   D. They all have six neutrons.

9. How do you identify a daughter isotope?
   A. It forms from the decay of a parent isotope.
   B. It causes parent isotopes to decay.
   C. It is heavier than its parent isotope.
   D. It has two stable forms. `4.d`

10. Which rock types are most commonly used in radiometric dating?
    A. igneous `4.d`
    B. metamorphic
    C. sedimentary
    D. all three are used

11. What process is illustrated below?

    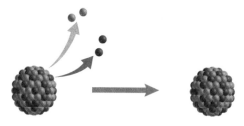

    A. daughter-to-parent isotope formation
    B. nuclear fusion
    C. radioactive decay
    D. half-life `4.d`

## Applying Science

**12.** **Hypothesize** what the crystal size would be in an igneous rock that cooled as soon as the magma reached the surface. **4.a**

**13.** **Describe** how water can provide the cement in sedimentary rocks. **4.a**

**14.** **Determine** the relationship between angular, poorly-sorted sediments and the distance the sediments were transported. **4.c**

**15.** **Construct** a diagram illustrating the concept of half-life. **4.d**

**16.** **Evaluate** the accuracy of a radiometric age date determined from a metamorphic rock. **4.d**

**17.** **Recommend** one of the radioactive isotopes listed below for use in dating an igneous rock estimated to be 1 billion years old. **4.d**

### Half-Lives of Selected Radioactive Isotopes

| Radioactive Isotope | Approximate Half-Life | Decay Product |
|---|---|---|
| Rubidium-87 | 48.6 billion years | strontium-87 |
| Thorium-232 | 14.0 billion years | lead-208 |
| Potassium-40 | 1.3 billion years | argon-40 |
| Uranium-238 | 4.5 billion years | lead-206 |
| Uranium-235 | 0.7 billion years | lead-207 |
| Carbon-14 | 5,730 years | nitrogen-14 |

### WRITING in Science

**18.** **Write** a paragraph explaining the difference in the formation of poorly sorted and well-sorted sediments.

## Cumulative Review

**19.** **Explain** the relationship between fossils and interpreting Earth history. **4.a**

**20.** **Predict** what would happen to a species of birds if the climate in their environment changed very quickly. **4.a**

## Applying Math

**Refer to the table on page 301 to answer questions 21–25.**

**21.** What is the total quantity of minerals produced in 1999? **MA7: NS 1.0, AF 1.5**

**22.** What is the total quantity of minerals produced in 2001? **MA7: NS 1.0, AF 1.5**

**23.** What percentage of the total minerals produced in 1999 is asbestos? **MA7: NS 1.0, AF 1.5**

**24.** What percentage of the total minerals produced in 2000 is asbestos? **MA7: NS 1.0, AF 1.5**

**25.** What percentage of the total minerals produced in 1999 is masonry cement? **MA7: NS 1.0, AF 1.5**

**1** Which principle states that the oldest rock layer is found at the bottom in an undisturbed stack of rock layers?

A half-life **4.d**

B absolute dating

C superposition

D uniformitarianism

**2** Which term means matching up rock layers in different places?

A superposition **4.a**

B correlation

C uniformitarianism

D absolute dating

**3** Which isotope is useful for dating wood and charcoal that is less than about 75,000 years old?

A carbon-14 **4.d**

B potassium-40

C uranium-238

D argon-40

**4** A substance at 1 half-life has 50 percent of a parent isotope remaining. What percentage of the parent isotope remains at 2 half-lives?

A 6.25 percent **4.d**

B 25 percent

C 3.125 percent

D 1.07 percent

**5** Which principle states that the same processes at work in Earth's past are still at work today?

A deposition **4.a**

B superposition

C unconformity

D uniformitarianism

The table below shows the percent remaining parent isotope per half-life of a radioisotope. Use the table to answer questions 6 and 7.

| Number of Half-Lives | Parent Isotope Remaining (%) |
|---|---|
| 1 | 100 |
| 2 | X |
| 3 | 25 |
| 4 | 12.5 |
| 5 | Y |

**6** Which percentage replaces the letter X?

A 40 **4.d**

B 50

C 6205

D 75

**7** Which percentage replaces the letter Y in the table above?

A 0 **4.d**

B 2.5

C 3.13

D 6.25

**8** While fossil hunting, Ana found fossils of three different types of trilobites in three different rock layers. She sketched the fossils she found in each layer. What principle is represented by the fossils Ana found?

**A** All animals that lived in an ancient sea looked like trilobites. `4.c`

**B** Fossils provide a record of all organisms that have lived on Earth.

**C** Trilobites that lived in the ocean became extinct millions of years ago.

**D** Evidence that animals have changed over time is found in the fossil record.

**9** Which type of scientist studies fossils?

**A** paleontologist `4.a`

**B** meteorologist

**C** chemist

**D** astronomer

**10** Which of the following is an igneous rock characteristic?

**A** made of sediments `4.c`

**B** changed by pressure

**C** found in layers

**D** came from magma

**11** Sedimentary rocks are formed by what process?

**A** cementation `4.c`

**B** deposition

**C** weathering

**D** lithification

**12** Which step of sedimentary rock formation results in sorted clasts?

**A** weathering `4.c`

**B** transportation

**C** deposition

**D** lithification

**Use the illustration below to answer questions 13 and 14.**

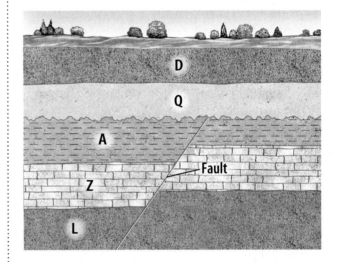

**13** Which sequence of letters describes the rock layers in the diagram from oldest to youngest?

**A** D, Q, A, Z, L `4.a`

**B** L, Z, A, Q, D

**C** Z, L, A, D, Q

**D** Q, D, L, Z, A

**14** Which correctly describes the relative age of the fault?

**A** younger than A, but older than Q `4.a`

**B** younger than Z, but older than L

**C** younger than Q, but older than A

**D** younger than D, but older than Q

# The History of Life on Earth

## The BIG Idea

Evidence from rocks helps us understand the history of life on Earth.

### LESSON 1 | 4.b, 4.e, 4.g, 7.c
**Geologic Time and Mass Extinctions**

**Main Idea** Fossils provide evidence of how life and environmental conditions have changed over time. Geologists used fossils to create the geologic time scale.

### LESSON 2 | 4.b, 4.e, 4.g, 7.d
**Early Earth History**

**Main Idea** Bacteria, the simplest organisms, were the first organisms to evolve on Earth. Increasingly complex organisms followed them.

### LESSON 3
4.b, 4.e, 4.g, 7.a, 7.c, 7.d

**Middle and Recent Earth History**

**Main Idea** Life continues to evolve into many of the forms we see on Earth today.

## Footprints in Stone

Did you ever go barefoot on a muddy beach? Your feet sink down and mud oozes between your toes. The next day the mud may dry out and your footprints remain. If they get filled in by sand or gravel, a mold may form. Cover them over with layers of sediment, wait a few thousand years, and your tracks will be in stone just like these dinosaur tracks.

**Science *Journal*** Write a one-page description about the dinosaur that might have left these tracks. What did it look like? What was it doing? What happened to it?

## How are events unscrambled?

The clues to Earth's past have appeared to humans out of sequence. How do scientists put events in order?

### Procedure

1. Find a **cartoon strip** that is at least a half page long.

2. Cut apart each frame of the cartoon strip.

3. Mix up the order of the frames and trade with a partner.

4. Try to put each other's cartoons back in to order. Try mixing three or four strips.

### Think about This

• **Analyze** How did you know which frame should go first and which should go last?

• **Explain** How did you put the other frames in order? What clues did you use?

• **Compare** How is putting the cartoon frames in order similar to the way scientists patch together the clues about the history of life on Earth?

 4.e, 4.g, 7.c

 Try at Home

## Science Online

Visit ca7.msscience.com to:

▶ view Concepts in Motion

▶ explore Virtual Labs

▶ access content-related Web links

▶ take the Standards Check

 **Mass Extinction** Make the following Foldable to show the causes of mass extinctions and which organisms were affected.

▷ **STEP 1** **Fold** a sheet of paper in half lengthwise. **Fold** the top down about 4 cm from the top.

▷ **STEP 2** **Unfold** and draw lines along all folds. **Label** as shown.

Causes Effects

**Reading Skill** **ELA7: R 2.3**

### Recognizing Cause and Effect
In the first column, explain the causes of mass extinctions throughout Earth's history. In the second column, explain why certain organisms became extinct as a result.

# Get Ready to Read

## Identify Cause and Effect

**1** **Learn It!** A *cause* is the reason something happens. The result of what happens is called an *effect*. Learning to identify causes and effects helps you understand why things happen. By using graphic organizers, you can sort and analyze causes and effects as you read.

**2** **Practice It!** Read the following paragraph. Then use the graphic organizer below to show what happened when oxygen entered the atmosphere.

> Recall that Earth's early atmosphere had no oxygen. Because cyanobacteria are photosynthetic, they released oxygen into the atmosphere. Over the next hundreds of millions of years, oxygen levels rose slowly as cyanobacteria and other early life-forms released oxygen. The earliest organisms did not consume oxygen. In fact, oxygen could kill them. During this period, natural selection favored organisms that could tolerate or even use oxygen. The amount of ozone in the atmosphere also increased during this time, shielding life on Earth from ultraviolet rays. These gradual changes to the atmosphere resulted in major changes in life on Earth.
>
> —*from page 327*

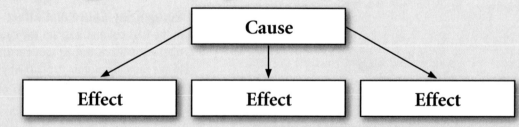

**3** **Apply It!** As you read the chapter, be aware of causes and effects of environmental changes. Find five causes and their effects.

# Target Your Reading

Use this to focus on the main ideas as you read the chapter.

**1 Before you read** the chapter, respond to the statements below on your worksheet or on a numbered sheet of paper.
- Write an **A** if you **agree** with the statement.
- Write a **D** if you **disagree** with the statement.

**2 After you read** the chapter, look back to this page to see if you've changed your mind about any of the statements.
- If any of your answers changed, explain why.
- Change any false statements into true statements.
- Use your revised statements as a study guide.

**Reading Tip**

Graphic organizers such as the Cause-Effect organizer help you organize what you are reading so you can remember it later.

| Before You Read A or D | Statement | After You Read A or D |
|---|---|---|
| | **1** Fossils are important to estimating the age of Earth. | |
| | **2** Establishing a geologic time scale of Earth events was easy once fossils were found. | |
| | **3** Catastrophic events have caused most extinctions of animals and plants. | |
| | **4** Volcanic eruptions and tsunamis have been the main source of mass extinctions. | |
| | **5** Over 90 percent of all species have gone extinct. | |
| | **6** There are no fossils older than 65 million years. | |
| | **7** At one time, there might have been little or no oxygen in the atmosphere. | |
| | **8** Flying reptiles evolved into birds. | |
| | **9** Mammals and dinosaurs were both alive on Earth at the same time. | |
| | **10** Turtles, frogs, crocodiles, dinosaurs, and reptiles all evolved during the same era. | |

**Science Online**

Print a worksheet of this page at ca7.msscience.com.

# LESSON 1

## Science Content Standards

**4.b** Students know the history of life on Earth has been disrupted by major catastrophic events, such as major volcanic eruptions or the impacts of asteroids.
**4.e** Students know fossils provide evidence of how life and environmental conditions have changed.
**4.g** Students know how to explain significant developments and extinctions of plant and animal life on the geologic time scale.
**Also covers:** 7.c

## Reading Guide

### What *You'll Learn*

▶ **Describe** how fossils were used to organize the geologic time scale.

▶ **Describe** the mass extinction events on the geologic time scale.

▶ **Explain** how catastrophic events can lead to mass extinctions.

### Why *It's Important*

The life and landscape around you are the result of change through geologic time.

### Vocabulary

index fossil
mass extinction
catastrophic event

### Review Vocabulary

**volcano:** land or underwater feature that forms when magma reaches Earth's surface (Grade 6)

# Geologic Time and Mass Extinctions

**Main Idea** Fossils provide evidence of how life and environmental conditions have changed over time. Geologists used fossils to create the geologic time scale.

**Real-World Reading Connection** The storage media for home computers has changed over the last 25 years. During that time people have used 5.25-inch floppy disks, 3.5-inch disks, and now read-writable CDs and portable flash drives. In a similar way, life on Earth has changed throughout Earth's history.

## Development of the Geologic Time Scale

The changes to life and Earth that have occurred throughout Earth's history are recorded on a time line called the geologic time scale. Because extinctions, growth rates, and environmental changes happen at different rates, the time scale's units are uneven. To organize geologic time into units, paleontologists (pay lee un TOL uh jihsts) study the types and ages of fossils in rock layers and decide where to mark the units.

### Index Fossils

Units of time on the geologic time scale are described by the presence and the absence of certain types of fossils called index fossils. An **index fossil** is the remains of a species that existed over vast regions of Earth for a short period of time. **Table 1** explains how a species is selected to be an index fossil.

| Table 1 Index Fossil Criteria |
|---|
| **1** The remains of species must have hard parts, so they will preserve easily in the rock record. |
| **2** The remains of species must be geographically widespread, so they are commonly found. |
| **3** The species must have lived in many types of environments. This ensures that they will be preserved in many different types of sedimentary rocks. |
| **4** The species must have lived for a short time before they became extinct. This allows rock layers to be divided into small units of geologic time. |

# Divisions of the Geologic Time Scale

**Figure 1** shows the geologic time scale used today. Notice that no two divisions of time have the same number of years. There are several major divisions of the geologic time scale. The largest divisions are called eons and are the longest units of time. Eons have been broken into smaller units called eras. Eras in turn are divided into periods and epochs.

**Eras** Paleontologists have defined three eras within the Phanerozoic (fan ayr oh ZOH ihk) eon. The Paleozoic (pay lee uh ZOH ihk) era, which means "ancient life," was dominated by invertebrate marine organisms. Although they might have a shell, invertebrate marine animals are those without a backbone. During the Mesozoic (mez uh ZOH ihk) era, which means "middle life," dinosaurs and mammals lived on land. The Cenozoic (sen uh ZOH ihk) era, which means "recent life," continues today. Modern mammals and humans evolved during this recent time.

 **Figure 1** For how many years did the Paleozoic era last?

**Periods and Epochs** Divisions of eras are called periods. The Cenozoic era was once divided into two periods, the Tertiary (TER shee ayr ee) period and the Quaternary (KWAH tur nayr ee) period. As scientists learn more and do more research, they sometimes change the way they describe and name things. Today we no longer use the term *Tertiary* to describe the first division of the Cenozoic. Instead paleontologists divide the Tertiary into two parts called the Paleogene period and Neogene period. You can find these listed in the chart in **Figure 1.**

The Quaternary period began about 1.8 million years ago. The periods have been divided into epochs. The Pleistocene (PLYS tuh seen) epoch ended about 8,000 years ago. The Holocene (HOH luh seen) is the epoch we live in.

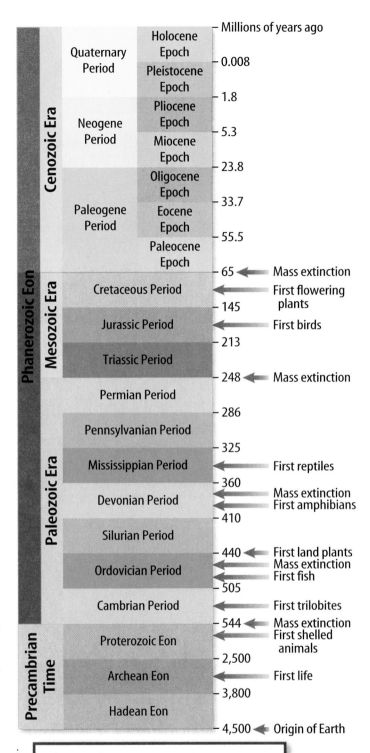

**Figure 1** The geologic time scale was developed using relative and absolute dating methods.

**Concepts In Motion**

Interactive Table Organize information about the geologic time scale at ca7.msscience.com.

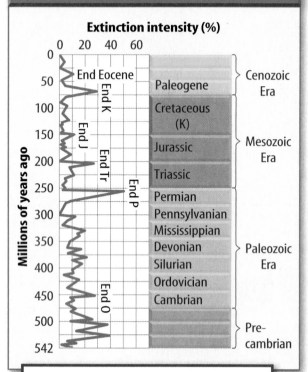

**Marine Genus Biodiversity: Extinction Intensity**

Extinction intensity (%)

Figure 2 The graph shows how some extinction events were used to mark changes in the geologic time scale.

# What are mass extinctions?

How do paleontologists determine when one unit on the geologic time scale ends and another begins? Scientists look for layers of rock that include more diversity and greater numbers of fossils than rock layers above them. This indicates that many organisms might have died over a short period of time. Several units on the geologic time scale begin and end with mass extinction, as shown in **Figure 2. Mass extinction** is the dying off of many different species of organisms over a short period in geologic time.

The extinction of a single species of organisms is common. In fact, 99 percent of all species that have lived on Earth are now extinct. However, the extinction of several species over a short period of time is rare. It is important to note that mass extinctions do not occur instantaneously. They can happen over as great a span of time as a few million years.

 **Visual Check** What percent of extinctions marked the end of the Eocene era, the Triassic era, the Permian era, and Precambrian time?

# Possible Causes of Mass Extinction

Once paleontologists recognized that mass extinctions occurred throughout geologic time, they began to search for catastrophic events that might cause them. A **catastrophic** (ca tuh STRAH fik) **event** is an event that causes a drastic change in the numbers of organisms of one or more species over a short period in geologic time. It may seem that all catastrophic events cause mass extinction, but that is not always true. Scientists still do not fully understand the specific catastrophic events that have caused each of the mass extinctions. They have identified several types of events, however, that have the ability to cause mass extinction. These events include changes in climate, volcanic eruptions, and asteroid impacts.

**WORD ORIGIN**

catastrophe
*kata*– prefix; from Greek; means *over*
*–strephein* from Greek; means *to turn*

## Climate Change

There is evidence that some mass extinctions were caused by relatively sudden changes in climate. **Figure 3** shows a diver collecting climatic evidence. Recall that climate is an average weather pattern over a long period of time. Species that are unable to survive a change in climate become extinct. Climate change can be caused by several events, including some volcanic eruptions and asteroid impacts. Global warming and global cooling are two types of climate change that might have caused some mass extinctions.

**Global Warming** Burning of fossil fuels, such as coal and oil, adds greenhouse gases, like carbon dioxide, to the atmosphere. Many scientists think greenhouse gases in the atmosphere contribute to global warming, a **global** increase in atmospheric temperature. If the overall temperature of the atmosphere increases, the temperature of the oceans also increases. Because warm water holds less oxygen than cold water, global warming could cause a decrease in oxygen levels in the water. If the oxygen levels drop in shallow waters, where most organisms live, mass extinctions could occur.

Global warming could also raise sea levels. Water from melting glaciers would flow into the oceans, causing sea levels to rise. Geologists have found evidence of warm temperatures, a rising sea level, and oxygen-poor waters flooding shallow-water areas during the Devonian mass extinction. Some scientists think global warming might have been the cause.

 **Reading Check** List possible effects of global warming.

**Figure 3** Nearly microscopic corals build on top of the skeletons of their ancestors. The core sample that is being taken here will tell scientists what the environment was like thousands or millions of years ago.

**Infer** What climatic conditions would you expect to produce the most coral life-forms?

**Global Cooling** Mass extinctions could also be caused by global cooling, an overall decrease in atmospheric temperatures. Global cooling could lower sea levels as large amounts of water are frozen in glacial ice. Less water in the oceans would mean fewer warm, shallow-water environments. With fewer warm-water environments, there would be less space to support marine ecosystems. Global cooling appears to have initiated the Ordovician mass extinction event. **Figure 4** shows how at that time, large glaciers were active near the south pole.

## Volcanoes

When you think of a volcanic eruption, you might think of a large explosion. However, volcanoes also produce nonexplosive eruptions. The dust, ash, lava, and gas emitted from volcanic eruptions can affect climate and organisms.

**Explosive Eruptions** Mt. Vesuvius, in Italy, erupted in A.D. 79. The ash and lava buried the cities of Pompeii and Herculaneum, killing thousands of people. The 1815 eruption of Tambora produced a flaming cloud of dust and gas that killed more than 30,000 people. The year after this eruption is referred to as the year without summer as the air was blanketed with ash, reducing the amount of sunlight that reached Earth. **Figure 5** shows part of the results of the violent, but relatively small, explosion of Mount St. Helens in Washington State. These eruptions are recent events in geologic time. Although catastrophic, these eruptions have not led to mass extinction. However, a volcanic eruption is one of several hypotheses proposed to explain the mass extinction event at the end of the Cretaceous period.

**Figure 4** The iceberg breaks off the glacier edge as it enters the ocean. It looks much the same now as it did during the Ordovician era.

 **Figure 5** What force might have knocked over these trees?

**Figure 5** Trees lie covered in ash in the blow-down zone after the eruption of Mount St. Helens in 1980.

**Figure 6** The lava is red hot as it flows across the surface of the island of Hawaii. Gases from this eruption are also being added to the atmosphere.

**Basalt Flows** Along divergent plate boundaries and in isolated hot spots, such as under the Hawaiian Islands, lava flows smoothly onto Earth's surface. These nonexplosive floods of molten basalt emit the largest volume of matter of any eruptions. This matter comes from Earth's mantle. Geologic evidence shows that large basalt flows occurred in Siberia during the Permian mass extinction. The flows are called the Siberian Traps. During the Cretaceous mass extinction, another large basalt flow, called the Deccan Traps, was released in India. Although small by comparison, **Figure 6** shows a basalt flow around a volcano in Hawaii.

**Volcanic Haze** The gases produced by basalt flows cause a complex sequence of effects. First, sulfur dioxide gas is released into the atmosphere, resulting in the formation of acid clouds. These clouds block some of the sunlight from reaching Earth's surface. Over the course of months to tens of years, global cooling occurs. This is called the volcanic haze effect. Over periods of tens to hundreds of thousands of years, global temperatures may increase because heat becomes trapped in Earth's atmosphere by the sulfuric acid clouds. It is uncertain whether basaltic flows and the gases they emit were enough to cause the Permian and Cretaceous mass extinctions.

 **Reading Check** How could acid clouds affect temperatures?

**Figure 7** Scientific evidence of crater formation and meteorite deposits have identified this site as the impact site that might have killed off all the dinosaurs.

**Discuss** the reasons scientists might have had trouble locating this asteroid impact site.

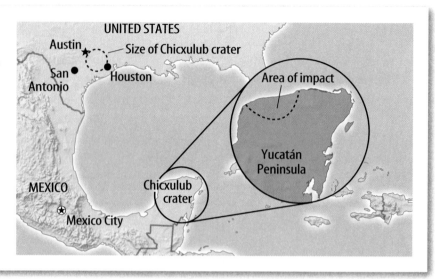

UNITED STATES
Austin
— Size of Chicxulub crater
San Antonio
Houston
Area of impact
Yucatán Peninsula
MEXICO
Chicxulub crater
Mexico City

**Figure 8** Plants wouldn't be able to photosynthesize if the atmosphere were full of the dust an asteroid impact might kick up. Mass extinction might follow.

## Asteroid Impacts

**Figure 7** shows the location of a possible asteroid impact site on the Yucatan Peninsula in Mexico. Scientists believe this impact may have contributed to the Cretaceous mass extinction.

**Effects of the Impact** Some geologists propose that this impact sent enough dust and other material into the atmosphere to block sunlight. **Figure 8** shows how a cold and dark Earth killed plants and other primary producers. Without primary producers, there was no source of food. Mass extinctions followed. Global cooling, created by the initial impact, turned into global warming as carbon dioxide was released from burning plants ignited by the impact. These greenhouse conditions lasted thousands of years.

**The Debate** Most scientists accept the hypothesis that a large asteroid, or possibly several asteroids, hit Earth at the end of the Cretaceous period. Evidence supports the hypothesis that many species became extinct around the time of the impact. However, paleontologists propose that the impact did not cause all the extinctions. The fossil record shows that many species were decreasing in number and diversity long before the impact. In fact, many became extinct at least one million years before the impact. The fossil record also shows that the extinction rate increased tens of thousands of years before the impact. It appears that while the impact did cause some extinctions, it clearly did not cause all of them.

## Is there an extinction pattern?

Although mass extinctions occur over a short geologic time span, they are not instantaneous. Fossil evidence indicates that mass extinctions can occur over a few million years or more. What caused the mass extinctions in geologic time? Investigations have revealed no clear patterns, although there are several types of catastrophic events that can cause mass extinction. It appears that each extinction event might have been caused by a unique series of events. Species that survive mass extinction inherit an environment with few competitors. In time, their descendents might repopulate Earth. In the next lesson, you will read about the organisms that populated Earth during major segments of geologic time.

# LESSON 1 Review

## Summarize

Create your own lesson summary as you write a script for a **television news report.**

1. **Review** the text after the **red** main headings and write one sentence about each. These are the headlines of your broadcast.

2. **Review** the text and write 2–3 sentences about each **blue** subheading. These sentences should tell *who, what, when, where,* and *why* information about each **red** heading.

3. **Include** descriptive details in your report, such as names of reporters and local places and events.

4. **Present** your news report to other classmates alone or with a team.

 ELA7: LS 2.2

## Standards Check

### Using Vocabulary

1. Use the term *index fossil* in a sentence. **4.e**

### Understanding Main Ideas

2. **List** the types of remains that can be preserved as fossils. **4.e**

3. **Compare and contrast** global warming and global cooling. **4.g**

4. The Siberian Traps were an example of which of these?

   A. greenhouse gases
   B. asteroid impact
   C. global warming
   D. basalt flow **4.b**

5. **Organize** the divisions of the geologic time scale in order from longest length of time to shortest length of time. **4.g**

### Applying Science

6. **Create** a worldwide technology time scale. Describe the criteria you used to create your time scale. **4.e**

7. **Predict** what criteria will be used to mark the end of the current era. **4.g**

8. **Describe** Fill in the features of global warming. **4.b**

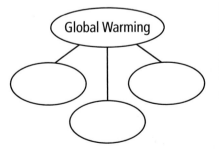

**Science Online**

For more practice, visit **Standards Check** at ca7.msscience.com.

00:30 minutes

Try at Home

# DataLab

# Which organisms return first following a catastrophic event?

Some catastrophic events cause mass extinctions. How do species survive after a catastrophic event?

## Data Collection

1. Study the graph of stream invertebrates.

2. How many species reappeared during the first ten years following the eruption of Mount St. Helens?

3. Study the graph of bird species.

4. How many species of birds reappeared during the first ten years following the eruption?

5. Compare the reappearance of bird species to that of stream invertebrates following the eruption.

## Data Analysis

1. **Infer** Which animals would you have expected to return first, birds or stream invertebrates? Explain.

2. **Interpret Data** Which had the greater number of species in the blowdown zone 10 years after the eruption?

3. **Form Hypotheses** Plants, birds, and stream invertebrates now thrive in areas once covered by volcanic ash. Write a hypothesis about how this repopulation occurred for each group.

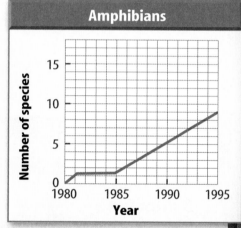

Source: USGS

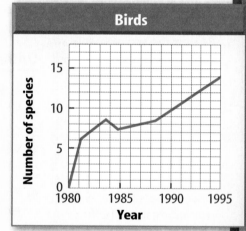

Source: USGS

 **Science Content Standards**

**7.c** Communicate the logical connection among hypotheses, science concepts, tests conducted, data collected, and conclusions drawn from the scientific evidence.

 **MA7:** MR 2.5

### Science Content Standards

**4.b** Students know the history of life on Earth has been disrupted by major catastrophic events, such as major volcanic eruptions or the impacts of asteroids.
**4.e** Students know fossils provide evidence of how life and environmental conditions have changed.
**4.g** Students know how to explain significant developments and extinctions of plant and animal life on the geologic time scale.
**7.d** Construct scale models, maps, and appropriately labeled diagrams to communicate scientific knowledge (e.g., motion of Earth's plates and cell structure).

## Reading Guide

### What You'll Learn

▶ **Describe** the environment and first life from Precambrian time.

▶ **Trace** the changes in life-forms in the Paleozoic after the Cambrian explosion.

▶ **Infer** the changes that lead to mass extinctions.

### Why It's Important
Learning about past events helps us predict the future.

### Vocabulary
amniote
cyanobacteria
vertebrate

### Review Vocabulary
**extinct:** no longer existing (species) (p. 224)

# Early Earth History

**Main Idea** Bacteria, the simplest organisms, were the first organisms to evolve on Earth. Increasingly complex organisms followed them.

**Real-World Reading Connection** Imagine that you go into the kitchen and there on the table you find a paper plate with icing and candle wax on it. You might ask yourself what happened. Your hypothesis might be that in the recent past there was a birthday party in the room. Scientists have a similar task when they find the fossilized remains of ancient organisms. They ask themselves this question: What was life on Earth like in the past?

## Life on Earth Changes

Fossils record the history of life on Earth. Paleontologists, who study fossils, discovered that the system used to classify modern organisms could also be used to classify fossils. They observed that fossils from rock layers that are touching are more similar to each other than fossils from widely separated layers. Geologists also recognized that the more recently a fossil was formed, the more it resembles a living organism. Perhaps you have been to the ocean and collected a sand dollar, or have seen a sand dollar skeleton. It likely looked most like the sand dollar in the first row of **Table 2.** In this lesson, you will read about these changes in life during the Precambrian (pree KAM bree un) time.

**Visual Check** **Table 2** How did the sand dollar change over time?

**Table 2 Sand Dollar Changes**

| | | Side View | Top View |
|---|---|---|---|
| Youngest → | **Middle Eocene** |  | |
| | **Early Eocene** | | |
| Oldest → | **Paleocene** | | |

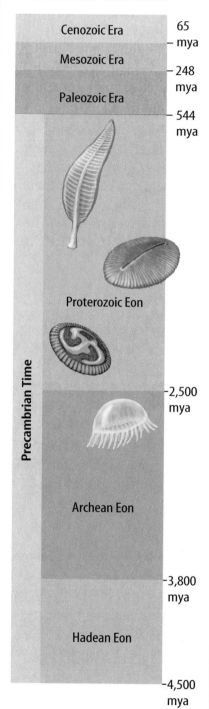

**Figure 9** Precambrian time is divided into three eons.

| | |
|---|---|
| Cenozoic Era | 65 mya |
| Mesozoic Era | 248 mya |
| Paleozoic Era | 544 mya |
| Proterozoic Eon | |
| Archean Eon | 2,500 mya |
| | 3,800 mya |
| Hadean Eon | |
| | 4,500 mya |

Precambrian Time

# Precambrian Time

**Figure 9** shows the portion of the geologic time scale that represents Precambrian time. Precambrian time is divided into three eons—Hadean (HAY dee un), Archean (ar KEE un), and Proterozoic (proh ter oh ZOH ihk). The Precambrian age represents 88 percent of Earth's history. Precambrian rocks are difficult for scientists to study because most of the rock has been changed through metamorphism. Recall that it is difficult for scientists to determine the absolute age of metamorphosed rock using radiometric dating. Also, much of the Precambrian rock has been destroyed at subduction zones. As the plates move together, the more dense plate sinks into the mantle. There the rock in the plate may melt or become metamorphic. Any fossil remains will be destroyed.

Fossils are not as abundant in Precambrian-aged rocks as they are in younger rocks. But, the fossils that have been discovered provide a great deal of information about Earth's early atmosphere and environment during this time.

## The Precambrian Atmosphere

Rocks of Archean age reveal that Earth's early atmosphere was very different from today's atmosphere. For example, Archean sediments contain large amounts of the minerals pyrite and uraninite. Today's atmosphere contains oxygen that quickly destroys these minerals through the chemical process of oxidation. We see oxidation today when water and oxygen react with iron to make rust. Pyrite contains lots of iron. It makes sense that the presence of pyrite and uranite in very old rocks tells us that Earth's early atmosphere had very little oxygen.

**Ozone** Because we know oxygen is required to make ozone, the absence of oxygen also suggests that there was no ozone layer during Precambrian time. Scientists are concerned that the ozone layer today has been partially destroyed by chemicals made by humans. Without atmospheric ozone to protect life on Earth from harmful ultraviolet rays, exposure of lifeforms to these rays could result in death or mutation. Recall how mutations occur in cells. Changes in one gene in an organism could result in new life-forms many, many generations later. Could this be the process leading up to the big changes in the Paleozoic era?

 **Reading Check** Why is ozone important to living organisms?

**Figure 10** Cyanobacteria use sand and salt from the oceans to build stromatolite mounds similar in some ways to how corals build reefs.

## The First Organisms

Stromatolites (stroh MAT uh lites) are mounds of alternating thin-layered sediments and photosynthetic cyanobacteria. They contain the fossils of one of the earliest known, ancient organisms. **Figure 10** shows how stromatolites form. **Cyanobacteria** are single-celled, blue-green algae thought to be one of the earliest organisms. Like other photosynthetic organisms, cyanobacteria take in carbon dioxide and release oxygen. Stromatolites were common during the Archaen eon until the late Proterozoic eon, when bacteria-eating animals evolved. Today, stromatolites exist only in water that is too salty and warm for other organisms to survive.

 How are cyanobacteria like other photosynthetic organisms?

## A Changing Environment

Recall that Earth's early atmosphere had no oxygen. Because cyanobacteria are photosynthetic, they released oxygen into the atmosphere. Over the next hundreds of millions of years, oxygen levels rose slowly as cyanobacteria and other early life-forms released oxygen. The earliest organisms did not consume oxygen. In fact, oxygen could kill them. During this period, natural selection favored organisms that could tolerate or even use oxygen. The amount of ozone in the atmosphere also increased during this time, shielding life on Earth from ultraviolet rays. These gradual changes to the atmosphere resulted in major changes in life on Earth.

## What makes the best fossils?

Paleontologists use fossils to determine what life was like in the past. Some life-forms formed better fossils than others. Determine what makes the best fossils.

**Procedure**

1. Complete a lab safety form.
2. Place a **rubber band**, a **paper clip**, a few **salt grains**, and a **bottle cap** on a flat surface.
3. Press some **clay** onto each of the objects.
4. Remove the objects from the clay and observe the fossil mold impression.

**Analysis**

1. **Determine** which made the best fossil.
2. **Explain** what is required for good fossils.
3. **Infer** why there are so few fossils from the Precambrian time.

7.d

Try at Home

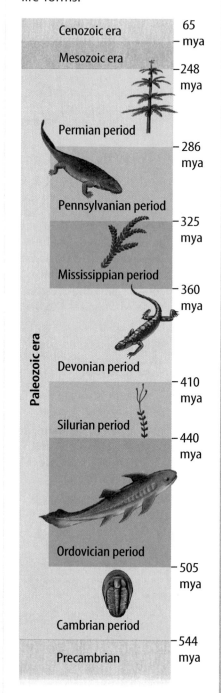

**Figure 11** The Paleozoic era ushered in a variety of new life-forms.

Cenozoic era — 65 mya

Mesozoic era — 248 mya

Paleozoic era

Permian period — 286 mya

Pennsylvanian period — 325 mya

Mississippian period — 360 mya

Devonian period — 410 mya

Silurian period — 440 mya

Ordovician period — 505 mya

Cambrian period — 544 mya

Precambrian

## Soft-Bodied Organisms

Organisms increased in complexity in the Proterozoic eon. During this eon, the first invertebrate organisms appeared. Invertebrates are animals without backbones. Unusual fossils of soft-bodied organisms were discovered in the Ediacara Hills of Australia. These organisms, called the Ediacaran (eddy uh KER uhn) fauna, had shapes similar to present-day jellies, worms, and corals. Some paleontologists believe that some present-day organisms are descended from the Ediacaran fauna. Others think these organisms became extinct at the end of the Proterozoic eon.

# The Paleozoic Era

The first appearance of fossils of organisms made from hard parts marks the end of the Proterozoic eon. Because organisms made from hard parts fossilize easier than those made of soft parts, fossils are easier to find in Paleozoic rocks than Precambrian rocks. **Figure 11** shows the portion of the geologic time scale that contains the Paleozoic era.

**Reading Check** What marked the end of the Proterozoic eon?

## The Cambrian Explosion

About five million years after the start of the Cambrian (KAM bree un) period, an event known as the Cambrian explosion occurred. The fossil record shows that during a relatively short period of time, the number of animals with shells greatly increased. Small-shelled organisms that looked like cones, plates, and tubes evolved along with larger-shelled organisms. Invertebrates, including sponges, jellies, and corals, also evolved during the Cambrian explosion. Trilobites, animals with hard outer skeletons, were the most commonly fossilized organisms of the Cambrian period. Some species of trilobites are shown in **Figure 12.**

**Figure 12** Changes in trilobite body forms matched changes in the environment.

Cambrian    Devonian    Mississippian

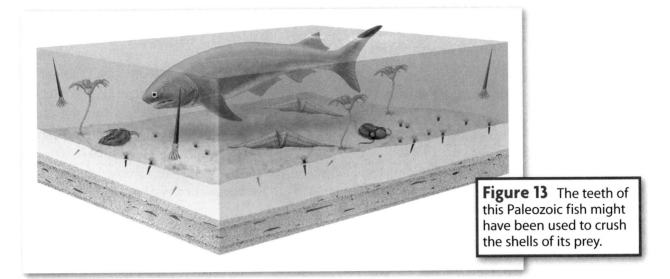

**Figure 13** The teeth of this Paleozoic fish might have been used to crush the shells of its prey.

## Invertebrates of the Paleozoic Era

Throughout the Paleozoic era, the oceans contained a wide **variety** of invertebrate organisms including corals, brachiopods (BRAY kee uh pahdz), crinoids (KRIH noydz), and bryozoans (bri UH zoh unz). **Figure 13** shows what the ocean floor may have looked like during the Ordovician (or duh VIH shun) period. Imagine a cockroach 10 cm long or a dragonfly with a wingspan of 74 cm. These insects would have lived during the Silurian (si LOOR ee un) period.

## Vertebrates of the Paleozoic Era

**Vertebrates,** animals with backbones, evolved during the early Paleozoic Era. The first of these lived in the oceans.

**Bony Fish** Early vertebrates included two groups of bony fish. One group had thin, bony rays which supported their fins. Another group of bony fish had thick fins supported by large bones and muscles. Scientists believe that the first group evolved into modern-day fish, while the second group evolved into amphibians that can live both in water and on land. Amphibians later evolved into reptiles and mammals.

**A New Egg** In order to reproduce, amphibians had to return to the water to lay their eggs. The water carries food and wastes into and out of the eggs. Amphibian eggs are not watertight and they would dry out and die on land. During the Pennsylvanian period a significant development occurred in the process of egg-laying. Early in the Pennsylvanian period an organism evolved that could lay its eggs on land. The organism is called an **amniote** and it lays water-tight, amniotic eggs. This means the eggs do not dry out on land. Since plants had moved on land during the Ordovician and provided a food source, this allowed the amniotes to spend all their time on land. Mammals, dinosaurs, and reptiles all evolved from amniotes.

**ACADEMIC VOCABULARY**

variety
*(noun)* the quality of having different forms *The shirt comes in a variety of colors.*

**SCIENCE USE V. COMMON USE**

sponge
*Science Use* an invertebrate animal of the ocean. *A sponge reproduces by budding.*
*Common Use* a device used for cleaning. *She used a sponge to wash her car.*

**Figure 14** Plants of the Mississippian and Pennsylvanian eras made up the biotic mass that produced the coal and oil we use as fuel today.

## Plants of the Paleozoic Era

The first plants developed in the ocean from green algae. During the Ordovician period, plants spread onto land. Because these early plants could not move water and nutrients to all their parts, the plants remained small and lived in low, moist areas. Vascular plants then evolved with vascular systems that could move water and nutrients between their roots and leaves. Vascular club mosses were small, but by the Late Devonian they became the trees shown in **Figure 14.** Ferns and groups that include the present-day conifers appeared during the Mississippian period. Large swamps containing abundant trees and ferns developed during the Mississippian and Pennsylvanian periods. These plants decayed, and became large coal deposits.

## Paleozoic Era Extinctions

The fossil record indicates that mass extinction events occurred during the Ordovician period and the Devonian period. The Paleozoic era ended with the late Permian extinction—the extinction of more than 90 percent of all marine species and more than 70 percent of all land species. **Figure 15** shows how the ocean might have looked before and after an extinction event. Several hypotheses have been proposed to explain the Permian extinction. One proposes that the uplifting formation of Pangaea left little room for shallow-water life-forms as marine terraces became dry land. Another proposes that the Siberian Traps released ash and sulfur into the atmosphere, causing global cooling and the formation of glaciers on land.

**Figure 15**
The Permian extinction killed off 90 percent of all marine species.

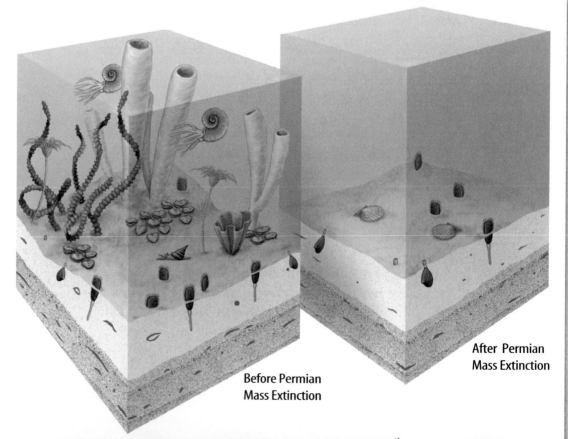

Before Permian
Mass Extinction

After Permian
Mass Extinction

**Mass Extinction Ends the Paleozoic Era** The early Cambrian period saw the expansion on Earth of many new species of life and the development of hard-shelled organisms that would leave fossil evidence of their existence. Before the Paleozoic era ended, there would be the evolution of the first fish, land plants, amphibians, and reptiles, all of which had hard parts that left fossil evidence. However, about 250 million years ago, the late Permian extinction resulted in the extinction of most marine and land species. Changes in species diversity usually follow an extinction event. Niches and habitats once inhabited by some organisms became empty and other species moved into these spaces. Extinction of predators allowed other organisms to increase in number and expand in distribution.

# LESSON 2  Review

## Summarize

Create your own lesson summary as you organize an **outline**.

1. **Scan** the lesson. Find and list the first **red** main heading.

2. **Review** the text after the heading and list 2–3 details about the heading.

3. **Find** and list each **blue** subheading that follows the **red** main heading.

4. **List** 2–3 details, key terms, and definitions under each **blue** subheading.

5. **Review** additional **red** main headings and their supporting **blue** subheadings. List 2–3 details about each.

## Standards Check

### Using Vocabulary

1. Write the definition for *mass extinction* in your own words.

### Understanding Main Ideas

2. **Explain** how the introduction of oxygen to the atmosphere changed the life-forms on Earth.

3. **Describe** the changes that mark the beginning of the Paleozoic era. **4.g**

4. **Infer** which changes during the Paleozoic era were most important to today's life-forms. **4.e**

5. Which is used as a record of Earth's history? **4.e**

 **A.** bacteria

 **B.** atmosphere

 **C.** fossils

 **D.** geologic time scale

6. **Trace** the evolution of vertebrates in the Paleozoic era. **4.e**

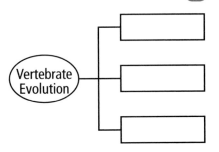

### Applying Science

7. **Compare and contrast** the amniote egg with the amphibian egg. **4.b**

8. **Solve** How many generations of cyanobacteria would there be in a million years if each bacterium lives for 24 hours? How many generations for an organism that lives 100 years? **4.g**

**Science** nline
For more practice, visit **Standards Check** at ca7.msscience.com.

**Science Content Standards**

**4.b** Students know the history of life on Earth has been disrupted by major catastrophic events, such as major volcanic eruptions or the impacts of asteroids.

**4.e** Students know fossils provide evidence of how life and environmental conditions have changed.

**4.g** Students know how to explain significant developments and extinctions of plant and animal life on the geologic time scale.

**Also covers:** 7.a, 7.c, 7.d

## Reading Guide

### What *You'll Learn*

▶ **Identify** the evolution of organisms on Earth today.

▶ **Determine** the changes that pressure organisms to evolve.

▶ **Examine** the diversity of life over time.

### Why *It's Important*

Many people are concerned with the rate of extinctions of life on Earth and the possibility that humans are the cause.

### Vocabulary

pterosaur
ectotherm
endotherm
gymnosperm
primate

### Review Vocabulary

**angiosperm:** a flowering seed plant (p. 138)

# Middle and Recent Earth History

**Main Idea** Life continues to evolve into many of the forms we see on Earth today.

**Real-World Reading Connection** After it rains, you may see a puddle in the street or in your yard. In a day or two it is gone—it evaporated. You didn't see it happen, but it was evaporating the whole time. Imagine how long it would take for a lake to evaporate. Now imagine the ocean evaporating into nothing. How long would it take?

## The Mesozoic Era

**Figure 17** on the facing page shows the three periods of the geologic time scale that make up the Mesozoic era—the Triassic period, the Jurassic period, and the Cretaceous period. Most organisms that survived the Permian mass extinction event diversified widely during the next 50 million years.

### A Changing Landscape

About 180 million years ago, the Pangaea land mass began to split into two land masses, Laurasia and Gondwanaland, as shown in **Figure 16.** The split started a new weather pattern that would create a warm, wet climate for a large area of these land masses.

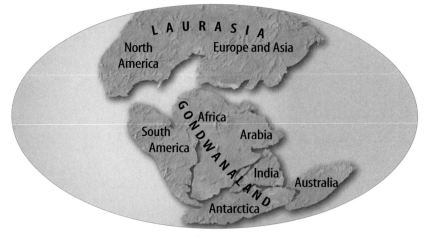

**Figure 16** The continent of Pangaea would split first into two continents and later into the present-day continents.

## Invertebrates of the Mesozoic Era

After the extinction event at the end of the Paleozoic era, many of the predators of stromatolites had become extinct. This allowed stromatolites to increase in numbers. Algae and large clams, like the rudistids, were the new life forms to evolve in the Cretaceous period. By the Triassic, however, the rudistids had been replaced by reef-building corals. We can still find the descendents of crinoids and brachiopods that populated the Mesozoic oceans. They live in polar seas and in deep oceans. Although most groups of organisms became more widely diversified during the Mesozoic era, the insects that had become so abundant during the late Paleozoic era declined in number and diversity during the Mesozoic era.

## Vertebrates of the Mesozoic Era

In addition to the fish that evolved during the Paleozoic era, the oceans of the Mesozoic era contained predatory reptiles such as plesiosaurs and mosasaurs. Amphibians, reptiles, and mammals that lived on land continued to evolve during the Mesozoic era. Frogs, turtles, crocodiles, pterosaurs, and dinosaurs evolved during this time. **Pterosaurs** were flying reptiles. Many were the size of today's predatory birds. The pterosaur shown in **Figure 18** had a wingspan of 12 m and might have weighed 200 kg. Although pterosaurs shared many characteristics with dinosaurs, they were not dinosaurs. Pterosaurs differed from dinosaurs in that they had hollow bones, thin and translucent wings, extra bones in their hands or wings, and were probably covered with a hairlike material. Although they could fly like birds and bats, they are not a related species to either.

 What Mesozoic animals still exist today?

**Figure 18** Some pterosaurs skimmed the water with their beaks to catch fish.

**Figure 17** The Mesozoic era included the Jurassic period, also know as the Age of Reptiles.

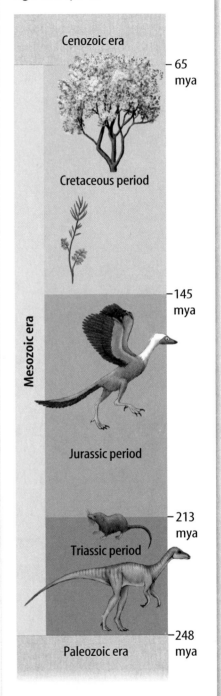

Cenozoic era

Cretaceous period

–65 mya

Mesozoic era

–145 mya

Jurassic period

–213 mya

Triassic period

–248 mya

Paleozoic era

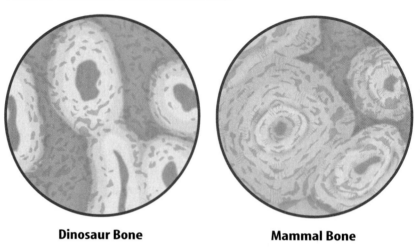

**Figure 19** Growth rings can be seen in this enlarged cross-section of dinosauar and mammal bones. The growth rate might be a clue to whether dinosaurs were endothermic.

Dinosaur Bone          Mammal Bone

**Dinosaurs** Dinosaurs evolved during the Triassic period. The first dinosaurs were small, but as new species evolved, they grew bigger. *Apatosaurus* and *Diplodocus* were some of the largest animals to walk on Earth. The first scientists to study dinosaur fossils thought their skulls, feet, and tails suggested that they were just very large reptiles. Because they imagined them to be reptiles, they believed that they lived and behaved like modern reptiles do today. That would mean that dinosaurs were **ectotherms,** relying on their surroundings and behavior to help them regulate their body temperatures. As such they would have to find sunlight to warm up and move into the shade to cool off. Recent studies of dinosaur bones show that their structure is more similar to endothermic species. **Endotherms** generate internal body heat to maintain a constant body temperature. **Figure 19** shows a comparison of dinosaur and mammal bones. Rings in bones indicate the organism's growth rate much like tree rings tell the age and rate of growth of a tree. Similarities in growth rate have led scientists to think that dinosaurs were endothermic and may have lived more like today's mammals and birds than like reptiles. Other comparisons include speed of travel, carrying the tail and not dragging it, and having an upright stance.

**Birds** By the 1970s scientists had proposed that birds are the descendants of dinosaurs. Read about the extinct reptiles in **Figure 20** and think about the debate. It has been many millions of years since the time of dinosaurs. Birds have had many opportunities to evolve to fit into new and different environments. Did they become endothermic or have they always been endotherms?

# Visualizing Extinct Reptiles

**Figure 20**

If you're like most people, the phrase "prehistoric reptiles" probably brings dinosaurs to mind. But not all ancient reptiles were dinosaurs. The first dinosaurs didn't appear until about 115 million years after the first reptiles. Paleontologists have unearthed the fossils of a variety of reptilian creatures that swam through the seas and waterways of ancient Earth. Several examples of these extinct aquatic reptiles are shown here.

▲ **MOSASAUR (MOH zuh sawr)** Marine-dwelling mosasaurs had snake-like bodies, large skulls, and long snouts. They also had jointed jaw-bones, an adaptation for grasping and swallowing large prey.

▲ **ICHTHYOSAUR (IHK thee uh sawr)** Ichthyosaurs resembled a cross between a dolphin and a shark, with large eyes, four paddle-like limbs, and a fishlike tail that moved from side to side. These extinct reptiles were fearsome predators with long jaws armed with numerous sharp teeth.

◄ **ELASMOSAURUS (uh laz muh SAWR us)** Predatory Elasmosaurus had a long neck—with as many as 76 vertebrae—topped by a small head.

▲ **CHAMPOSAUR (CHAMP uh sawr)** This ancient reptile looked something like a modern crocodile, with a long snout studded with razor-sharp teeth. Champosaurs lived in the freshwater lakes and streams and preyed on fish and turtles. They were topped by a small head.

▲ **PLESIOSAUR (PLEE see uh sawr)** These marine reptiles had stout bodies, paddle-like limbs, and long necks. Plesiosaurs might have fed by swinging their heads from side to side through schools of fish.

**Figure 21** Observe the fossil skeleton and decide if *Archaeopteryx* looked like this.

**Decide** what features of the *Archaeopteryx* fossil link it to birds and to dinosaurs.

**Archaeopteryx** Once scientists discovered a dinosaurlike skeleton with fossilized feathers in Jurassic-aged rocks, they knew they had the support they needed for their theory that birds evolved from dinosaurs. *Archaeopteryx* is the name that has been given to one ancestral bird species. The fossil and a reconstruction are shown in **Figure 21.**

**Mammals** evolved during the Triassic period, alongside the dinosaurs. Early mammals, shown in **Figure 22,** were small in size and not very numerous or diverse for most of the Mesozoic era. In the late Cretaceous period, they increased in both number and diversity. As dinosaur species became extinct, mammals were able to move into the niches that dinosaurs once occupied. You will read more about mammals later in this lesson.

**Figure 22** The first mammals were small, rarely getting larger than an opossum.

**Figure 23** Angiosperms evolved to fit many niches. Their water-tight seeds allowed them to move away from water and become the dominant plant form.

## Plants of the Mesozoic Era

Plants called gymnosperms dominated the plant population of the Mesozoic era. **Gymnosperms** produce seeds but no flowers. Some gymnosperms, such as the pine and ginkgo trees, still exist today. Angiosperms evolved near the end of the Mesozoic era. Angiosperms are flowering plants that bear seeds with hard outer coverings. This gave them the ability to live in many different environments and to survive harsh climatic conditions. **Figure 23** shows what a plant landscape might have looked like during the Mesozoic era.

 How are gymnosperms and angiosperms different?

## Mesozoic Era Extinction Events

Scientists have observed evidence of extinction events in rocks of Mesozoic era age. The Triassic period ended with a mass extinction event that killed off approximately 20 percent of all marine families. Another mass extinction event occurred at the end of the Jurassic period. Several dinosaur groups including some of the largest dinosaurs, such as *Diplodocus,* became extinct during this event. One of the most well-known extinction events occurred at the end of the Cretaceous period. Almost 85 percent of all species in the oceans and all of the remaining dinosaurs became extinct, yet many mammal, bird, and reptile species survived. This event marked the end of the Mesozoic era.

## The Cenozoic Era

**Figure 24** shows the portion of the geologic time scale that includes the Cenozoic era. The Cenozoic era is divided into seven epochs. During the Cenozoic era, marine life began to recover from the Cretaceous mass extinction event. The offspring of organisms that survived the Cretaceous extinction event make up the present marine ecosystems. A reconstruction of life in the early Cenozoic oceans is shown in **Figure 25.** How similar do these animals look to today's marine populations?

### Animals on Land

By the beginning of the Cenozoic era, the modern mammals had evolved. Some mammals returned to the ocean. During the Eocene epoch, whales evolved from carnivorous, meat-eating, land mammals to the modern marine mammals they are today. **Primates,** animals with opposable thumbs and two eyes that look directly forward, evolved during the Eocene epoch. They diversified rapidly and lived in both the trees and on the ground. About 4.4 million years ago, during the Pliocene epoch, the hominids evolved. Hominids are descendants of these early primates. Hominids walk upright on two legs. The human species, *Homo sapiens,* belongs to the hominid group.

### Plants of the Cenozoic Era

Recall that flowering plants evolved near the end of the Mesozoic era. They have continued to evolve ever since. Today, there are more than 250,000 species of flowering plants. Fruits, vegetables, and nuts are all produced by flowering plants. Grasses are flowering plants and during the Eocene epoch supported a large diversity of mammals, which enabled the mammals to multiply and diversify.

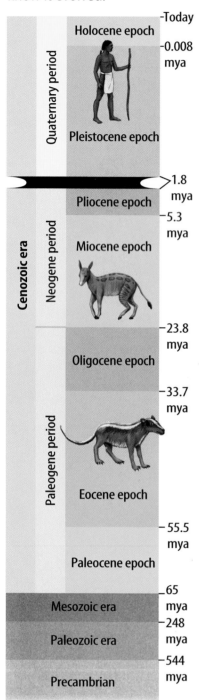

**Figure 24** The modern era, the Cenozoic, is when life as we know it evolved.

**Figure 25** Fish, mammals, and many invertebrates and plants have become common life forms in today's oceans.

## Cenozoic-Era Extinctions

Cenozoic mass extinction events have not occurred on the scale of those previously discussed in this chapter. Some extinctions are the result of natural selection while others have been **induced** by humans. Can you think of animals that have become extinct during the Cenozoic era?

## Complexity Increases over Time

Fossil sequences from the Archean eon to the Cenozoic era show that complexity increases over time. Life began as simple bacteria. Then more complex organisms with shells evolved. Organisms became more diversified and continued to evolve from marine invertebrates to marine and land vertebrates and plants. The fossil record reveals this change.

**ACADEMIC VOCABULARY**
induce (en DOOS)
*(verb)* to move by persuasion or influence
*The candidate's editorial induced me to vote for her.*

# LESSON 3 Review

## Summarize

Create your own lesson summary as you write a **newsletter**.

1. **Write** this lesson title, number, and page numbers at the top of a sheet of paper.

2. **Review** the text after the red main headings and write one sentence about each. These will be the headlines of your newsletter.

3. **Review** the text and write 2–3 sentences about each **blue** subheading. These sentences should tell *who, what, when, where,* and *why* information about each headline.

4. **Illustrate** your newsletter with diagrams of important structures and processes next to each headline.

 ELA7: W 2.5

 **Standards Check**

## Using Vocabulary

1. Use the term *angiosperm* in a sentence. **4.g**

**Select the correct term to complete the sentences.**

ectotherm  endotherm  primate

2. An animal that warms itself in the Sun is a(n) _____. **4.g**

3. An animal with opposable thumbs is a(n) _____. **4.g**

## Understanding Main Ideas

4. Which of the following began the Mesozoic era? **4.e**

   A. the breakup of Pangaea
   B. the formation of continental ice sheets
   C. the melting of European glaciers
   D. the extinction of the dinosaurs

5. **Compare and contrast** the organisms in the Mesozoic and Cenozoic eras. **4.g**

| Mesozoic | Cenozoic |
|----------|----------|
|          |          |
|          |          |
|          |          |

## Applying Science

6. **Think Critically** In the last several decades birds have been identified as descendents of dinosaurs. What discoveries allowed this change to occur? **4.g**

7. **Explain** why Earth's life-forms became so diverse after an extinction event. **4.b**

**Science** nline
For more practice, visit **Standards Check** at ca7.msscience.com.

# MiniLab

# What happened here?

00:20 minutes

Geologists can determine what an area was like in the past by studying evidence in the rock record. The rock record refers to the information that is stored by the way rocks are formed. The diagram below shows rock layers from three separate locations.

## Procedure

1. Study the diagram below.

2. Compare the locations of different fossils in the layers.

3. Decide what each layer tells you about the relative age of the fossils.

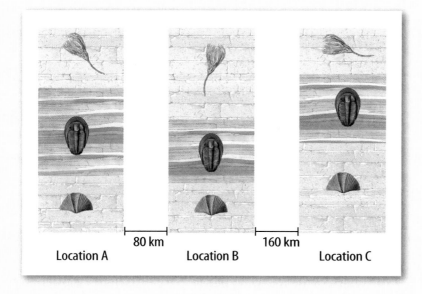

Location A     80 km     Location B     160 km     Location C

## Analysis

1. **Analyze** Which rocks in the diagram are oldest? Which are the youngest? What principle explains how you know this?

2. **Analyze** What can you infer about the relative ages of the fossils in each of the three locations? Explain.

3. **Infer** What might have occurred at the boundaries between each layer? What might scientists look for to verify this?

 **Science Content Standards**

**7.c** Communicate the logical connection among hypotheses, science concepts, tests conducted, data collected, and conclusions drawn from the scientific evidence.

# Applying Math

## Scientific Notation and Age of Meteorites

The Gao Meteorite fell on March 5, 1960, at Gao, Sissili, Burkina. The composition of the silicate spheres of the meteorite formed from solar dust and gas about 4.6 billion years ago.

### Example

Write 4.6 billion in standard notation and in scientific notation.

**What you know:**   4.6 billion years

**What you need to find:**   Standard notation
Scientific notation

**Write the number in standard notation:**   Write the number form for billion, 1,000,000,000.
4.6 billion is 4.6 × 1,000,000,000 or 4,600,000,000.

**Now write 4,600,000,000 in scientific notation:**

**1** Move the decimal 9 places to the left.
4,600,000,000.

**2** Drop the zeros to the right of the decimal.
4.6

**3** Add × $10^9$ after 4.6. The exponent equals the number of places the decimal was moved. If it was moved left, the exponent is positive. If it was moved right, the exponent is negative.

**Answer:** 4.6 billion is 4.6 × $10^9$ in scientific notation.

---

### Practice Problems

In 1996 a meteorite from Mars was found in Alan Hills, Antarctica. The meteorite provided evidence of possible life on Mars dating to about 3.6 billion years ago.

**1.** Write this number in standard notation.

**2.** Write this number in scientific notation.

**Science Online**
For more math practice, visit Math Practice at ca7.msscience.com.

# Use the Internet:
# How has California changed over geologic time?

## Materials
computer with internet access

## Science Content Standards

**7.a** Select and use appropriate tools and technology (including calculators, computers, balances, spring scales, microscopes, and binoculars) to perform tests, collect data, and display data.

**7.d** Construct scale models, maps, and appropriately labeled diagrams to communicate scientific knowledge (e.g., motion of Earth's plates and cell structure).

## Problem

Imagine what California was like millions of years ago. What animals might have been roaming around the spot where you now sit? Fossils can help uncover clues about how plants and animals evolved over time. By using Internet resources and sharing data with your peers, you can learn more about how life in California has changed over time.

## Form a Hypothesis

Predict how the plants and animals have changed over time.

## Collect Data and Make Observations

1. Make a data table like the one below with your region name in the title. Leave a larger space for the sixth row.

| Species that Lived in (Your Region) California | | | | |
|---|---|---|---|---|
| Species name | | | | |
| Location fossils are found | | | | |
| Period or epoch species lived | | | | |
| Plant or animal | plant | plant | animal | animal |
| Type of plant or animal | | | | |
| Sketch of the species | | | | |
| Descendants (if any) | | | | |

2. Use library resources and <u>ca7.msscience.com</u> to gather information about two plants and two animals found in your region during one of these geologic time intervals—Precambrian time, the Paleozoic era, the Mesozoic era, or the Cenozoic era.

3. List the species' names, and the locations and geologic time interval in which they lived on the data table.

4. Determine the group each species belongs to. Is it a vertebrate or invertebrate animal? Is it a bird, fish, amphibian, reptile, insect, or mammal? Is it a gymnosperm or an angiosperm? List this in the data table.

5. Draw a sketch of the species in the data table.

6. Determine if any present-day species might have descended from the selected species.

7. Post your data at <u>ca7.msscience.com</u>.

## Analyze and Conclude

1. **Analyze** your data, those of your classmates, and those posted at <u>ca7.msscience.com.</u> What similarities exist among species that lived during the same time period?

2. **Infer** What clues do the plant and animal fossils provide about the environment in which these species lived? How do these environments compare to the present-day environment in your area?

3. **Form a Hypothesis** Which time periods showed the greatest diversity of fossils? For time periods that had fewer types of fossils, provide two hypotheses as to why this might be true.

4. **Predict** when the species you studied died out and form a hypothesis to explain why they are no longer living. Explain how paleontologists would determine this information.

## Communicate

Write a two-page story about your four organisms. Give a general description of the organism, its habitat, and the niche it belonged to. If any two of the organisms are from the same era, write about how they interacted. If they are from different eras, explain how things might have been different if they had existed at the same time.

# Real World Science

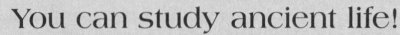

## Science & Career

### You can study ancient life!

Would you like to learn more about ancient plants, sea creatures, dinosaurs, and early mammals? Paleontology is a multidisciplinary science incorporating biology, geology, chemistry, physics, and mathematics. It is the study of all types of ancient life—their structure, evolution, and environment—as shown through their fossils. The paleontologist in this picture is shown with a dinosaur fossil collected from El Chocon, Argentina. To become a paleontologist you should study math, science, and computer courses in high school.

Go to **Careers** at **ca7.msscience.com** to learn more about what you can do as a paleontologist. Write a paragraph on how paleontology aids in the understanding of ancient Earth. Your paragraph should show proper sentence structure, punctuation, grammar, and spelling.

**ELA7:** W 1.1

## How old is it?

Radiometric dating continues to be the most common way scientists date geologic timescales. It's based on the half-lives of radioactive isotopes. Dating can be conducted on objects as small as 0.0000000001 g using a mass spectrometer. The ages are not taken from fossils but from the rocks surrounding them. This technician at the U.S. Geological Survey is using a mass spectrometer to determine the proportions of carbon isotopes contained in a sample of organic remains.

Visit **Technology** at **ca7.msscience.com** to find out more about radiometric dating. Divide into groups and pick one dating isotope to research. Create a table listing information about the isotope.

## Science & Technology

# The "Age of the Fishes"

Picture warm, tropical seas filled with brachiopods, swimming trilobites, "sea flowers" (crinoids), sea scorpions, ammonites, and corals. That would be the Devonian period. Many new kinds of fish appeared during this time. Placoderms, armored fish with bony plates in their mouths instead of teeth, reached their greatest diversity. The photo shows the head and trunk plate of a placoderm fossil. Early sharks and rays became abundant during this period. The first ray-finned and lobe-finned fishes also appeared.

Visit **History** at ca7.msscience.com to find out more about the Devonian time period. Create a bar graph showing the length of the time period on one axis and the appearance and duration of the different fishes from this time including, but not limited to, placoderms, sharks, rays, and early finned fishes. What does this tell us about the evolution of these organisms? Draw or paste pictures of these organisms onto the graph.

## Changing Climate and Our World

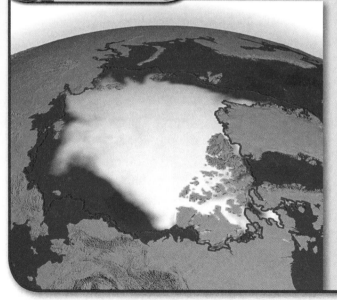

Paleoecology is the study of the ecology and climate of the past, as revealed both by fossils and by other methods. Since 1979, the size of the summer polar ice cap has shrunk more than 20 percent, which could indicate global warming. But how do we know if it is warming or cooling?

Visit **Society** at ca7.msscience.com to learn more about paleoecology and global warming. If Earth warmed up by 10°C, what would the ramifications be? Assign each student to a group to research the effects of this rise for one of the continents. Explore the organisms, environments, countries, and societies.

## The BIG Idea — Evidence from rocks helps us understand the history of life on Earth.

### Lesson 1 Geologic Time and Mass Extinctions
**4.b, 4.e, 4.g, 7.c**

**Main Idea** Fossils provide evidence of how life and environmental conditions have changed over time. Geologists used fossils to create the geologic time scale.

- Fossils were used to organize the geologic time scale.
- The geologic time scale is divided into eras, periods, and epochs.
- Scientists use extinctions and developments to mark the time scale divisions.
- Mass extinctions may be caused by global warming, global cooling, volcanoes, asteroid impacts, or combinations of all of these.

- **catastrophic event** (p. 318)
- **index fossil** (p. 316)
- **mass extinction** (p. 318)

### Lesson 2 Early Earth History
**4.b, 4.e, 4.g, 7.d**

**Main Idea** Bacteria, the simplest organisms, were the first organisms to evolve on Earth. Increasingly complex organisms followed them.

- The first life-forms were bacteria. They began to evolve into more complex life forms.
- Newer life-forms evolved to tolerate or use oxygen.
- The Paleozoic era evolved organisms with hard shells during the Cambrian explosion.
- Some of the life-forms, including fish, evolved a spinal column.
- The amniotes developed an egg with a shell so they could survive on land.
- Plants moved onto land first, followed by animals that used them for food.
- The Permian extinction killed off most of the species on Earth and ended the Paleozoic era.

- **amniote** (p. 329)
- **cyanobacteria** (p. 327)
- **vertebrate** (p. 329)

### Lesson 3 Middle and Recent Earth History
**4.b, 4.e, 4.g, 7.a, 7.c, 7.d**

**Main Idea** Life continues to evolve into many of the forms we see on Earth today.

- Pangaea begins to break up and creates changes in the environment and climate.
- The dominant creatures of the Mesozoic era are reptiles and dinosaurs.
- The extinction of the dinosaurs marks the beginning of the Cenozoic era.
- In the Cenozoic era, organisms that we see today evolved.
- Cooling climates gave an advantage to plants that could produce seeds and animals with body coverings and temperature regulation.

- **ectotherm** (p. 334)
- **endotherm** (p. 334)
- **gymnosperm** (p. 337)
- **primate** (p. 338)
- **pterosaur** (p. 333)

Download quizzes, key terms, and flash cards from ca7.msscience.com.

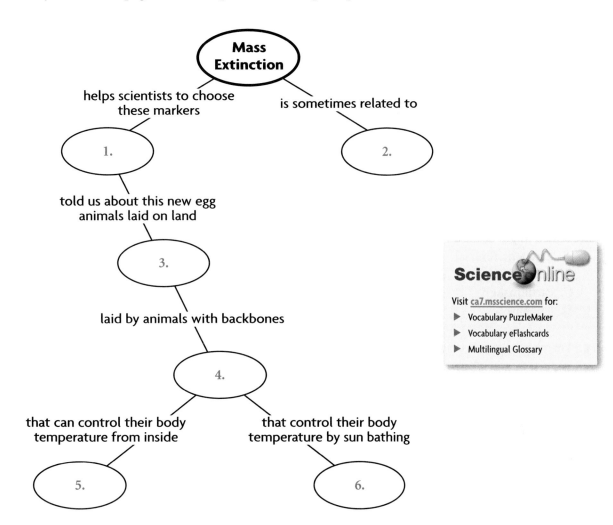

# Linking Vocabulary and Main Ideas

Use vocabulary terms from page 346 to complete this concept map.

**Mass Extinction**

helps scientists to choose these markers

is sometimes related to

1.

2.

told us about this new egg animals laid on land

3.

laid by animals with backbones

4.

that can control their body temperature from inside

that control their body temperature by sun bathing

5.

6.

**Science Online**

Visit ca7.msscience.com for:
▶ Vocabulary PuzzleMaker
▶ Vocabulary eFlashcards
▶ Multilingual Glossary

## Using Vocabulary

**Fill in the blanks with the correct vocabulary word from this chapter.**

_____7._____ are used by scientists to identify the start or the end of a geologic time period. These are usually in the fossil record because of some ____8.____ that may have been caused by a(n) ____9.____ .

The fossil record tells us that ____10.____ were probably the first organisms on Earth and they still live in extreme conditions today. Most of the major life forms on Earth today are ____11.____ that descended when animals moved on to land. This was made possible by the evolution of a new egg form, the ____12.____ egg.

## Understanding Main Ideas

1. Which type of fossil is used to mark geologic time?
   A. mold fossil
   B. cast fossil
   C. dinosaur fossil
   D. index fossil  `4.e`

2. Which is the largest segment of time on the geologic time scale?
   A. epoch
   B. period
   C. eon
   D. era  `4.g`

3. Which might cause a mass extinction?
   A. magnetic reversal
   B. asteroid impact
   C. earthquake
   D. tsunami  `4.b`

4. The map below shows the location of an asteroid impact.

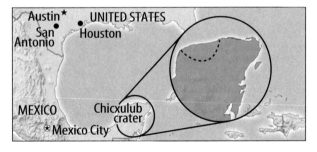

   Why was the asteroid impact site so difficult to find?
   A. It was in Mexico.
   B. It had a different shape from other impact sites.
   C. It was so old.
   D. It was mostly underwater.  `4.b`

5. Global warming is generally the result of which?
   A. global cooling
   B. fire
   C. greenhouse gases
   D. basaltic flow  `4.g`

6. Precambrian fossils are hard to find because they are which?
   A. soft-bodied organisms
   B. shelled organisms
   C. in rock buried very deep
   D. microscopic  `4.b`

7. The Cambrian explosion produced lots of which organisms?
   A. vertebrates
   B. shelled animals
   C. algae
   D. plankton  `4.g`

8. The figures below show bone cells of dinosaur and mammal bone.

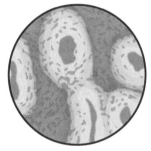

   What were scientists trying to determine by comparing dinosaur and mammal bone cells?
   A. that dinosaurs had feathers
   B. that dinosaurs were endotherms
   C. that dinosaurs could walk upright
   D. that dinosaurs could run fast  `4.e`

9. Which could be said about the Archaeopteryx fossil?
   A. It is the first bird fossil.
   B. It is the first fossil found with feathers.
   C. It is the missing link.
   D. It is a hoax.  `4.e`

10. Differences between angiosperms and gymnosperms are most obvious in which part?
    A. seeds
    B. roots
    C. leaves
    D. pollen  `4.e`

## Applying Science

**11. Analyze** Your class is examining a road cut and finds several trilobite fossils. One is found at the bottom of the road cut and the other is found at the top. They look identical. Which one is older? **4.e**

**12. Infer** A middle Eocene sand dollar is thinner than an early Eocene sand dollar. What might have caused the evolution in thickness? **4.g**

**13. Explain** how a catastrophic event may not cause a mass extinction. **4.b**

**14. Hypothesize** why Precambrian organisms had no shells, but after the Cambrian explosion, there were many species with shells. **4.g**

**The image below shows an iceberg breaking off from a glacier.**

**15. Explain** how glaciers might be affected during both global warming and global cooling. **4.b**

**WRITING in Science**

**16. Select** an epoch from the Cenozoic Era and write three paragraphs about life during that time. **ELA7: W 1.1**

## Cumulative Review

**17. Explain** how the principle of superposition helps us understand that dinosaurs and humans didn't live at the same time. **4.c**

**18. Explain** how radioactive decay tells us the age of a dinosaur fossil. **4.d**

**19. Describe** how Steno's principle of original horizontality is related to the geologic time scale. **4.g**

**20. Explain** the relationship between the principle of original lateral continuity, index fossils, and the geologic time scale. **4.g**

## Applying Math

**21.** Radiometric dating of chondrites has placed them at the age of 4.55 billion years, which is the approximate age of the solar system. Write this number in standard notation and in scientific notation. **MA7: NS 1.1**

**22.** A basalt meteorite found on the ice in Antarctica was likely formed in a volcanic eruption about 180 million years ago. Write this number in standard notation and in scientific notation. **MA7: NS 1.1**

**23.** The Barringer Meteor Crater in Arizona is about 49,000 years old. Write this number in scientific notation. **MA7: NS 1.1**

**24.** The Paleozoic era started $5.44 \times 10^8$ years ago. Write this as standard notation. **MA7: NS 1.1**

Use this diagram to answer questions 1–3.

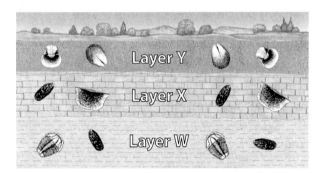

 Silurian-Triassic     Cambrian-Ordovician

 Silurian     Cambrian

 Ordovician

**1** **During which geologic time period did layer W form?**

A   Cambrian

B   Ordovician

C   Devonian

D   Silurian    4.e

**2** **During which geologic time period did layer X form?**

A   Devonian

B   Silurian

C   Ordovician

D   Cambrian    4.e

**3** **During which geologic time period did layer Y form?**

A   Cambrian

B   Silurian

C   Mississippian

D   Ordovician    4.e

**4** **When did dinosaurs roam Earth?**

A   Precambrian time

B   Paleozoic era

C   Mesozoic era

D   Cenozoic era    4.e

**5** **The diagram below shows the breakup of supercontinent that formed at the end of the Paleozoic Era.**

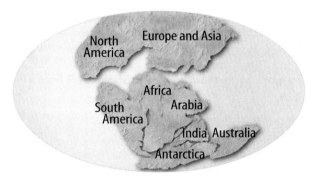

**What is the name of this continent?**

A   Gondwanaland

B   Eurasia

C   Laurasia

D   Pangaea    4.g

**6** **During which geologic period did modern humans evolve?**

A   Quaternary

B   Triassic

C   Ordovician

D   Tertiary    4.e

Science online   Standards Assessment ca7.msscience.com

**7** The figure below shows the collision of India and the Asian continent.

**Which mountain range formed because India collided with Asia?**

**A** Alps

**B** Andes

**C** Ural

**D** Himalayas    `4.g`

**8** **What is the oldest epoch in the Cenozoic era?**

**A** Pleistocene

**B** Paleocene

**C** Miocene

**D** Holocene    `4.g`

**9** **What is the youngest epoch in the Cenozoic era?**

**A** Miocene

**B** Holocene

**C** Paleocene

**D** Eocene    `4.g`

**10** **Which epoch is part of the Quaternary period?**

**A** Oligocene

**B** Eocene

**C** Pleistocene

**D** Pliocene    `4.g`

**11** The figure below shows a strand from a stromatolite.

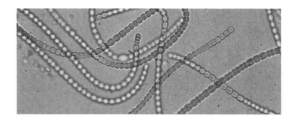

**What is the oldest life-form on Earth?**

**A** dinosaurs

**B** pterosaurs

**C** cyanobacteria

**D** algae    `4.e`

**12** **Environmental changes brought on by catastrophic events caused which to happen?**

**A** mass extinction

**B** volcano formation

**C** asteroid impacts

**D** cracks in Earth's plates    `4.b`

**13** **Which is the best definition of mass extinction?**

**A** the end of an era

**B** the dying off of one species

**C** the dying off of just dinosaurs

**D** the dying off of many species of plants and animals    `4.b`

**14** **After a mass extinction, life-forms evolved because of which reason?**

**A** New niches were created.

**B** Old niches were left empty.

**C** Temperature changes always cause mutations.

**D** Global temperatures increased.    `4.b`

**Chapter 8 • Standards Assessment** **351**

Are you interested in learning more about how Earth and life on Earth have changed? If so, check out these great books.

## Poetry

**Sierra,** by Diane Siebert, is a poem in which one of the Sierra Mountains speaks of the beauty and timelessness of herself and her sister peaks. The poem includes references to the geologic processes that created the mountains. ***The content of this book is related to*** *Science Standard 7.4.*

## Narrative Nonfiction

**Asteroid Impact,** by Douglas Henderson, tells the story of an enormous asteroid that struck Earth 65 million years ago. This impact may have been responsible for the extinction of dinosaurs at the end of the Cretaceous Period. ***The content of this book is related to*** *Science Standard 7.4.*

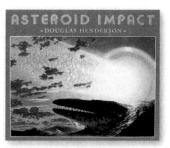

## Nonfiction

**Giant Shark: Megalodon, Prehistoric Super Predator,** by Caroline Arnold, describes the life cycle and habits of the "largest ocean predator." Extinct for over two million years, this enormous shark comes to life in double-spread watercolor illustrations. ***The content of this book is related to*** *Science Standard 7.4.*

## Nonfiction

**Plate Tectonics,** by Alvin Silverstein, is a thorough discussion of plate tectonics. The book provides details about how continental drift has affected the evolution of life on the planet, how volcanoes act as Earth's safety valves, and the causes of earthquakes. ***The content of this book is related to*** *Science Standard 7.4.*

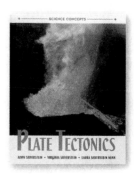

Choose the word or phrase that best answers the question.

1. The figure shows a series of rock layers.

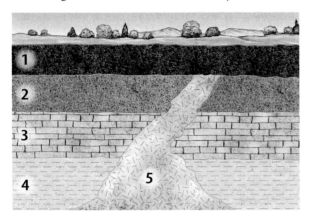

Which lists the layers in order from oldest to youngest?
A. 5-4-3-2-1
B. 1-2-3-4-5
C. 2-3-4-5-1
D. 4-3-2-5-1  **4.b**

2. A fault can be used to determine which of the following for a group of rocks?
A. absolute age
B. index age
C. radiometric age
D. relative age  **4.a**

3. "The present is the key to the past" summarizes which principle?
A. superposition
B. succession
C. radioactivity
D. uniformitarianism  **4.a**

4. Which are the remains of species that existed on Earth for short periods of time and were abundant geographically wide-spread?
A. trace fossils
B. index fossils
C. carbon films
D. body fossils  **4.g**

Write your responses on a sheet of paper.

5. **Explain** how scientists hypothesize that Earth is about 4.5 billion years old.  **4.d**

6. **Predict** Suppose you are trying to determine the ages of rock layers in the western United States. You find a layer of volcanic ash deposits. How might this layer help you determine the ages of the rock layers?  **4.b**

7. **Analyze** Suppose you discover layers of rocks. How can you tell if the layers have not been disturbed?  **4.a**

8. **Design** In a canyon, erosion by water and wind has cut through the sedimentary rock, exposing layers of rock. Infer the relative age of rocks in the lowest layers compared to the top layer. Design a sequence chart similar to the one shown below to compare plant and animal fossils you might find in the different layers.  **4.e**

| Relative Age of Rock | Examples of Plant and Animal Fossils |
|---|---|
|  |  |
|  |  |
|  |  |
|  | Trilobites |

~9. **Explain** why relative dating can only estimate the age of a fossil.  **4.e**

10. **Hypothesize** how a fossil of an organism that lived in ocean water millions of years ago might be found in the middle of North America.  **4.a**

11. **Summarize** how early photosynthetic organisms changed the conditions on Earth to allow more advanced organisms to flourish.  **4.g**

# UNIT 5

# Structure, Function, and Physical Principles in Living Systems

**Huge Skeleton** Your skeletal system supports your body much like the steel beams support the Golden Gate Bridge connecting the city of San Francisco and Marin County in California.

**West Coast EVENTS**

**1867**
The United States purchases Alaska from Russia.

**1898**
The United States, during the presidency of William McKinley, gains control of the Hawaiian Islands.

A.D. 1 ⚡ 1200   1300   1400   1500   1600   1700   1800   1900

**WORLD EVENTS**

**1284**
First known eyeglasses are invented.

**1660**
Marcello Malpighi proves previous blood circulation theories when he discovers capillaries connecting to arteries and veins in an eel.

**1876**
Alexander Graham Bell, at his laboratory in Boston, Massachusetts, invents the telephone, sending the sound of voices over electrical wires.

**Science Online**

To learn more about biophysicists and their work, visit ca7.msscience.com.

**Concepts In Motion**

**Interactive Time Line** To learn more about these events and others, visit ca7.msscience.com.

**May 1937**
The Golden Gate Bridge opens; its 1,260-m span— a world record that held for 27 years.

**1984**
Athletes from around the world meet at Los Angeles, California, to test their athletic skills at the Olympic Games.

**June 2001**
Scientists at the Lawrence Livermore Laboratory in California, announce they have discovered how organisms modify crystal shape and growth to form bone and shell structures.

**1920      1940      1960      1980      2000      2020**

**1940s**
Charles Richard Drew organizes a blood bank in NYC. It served as a model for the system run by the American Red Cross.

**1950s**
Ultrasound scans become useful tools for safely checking fetuses for size and growth patterns.

**2001–2005**
Paraplegic Matt Nagle uses a computer chip implanted in his brain to allow him to grasp objects with an artificial hand by thinking about moving his paralyzed hand.

# The Musculoskeletal System and Levers

## The BIG Idea

Muscles, bones, and joints form simple machines in the body that produce movement and mechanical advantage.

### LESSON 1   5.a, 5.c, 6.h, 7.a
**The Musculoskeletal System**

**Main Idea** Muscles, tendons, and bones work in a coordinated fashion to produce movement.

### LESSON 2
  6.h, 6.i, 7.a, 7.c, 7.d

**The Body and Levers**

**Main Idea** Muscles and bones are joined in a way that allows them to act as levers, providing force or speed advantages.

## How does he *do* that?

This skateboarder is showing great control of his musculoskeletal system. His muscles and bones are working together to produce smooth, controlled movements that allow him to perform this trick.

**Science Journal** Write a paragraph about the activities you perform that you think require your muscles and bones to work together.

## Launch Lab

### Is it easy to lift?

You might find it easier to carry your science book close to your chest rather than far away from it. Why?

**Procedure**

1. Read and complete a lab safety form.

2. Hold a **soup can** in one hand.

3. Lift the can using only your wrist.

4. Hold your elbow at your waist and lift the can by bending your arm at your elbow.

5. Hang your arm down and then without bending your elbow, raise the can in front of you to shoulder height and back.

### Think About This

- **Report** Which of the actions moved the can the shortest distance? The longest?

- **Choose** Which movement felt easiest? Which felt hardest?

- **Differentiate** Did all the movements use the same parts of the arm? Which parts of your arm did you use?

 5.c, 7.a

## Science Online

Visit ca7.msscience.com to:

▶ view Concepts in Motion

▶ explore Virtual Labs

▶ access content-related Web links

▶ take the Standards Check

---

**FOLDABLES™ Study Organizer**

**Levers in the Body** Make the following Foldable to identify the levers found in the human body.

▷ **STEP 1 Fold** a sheet of paper into thirds lengthwise.

▷ **STEP 2 Unfold** and **draw** vertical lines along the folds. **Draw** three horizontal lines to divide the paper into four rows. **Label** as shown.

**Reading Skill**

**Visualizing** As you read this chapter, you will learn about parts of the body that act as levers. Identify each type of lever in the first column. Give examples in column 2. Explain the mechanical advantage to the body for each type of lever in column 3.

# Get Ready to Read

# Make Connections

**❶ Learn It!** Make connections between what you read and what you already know. Connections can be based on personal experiences (text-to-self), what you have read before (text-to-text), or events in other places (text-to-world).

As you read, ask connecting questions. Are you reminded of a personal experience? Have you read about the topic before? Did you think of a person, a place, or an event in another part of the world?

**❷ Practice It!** Read the excerpt below and make connections to your own knowledge and experience.

*Text-to-self:*
When you exercise, how long does it take your muscles to get tired?

*Text-to-text:*
What did you read about mitochondria and cellular respiration in earlier chapters?

*Text-to-world:*
Think about Olympic athletes. How do you think the network of blood vessels going to their muscle cells would compare to nonathletes?

> Movement of the muscle filaments during contraction requires energy. Muscle cells contain more mitochondria than other cells in order to produce the energy needed for contraction. A large network of blood vessels supplies muscles with the oxygen the mitochondria need for cellular respiration.
>
> —*from page 364*

**❸ Apply It!** As you read this chapter, choose five words or phrases that help you make a connection to something you already know.

# Target Your Reading

Use this to focus on the main ideas as you read the chapter.

**Reading Tip**

Make connections with memorable events, places, or people in your life. The better the connection, the more likely you will remember.

**1** **Before you read** the chapter, respond to the statements below on your worksheet or on a numbered sheet of paper.
- Write an **A** if you **agree** with the statement.
- Write a **D** if you **disagree** with the statement.

**2** **After you read** the chapter, look back to this page to see if you've changed your mind about any of the statements.
- If any of your answers changed, explain why.
- Change any false statements into true statements.
- Use your revised statements as a study guide.

**Science Online**

Print a worksheet of this page at ca7.msscience.com.

| Before You Read A or D | Statement | After You Read A or D |
|---|---|---|
| | **1** Your bones allow you flexibility in movement. | |
| | **2** Your nose is not made from bone. | |
| | **3** When a muscle relaxes, it causes the bone it moved to return to its original position. | |
| | **4** Muscle fibers can actively lengthen. | |
| | **5** A lever helps you complete a task with less work. | |
| | **6** A shovel is a type of lever. | |
| | **7** Some levers require you to use more force than you would need to complete the task without them. | |
| | **8** Your body contains all three classes of levers. | |
| | **9** Most of the levers in your body make the work you do require more effort. | |
| | **10** Bones provide the effort force, while muscles are the levers. | |

## Reading Guide

### What *You'll Learn*

▶ **Identify** the main characteristics of the skeletal system.

▶ **Examine** how muscles contract and relax.

▶ **Explain** how bones and muscles work together.

### Why *It's Important*
Understanding the musculoskeletal systems helps you better appreciate how your body moves.

### Vocabulary

| | |
|---|---|
| skeletal system | contraction |
| bone | relaxation |
| joint | tendon |
| cartilage | flexion |
| muscle | extension |

### Review Vocabulary
**mitochondrion:** organelle that converts food molecules into usable energy (p. 61)

# The Musculoskeletal System

**Main Idea** Muscles, tendons, and bones work in a coordinated fashion to produce movement.

**Real-World Reading Connection** What holds up the walls and the roof of a building and protects it from the outside elements? There are beams, braces, and insulation inside the walls and under the roof that you cannot see. What structures support and protect our bodies?

## The Skeletal System

The hard structures within our bodies are part of the **skeletal system** (SKE luh tul • SIS tum), which provides support, protection, and movement. Press on your wrist, ankle, knee, or elbow. Do you feel something hard under your skin? You are feeling **bone,** a hard tissue made mostly of cells, collagen, and calcium. Collagen is a protein that forms strong fibers. Calcium is a mineral that adds strength to the collagen fibers. The human body has over 200 bones that make up the skeleton, shown in **Figure 1.**

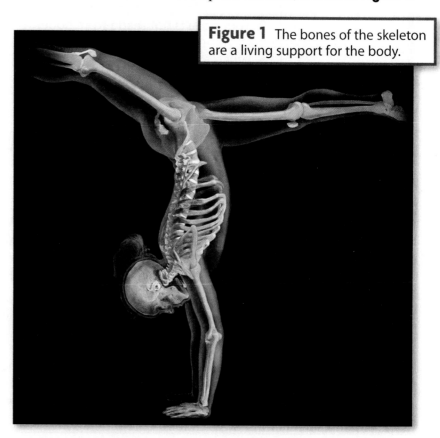

**Figure 1** The bones of the skeleton are a living support for the body.

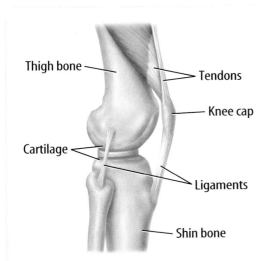

**Figure 2** Ligaments and tendons hold bones and muscles together. There is very little space between the bones of many joints. Cartilage covers the ends of the bone and prevents the bones from rubbing against each other.

**Infer** why it would be important for bones to not rub directly against each other.

Thigh bone

Tendons

Knee cap

Cartilage

Ligaments

Shin bone

## Functions of the Skeletal System

If you look at bones, you'll probably notice that they have different sizes and shapes. The surfaces of bones are not smooth. You'll see bumps, edges, round ends, rough spots, and many pits and holes where blood vessels and nerves enter and leave. Bones have many small, open spaces so they are not too heavy to move. These features allow the bones to perform all of their functions.

You might be wondering how your skeletal system can protect you from inside your body. The bones of your skull and vertebrae protect your brain and spinal cord. Ribs—the bones in your chest—protect the soft organs underneath, such as the heart and lungs. Without support from the skeletal system, you would be a soft mass without definite shape. The skeletal system also gives your muscles attachment points, which allow you to move. Your skeletal system stores calcium and phosphorus for later use. Both these minerals keep your bones hard. Finally, the middle of some bones, called marrow, is the place where blood cells are formed.

 How does the skeletal system benefit the body?

## Bones Connect at Joints

Because bones are hard, they cannot bend. However, our bodies are flexible and we can bend, twist, and rotate. This is possible because bones connect at **joints.** The softer tissues of the skeletal system, shown in **Figure 2,** help hold bones together at joints and add to our flexibility. Ligaments connect bones. Ligaments are similar to strong rubber bands that stretch when we move. **Cartilage** is a strong, yet flexible and elastic tissue that reduces friction and increases flexibility. You can twist your lower arm without moving your upper arm. Can you do the same with your leg? The structure of a joint determines the movement.

**WORD ORIGIN**
joint
from Latin *junctus;* means *join*

## Types of Joints

**1** **Hinge Joint** The joints in your fingers, elbows, and knees are hinge joints. Hinge joints only allow bones to move back and forth, like the hinges of a door. **Table 1** shows the joints in the body, and simple machines that work similarly.

**2** **Saddle Joint** Compare the movement of your thumb to the other fingers in your hand. The thumb has a wider range of motion. This is because the joint in the thumb is a saddle joint. In a saddle joint, both bones have ends shaped liked saddles. The thumb is the only saddle joint in the body.

**3** **Ball-and-Socket Joint** The shoulder joints and hip joints can rotate and move in nearly every direction. Hip and shoulder joints are ball-and-socket joints. Ball-and-socket joints are made of a bone that has a round end that fits into a cuplike depression of another bone. An ellipsoid joint is similar to a ball-and-socket joint, except the end of the bone is shaped like an ellipse instead of being round. The knuckles of our hands are examples of ellipsoid joints. An ellipsoid joint cannot move in as many directions as a ball-and-socket joint.

 Where are your four ball-and-socket joints located?

**4** **Pivot Joint** The cylindrical region of one bone fits into a ring-shaped structure of another bone in a pivot joint. Pivot joints only allow bones to rotate. The joint between the first two vertebrae in the neck is a pivot joint. This pivot joint allows you to turn your head from side to side. The pivot joint that connects the two bones in your forearm allows you to rotate your lower arm.

**5** **Gliding Joint** Two bones that connect at flat surfaces are a gliding joint. The bones in a gliding joint can only move from side to side or front to back. Our ankles and wrists have gliding joints.

**6** **Immovable Joint** Two bones held firmly together, allowing very little or no movement, form an immovable joint. You might be wondering why a joint would be immovable. Your skull contains immovable joints. When you were born, there was space between some of the bones of your skull. These spaces allowed your brain to increase in size. Eventually, the immovable joints fused the bones together. Your lower jaw is the only bone of the skull that moves after the immovable joints of the skull join.

 **Table 1** Which of these types of joints has the widest range of motion? The narrowest?

## Table 1 Joints in the Human Body

| Description of Joint | Mechanical Object and Joint |
|---|---|
| **1 Hinge Joints**<br>Allow bones to move back and forth<br>**Examples:** fingers, elbows, and knees | <br>Hinge joint |
| **2 Saddle Joints**<br>Allow bones to move back and forth and side to side, but have limited rotational ability<br>**Example:** thumbs | <br>Saddle joint |
| **3 Ball-and-Socket Joints**<br>Allow bones to move and rotate in nearly all directions<br>**Examples:** hips and shoulders | <br>Ball-and-socket joint |
| **4 Pivot Joint**<br>Allows bones to rotate<br>**Example:** neck | <br>Pivot joint |
| **5 Gliding Joint**<br>Allows bones to move side to side or front to back<br>**Examples:** ankles and wrists | <br>Gliding joint |
| **6 Immovable Joint**<br>Allows very little or no movement<br>**Example:** skull | <br>Immovable joint |

# The Muscular System

**ACADEMIC VOCABULARY**

contract (kun TRAKT)
*(verb)* to make a smaller size
by squeezing or forcing
together *The word* cannot *can*
*be contracted to* can't.

When you think of the parts of your body that allow you to move, you probably think of muscles. **Muscle** (MUH sul) is tissue made of long cells that **contract.** There are more than 620 muscles in the human body. **Figure 3** shows that muscles are made of bundles of muscle cells called muscle fibers. Muscle fibers are not like most other cells. A single muscle fiber has hundreds of nuclei and many mitchondria. Some muscle fibers are as long as the muscle, which can be up to 30 cm. Muscle fibers contain bundles of small tubes that contain bundles of two different threadlike proteins, or muscle filaments. The arrangement of muscle filaments is lengthwise, with their ends partially overlapping. During muscle **contraction,** the muscle filaments move closer to each other. All the cells of a muscle contract at the same time and the muscle shortens. During muscle **relaxation,** all the muscle filaments move away from each other.

 **Figure 3** How do muscles get smaller when they contract?

## Muscle Contractions

What makes our muscles contract? Muscles have nerve cells that receive signals from the nervous system. The nerve cells start a chemical reaction in the muscle cells that leads to contraction of the muscle. Movement of the muscle filaments during contraction requires energy. Muscle cells contain more mitochondria than other cells in order to produce the energy needed for contraction. A large network of blood vessels supplies muscles with the oxygen the mitochondria need for cellular respiration.

## Types of Muscle

Your hand, arm, and leg muscles are voluntary muscles. A voluntary muscle is a muscle that you are able to control. Your heart and stomach are involuntary muscles. An involuntary muscle is one that you cannot control by thinking about it. These muscles work all day, every day, without your active involvement.

Recall from Chapter 2 that cells form tissues, tissues form organs, organs form organ systems, and organ systems form an organism. The same is true in the muscular system. Muscle cells form muscle tissue. There are three types of muscle tissue. Muscles that cause movement of your body are made up of skeletal muscle tissue. Cardiac muscle tissue is found only in your heart. Smooth muscle tissue is found in your internal organs, such as your stomach and blood vessels.

 What are the three types of muscle tissue?

# Visualizing Muscle Contractions

**Figure 3**
When a muscle contracts, the proteins in all the individual muscle fibers move closer together. This usually makes the muscle shorter and thicker.

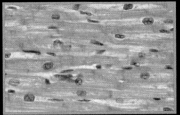

▲ Muscle cells contain more mitochondria than other cells in order to have more energy available to perform their functions.

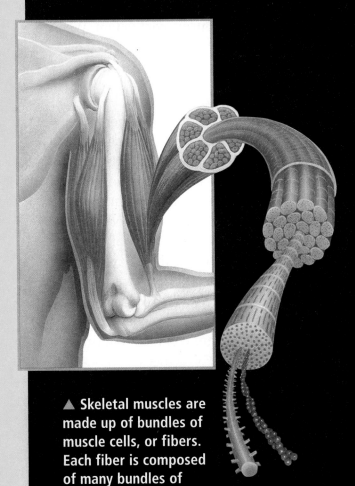

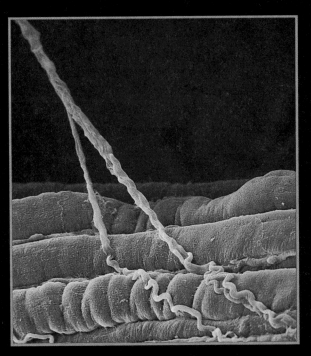

▲ Skeletal muscles are made up of bundles of muscle cells, or fibers. Each fiber is composed of many bundles of muscle filaments.

▲ A signal from a nerve fiber starts a chemical reaction in the muscle filament. This causes molecules in the muscle filament to gain energy and move. Many filaments moving together cause the muscle to contract.

*Contributed by National Geographic*

## MiniLab

### How do bones and muscles interact?

The interaction of your muscles and bones makes every movement of your body possible.

**Procedure**

1. Read and complete a lab safety form.

2. Feel your leg as you perform the following movements:
   • Flex your foot upward
   • Bend your knee
   • Pretend to kick a soccer ball

3. Feel your partner's arm as he or she performs the same movements you did earlier.

**Analysis**

1. **Compare and contrast** the location of the muscles with the location of the joint being moved.

2. **Describe** any differences you felt in the muscles of the arm versus the muscles of the leg. What can you infer from these differences?

 5.c, 7.a        Try at Home

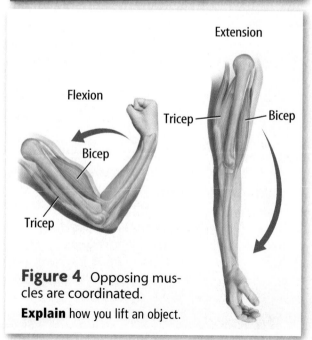

Extension

Flexion

Tricep — Bicep

Bicep

Tricep

Tricep

**Figure 4** Opposing muscles are coordinated.

**Explain** how you lift an object.

# Interactions of the Musculoskeletal System

Our bones alone cannot move our bodies. Similarly, muscle contraction is only part of movement. In order for us to move, the muscular system must function with the skeletal system. Our skeleton provides support for our muscles.

## How do you move?

Usually a muscle connects to at least two different bones. **Tendons** (TEN dunz) connect bones to muscles and do not stretch as much as ligaments. Tendons, ligaments, and cartilage are connective tissues. The rough spots on bones are places where the tendons and ligaments attach.

The biceps muscle causes your arm to bend. **Flexion** (FLEK shun) is the bending of a limb that decreases the angle between the bones of the limb. Flexion of your arm happens when the biceps muscle shortens during contraction. When the biceps muscle shortens, the lower arm moves closer to the upper arm, and the arm bends.

## Opposing Muscle Groups

Muscles can contract and become shorter, but they cannot actively lengthen. **Extension** (eks TEN shun) is the straightening of a limb that increases the angle between the bones of the limb. How does your arm straighten during extension? Arrangement of muscles is often in opposing groups. Look at the muscles of the upper arm in **Figure 4.** Notice that there are muscles on each side of the arm. The triceps muscle is at the back of the arm, opposite from the biceps. Your arm bends when the biceps contract. The biceps relax and the triceps contract, resulting in an extension of the arm.

It is important to realize that opposing muscle groups, such as the biceps and triceps, may be contracting at the same time. At the same time the biceps muscle contracts, the triceps muscle is also slightly contracting. The triceps muscle contracts so the lifting motion is smooth and controlled.

 **Reading Check** How is it that when you flex your arm, you contract your tricep?

# What have you learned?

The musculoskeletal system works to move the body. The skeletal system—made of bones, ligaments, tendons, and cartilage—supports and protects the body. Muscles provide the contractions necessary to move bones when signaled by the nervous system. Joints maintain flexible connections between bones. The body has different types of joints that allow for motion in different directions. Opposing muscle groups function together to achieve controlled and smooth motion.

In the next lesson you will read that your bones and muscles work together as levers in the body. This important relationship in the body helps you gain speed and distance in doing even very routine activities, such as taking a step. It also helps to make work easier.

## LESSON 1 Review

### Summarize

Create your own lesson summary as you write a script for a **television news report.**

1. **Review** the text after the **red** main headings and write one sentence about each. These are the headlines of your broadcast.

2. **Review** the text and write 2–3 sentences about each **blue** subheading. These sentences should tell *who, what, when, where,* and *why* information about each **red** heading.

3. **Include** descriptive details in your report, such as names of reporters and local places and events.

4. **Present** your news report to other classmates alone or with a team.

 **ELA7: LS 2.2**

### Standards Check

#### Using Vocabulary

1. **Distinguish** between cartilage and tendons. **5.c**

2. Use the words *bone* and *muscle* in a sentence. **5.c**

3. Bones are connected at _____. **5.c**

#### Understanding Main Ideas

4. **Explain** why the skeletal and muscular systems cannot function without each other. **5.c**

5. **Give another example** of this joint that was not discussed in the text. **6.h**

6. **Construct** an events-chain map to illustrate the movement of a muscle. **5.a**

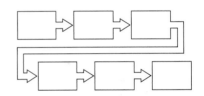

#### Applying Science

7. **Compare** your body, which has an internal skeleton, to the body of a slug, which has no internal skeleton. **5.c**

8. **Relate** everyday objects to the actions of your joints. How are they similar? What functions do the joints in machines serve? **6.h**

 **Science** nline

For more practice, visit **Standards Check** at ca7.msscience.com.

### Science Content Standards

**6.h** Students know how to compare joints in the body (wrist, shoulder, thigh) with structures used in machines and simple devices (hinge, ball-and-socket, and sliding joints).

**6.i** Students know how levers confer mechanical advantage and how the application of this principle applies to the musculoskeletal system.

**Also covers:** 7.a, 7.c, 7.d

## Reading Guide

### What *You'll Learn*

▶ **Distinguish** the three classes of levers.

▶ **Identify** levers in the human body.

▶ **Describe** the advantage to having levers in the body.

### Why *It's Important*

It's helpful to understand how levers work to understand your body.

### Vocabulary

lever
fulcrum
first-class lever
second-class lever
third-class lever
mechanical advantage

### Review Vocabulary

**work:** transfer of energy that occurs when a push or a pull causes movement (Grade 6)

# The Body and Levers

**(Main Idea)** Muscles and bones are joined in a way that allows them to act as levers, providing force or speed advantages.

**Real-World Reading Connection** Can you imagine playing baseball without a bat or cutting paper without scissors? How long would it take you to dig a hole without a shovel? All of these tasks are easier when we use simple machines. However, you do not need to find any tools or common objects to see a lever in action. Your body is a living example of levers.

## What is a lever?

"Give me a place to stand, and I will move the Earth" is a quote by the ancient Greek mathematician Archimedes (287–212 B.C.), usually credited with first describing the uses of simple machines called levers. A **lever** (LEE ver) is a simple machine made of anything rigid that pivots around a fixed point. The **fulcrum** (FUL krum) is the fixed point that a lever pivots around, also known as a pivot point. **Figure 5** is an example of a lever. Archimedes used the concept of levers to devise war machines used against the Roman Empire.

We use levers to make work easier. Sometimes levers allow the operator to perform a task using less force. Other times, the task can be completed in less time or by moving a shorter distance. By the end of this lesson, you'll be presented with clues to help you discover why Archimedes said he could move the world.

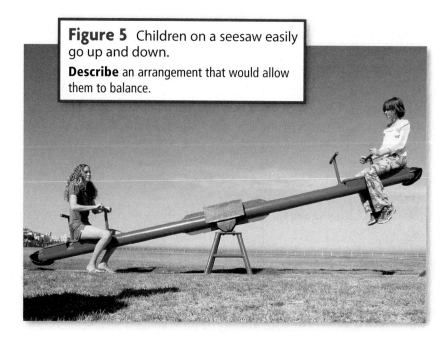

**Figure 5** Children on a seesaw easily go up and down.
**Describe** an arrangement that would allow them to balance.

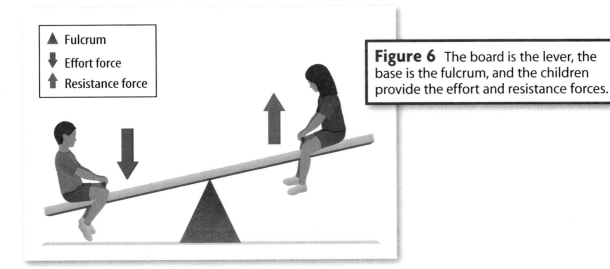

- ▲ Fulcrum
- ↓ Effort force
- ↑ Resistance force

**Figure 6** The board is the lever, the base is the fulcrum, and the children provide the effort and resistance forces.

# The Three Classes of Levers

On a seesaw, the board the two people sit on is the lever. The base that the board rests upon is the fulcrum. Two forces act upon different parts of a lever. A force is a push or a pull on an object when it interacts with another object. The effort force moves an object over a distance. The resistance force opposes the effort force. In **Figure 6,** a child sitting on a seesaw provides the effort force needed to move the right side down. The child being pushed up on the opposite side exerts the resistance force. Note that while one child moves up when the other child moves down, they both move in the same direction around the fulcrum—either clockwise or counterclockwise.

 What is the difference between the effort force and the resistance force?

The distance between the forces and the fulcrum determines how easy or how hard it will be to use the lever. If the effort force is very close to the fulcrum, it will take a lot of force to use the lever. The farther the effort force is from the fulcrum, the easier it will be to use. The situation is reversed for the resistance force: the closer to the fulcrum, the easier the resistance force will be to move. Likewise, the farther the resistance force is located from the fulcrum, the harder the lever will be to move.

In your body, if a bone is the lever and muscles supply the force, which part of your body is the fulcrum? The joints act as the fulcrum, the point around which the lever rotates. The connective tissues transfer the force to locations from bones to bones or from bones to muscles.

A seesaw is one of three different types of levers. Each type of lever is suited for different tasks. The location of the fulcrum, load, and applied force determines the type of lever. **Table 2** shows the three classes of levers.

**WORD ORIGIN**

lever
from Latin *levare;* means *to raise*

fulcrum
from Latin *fulcire;* means *to support*

## First-Class Levers

The resistance force and the effort force are on opposite sides of the fulcrum in a **first-class lever.** A seesaw, pliers, and scissors are examples of first-class levers. Scissors, shown in **Table 2,** are made of two first-class levers. When you open and close the scissors, the direction of the effort force changes.

The body has few first-class levers. Nodding your head uses a first-class lever. **Table 2** shows that the fulcrum is the joint connecting your skull to your backbone. The weight of your head is the resistance force. Your neck muscles provide the effort force.

## Second-Class Levers

The resistance force is between the fulcrum and the effort force in a **second-class lever,** as shown in **Table 2.** Backpacks and luggage with wheels on the bottom are examples of second-class levers. The handle is where you exert the effort force. The weight of the backpack or luggage is the resistance force. The wheels act as a fulcrum. Another example of second-class levers is a wheelbarrow.

When you lift your heels off the ground and stand on your toes, as shown in **Table 2,** you are using a second-class lever. The fulcrum is at your toes. The resistance force is the weight of your body. The calf muscle in your lower leg supplies the effort force.

 **Table 2** Relative to the effort force provided by your calf muscle, what direction does the resistance force move?

## Third-Class Levers

The effort force is between the resistance force and fulcrum in a **third-class lever.** This arrangement requires more effort force than the resistance force it produces. This means that using the lever to move the object is more difficult than moving the object without the lever. However, you are able to move the object farther or faster than you could without the lever. Most hand tools and sports equipment are third-class levers, such as baseball bats and rakes. **Table 2** shows a person gripping the end of a shovel. One hand grips the handle, **stabilizing** the shovel and acting as the fulcrum point. The other hand exerts the effort force. The effort force moves the resistance force, the weight of the dirt, at the end of the shovel.

The most common levers in the body are third-class levers. An example of a third-class lever is your upper arm and lower arm. **Table 2** shows that the fulcrum is the elbow joint. The lever is one of the bones of the lower arm. The resistance force is the weight of your lower arm and any object you may be lifting. The effort force is supplied by the biceps muscle.

 Which class of levers is most common in your body?

**ACADEMIC VOCABULARY**

stable (STAY buhl)
*(adjective)* resistant to change of position or condition
*A chair or stool with three legs is more stable than one with four.*

**370 Chapter 9**

Concepts In Motion

Interactive Table To explore more about levers, visit Tables at ca7.msscience.com.

## Table 2 Levers in the Human Body

| Common Object | Physics | In Human Body |
|---|---|---|
| **First class**<br>The fulcrum is between the resistance force and effort force in a first-class lever. | Effort force / Resistance force / Fulcrum | This first-class lever reduces the strain on your neck muscles caused by the weight of your head. |
| **Second class**<br>The resistance force is between the fulcrum and effort force in a second-class lever. | Effort force / Resistance force / Fulcrum | This second-class lever allows your calf muscles to easily lift nearly your entire body weight. |
| **Third class**<br>The effort force is between the resistance force and fulcrum in a third-class lever. | Resistance force / Effort force / Fulcrum | This third-class lever allows you to quickly lift an object in your hand. |

**Figure 7** The position he is holding demonstrates his skill in balancing multiple forces using the multiple lever systems of his body.

## Effort Forces and Resistance Forces in Levers

Levers in the human body can exert forces on objects, such as the gymnastic rings in **Figure 7.** When a lever is used, an effort force is applied to one end. This end moves as the effort force is applied. For example, if you push down on one end of a seesaw, that end moves. The distance this end moves is the effort distance.

When you push down, the other end of the seesaw moves up. This end of the seesaw exerts the resistance force. This distance this end of the seesaw moves is the resistance distance. The effort distance and resistance distance determine how the resistance force compares to the effort force.

**Levers that Increase the Effort Force** For first-class levers and second-class levers, the resistance distance is less than the effort distance. This means the point where the effort force is applied moves a greater distance than the point where the resistance force is applied. When the effort distance is greater than the resistance distance, the resistance force is greater than the effort force. As a result, for first-class and second-class levers the resistance force is greater than the effort force.

**Levers that Decrease the Effort Force** For third-class levers, the opposite is true—the resistance distance is greater than the effort distance. For example, when you use a broom, the distance your upper hand moves is shorter than the distance the bottom of the broom moves. However, when the effort distance is less than the resistance distance, the resistance force is less than the effort force. As a result, third-class levers decrease the effort force.

**Figure 8** A jack is a lever commonly used to lift cars. Instead of lifting the car a short distance all at once, the girl will move it bit by bit over a longer distance.

**Identify** the class of levers to which the car jack belongs.

# Why use levers?

Some levers make it easier to lift heavy objects, others make it easier to move objects faster and farther. How is this possible? The person in **Figure 8** is lifting a car with a jack. The jack makes it easier to do the work.

## Mechanical Advantage

You just read that a lever could decrease the amount of force needed to do a task. **Mechanical advantage** (MA) is the ability of a machine to increase the amount of force put into the machine, a ratio of resistance force ($F_R$) to effort force ($F_E$).

$$\text{Mechanical advantage (MA)} = \frac{\text{Resistance force } (F_R)}{\text{Effort force } (F_E)}$$

What is the mechanical advantage of the lever in **Figure 9?**

$$MA = \frac{60 \text{ N}}{20 \text{ N}}$$
$$MA = 3$$

Therefore, the machine tripled the force applied to it. This is sometimes measured as the ratio of the distance the resistance force is from the fulcrum to the distance the effort force is from the fulcrum. This looks like this:

$$MA = \frac{\text{distance resistance force is from fulcrum } (D_R)}{\text{distance effort force is from fulcrum } (D_E)}$$

**SCIENCE USE V. COMMON USE**
work
*Science Use* the force needed to move the object multiplied by the distance the object moves. *The work needed to move an object cannot be decreased by using a lever, but the amount of force needed can be changed.*
*Common Use* the occupation for which you are paid. *In high school, many students decide what line of work they would like to pursue.*

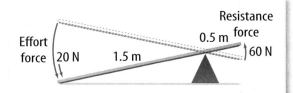

Effort force 20 N    1.5 m    0.5 m    Resistance force 60 N

**Figure 9** The effort force moves the lever 1.5 m. The lever moves only 0.5 m in the direction of the resistance force.

**Figure 10** The end of the bat travels the greatest distance and therefore has the greatest velocity. A person playing baseball tries to hit the baseball with the end of the bat. This will result in the baseball traveling much faster and usually farther than if the ball were thrown.

## Speed Advantage

Sometimes we need help moving objects quickly over long distances. Third-class levers can make it easier to move an object a long distance quickly. Recall that a baseball bat is an example of a third-class lever. **Figure 10** shows when you swing a bat, the handle moves a short distance. However, the end of the bat travels a longer distance and at a greater speed.

 **Figure 10** Compare the speeds of the parts of the bat where resistance force and effort force are exerted.

Having bones as levers helps us do work by giving us more efficient ways of using force. This usually allows us to move faster. The end of a swinging baseball bat moves farther and faster than the end grasped by the batter. The same is true for your limbs. Your limbs contain multiple joints and therefore multiple levers. As a result, your feet move much farther and faster than your upper leg when you walk. Therefore, levers allow you to have long, quick strides. Similar to your legs, levers increase the speed of your arms and hands as well.

 How do levers allow parts of the body to move farther than others?

## Levers in the Body

How can a length of a lever affect the way your body works? Consider arm wrestling. If you are facing an opponent whose arm is the same length as your own, who will win the match? Since the distance is the same, and work equals force times distance, the person who is able to produce more force will win. What if one person's arm is shorter? In this case, the person with the shorter arm will have to produce more force to win the match. However, it will be easier for the person with the shorter arm to produce more force because the effort and resistance force are closer together on a shorter arm. Less effort is required to match the resistance provided by the opponent. This is why shorter men and women have a natural advantage in sports such as gymnastics, diving, and figure skating.

# What have you learned?

A lever is a simple machine that makes work easier. The force applied to a lever is changed in size or direction, but the work done by the lever cannot exceed the work put into it. There are three classes of levers. The location of the fulcrum, effort force, and resistance force determine the class of the lever. First- and second-class levers make work easier by multiplying the force you put into the machine. Third-class levers make work easier by increasing the range or speed of motion beyond what you are naturally capable of doing. In our bodies, bones act as levers, and muscles provide the force to move objects. The arrangement of multiple levers needed to perform even simple movements creates an advantage. You have each class of levers in your body, but most levers in the body are third-class levers. This is because of the necessary arrangement of muscles and bones.

# LESSON 2 Review

## Summarize

Create your own lesson summary as you design a **study web.**

1. **Write** the lesson title, number, and page numbers at the top of a sheet of paper.

2. **Scan** the lesson to find the **red** main headings.

3. **Organize** these headings clockwise on branches around the lesson title.

4. **Review** the information under each **red** heading to design a branch for each **blue** subheading.

5. **List** 2–3 details, key terms, and definitions from each **blue** subheading on branches extending from the main heading branches.

 **ELA7: W 2.5**

## Standards Check

### Using Vocabulary

1. **Define** lever. **6.i**

2. **Describe** a first-class lever, a second-class lever, and a third-class lever. **6.i**

3. The ability of a machine to increase the amount of force put into a machine is _____. **6.i**

### Understanding Main Ideas

4. **Calculate** If a lever has a resistance force of 40 N and an effort force of 10 N, what is the mechanical advantage of this lever? **6.i**

   **A.** 0.25 N
   **B.** 4 N
   **C.** 40 N
   **D.** 400 N

5. **Compare** the advantages of first-class levers and third-class levers in the body. **6.i**

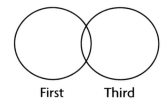

First class  Third class

### Applying Science

6. **Suggest** a reason why it may be advantageous to have a shorter forearm when lifting a heavy weight. **6.i**

7. **Decide** which joint would be better for creating increased speed of a resistance force—the elbow joint or the ankle joint? Explain your answer. **6.i**

**Science** nline

For more practice, visit **Standards Check** at ca7.msscience.com.

# What is the mechanical advantage of a lever?

One important aspect of science is being able to base conclusions upon numeric data. Mechanical advantage can be used to compare levers.

## Data

| Comparing Levers | | | |
|---|---|---|---|
| | **Lever 1** | **Lever 2** | **Lever 3** |
| $D_E$ (in cm) | 10 cm | 30 cm | 50 cm |
| $D_R$ (in cm) | 50 cm | 30 cm | 10 cm |
| MA | ? | ? | ? |
| Type of lever | ? | ? | ? |

## Data Analysis

1. **Calculate** the mechanical advantage (MA) of a lever at each fulcrum point. Recall that MA $= \dfrac{D_E}{D_R}$.

2. **Identify** which type of lever the data are describing.

3. **Compare and contrast** the MA at each fulcrum point. Which $D_E$ and $D_R$ gave you the highest MA? The lowest?

4. **Diagram** each lever. Be sure to include the correct labels.

 **Science Content Standards**

**6.i** Students know how levers confer mechanical advantage and how the application of this principle applies to the musculoskeletal system.

**7.d** Construct scale models, maps, and appropriately labeled diagrams to communicate scientific knowledge (e.g., motion of Earth's plates and cell structure).

# Applying Math

## Degree of Joint Rotation

Lumbar spine vertebrae have three-dimensional degrees of rotation to allow the spine to move. Similar to a three-dimensional coordinate graph, the lumbar spine has three axes of rotation shown in the diagram below.

**Three-Dimensional Graph**

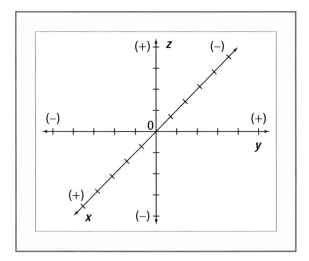

**Lumbar Rotations**

An extension is a bending of the torso in an angle along the *y*-axis. Lateral bending is a sideways rotation about the *x*-axis. Axial rotation is a twisting of the lumbar vertebrae around the *z*-axis.

## Example

Which angle of rotation is associated with bending forward?

**Answer:** Bending forward is an extension rotation in the positive *y*-direction.

---

### Practice Problems

1. Which angle of rotation is associated with bending backward?
2. Which angle of rotation is associated with twisting to the right?

**Science Online**
For more math practice, visit Math Practice at ca7.msscience.com.

# Model and Invent:
# Build Your Own Levers

## Possible Materials

soup cans
weights
rulers
metersticks

## Safety Precautions

## Problem

You can calculate the mechanical advantage of the levers present in your body, but without very complicated equipment, you cannot measure the force exerted by your muscles.

## Form a Hypothesis

By building a model of a lever, you can determine the input mass necessary to move the soup can the distance you recorded earlier. Predict the input that will move the soup can. How did you arrive at that prediction?

## Collect Data and Make Observations

1. Read and complete a lab safety form.
2. Review your notes from the previous labs and recall how you have modeled levers in the past.
3. Choose a lever to model.
4. Measure, using centimeters, the $D_E$ and $D_R$ of your chosen lever.
5. Experiment to find an input that will move the load efficiently.
6. Model other classes of levers.
7. If materials are available, make scale models of levers in the body, with accurate weights and lengths.

## Science Content Standards

**6.h** Students know how to compare joints in the body (wrist, shoulder, thigh) with structures used in machines and simple devices (hinge, ball-and-socket, and sliding joints).
**6.i** Students know how levers confer mechanical advantage and how the application of this principle applies to the musculoskeletal system.
**7.a** Select and use appropriate tools and technology (including calculators, computers, balances, spring scales, microscopes, and binoculars) to perform tests, collect data, and display data.
**7.c** Communicate the logical connection among hypotheses, science concepts, tests conducted, data collected, and conclusions drawn from the scientific evidence.
**7.d** Construct scale models, maps, and appropriately labeled diagrams to communicate scientific knowledge (e.g., motion of Earth's plates and cell structure).

## Analyze and Conclude

1. **Explain** the process you used to come up with your model.
2. **Describe** your model by drawing and labeling it. What lever did you choose to model? What did you use for a fulcrum? What was the final input mass? Did you predict correctly?
3. **Calculate** the MA for the lever you modeled.
4. **Compare and contrast** the model you used for this lever with potential models for another lever.
5. **Calculate** the MA for the other levers you identified in Step 6. Which lever has the highest MA? Which has the lowest?
6. **Summarize** what you have learned about MA in the levers of your own body.

## Communicate

**Demonstrate** your model to the class. **Share** your calculated mechanical advantage. What were other mechanical advantages? Were they all similar to yours or were they all different?

# Real World Science

## You can be an athletic trainer!

Athletic trainers help athletes get and stay in shape by designing training and nutrition programs. They work on injury prevention through training, education, and intervention techniques (tape, wraps, padding, braces, etc.). Working with a physician, they provide rehabilitation and therapy when an athlete is injured. The athletes pictured are performing leg exercises.

Visit **Careers** at **ca7.msscience.com** to find out more about what it takes to be an athletic trainer. Write a help wanted ad for a professional sports team's athletic trainer. List the education and certification required for this position. Give the salary range and any benefits.

## Checking Out Your Knees

Many people will injure their knees in their lifetime, not just athletes. Most of these injuries involve tears in the cartilage within the joint. The traditional way to check for this is through arthroscopic surgery, where small incisions are made around the knee and a tiny camera is inserted to view the joint. Recently, a new type of magnetic resonance imaging (MRI) has become precise enough to look at the joint from the outside. It's called 3-Tesla MRI and is pictured here.

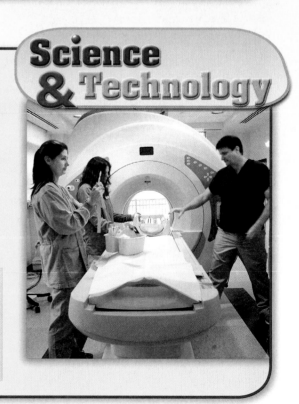

Visit **Technology** at **ca7.msscience.com** to find out more about options for finding problems in the knee. Create a table to compare and contrast arthroscopy versus MRI imaging for identifying knee joint problems. Make sure to consider the advantages and disadvantages of each method.

# Archimedes, Levers, and the Human Body

Archimedes is considered one of the greatest mathematicians of all time. He is called the "father of integral calculus" and also the "father of mathematical physics." He provided the earliest writings that still exist about levers in the third century B.C. He has been quoted by Pappus of Alexandria as saying, "Give me the place to stand, and I shall move the earth." Man has always been fascinated by levers and understanding them, as shown in this wall painting from around A.D. 1600.

Visit **History** at ca7.msscience.com to find out more about Archimedes and levers in the human body. If the foreman is 30 cm in length and the distance to the bicep is 6.5 cm, what is the force needed to create balance with barbells of 0.9, 2.3, 3.6, and 5.5 kg? Create a chart showing the equations and your answers.

# Artificial People?

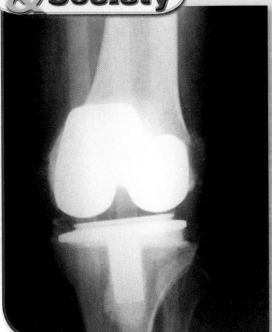

Recent studies have shown that people in the United States are living longer and remain healthier and more active as they age. But with this longevity, musculoskeletal conditions, such as arthritis, are increasing. Today, joint replacement is an option for some people. Joints of the ankle, hip, knee, shoulder, and finger can be replaced with synthetic ones, such as this artificial knee joint. These artificial joints allow better mobility and less pain for up to 15 years, sometimes longer.

Visit **Society** at ca7.msscience.com to find out more. Divide the students into groups to research and discuss the societal impacts of living longer with regard to musculoskeletal conditions. Create a list of at least four impacts to society. Discuss the findings within the class. Make sure to use correct spelling, capitalization, and grammar.

**The BIG Idea** Muscles, bones, and joints form simple machines in the body that produce movement and mechanical advantage.

## Lesson 1 The Musculoskeletal System
*5.a, 5.c, 6.h, 7.a*

**Main Idea** Muscles, tendons, and bones work in a coordinated fashion to produce movement.

- The musculoskeletal system works to move the body.

- The skeletal system—made of bones, ligaments, tendons, and cartilage—supports and protects the body.

- Muscles provide the contractions necessary to move bones when signaled by the nervous system.

- Joints maintain flexible connections between bones, different types of joints allow for motion in different directions.

- Opposing muscle groups function together to achieve controlled and smooth motion.

- **bone** (p. 360)
- **cartilage** (p. 361)
- **contraction** (p. 364)
- **extension** (p. 366)
- **flexion** (p. 366)
- **joint** (p. 361)
- **muscle** (p. 364)
- **relaxation** (p. 364)
- **skeletal system** (p. 360)
- **tendon** (p. 366)

## Lesson 2 The Body and Levers
*6.h, 6.i, 7.a, 7.c, 7.d*

**Main Idea** Muscles and bones are joined in a way that allows them to act as levers, providing force or speed advantages.

- In our bodies, bones act as levers, and muscles provide the force to move objects.

- The arrangement of multiple levers needed to perform even simple movements creates lever advantage.

- You have each class of levers in your body, but most levers are third-class levers. This is because of the necessary arrangement of muscles and bones.

- **first-class lever** (p. 370)
- **fulcrum** (p. 368)
- **lever** (p. 368)
- **mechanical advantage** (p. 373)
- **second-class lever** (p. 370)
- **third-class lever** (p. 370)

 **STUDY TO GO** Download quizzes, key terms, and flash cards from ca7.msscience.com.

Science Online Interactive Tutor ca7.msscience.com

# Linking Vocabulary and Main Ideas

Use the vocabulary terms on page 382 to complete the concept map.

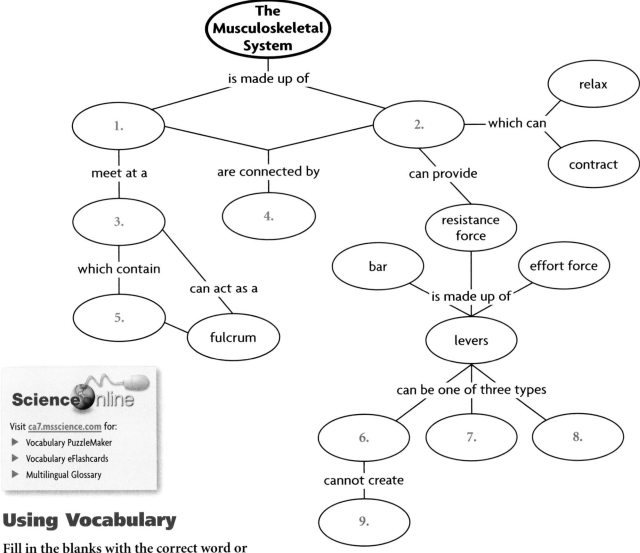

## Using Vocabulary

**Fill in the blanks with the correct word or words.**

**10.** _____ are a type of simple machine that makes tasks easier.

**11.** Levers can create _____, which can be increased by increasing the length of a lever in a first-class lever.

**12.** Bones connect at _____.

**13.** When muscles _____, they become shorter and bones move.

**14.** Muscles are coordinated. For example, the biceps cause flexion, while the triceps cause _____ of the arm.

**15.** Joints are the _____ of a lever.

**16.** Most of the bones in the body are _____, which allow us to make long, quick movements.

**17.** Your neck is a(n) _____ lever.

## Understanding Main Ideas

*Choose the word or phrase that best answers the question.*

1. Scissors are an example of which class of lever?
   A. first-class
   B. second-class
   C. third-class
   D. fourth-class  `6.i`

2. What is the purpose of simple machines?
   A. to make work harder
   B. to make work easier
   C. to create energy
   D. to create work  `6.i`

3. What is an example of a second-class lever?
   A. the knee
   B. the elbow
   C. the ankle
   D. the pelvis  `6.i`

4. Mechanical advantage is the ratio of the resistance force divided by what?
   A. resistance distance
   B. work
   C. effort distance
   D. effort force  `6.i`

5. Below is an image of a lever.

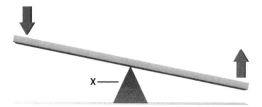

   What does X point to?
   A. lever
   B. wheelbarrow
   C. resistance
   D. fulcrum  `6.i`

6. What connects bone to muscle?
   A. cartilage
   B. tendons
   C. ligaments
   D. collagen  `5.c`

7. What is another job of the skeletal system, besides support?
   A. to conduct nerve impulses
   B. to protect internal organs
   C. to clean blood
   D. to contract  `5.c`

8. What is the opposite of flexion?
   A. extension
   B. contraction
   C. hinge joint
   D. mechanical advantage  `5.c`

9. What types of joints are in the skull?
   A. ball-and-socket  `6.h`
   B. hinge
   C. saddle
   D. immovable

10. The figure to the right is a picture of which kind of joint?
    A. ball-and-socket
    B. hinge
    C. immovable
    D. pivot  `6.h`

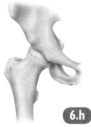

11. The elbow joint is a fulcrum for which class of lever?
    A. first-class
    B. second-class
    C. third-class
    D. all classes  `6.h`

12. What does a mechanical advantage greater than one usually mean?
    A. Resistance is greater.
    B. Heavy objects can be lifted.
    C. Only light objects can be lifted.
    D. Input force is very high.  `6.i`

Science Online Standards Review ca7.msscience.com

## Applying Science

**13. Compare** second-class levers and third-class levers. `6.i`

**14. Explain** the interactions between the biceps muscles and the bones of the arms when drinking a glass of water. `5.c`

**15. Hypothesize** about what kind of joints are in your toes, based on what you learned about joints. `6.h`

**16. Draw** a diagram of the arm. Label the lever, the fulcrum, and where the force would be applied for movement if the bicep contracts. `6.h`

**17. Hypothesize** why bone is a lever, based on what you know about bone and muscle tissue. `6.h`

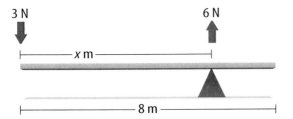

**18. Calculate** the resistance distance in the lever in the figure. `6.i`

**19. Determine** a way to use a shovel as either a first-class lever or a third-class lever without moving your hands. `6.i`

**20. Explain** how a muscle returns to the length it was before contraction, given that muscles can only contract. `5.c`

**21. Imagine** you could increase the length of your forearm. What would this do to the mechanical advantage you would experience? `6.i`

**22. Consider** how you would adjust the distance of the effort force from the fulcrum so that you could lift more weight, based on what you know about first-class levers. `6.i`

**23. Explain** how a third-class lever is different from the other level classes. `6.i`

## WRITING in Science

**24.** Write a manual that explains how to open a screw-top jar. Be sure to note the muscles, joints, and levers needed to complete each action. `ELA7: 1.3`

## Applying Math

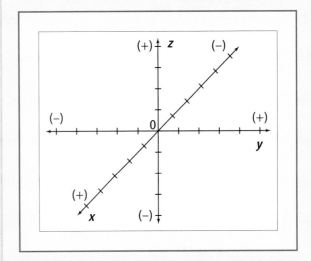

**25.** Which angle of rotation is associated with twisting to the left? `MA7: MR 1.2`

**26.** Which angle of rotation is associated with twisting the hips? `MA7: MR 1.2`

**27.** Which angle of rotation is associated with twisting the head? `MA7: MR 1.2`

**28.** An extension is a movement around which axis? `MA7: MR 1.2`

**29.** An axial rotation is a movement around which axis? `MA7: MR 1.2`

**1** Which is true about voluntary and involuntary muscles?

**A** Involuntary muscles can be consciously controlled; voluntary muscles are muscles that cannot be controlled consciously.

**B** Involuntary muscles work randomly; voluntary muscles are always working.

**C** Voluntary muscles can be consciously controlled; involuntary muscles cannot be controlled consciously.

**D** Voluntary muscles are located in the heart and organs; involuntary muscles are located in the limbs. **5.c**

Use the illustration below to answer to answer questions 2 and 3.

Ball-and-socket joint

Pivot joint

Gliding joint

Hinge joint

**2** Which type of joint do your elbows have?

**A** hinge **6.h**

**B** gliding

**C** ball and socket

**D** pivot

**3** Which type of joint allows your legs and arms to swing in almost any direction?

**A** hinge **6.h**

**B** gliding

**C** ball and socket

**D** pivot

**4** What is the most important difference between cardiac muscle and skeletal muscle?

**A** Their cells contain different materials. **5.a**

**B** Their cells have different shapes.

**C** They have different sizes of cells.

**D** They have different functions.

Use the image below of a lever for questions 5 and 6.

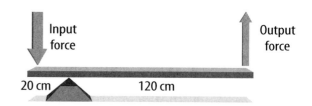

**5** What is the mechanical advantage of the lever shown above?

**A** $\frac{1}{6}$ **6.i**

**B** $\frac{1}{2}$

**C** 2

**D** 6

**6** What is the mechanical advantage of the lever if the triangular block is moved 60 cm to the right.

**A** $\frac{1}{4}$ **6.i**

**B** $\frac{1}{2}$

**C** 2

**D** 4

Science Online  Standards Assessment ca7.msscience.com

**7** Which statement is *always* true when you use a lever?

**A** An object moves a shorter distance.  `6.i`

**B** An object moves a longer distance.

**C** Less force is needed.

**D** More force is needed.

**8** Explain the differences between the three classes of levers in terms of the location of the fulcrum, input force, and output force or load.

**A** first-class lever: fulcrum is between input and output force; second-class lever: output force is between input force and fulcrum; third-class lever: input force is between fulcrum and output force  `6.i`

**B** second-class lever: fulcrum is between input and output force; first-class lever: output force is between input force and fulcrum; third-class lever: input force is between fulcrum and output force

**C** third-class lever: fulcrum is between input and output force; first-class lever: output force is between input force and fulcrum; second-class lever: input force is between fulcrum and output force

**D** third-class lever: fulcrum is between input and output force; second-class lever: output force is between input force and fulcrum; first-class lever: input force is between fulcrum and output force

**9** What is the name of the place about which a lever rotates?

**A** center point  `6.i`

**B** fulcrum

**C** hinge

**D** vertex

**10** Hannah is using a shovel as a lever to lift rock in her garden. She is using a second rock as the fulcrum and pushing down on the handle of the shovel. She is not able to lift the rock. How can she increase the mechanical advantage of the lever?

**A** She can place the fulcrum closer to the rock he is lifting.  `6.i`

**B** She can move the fulcrum away from the rock she is lifting.

**C** She can remove the fulcrum and lift on the end of the shovel instead.

**D** She can push down on the shovel between the fulcrum and the rock.

**11** The diagram below shows several levers.

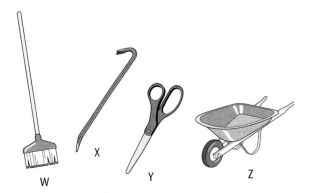

Which is a second-class lever?

**A** W  `6.i`

**B** X

**C** Y

**D** Z

### CHAPTER 10

# The Cardiopulmonary System and Pressure

## The BIG Idea

The pulmonary-circulatory system, driven by pressure generated by the heart, functions as a whole to supply oxygen to and remove carbon dioxide from your cells.

### LESSON 1  5.b, 7.c
### The Pulmonary-Circulatory System

**Main Idea** The pulmonary and circulatory systems work together to transport oxygen to your cells and to remove carbon dioxide from your cells.

### LESSON 2
5.b, 6.j, 7.a, 7.c, 7.e

### Pressure and the Body

**Main Idea** Pressure allows us to breathe and keeps blood flowing throughout the circulatory system.

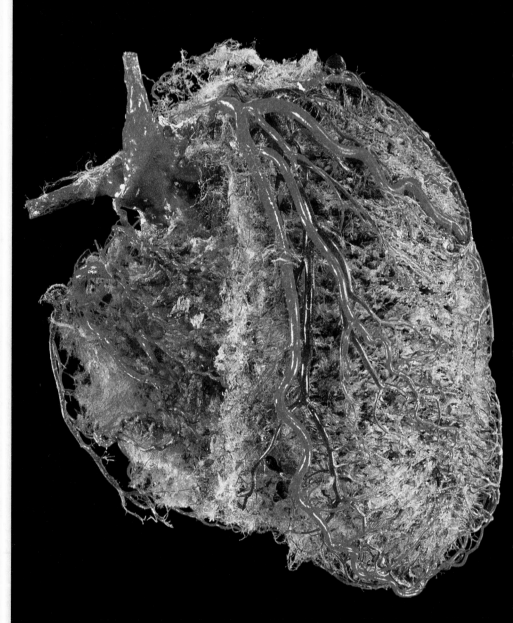

### What's *that?*

The heart is one of the main organs of the cardiopulmonary system. It pumps blood to every part of your body, including itself. The blood vessels shown here nourish the heart with blood.

**Science *Journal*** Write a paragraph that explains how you think blood flows through your body.

## Launch Lab

**00:10 minutes**

### Does your pulse change?

You probably know that you can feel your pulse, or heartbeat, in your wrist. Did you know that it also can be felt in your neck and even in your ankle?

**Procedure**

1. Using two fingers, but not your thumb, find your pulse.

2. Using a **clock with a second hand,** count the number of beats for 15 s; multiply this number by 4 and record.

3. Record the number of times you take a breath in 1 min.

4. Perform a physical task.

5. Record your pulse and breathing rate.

**Think About This**

- **Report** Did your heart rate increase or decrease after the activity? Breathing rate?

- **Hypothesize** Think of a reason your breathing rate and heart rate would both change.

 **5.b, 7.c**

## Science Online

Visit ca7.msscience.com to:

▶ view **Concepts in Motion**

▶ explore Virtual Labs

▶ access content-related Web links

▶ take the Standards Check

**FOLDABLES™**
**Study Organizer**

**Circulatory System Failure** Make the following Foldable to summarize conditions that result from failure of the cardiopulmonary system.

▷ **STEP 1 Fold** the bottom of a horizontal sheet of paper up about 5 cm.

▷ **STEP 2 Fold** into thirds.

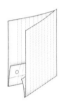

▷ **STEP 3 Unfold** twice and dot with glue or staple to make three pockets. **Label** as shown.

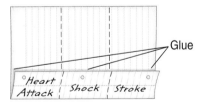

Glue

°Heart Attack | °Shock | °Stroke

**Reading** *Skill*    **ELA7: R 2.3**

**Recognizing Cause and Effect** As you read this chapter, record information about the causes and effects of the conditions on note cards and place them in the appropriate pockets.

# Get Ready to Read

# Summarize

**1. Learn It!** Summarizing helps you organize information, focus on main ideas, and reduce the amount of information to remember. To summarize, restate the important facts in a short sentence or paragraph. Be brief and do not include too many details.

**2. Practice It!** Read the text on page 408 labeled The Heart as a Pump. Then read the summary below and look at the important facts from that passage.

**Important Facts**

The heart is a muscle that can contract and relax.

Pressure can be increased by increasing force or decreasing area.

When the heart contracts, the chamber the blood is in gets smaller.

A smaller chamber has less area.

**Summary**

Changes in pressure are how the heart pumps blood through the body.

**3. Apply It!** Practice summarizing as you read this chapter. Stop after each lesson and write a brief summary.

# Target Your Reading

Use this to focus on the main ideas as you read the chapter.

**Reading Tip**

Reread your summary to make sure you didn't change the author's original meaning or ideas.

**1** **Before you read** the chapter, respond to the statements below on your worksheet or on a numbered sheet of paper.

- Write an **A** if you **agree** with the statement.
- Write a **D** if you **disagree** with the statement.

**2** **After you read** the chapter, look back to this page to see if you've changed your mind about any of the statements.

- If any of your answers changed, explain why.
- Change any false statements into true statements.
- Use your revised statements as a study guide.

**Science Online**

Print a worksheet of this page at ca7.msscience.com.

| Before You Read<br>A or D | Statement | After You Read<br>A or D |
|---|---|---|
| | **1** All arteries contain oxygenated blood. | |
| | **2** Veins and arteries are identical in structure but take blood in different directions. | |
| | **3** Your lungs have a greater surface area inside than they do outside. | |
| | **4** If more than two of your grandparents develop heart disease, you probably will too. | |
| | **5** Blood flows through your lungs. | |
| | **6** If you have high blood pressure, your heart could explode. | |
| | **7** It is better to have low blood pressure than high blood pressure. | |
| | **8** Air is pulled into your lungs. | |
| | **9** Blood flows in one direction in your body. | |
| | **10** You can increase pressure by decreasing surface area. | |

### Science Content Standards

**5.b** Students know organ systems function because of the contributions of individual organs, tissues, and cells. The failure of any part can affect the entire system.

**7.c** Communicate the logical connection among hypotheses, science concepts, tests conducted, data collected, and conclusions drawn from the scientific evidence.

## Reading Guide

### What *You'll Learn*

▶ **Investigate** the pulmonary and circulatory systems.

▶ **Describe** the interaction of the pulmonary and circulatory systems.

▶ **Explain** how problems can occur in the pulmonary and circulatory systems.

### Why *It's Important*

Understanding how these systems work will help you decrease your risks for diseases.

### Vocabulary

| | |
|---|---|
| pulmonary system | atrium |
| breathing | ventricle |
| lungs | artery |
| pneumonia | capillary |
| suffocation | vein |
| asthma | heart attack |
| circulatory system | stroke |
| | heart |

### Review Vocabulary

**respiration:** a series of chemical reactions that transforms the energy in food molecules to usable cellular energy (p. 68)

# The Pulmonary-Circulatory System

**Main Idea** The pulmonary and circulatory systems work together to transport oxygen to your cells and to remove carbon dioxide from your cells.

**Real-World Reading Connection** Take a deep breath. Notice how your chest expands. Every time you breathe, air enters and exits your lungs. At the same time, your heart is constantly beating. How do these events happen and why are they necessary for survival?

## The Pulmonary System

You may already know that we, like all animals, need oxygen to live. We get oxygen from the air we breathe. We also need to rid our bodies of carbon dioxide. Recall from Chapter 1 that carbon dioxide is a waste product of cellular respiration. How do we take in oxygen and remove carbon dioxide? Our **pulmonary system** (PUL muh nar ee • SIHS tehm) contains tissues and organs specialized for taking in oxygen and removing carbon dioxide from our bodies and for exchanging oxygen and carbon dioxide. The pulmonary system is also often referred to as the respiratory system. **Figure 1** highlights the organs and tissues of the pulmonary system. Take a deep breath. Think about where you feel the air moving through your body. Look at **Figure 1** and trace the path you think the air follows.

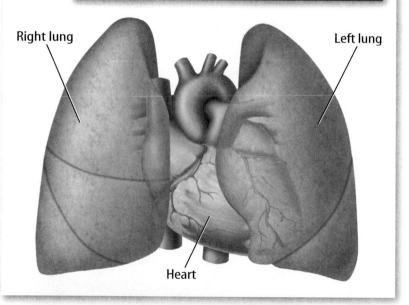

**Figure 1** The pulmonary system includes all the passageways that bring air in and out of the body.

Right lung

Left lung

Heart

## Breathing

The pulmonary system is open to the atmosphere, so atmospheric air can move into and out of your body. **Breathing** is the process of air entering and exiting the lungs. Inhalation is breathing in air, while exhalation is breathing air out. Both phases are shown in **Figure 2.** The muscles between your ribs play an important role, allowing your rib cage to expand and contract. This alone is responsible for 25 percent of the breathing process. When the flat muscle below your rib cage called the diaphragm contracts, inhalation begins. When it relaxes, exhalation begins.

When you inhale, air enters the pulmonary system through your nose or mouth. Air from the nose and mouth first passes through the pharynx, a tubelike passageway in the throat. Then air moves into your larynx, the valve separating the upper and lower portions of the throat where sound is produced. Beyond the larynx food objects proceed to the digestive system. Air goes to the trachea, a 12-cm-long tube lined with C-shaped rings of cartilage to prevent it from collapsing. The trachea forks into two branches, called bronchi (BRAHN ki) (singular, bronchus). Air continues its path through the bronchi.

The bronchi are connected to the **lungs,** the organs of the pulmonary system. Air enters the lungs through the bronchi and the bronchi then divide into branched tubes called bronchioles (BRON kee ohlz). These tubes continue to divide like branches of a tree getting smaller and smaller. At the end of the bronchioles, like leaves at the end of twigs, are millions of microscopic sacs called alveoli (al VEE uh li)(singular, alveolus). Alveoli are like tiny balloons that fill with air as you breathe. In the alveoli, oxygen from the air that was breathed in and carbon dioxide from the cells are exchanged. The air that now has little oxygen and is high in carbon dioxide is exhaled and flows out in the reverse path.

 **Reading Check** Where does gas exchange take place in the lungs?

**Figure 2** The lungs expand and contract, allowing for inhalation and exhalation.

**Describe** the physical differences that would occur in the inhalation and exhalation images if the diaphragm had a hole in it.

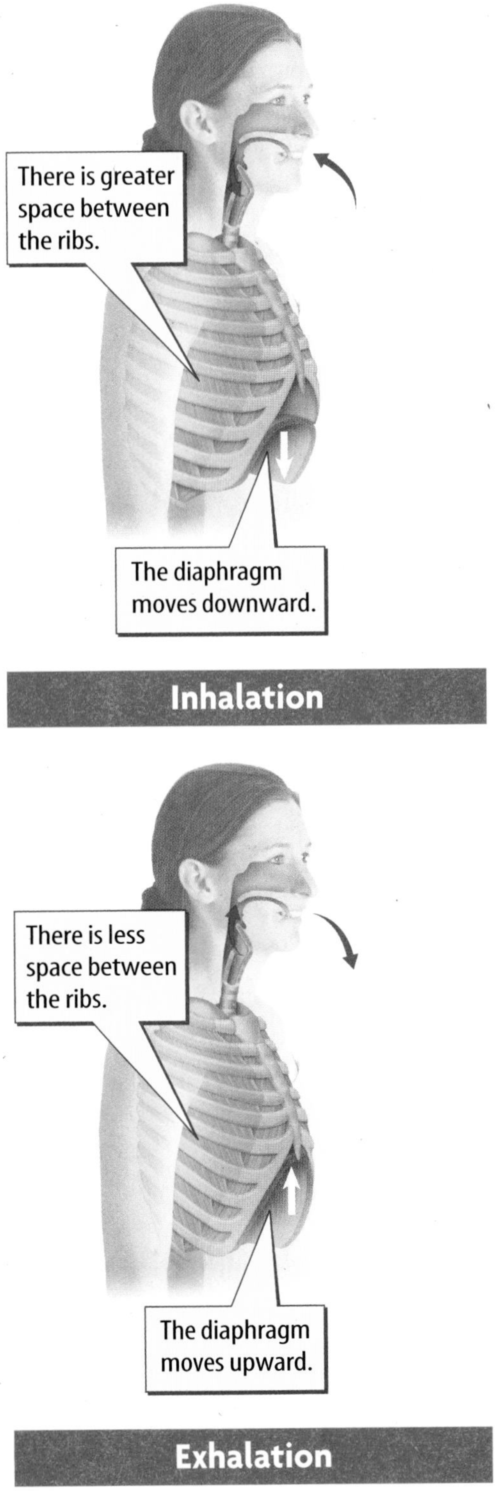

There is greater space between the ribs.

The diaphragm moves downward.

**Inhalation**

There is less space between the ribs.

The diaphragm moves upward.

**Exhalation**

**Figure 3** In an X ray, healthy lungs are transparent because they are filled with air. Cloudy, white areas in the lungs are a sign of pneumonia.

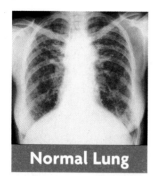

**Normal Lung**

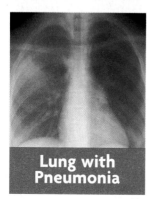

**Lung with Pneumonia**

## Problems in the Pulmonary System

We could live days without water and longer than a month without food. However, we cannot live even an hour without oxygen. Cells combine the food and oxygen to produce energy. You have probably had nasal congestion from colds or other illnesses. Congestion from colds sometimes makes it hard to breathe because your swollen sinuses fill with fluid and mucus blocks air passageways in your lungs. Other problems in the pulmonary system, such as pneumonia, suffocation, and asthma, make it difficult to breathe and can lead to severe health problems. Problems in the pulmonary system prevent oxygen from reaching the lungs.

**Pneumonia** One of the leading causes of death in the United States is **pneumonia** (noo MOH nyuh), an infection of the lungs. Viruses, bacteria, fungi, and parasites can cause pneumonia. Thick fluid may build up in the lungs of a person with pneumonia. Fluid in the lungs interferes with gas exchange. This causes less oxygen to be absorbed into the blood. X rays are often used to diagnose pneumonia. Compare the X rays in **Figure 3** of the lungs of a healthy person and a person with pneumonia.

Pneumonia is caused by contact with mucus from an infected person or the introduction of bacteria or viruses normally present in the mouth and throat into the lungs. Many times, people weakened by environmental conditions, other illnesses, and infections may also contract pneumonia. This is why people who contract pneumonia in the hospital while being treated for other conditions are at a greater risk.

 **Reading Check** Identify how pneumonia makes it difficult to breathe.

**Suffocation** Have you ever seen someone choking? Food or other objects can become stuck in a person's airway. When this happens, oxygen cannot be supplied to the lungs. **Suffocation** occurs when the lungs and body do not receive enough oxygen. **Figure 4** shows abdominal thrusts, used to dislodge an object from a person's airway. Choking is not the only cause of suffocation. Infants and children can suffocate if blankets or plastic bags cover their faces. Gases such as carbon monoxide can also cause suffocation. Carbon monoxide takes the place of oxygen in the blood and is dangerous because it is odorless. Therefore, a person unknowingly can be exposed to high levels of carbon monoxide.

 **Visual Check** **Figure 4** What signs are present when someone is choking and unable to breathe?

# Visualizing Abdominal Thrusts

**Figure 4**

When food or other objects become lodged in the trachea, airflow between the lungs and the mouth and nasal cavity is blocked. Death can occur in minutes. However, prompt action by someone can save the life of a choking victim.

The rescuer uses abdominal thrusts to force the victim's diaphragm up. This decreases the volume of the chest cavity and forces air up in the trachea. The result is a rush of air that dislodges and expels the food or other object. The victim can breathe again. This techinque is shown at right and should only be performed in emergency situations.

**A** The rescuer stands behind the choking victim and wraps her arms around the victim's upper abdomen. She places a fist (thumb side in) against the victim's stomach. The fist should be below the ribs and above the navel.

Food is lodged in the victim's trachea.

The rescuer places her fist against the victim's stomach.

The rescuer's second hand adds force to the fist.

An upward thrust dislodges the food from the victim's trachea.

**B** With a forceful, quick movement, the rescuer thrusts her fist up into the area below the ribs. This action should be repeated as many times as necessary.

*Contributed by National Geographic*

**Asthma** The most common long-term disease in children is **asthma** (AZ muh), a disease of the airways to the lungs. Common substances that cause allergies, such as cigarette smoke, pollen, pet dander, insect droppings, mold, and ozone, cause a more severe reaction in people with asthma. Their airways become swollen, making them narrower than normal. This narrowing makes it difficult to take in enough oxygen, as shown in **Figure 5.** This causes wheezing, chest tightness, coughing, and trouble breathing. Nearly one in five children in California has asthma. The symptoms of asthma come and go with exposure to allergens. Therefore, people with asthma should be careful to avoid situations in which they are exposed to allergens.

**Reading Check** What is the best way to relieve symptoms of asthma?

Many asthma triggers can be difficult to avoid, but it is still possible to lead a normal life with proper treatment. Air pollution, such as smog and ozone, is the primary trigger of most asthma attacks. In some cities, all residents, not just those with asthma, are warned to stay indoors on days when high levels of pollution are measured. Smog levels in California exceeded federal health limits on 109 days in 2004. Exercise can trigger asthma attacks in some people. People with this condition do not have to avoid exercise, but they should seek medical advice before beginning a fitness program. With a plan for prevention and treatment of asthma, athletes are unlimited by their condition. Some Olympic athletes, such as swimmer Tom Dolan and track-and-field star Jackie Joyner-Kersee, have won many gold medals with correct monitoring and treatment of their asthma.

**Figure 5** This doctor is checking the breathing of an asthmatic patient. An asthma patient has swollen airways.

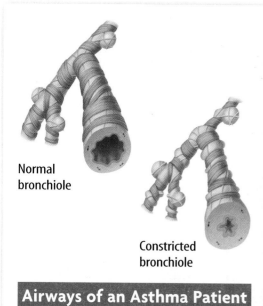

Normal bronchiole

Constricted bronchiole

**Airways of an Asthma Patient**

**Asthma Patient**

# The Circulatory System

All the cells of our bodies need oxygen, food, and other nutrients. Cells also produce waste products that need to be removed. How do substances get to and from cells? All these substances are transported by the blood in the circulatory system. The **circulatory system** is the system that contains the heart and blood vessels and transports blood throughout the body.

## Blood

If you have seen your blood, you know that it is a dark red liquid. Blood is a tissue that contains many different substances—even cells. Blood is about 55 percent plasma, which is 90 percent water. The remaining 10 percent is composed of ions, proteins, and other substances the body produces or requires.

**Platelets and White Blood Cells** Platelets and white and red blood cells, listed on **Table 1,** make up the remaining portion of blood. Platelets are fragments of cells contained in your blood. After an injury, proteins in the blood cause platelets to form a plug which stops the bleeding. Without platelets, even a small cut would continue bleeding because a scab would not form. White blood cells are part of the immune system, which fights infections.

**WORD ORIGIN** · · · · · · · · · · · ·

circulatory system
*circ*– from Greek word *circe* meaning *circle*

 **Table 1** What are the functions of each of the whole blood components?

| Table 1 Components in Whole Blood | | |
| --- | --- | --- |
| **Blood Cells** | **Example** | **Function** |
| Red blood cells | | Transport oxygen, help transport carbon dioxide |
| White blood cells | | Defense and immunity |
| Platelets | | Clotting |

**COncepts In MOtion**
Interactive Table Organize information about the components of whole blood at ca7.msscience.com.

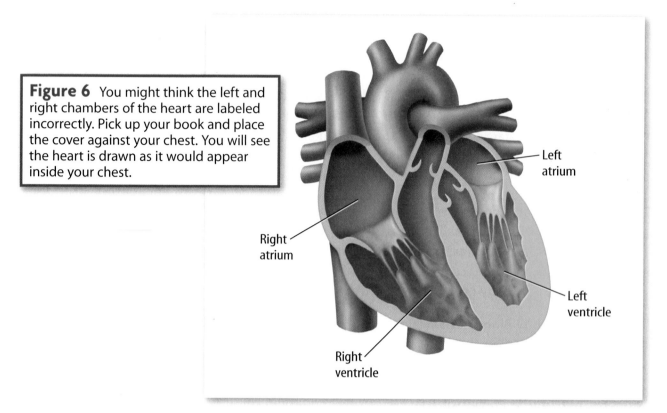

**Figure 6** You might think the left and right chambers of the heart are labeled incorrectly. Pick up your book and place the cover against your chest. You will see the heart is drawn as it would appear inside your chest.

Left atrium

Right atrium

Left ventricle

Right ventricle

**Red Blood Cells** Your body contains about 25 trillion red blood cells. Red blood cells are normally shaped like a disc that is flattened on both sides. Red blood cells have iron-containing proteins called hemoglobin that carry oxygen. Because of this protein and their shape, red blood cells can transport about one billion oxygen molecules.

 How do red blood cells carry oxygen?

Red blood cells constantly wear out and your body replaces them. They last about 120 days, so you have a completely new population of red blood cells every two months. Because of this, people can donate blood about every eight weeks.

## Heart

The **heart** is the organ of the circulatory system that pumps blood. It is hollow, muscular, about the size of your fist, and located in the middle of the chest between the lungs.

**Figure 6** shows how the heart is divided into four chambers. The two upper chambers of the heart that receive blood are called **atria** (singular, atrium). The **ventricles** are the two lower chambers that pump blood out of the heart. Deoxygenated blood enters the right atrium of the heart. The heart pumps this blood through the right ventricle and into the lungs. Then the blood flows back to the left atrium of the heart where it is pumped through the left ventricle and to the body.

## Blood Vessels

Blood travels to and from the heart in vessels, as shown in **Figure 7.** The vessels of the circulatory system are like the roads of a city. A city has large interstates, smaller highways, and even smaller neighborhood streets. Similarly, the circulatory system has large blood vessels that are connected to smaller vessels. **Arteries** are vessels that carry blood away from the heart to organs in the body. Arteries branch into smaller vessels, and then even smaller vessels called capillaries. **Capillaries** are the blood vessels that deliver oxygen and nutrients to the organs, as shown in **Figure 8.** Just as oxygenated blood flows away from the heart, deoxygenated blood carrying carbon dioxide must return to the heart. The capillaries take up carbon dioxide and other wastes before joining with larger vessels that carry the blood on its return path. These vessels connect to larger vessels called **veins** that carry blood to the heart.

All blood vessels have the same basic structure. The inner lining is is a thin, flat layer of cells where the blood and the vessel wall meet. Every part of the circulatory system is lined by this thin layer of cells. Capillaries sometimes only have this thin layer of cells. The next layer is of connective tissue followed by a layer of smooth muscle. The muscle layer is more highly developed in the arteries. Why do you think this is? Finally, there is another layer of connective tissue that contains the nerves and supplies the larger blood vessels with nutrients.

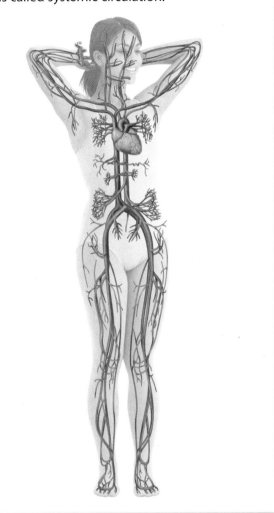

**Figure 7** Blood flow throughout the body is called systemic circulation.

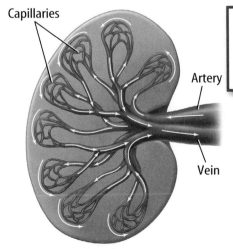

**Figure 8** The blood vessels supply the body with blood and oxygen while taking away waste products such as carbon dioxide.

**Describe** how blood flows into and out of the organs.

**Figure 9** Notice the cause of these cardiovascular diseases.

**Infer** why a disruption of blood flow to the brain or heart would be harmful to a person's health.

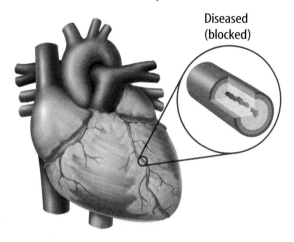

Diseased (blocked)

**Heart Attack**

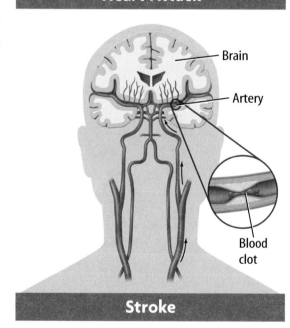

Brain

Artery

Blood clot

**Stroke**

## Problems in the Circulatory System

Problems in the circulatory system prevent oxygen from reaching the cells and can lead to serious health problems and death. Diseases of the heart and blood vessels are called **cardiovascular diseases** (kar dee oh VAS kyuh lur • dih ZEEZ ez). Cardiovascular disease causes more than half the deaths in the United States.

Risk factors for cardiovascular disease include being overweight, eating a diet high in saturated fat and cholesterol, smoking, having high sugar in the blood, being physically inactive, and consuming too much alcohol. Older men are more likely to show symptoms of cardiovascular disease than anyone else. Although tests are available to screen for heart disease, it is instead recommended that people who do not show symptoms, such as heart attack and stroke, identify and eliminate risk factors in their lives.

**Heart Attack** The arteries that supply the heart muscle with blood and oxygen are the coronary arteries. A **heart attack** occurs if the coronary arteries cannot supply enough blood to the heart. This happens when the coronary arteries clog, as shown in **Figure 9.** The heart muscle may die and the heart may stop working if the muscle does not receive enough oxygen. Symptoms of a heart attack include chest pain, pain in the arms and back, shortness of breath, and dizziness.

**Stroke** Without oxygen, brain tissue will die within 4–5 minutes. A **stroke** is the death of brain tissue. A stroke can happen if a blood vessel to the brain is blocked or if one of these blood vessels breaks. A ruptured blood vessel, or a blocked vessel, also shown in **Figure 9,** prevents blood flow to the brain. Once brain tissue dies, it is not replaced. A stroke may result in memory loss, loss of muscle control, or other loss of nerve function, depending on where in the brain the stroke occurs.

Stroke is the third leading cause of death in adults. When the blood vessels in the brain have degenerated enough in one place to have a stroke, the overall condition is usually not healthy.

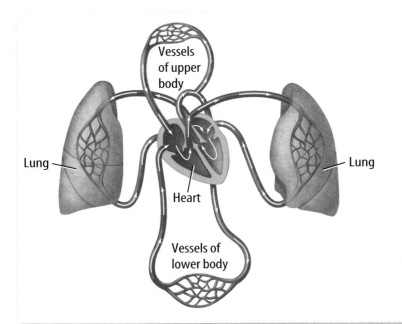

**Figure 10** The pulmonary system and circulatory system work together to supply all the tissues of the body with oxygen.

Vessels of upper body

Lung

Lung

Heart

Vessels of lower body

# Exchanges Between the Pulmonary and Circulatory Systems

The pulmonary and circulatory systems must both function properly for us to survive. The circulatory system cannot deliver oxygen unless the blood has been successfully oxygenated by the pulmonary system. Similarly, the muscles of the rib cage and diaphragm cannot function unless the circulatory system supplies them with oxygenated blood. The air in the alveoli and the blood in the capillaries must be able to exchange oxygen and carbon dioxide freely over the thin membrane that separates them. All the organs, tissues, and cells of both systems must function properly for the systems to function normally. **Figure 10** illustrates some of the interactions of the pulmonary and circulatory systems.

## Gas Exchange

Perhaps the most important exchange between the pulmonary and circulatory systems is the gas exchange in the lungs. The membrane separating the capillaries and the alveoli allows gases to move across it. No energy is needed for the exchange of oxygen and carbon dioxide—the gases move from regions where they are at a higher **concentration** to regions where they are at a lower concentration.

 What two gases are exchanged in the lungs?

The structure of your lungs allows a great amount of oxygen and carbon dioxide to be exchanged between the air you breathe and your blood because the structure within the lungs greatly increases the surface area of the lungs.

**ACADEMIC VOCABULARY**
concentration (kahn sen TRAY shun)
*(noun)* the measure of how much of a given substance is mixed with another substance
*The concentration of sugar in soft drinks is high.*

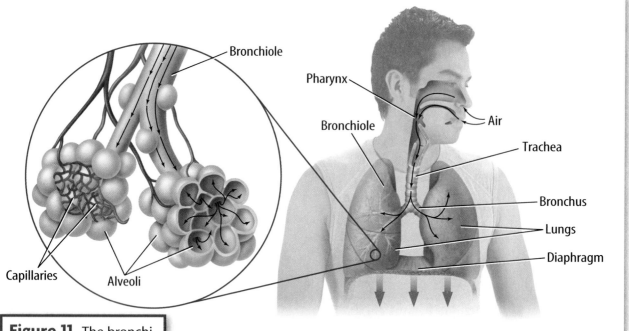

Bronchiole
Pharynx
Bronchiole
Air
Trachea
Bronchus
Lungs
Diaphragm
Capillaries
Alveoli

**Figure 11** The bronchioles in the lungs are similar in form to the branches of a tree. The alveoli at the end of each bronchiole are surrounded by small vessels.

**Describe** how gases are exchanged in the pulmonary system.

## Exchange in the Lungs

Alveoli are surrounded by capillaries. Oxygen gas is removed from the air you breathe and passes across a thin membrane between the alveoli and the capillaries. At the same time, carbon dioxide passes in the opposite direction, from the capillaries to the alveoli into the air you had breathed in. This process is shown in **Figure 11.** When the level of carbon dioxide in the air in your lungs becomes great enough, you exhale without thinking about it.

You may have heard the word *respiration* used interchangeably with the word *breathing*. However, they are not the same. Respiration is the use of oxygen and food and the production of carbon dioxide in your cells to produce energy, as discussed in Chapter 3. Breathing is the physical process of inhalation and exhalation.

# Preventing Problems in the Pulmonary and Circulatory Systems

What can you do to reduce your risk of stroke and heart attack? Family history, or genetics, partially determines your risk. However, a healthy lifestyle is the best way to prevent cardiopulmonary problems. Exercise reduces the risk of cardiovascular disease by improving the flow of blood and oxygen throughout your body and by keeping your blood vessels flexible. Choosing not to smoke and eating a diet low in saturated fat and cholesterol also helps prevent cardiovascular disease.

 Name something you do that reduces your risk of cardiopulmonary disease.

# What have you learned?

The pulmonary and cardiovascular systems work together to provide your body with the oxygen it needs and to remove carbon dioxide. Your lungs are made up of millions of alveoli, which provide a place for gas exchange. Your heart pumps blood through your body, picking up oxygen in your lungs and delivering it to your tissues. It also takes carbon dioxide from your cells and returns it to the lungs, to be expelled from the body. These two systems are dependent on one another. Any failure in either system affects the other system. Common failures include stroke, heart attack, pneumonia, and suffocation. Living a healthy lifestyle is the best way to avoid these problems in the cardiopulmonary system.

# LESSON 1 Review

## Summarize

Create your own lesson summary as you write a **newsletter.**

1. **Write** this lesson title, number, and page numbers at the top of a sheet of paper.

2. **Review** the text after the **red** main headings and write one sentence about each. These will be the headlines of your newsletter.

3. **Review** the text and write 2–3 sentences about each **blue** subheading. These sentences should tell *who, what, when, where,* and *why* information about each headline.

4. **Illustrate** your newsletter with diagrams of important structures and processes next to each headline.

 **ELA7:** W 2.5

## Standards Check

### Using Vocabulary

1. **Name** three characteristics of alveoli. **5.b**

2. **Explain** the function of hemoglobin. **5.b**

### Understanding Main Ideas

3. **Give an example** of how the pulmonary and circulatory systems are dependent on each other. **5.b**

4. **Draw** a picture and trace the path of oxygen from the air outside your body to your cells. **5.b**

5. **State** the reason why loss of oxygen to the brain is especially dangerous. **5.b**

6. **Compare and contrast** veins and arteries. **5.b**

Veins            Arteries

7. How does pneumonia prevent oxygen from being absorbed into the blood? **5.b**

   A. Fluid built up in the lungs blocks the air flow.

   B. The alveolar membranes get thicker.

   C. The capillaries of the lungs become clogged.

   D. Bacteria destroy alveoli.

### Applying Science

8. **Predict** what would happen if you were to decrease the number of red blood cells in your blood. **5.b**

9. **Assess** your current lifestyle—how heart-healthy are you? Make a list of risk factors of the typical student your age. **5.b**

**Science Online**

For more practice, visit **Standards Check** at ca7.msscience.com.

# DataLab

 Try at Home

# How does illness affect the cardiopulmonary system?

Illness affects all systems of the body. What happens to one system affects what happens to others. The data below were collected at a hospital for three different patients.

## Data

See data to the right.

## Data Analysis

1. **Graph Data** Using the data in the medical chart above, graph each vital sign (variable) versus time. Graph each dependent variable versus time on one graph.

2. **Interpreting Graphs** What relationship do you see between the dependent variables?

3. **Conclude** How are the two patients different from the control?

| Control | Heart Rate (beats per minute) | Blood Pressure | Breathing Rate (breaths per minute) |
|---|---|---|---|
| Time point 1 | 70 | 120/80 | 16 |
| Time point 2 | 72 | 119/80 | 16 |
| Time point 3 | 75 | 116/78 | 17 |
| Time point 4 | 72 | 118/77 | 16 |
| Time point 5 | 73 | 116/76 | 18 |

| Illness 1 | Heart Rate (beats per minute) | Blood Pressure | Breathing Rate (breaths per minute) |
|---|---|---|---|
| Time point 1 | 102 | 118/62 | 22 |
| Time point 2 | 104 | 118/68 | 22 |
| Time point 3 | 100 | 132/68 | 24 |
| Time point 4 | 106 | 138/84 | 24 |
| Time point 5 | 102 | 118/74 | 22 |

| Illness 2 | Heart Rate (beats per minute) | Blood Pressure | Breathing Rate (breaths per minute) |
|---|---|---|---|
| Time point 1 | 68 | 138/80 | 20 |
| Time point 2 | 70 | 118/68 | 20 |
| Time point 3 | 72 | 120/74 | 22 |
| Time point 4 | 84 | 118/72 | 23 |
| Time point 5 | 84 | 90/60 | 24 |

 **Science Content Standards**

**5.b** Students know organ systems function because of the contributions of individual organs, tissues, and cells. The failure of any part can affect the entire system.

**7.c** Communicate the logical connection among hypotheses, science concepts, tests conducted, data collected, and conclusions drawn from the scientific evidence.

## Reading Guide

### What *You'll Learn*

▶ **Define** *pressure.*

▶ **Explain** the role that pressure plays in the circulatory system.

### Why *It's Important*

The pressure in the cardiopulmonary system maintains the proper working order of your body.

### Vocabulary

pressure
hypertension
shock

### Review Vocabulary

**atmosphere:** mixture of gases that surrounds Earth (Grade 6)

# Pressure and the Body

**Main Idea** Pressure allows us to breathe and keeps blood flowing throughout the circulatory system.

**Real-World Reading Connection** What happens when you pump air into a ball? The ball becomes more firm as it fills with air. The air pushes against the walls of the ball. In the circulatory system, blood pushes against the walls of blood vessels.

## What is pressure?

Air in a ball places pressure on the inside walls of the ball, keeping it inflated. **Figure 12** shows another example of pressure. **Pressure** is the amount of force per unit area. Many different units are used to measure pressure. Atmospheric pressure, the pressure of air on Earth's surface, often is measured in millimeters of mercury (mmHg). So is your blood presssure. You may be familiar with pounds per square inch (psi), a common measure for tire pressure. The pascal (Pa) is the SI unit of pressure.

 **Reading Check** What is pressure?

**Figure 12** A flat or underinflated tire has very low pressure and cannot support the weight of the bike. A fully inflated tire has enough pressure to support the bike and the rider.

Deflated Tire

Inflated Tire

**Figure 13** An under-inflated ball has very low pressure. The ball flattens when a brick is placed on top of it. When more air is added, the pressure inside the ball increases. The brick no longer can flatten the ball. The pressure on a ballerina's toes is greater when all of her weight is only on her toes.

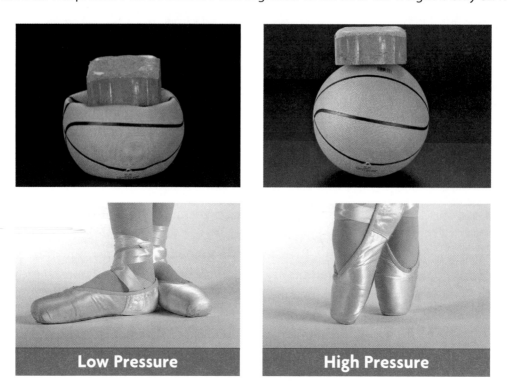

**Low Pressure**          **High Pressure**

## Changing Pressure

There are two ways to change pressure, as shown in **Figure 13.** First, pressure increases as you increase the amount of force applied to a constant area. For example, the force against the walls of a ball increases as more air pumps into the ball. Second, pressure increases as you decrease the size of the area to which a constant force is applied. For example, the pressure on a ballet dancer's toes increases when she stands on her toes, as compared to standing on flat feet. This is because the dancer's body weight is spread over the entire area of the foot. When the dancer is on her toes, the pressure is concentrated on a much smaller area. Similarly, you can decrease the pressure on a surface by applying less force to it. You can also decrease pressure by spreading a force over a larger area. The equation for finding pressure is:

$$\text{Pressure (Pa)} = \frac{\text{Force (N)}}{\text{Area (m)}}$$

$$P = \frac{F}{A}$$

**SCIENCE USE v. COMMON USE**

**pressure**

*Science Use* the amount of force per unit area. *When the pressure reached a critical point, the tea kettle began to whistle.*

*Common Use* a constant state of worry or urgency. *Adrian began to feel pressure from increasing amounts of home-work and lengthier soccer practices.*

**Figure 13** Identify in each set of photographs which factor of pressure has increased or decreased.

# Pressure in the Pulmonary System

When you inhale, do you push air into your lungs? You may think so, but air is pulled into your lungs, not pushed. Mammals, including humans, use this type of breathing to pull air into the lungs. The diaphragm and rib muscles move the chest cavity, as shown in **Figure 14.** During an inhalation they cause the chest cavity to expand. The volume of the lungs is expanded and the pressure in the alveoli decreases. This causes the pressure in the lungs to become lower than atmospheric pressure. Air moves from areas of high pressure to areas of low pressure, so air is pulled into the lungs. When we exhale, the chest contracts. The volume of the lungs decreases and forces the air out of the lungs and eventually through the mouth and nostrils.

 Describe what happens when pressure in the lungs is higher than atmospheric pressure.

# Pressure in the Circulatory System

Have you ever tried to use a water hose when the water was turned on low? You probably had a hard time spraying the water. That is because the water in a hose must be under pressure in order to have a strong, far-reaching spray. Similarly, pressure is needed in the circulatory system. Without pressure, blood vessels would not be able to transport blood to all tissues.

**Figure 14** Air moves from areas of high pressure to areas of lower pressure.

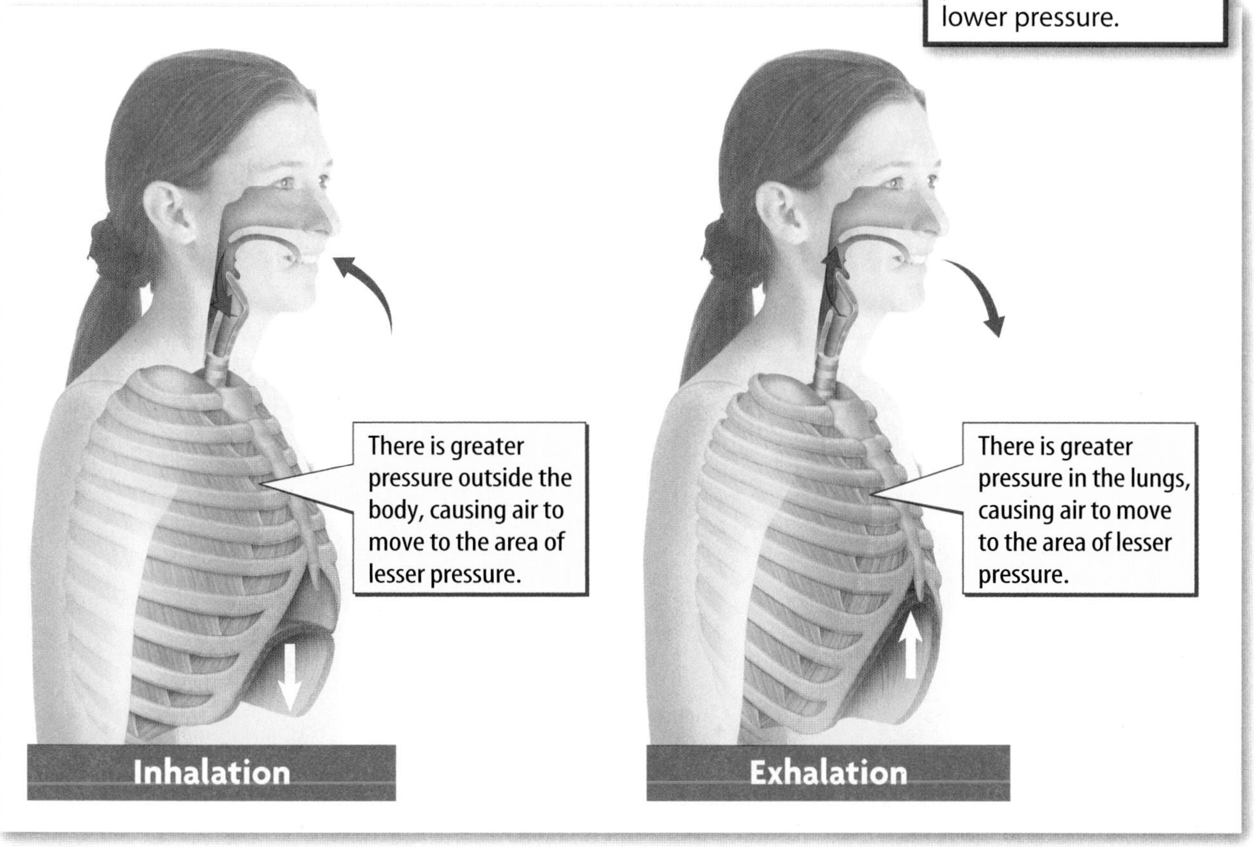

There is greater pressure outside the body, causing air to move to the area of lesser pressure.

**Inhalation**

There is greater pressure in the lungs, causing air to move to the area of lesser pressure.

**Exhalation**

## The Heart as a Pump

You use a pump to increase the air pressure of a tire or a ball. In the circulatory system, the heart is the pump. Recall from Chapter 9 that muscle fibers shorten when a muscle contracts. The heart is also a muscle that contracts. When the heart contracts, the volume inside the chamber decreases. Blood is forced out of the chamber as the chamber gets smaller. This is similar to how toothpaste is squeezed out of a tube.

## Pumping in One Direction

What happens if you squeeze the middle of a tube of toothpaste? Toothpaste moves in both directions. It is important for blood to move in one direction as the heart pumps. The heart and veins have valves that keep blood flowing in one direction through the circulatory system. Valves act like doors that open in only one direction. **Figure 15** shows the valves in the heart.

The contractions of the muscles of the heart create areas of greater and lesser pressure, pumping blood through the heart. Valves, shown in **Figure 15,** open and close and also contribute to the different pressures in the chambers. When the muscles of a chamber contract, the pressure in that chamber increases. When the muscles of a chamber relax, there is less pressure. The heart works like two pumps—the right and left atria contract nearly simultaneously and the right and left ventricles contract simultaneously.

 **Reading Check** How does changing pressure make the heart work?

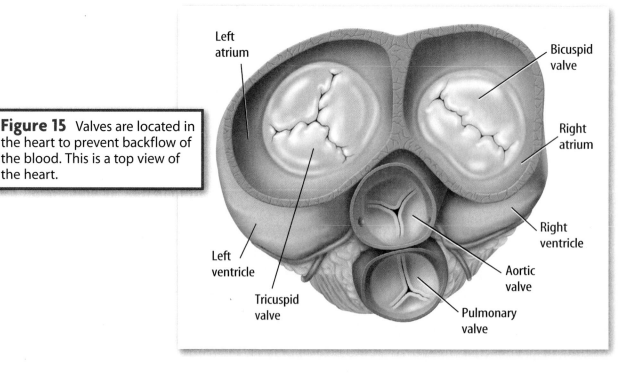

**Figure 15** Valves are located in the heart to prevent backflow of the blood. This is a top view of the heart.

Left atrium

Bicuspid valve

Right atrium

Left ventricle

Right ventricle

Tricuspid valve

Aortic valve

Pulmonary valve

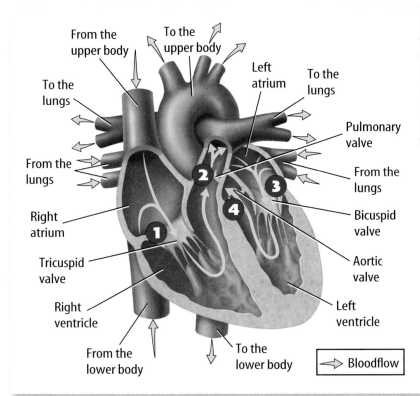

From the upper body
To the upper body
Left atrium
To the lungs
To the lungs
Pulmonary valve
From the lungs
From the lungs
Bicuspid valve
Right atrium
Tricuspid valve
Aortic valve
Right ventricle
Left ventricle
From the lower body
To the lower body

→ Bloodflow

**Figure 16** Notice that the atria have thinner walls than the ventricles because the atria pump blood a shorter distance.

**Describe** what causes the pressure changes as the blood flows through the heart.

**Concepts In Motion**
To see an animation of bloodflow through the heart, visit ca7.msscience.com.

**❶ Right Atrium to Right Ventricle**

Using **Figure 16,** trace the flow of blood through the heart. The right atrium receives blood from the body. The right ventricle relaxes and the tricuspid valve opens, blood flows into the right ventricle. When the right ventricle contracts, the tricuspid valve closes, preventing the blood from returning to the atrium.

**❷ Right Ventricle to Lungs**

The increased pressure in the right ventricle causes the pulmonary valve to open. The blood is pumped to the lungs. The pressure of the blood in the arteries causes the pulmonary valve to close.

**❸ Left Atrium to Left Ventricle**

After gas exchange occurs, the blood returns to the heart. This time, it flows into the left atrium. When the left ventricle relaxes, the bicuspid valve opens and blood flows into the left ventricle.

**❹ Left Ventricle to Body**

The left ventricle contracts, the bicuspid valve closes and the aortic valve opens. This pumps blood into the aorta and to the body. The pressure in the aorta causes the aortic valve to close.

Continuous surges keep the blood moving through the arteries. As the blood enters the veins, far from the heart, blood pressure decreases. The valves in the veins, shown in **Figure 17,** prevent backflow, allowing the blood to return to the heart.

**Figure 17** Valves in the veins, like those in the heart, prevent the backflow of blood.

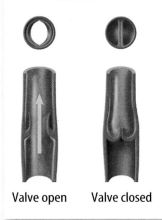

Valve open      Valve closed

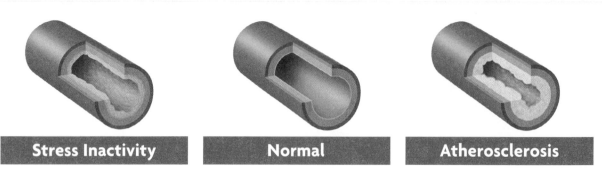

**Stress Inactivity** | **Normal** | **Atherosclerosis**

**Figure 18** The normal blood vessel in the middle has smooth, elastic walls. The vessel on the left has been damaged by stress and lack of use. On the right, the vessel has been partially filled by fat and cholesterol.

**Describe** What damage can hypertension do to blood vessels?

## Problems with Blood Pressure

Have you ever noticed what happens when water pressure to a faucet changes? The water either slows to a trickle or flows out much faster than expected. In a faucet, a short-term change in water pressure usually does not have a negative impact. However, changes in pressure can lead to life-threatening problems in the human circulatory system.

**Hypertension** Healthy blood vessels are elastic. When blood vessels lose elasticity, they cannot regulate blood flow as well. Sometimes the walls of blood vessels harden or vessels become blocked. This can lead to **hypertension** (HI pur ten shun), a dangerous rise in blood pressure caused by blockages in or the hardening of blood vessels. Since all organs are linked by the circulatory system, a dangerous rise in blood pressure can damage other organs. Hypertension is a disease caused by genetic and environmental factors. A diet high in saturated fat, cholesterol, and salt is one environmental cause that increases a person's risk of developing hypertension.

**Shock** As with high blood pressure, blood pressure that is too low can be very dangerous and life threatening. **Shock** is a condition in which a large amount of blood is lost, usually in a short **period** of time. Under certain circumstances, such as internal bleeding, a severe allergic reaction, or traumatic injury, blood leaves the vessels and shock occurs. When this happens, blood pressure decreases. The circulatory system, like a water hose, cannot function properly without pressure. The heart is not able to pump blood to all tissues without pressure. In some emergencies, shock is treated by stopping the blood loss and giving a blood transfusion, if blood loss has been severe.

**ACADEMIC VOCABULARY**
**period**
*(noun)* an amount of time
*In a short period of time, Hector was able to complete all of his science homework.*

 **Reading Check** Does shock cause an increase or a decrease in blood pressure?

# What have you learned?

Pressure on a surface is determined by the area of the surface and the amount of force applied to it. Changing the air pressure in your lungs relative to atmospheric pressure allows you to breathe. The heart provides pressure to pump blood through the body in one direction. If blood pressure becomes too high, as can happen when blood vessels become damaged, organs including the heart can become damaged from hypertension. If blood is lost due to a sudden injury, the drop in blood pressure due to shock can also be life-threatening.

# LESSON 2 Review

## Summarize

Create your own lesson summary as you design a **visual aid.**

1. **Write** the lesson title, number, and page numbers at the top of your poster.

2. **Scan** the lesson to find the **red** main headings. Organize these headings on your poster, leaving space between each.

3. **Design** an information box beneath each **red** heading. In the box, list 2–3 details, key terms, and definitions from each **blue** subheading.

4. **Illustrate** your poster with diagrams of important structures or processes next to each information box.

 ELA7: W 2.5

##  Standards Check

### Using Vocabulary

1. Use *pressure* in a scientific sentence. **6.j**

### Understanding Main Ideas

2. **State** the purpose of valves in the heart and the veins. **6.j**

3. **Describe** a situation in which you need to use pressure to accomplish a task. **6.j**

4. Choose the correct flow of blood through the heart. **6.j**

   **A.** left atrium, left ventricle, right atrium, right ventricle

   **B.** left ventricle, left atrium, right atrium, right ventricle

   **C.** right atrium, right ventricle, left atrium, left ventricle

   **D.** right ventricle, right atrium, left atrium, left ventricle

5. **Assess** the importance of pressure on our survivial. **6.j**

6. **Organize Information** Copy and complete the chart below, distinguishing the difference between hypertension and shock. **6.j**

| Disease | |
|---|---|
| Hypertension | |
| Shock | |

### Applying Science

7. **Predict** what would happen if blood flow in your body suddenly stopped. **6.j**

8. **Applying Math** If your heart beats 70 times per minute, predict how many times it will beat in an hour. **6.j**

**Science** nline

For more practice, visit **Standards Check** at ca7.msscience.com.

# MiniLab

# How does the cardiopulmonary system work?

## Procedure

1. Read and complete a lab safety form.

2. Obtain **tubing, bulbs,** and **sponges** to model blood vessels, the heart, and the lungs.

3. Before you test your model, make some predictions:

   - Will narrow or wide tubing allow more water through? Why?

   - Will the size of the bulb affect the amount of water pumped in one squeeze? How?

   - Will sponges hold more water if they are very dry or slightly damp? Justify your answer.

4. Collect the following data three times and average:

   - amount of water that can be pumped with one squeeze

   - amount of water in model with dry and wet sponges

5. Create a class data table to record the information from step 4.

## Analysis

1. **Identify** why these materials were chosen to make the model.

2. **Describe** the model system, including size and length of tubing and size of bulb, that produced the highest pressure. How did you determine which pressure was the highest?

3. **Decide** if the sponges absorbed more water when they were dry or when they were damp. Do you think the lungs are dry or wet, based on your experiments?

 **Science Content Standards**

**5.b** Students know organ systems function because of the contributions of individual organs, tissues, and cells. The failure of any part can affect the entire system.

**6.j** Students know that contractions of the heart generate blood pressure and that heart valves prevent backflow of blood in the circulatory system.

**7.a** Select and use appropriate tools and technology (including calculators, computers, balances, spring scales, microscopes, and binoculars) to perform tests, collect data, and display data.

# Applying Math

## Blood Pressure Variations

Blood pressure is the pressure of blood against the walls of the blood vessels as the blood moves through them. Blood pressure is measured with a sphygmomanometer (sfig moh muh NAH muh tur). Systolic pressure, the top number, is the pressure on your arteries when your heart is forcing blood through them. The bottom number, the diastolic pressure, is the pressure in your arteries when your heart relaxes. The following graph shows the blood pressure measurements of a man during an eight-hour time period.

### Example

Use the graph to determine if the systolic blood pressure changed during the time between 3 P.M. and 6 P.M. If so, by how much did it change?

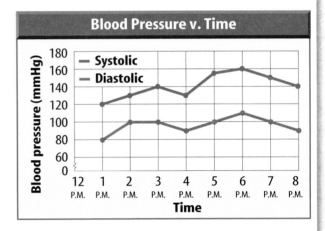

| What you know: | 3 P.M.: 140 mmHg |
| | 6 P.M.: 160 mmHg |
| What you want to know: | the difference between those measures |
| Subtract: | $160 - 140 = 20$ mmHg |

**Answer:** The systolic blood pressure increased by 20 mmHg during the time between 3 P.M. and 6 P.M.

### Practice Problems

1. According to the graph, at which time of day was the systolic blood pressure the highest?
2. According to the graph, what was the range for diastolic blood pressure during that eight-hour time period?

For more math practice, visit Math Practice at ca7.msscience.com.

## Model and Invent:
# What happens when the cardiopulmonary system breaks down?

### Materials

bulbs or turkey baster

plastic tubing

sponges

beaker

### Safety Precautions

### Science Content Standards

**5.b** Students know organ systems function because of the contributions of individual organs, tissues, and cells. The failure of any part can affect the entire system.

**6.j** Students know that contractions of the heart generate blood pressure and that heart valves prevent backflow of blood in the circulatory system.

**Also covers:** 7.a, 7.c, 7.e

## Problem

Diseases affecting the cardiopulmonary system, including heart attacks and strokes, are among the leading causes of death in the United States. Using your knowledge of this important organ system, investigate different ways the system can break down.

## Form a Hypothesis

➤ **Review** the data you collected in the Lesson 2 MiniLab or examine the model your teacher will show you.

➤ **Predict** which part of the model is most vulnerable and which could withstand the most damage before failing. Which variable would be most affected?

## Collect Data and Make Observations

1. Read and complete a lab safety form.

2. Using the bulb, tubing, and sponge your teacher will distribute, recreate the model from the Lesson 2 MiniLab.

3. Use the data collected in the Lesson 2 MiniLab as your control model.

4. Now create a model of cardiopulmonary disease. Decide the best way to model that disease.

5. Add to the data table from step 3, and record the mL of water that can be pumped with one squeeze. Collect data three times and average the results.

## Analyze and Conclude

1. **Interpret Your Data** Explain how the disease model is different from the control model. What variables did you change? What variables remained the same? Compare the averaged data.

2. **Explain** why you chose to model your disease in this manner.

3. **Identify** the strengths and weaknesses of your model.

4. **Describe and explain** the differences between your control data and your disease data. Which variable changed the most? Was your hypothesis supported?

5. **Compare** your disease model data to that of your classmates. Which "disease" seemed to have the greatest effect on the data when compared with the control data?

6. **Formulate** a model on paper that would show the effects of regular exercise. Would this model be able to withstand more or less damage than your disease model?

## Communicate

**WRITING in Science**  ELA7: W 2.3

**Share your Data** Summarize your procedure, data, and interpretation in a 500- to 700-word report, using the cardiopulmonary disease you modeled as a title. Present it to the class.

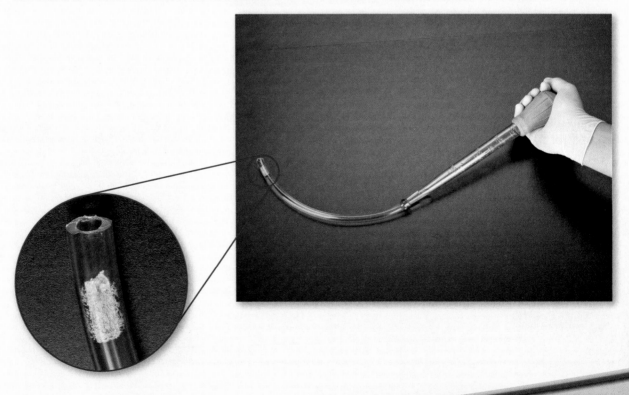

# Real World Science

Science & Career

## A Surgical Pioneer

Although the Great Depression prevented Vivien Thomas from going to medical school, he proved that intelligence, hard work, and creativity can produce extraordinary results. He was able to overcome racial prejudice to become a surgical researcher, instructor, and inventor. His important work led to a more complete understanding of shock, and helped pioneer heart surgery to cure the heart defect causing "blue baby syndrome."

Visit **Careers** at **ca7.msscience.com** to research Vivien Thomas's life, career, and achievements. Then write a help-wanted advertisement for which only Mr. Thomas would be qualified.

 **ELA7:** W 2.5

## Have a Heart

If donated hearts are old or diseased, they often cannot be used for transplant into the roughly 3,000 patients on the national waiting list. Dr. Hillel Laks at UCLA uses these "alternate" hearts for people who would be rejected as transplant patients. Some people think it is unfair to give anyone a "second-rate" heart.

Visit **Technology** at **ca7.msscience.com** to learn more about this issue. Then stage a debate between the "pro" side, that the transplants are valuable, and the "con" side, that they are discriminatory.

 **ELA7:** LS 2.4

Science & Technology

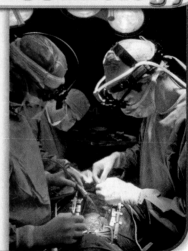

# The Blood Course of a Horse

Without adequate blood pressure, nothing in the cardio-pulmonary system can work. The first time blood pressure was measured, it was for a horse. Reverend Stephen Hales made this first measurement in 1733 by inserting a brass tube directly into the horse's vein. Luckily, things have progressed since then and doctors now use various nonin-vasive methods to take blood pressure measurements.

Blood pressure measurements have two numbers. A normal blood pressure is 120/90. Research what these numbers mean by visiting **History** at **ca7.msscience.com**. Then write a short report explaining them.

# Asthma in California

You probably know someone who has asthma, because California has the highest asthma rate in the country. In 2003 the rate was about 14.8 percent for people under 18. The disease causes the airways in the lungs to narrow, limiting the amount of air that gets in, which makes breathing difficult. An asthma attack is frightening and serious. Scientists think that certain types of air pollution can cause asthma attacks.

Make a bar graph comparing asthma rates in all of California with the rates for three California counties, including the one you live in. Find rates at **Society** at **ca7.msscience.com**.

## The BIG Idea

The pulmonary-circulatory system, driven by pressure generated by the heart, functions as a whole to supply oxygen to and remove carbon dioxide from your cells.

### Lesson 1 The Pulmonary-Circulatory System

5.b, 7.c

**Main Idea** The pulmonary and circulatory systems work together to transport oxygen to your cells and to remove carbon dioxide from your cells.

- The pulmonary system brings oxygen into the blood while helping dispose of carbon dioxide.
- The lungs are composed of small air sacs called alveoli, where gas exchange with the blood takes place.
- Problems in the pulmonary system usually involve a blockage in airflow and tissue death.
- The circulatory system transports blood to the tissues through blood vessels.
- The heart is the pump that keeps blood flowing constantly in the body.
- Problems in the circulatory system occur when blood flow stops and tissues cannot get necessary oxygen and nutrients.
- Lifestyle choices determine most of your risk for cardiovascular diseases.

- **artery** (p. 399)
- **asthma** (p. 396)
- **atrium** (p. 398)
- **breathing** (p. 393)
- **capillary** (p. 399)
- **circulatory system** (p. 397)
- **cardiovascular disease** (p. 400)
- **heart** (p. 398)
- **heart attack** (p. 400)
- **lungs** (p. 393)
- **pneumonia** (p. 394)
- **pulmonary system** (p. 392)
- **stroke** (p. 400)
- **suffocation** (p. 394)
- **vein** (p. 399)
- **ventricle** (p. 398)

### Lesson 2 Pressure and the Body

5.b, 6.j, 7.a, 7.c, 7.e

**Main Idea** Pressure allows us to breathe and keeps blood flowing throughout the circulatory system.

- Pressure is the amount of force divided by the area in which it is applied.
- Pressure changes with the amount of force applied to a surface or a change in the surface area upon which it is applied.
- Pressure in the circulatory system keeps blood flowing through your body.
- The heart and valves maintain pressure and blood movement in one direction.
- Changes in blood pressure are serious threats to good health.

- **hypertension** (p. 410)
- **pressure** (p. 405)
- **shock** (p. 410)

**STUDY TO GO** Download quizzes, key terms, and flash cards from **ca7.msscience.com.**

# Linking Vocabulary and Main Ideas

Use vocabulary terms from the previous page to complete this concept map.

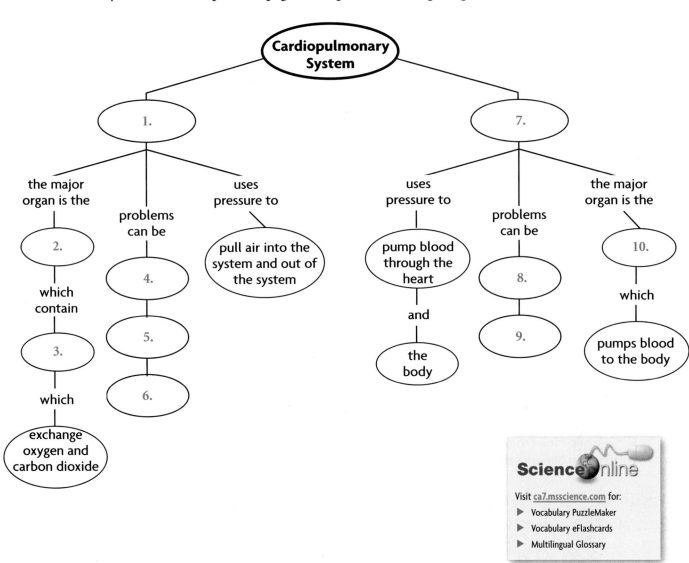

## Using Vocabulary

**Fill in the blanks with the correct vocabulary words.**

Blood vessels are located throughout the body to provide blood to the tissues. Three types of blood vessels are _____11._____, _____12._____, and _____13._____. The heart is made up of two _____14._____ and two _____15._____. _____16._____ drives the cardio-pulmonary system, ensuring that blood and air are where they are needed. Two problems that may arise if this fails are _____17._____, when the blood vessels are narrowed, and _____18._____, when not enough blood is pumping through the system.

Science Online

Visit ca7.msscience.com for:
▶ Vocabulary PuzzleMaker
▶ Vocabulary eFlashcards
▶ Multilingual Glossary

## Understanding Main Ideas

*Choose the word or phrase that best answers the question.*

1. What best describes the function of the lungs?
   A. to transport blood to the other side of the heart    `5.b`
   B. to pump blood through the body
   C. to prevent blood from flowing backward
   D. to provide a site for gas exchange with blood

2. If you hold your breath, what builds up as a waste material in your tissues?
   A. carbon dioxide    `5.b`
   B. oxygen
   C. sugars
   D. water

3. What is the name for the smallest blood vessels?
   A. arteries    `5.b`
   B. capillaries
   C. atria
   D. veins

4. What is the function of the right atrium?
   A. to pump blood to the arteries    `5.b`
   B. to pump blood to the veins
   C. to pump blood to the left atrium
   D. to pump blood to the right ventricle

5. The figure below shows an area of the lungs.

   What is this area in the lungs called?
   A. diaphragm    `5.b`
   B. trachea
   C. alveoli
   D. capillaries

6. The arrow in the figure below is pointing to a specific structure of the heart.

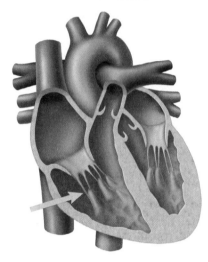

   What is the function of this structure?
   A. to pump blood to the body tissues    `5.b`
   B. to pump blood to the left atrium
   C. to pump blood to the left ventricle
   D. to pump blood to the lungs

7. The circulatory system is important for transporting nutrients and oxygen-rich blood through the body. What is another function of the circulatory system?
   A. to absorb nutrients from the air    `5.b`
   B. to absorb oxygen from the air
   C. to transport air to the lungs
   D. to transport carbon dioxide to the lungs

8. Which is the definition of pressure?
   A. area divided by force    `6.j`
   B. force divided by volume
   C. area divided by length
   D. force divided by length

9. Which describes how blood moves into the circulatory system?
   A. high pressure to low pressure    `6.j`
   B. low pressure to high pressure
   C. left to right
   D. top to bottom

## Applying Science

**10.** **Explain** the function of capillaries. `5.b`

**11.** **Diagram** how carbon dioxide and oxygen are exchanged across the membrane in alveoli. `5.b`

**12.** **Compare and contrast** a heart attack and a stroke. `5.b`

**13.** **Hypothesize** whether the brain or the heart has a higher rate of oxygen consumption. `5.b`

**14.** **Decide** if breathing and heart pumping are voluntary or involuntary processes. `5.b`

**15.** **Describe** some possible problems in the pulmonary system. `5.b`

**16.** **Describe** how this ballet dancer, in the image below, can decrease the pressure on the toes. Why is the pressure decreased? `6.j`

**17.** **Describe** the pressure inside the chamber "squeezing" the blood during the contraction phase of a heartbeat. `6.j`

**18.** **Form a plan** to reduce blood pressure in a person with hypertension. `6.j`

**19.** **Choose** the group of veins that would most need valves to prevent backflow: those running from the head to the heart or those running from the feet to the heart. Why? `6.j`

**20.** **Give a reason** why it is important to keep blood flow constant and moving in one direction through the body. `6.j`

**21.** **Hypothesize** why the ventricles of the heart are more muscular than the atria. `6.j`

### *WRITING in* ▸ Science

**22.** Write a paragraph summarizing the pressure changes that occur in the heart during one cycle. `ELA7: W 2.5`

## Cumulative Review

**23.** **List** the three classes of levers and give an example of each. `6.h`

**24.** **Describe** how the heart muscle contracts. `5.a`

**25.** **Identify** how the skeletal and muscular systems interact. `5.c`

## Applying Math

Use the graph below to answer questions 25–29.

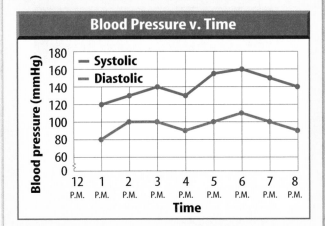

**Blood Pressure v. Time**

**26.** According to the graph, which time of day is the diastolic blood pressure the highest? `MA7: 1.2`

**27.** According to the graph, which time of the day is the man in question most active? `MA7: 1.2`

**28.** How does the systolic blood pressure change between 1 PM and 2 PM? `MA7: 1.2`

**29.** How does the diastolic blood pressure change between 1 PM and 2 PM? `MA7: 1.2`

**30.** How does the systolic blood pressure change between 2 PM and 3 PM? `MA7: 1.2`

**1** Which is the movement of the chest that brings air into the lungs and removes waste gases?

A breathing

B expiration

C oxidation

D respiration  5.b

Use the table below, which shows the heart rate of a student, Ashley, while performing different activities, to answer questions 2 and 3.

**Results from Ashley's Activities**

| Activity | Pulse Rate (beats/min) | Body Temperature | Degree of Sweating |
|---|---|---|---|
| 1 | 80 | 98.6° F | None |
| 2 | 90 | 98.8° F | Minimal |
| 3 | 100 | 98.9° F | Little |
| 4 | 120 | 99.1° F | Moderate |
| 5 | 150 | 99.5° F | Considerable |

**2** Which activity indicates that Ashley was exercising vigorously?

A Activity 2

B Activity 3

C Activity 4

D Activity 5  5.b

**3** Which activity was Ashley *most likely* performing during Activity 2?

A marching

B resting

C sprinting

D walking slowly  5.b

**4** Which statement *best* describes the interaction between the circulatory and respiratory systems?

A Blood carries carbon dioxide from the body cells to the lungs.

B Blood carries carbon dioxide from the lungs to the body cells.

C Blood carries oxygen from the body cells to the lungs.

D Blood carries oxygen from the heart to the lungs.  5.b

**5** The illustration below shows part of a human's circulatory system.

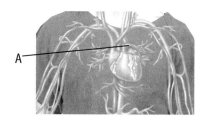

What might happen if vessel A became blocked?

A Blood could not flow to the body.

B Blood could not flow to the lungs.

C Blood could not return to the heart from the body.

D Blood could not return to the heart from the lungs.  5.b

**6** Which gases are exchanged between an alveolus and a capillary?

A carbon dioxide and oxygen

B carbon dioxide and water

C nitrogen and oxygen

D water and oxygen  5.b

Use the illustration of the interior of the heart below to answer questions 7–9.

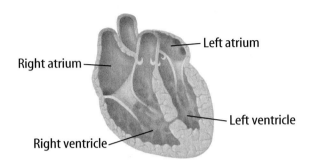

Right atrium — 
Left atrium
Left ventricle
Right ventricle —

**7** **What is wrong with the heart in the illustration above?**

 **A** The left atrium is too small.

 **B** The left ventricle wall is too thick.

 **C** There is a hole between the ventricles

 **D** The right atrium is too big.      5.b

**8** **How does this defect prevent normal blood flow?**

 **A** The blood will circulate only within the heart.

 **B** It allows the blood in the ventricles to mix.

 **C** The pressure in the heart is decreased.

 **D** The pressure in the heart is increased.      6.j

**9** **Why does the left ventricle pump blood with more pressure than the right ventricle?**

 **A** It has a greater surface area.

 **B** More oxygen in the blood creates more pressure.

 **C** The blood only has to travel a short distance.

 **D** The more muscular wall pumps with more force.      6.j

Use the image below of a dancer to answer questions 10 and 11.

Force = 530 N
Area = 37 cm²

**10** **Why is the pressure exerted on the floor by the dancer greater when she is on her toes?**

 **A** The area is greater.

 **B** The area is smaller.

 **C** The force is greater.

 **D** The force is smaller.      6.j

**11** **Compare the pressure the dancer would exert on the floor if she was wearing large clown shoes rather than the shoes in the photo.**

 **A** force would be divided by a larger area, less pressure

 **B** force would be divided by a larger area, more pressure

 **C** force would be divided by a smaller area, less pressure

 **D** force would be divided by a smaller area, more pressure      6.j

# The Eye and Light

## The BIG Idea

Light is a wave that interacts with everything you see.

**LESSON 1** 6.a, 6.e
### What is light?
**Main Idea** Visible light is an electromagnetic wave.

**LESSON 2** 6.b, 6.c, 6.f, 6.g
### Light and Matter
**Main Idea** Light interacts with matter in different ways.

**LESSON 3** 6.d
### Using Lenses
**Main Idea** Lenses form images by causing light rays to bend.

**LESSON 4** 5.g, 6.b, 6.d, 6.e
### The Eye and Vision
**Main Idea** The eye is a complex organ made up of different parts.

## Seeing the Light

The Sun looks like a glowing yellow ball as it sets behind the Golden Gate Bridge in San Francisco, California. You see the light waves emitted by the Sun and other light sources when these light waves enter your eyes. Your eyes are made of structures that function together to enable you to see the world around you.

**Science Journal** List five things that emit light.

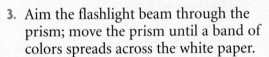

## Can you make a rainbow?

What colors are produced when white light passes through a prism?

### Procedure

1. Complete a lab safety form.

2. Place a **prism** between a **flashlight** and a sheet of clean **white paper.**

3. Aim the flashlight beam through the prism; move the prism until a band of colors spreads across the white paper.

4. In your Science Journal, draw the colors you observe in order and identify each.

5. Determine if you can change the order of the colors.

### Think About This

- **Describe** how the order of colors changed as the direction of the flashlight beam changed.

- **Infer** which color light waves have changed direction the most and the least after passing through the prism.

 6.e

## Science Online

Visit ca7.msscience.com to:

▶ view **Concepts in Motion**

▶ explore Virtual Labs

▶ access content-related Web links

▶ take the Standards Check

**The Eye** Make the following Foldable to record the structure and function of the different parts of the eye.

**STEP 1 Fold** a sheet of paper in half lengthwise.

**STEP 2 Cut** along the first line and then every fifth or sixth line of the top flap to form seven tabs.

### Reading Skill

#### Visualizing

As you read this chapter, list the names of the parts of the eye on the tabs. Beneath each tab, describe the structure and function of that part.

# Get Ready to Read

## Compare and Contrast

**①Learn It!** Good readers compare and contrast information as they read. This means they look for similarities and differences to help them to remember important ideas. Look for signal words in the text to let you know when the author is comparing or contrasting.

### Compare and Contrast Signal Words

| Compare | Contrast |
|---|---|
| as | but |
| like | or |
| likewise | unlike |
| similarly | however |
| at the same time | although |
| in a similar way | on the other hand |

**②Practice It!** Read the excerpt below and notice how the author uses contrast signal words to describe the differences between the refraction of different wavelengths by a prism.

> When white light passes through the prism, light waves with **different** wavelengths are refracted by **different** amounts. Violet light waves have the **shortest** wavelengths and are bent the **most.** Red light waves are bent the **least.**

**③Apply It!** Compare and contrast the concave lens and the convex lens on page 443.

# Target Your Reading

**Use this to focus on the main ideas as you read the chapter.**

**Reading Tip**

As you read, use other skills, such as summarizing and connecting, to help you understand comparisons and contrasts.

**1 Before you read** the chapter, respond to the statements below on your worksheet or on a numbered sheet of paper.

• Write an **A** if you **agree** with the statement.

• Write a **D** if you **disagree** with the statement.

**2 After you read** the chapter, look back to this page to see if you've changed your mind about any of the statements.

• If any of your answers changed, explain why.

• Change any false statements into true statements.

• Use your revised statements as a study guide.

**Science Online**

Print a worksheet of this page at ca7.msscience.com.

| Before You Read A or D | Statement | After You Read A or D |
|---|---|---|
| | **1** Light always travels at the same speed. | |
| | **2** Light can travel through empty space. | |
| | **3** Light rays always travel in straight lines from one point to another. | |
| | **4** Only shiny objects, such as mirrors, reflect light. | |
| | **5** The color of an object depends on the light the object reflects. | |
| | **6** The human eye sends light out to objects and detects the light that is reflected back to the eye. | |
| | **7** Three colors of light can be mixed together to make almost all the colors that you see. | |
| | **8** Eyeglasses magnify objects so the eyes can see them. | |
| | **9** The lens in the human eye does not change shape. | |
| | **10** Not eating enough leafy, green vegetables is the most common cause of the inability to see colors. | |

### Science Content Standards

**6.a** Students know visible light is a small band within a very broad electromagnetic spectrum.

**6.e** Students know that white light is a mixture of many wavelengths (colors) and that retinal cells react differently to different wavelengths.

## Reading Guide

### What *You'll Learn*

▶ **Describe** the properties of light waves.

▶ **Identify** the different types of waves in the electromagnetic spectrum.

▶ **Explain** what makes light appear as different colors.

### Why *It's Important*

Electromagnetic waves allow you to see, listen to the radio, and talk on a cellular phone.

### Vocabulary
wavelength
frequency
medium
electromagnetic spectrum

### Review Vocabulary
**emit:** to give off

# What is light?

**Main Idea** Visible light is an electromagnetic wave.

**Real-World Reading Connection** Imagine you are standing on a beach watching giant waves rolling toward you. As they reach the beach, you hear them crashing down and feel them pound the sand. The energy that shakes the ground and creates the noise is energy transferred by the waves. Light is also a type of wave that transfers energy from one place to another.

## Light Transfers Energy

Think about what happens when you throw a rock into a still pool of water, as in **Figure 1.** The rock hits the water and changes, or disturbs, the flat surface of the pool. This disturbance is caused by the energy transferred to the water from the moving rock. As you watch, waves move outward from the place where the rock entered the water. These waves carry energy to other parts of the pool.

Similar to water waves, light waves also carry energy from place to place. A source of light, such as the candle shown in **Figure 1,** or the Sun, emits light waves. These waves spread out in all directions. Sometimes, however, it is easier to think of light in a different way. A light ray is a narrow beam of light that travels in a straight line. In **Figure 1,** the light rays emitted by the candle are represented by arrows. You can think of a source of light as emitting light rays that travel away from the source in all directions.

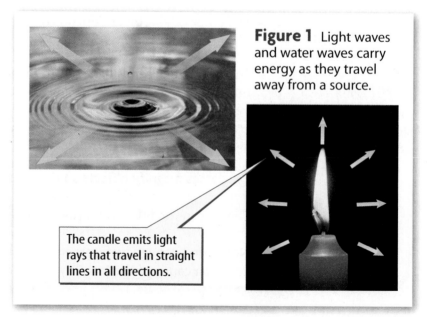

**Figure 1** Light waves and water waves carry energy as they travel away from a source.

The candle emits light rays that travel in straight lines in all directions.

## Parts of a Wave

**1** Imagine that you are holding one end of a rope that is attached to a wall, as shown in **Figure 2.** The rope is in its resting position when it is held so that it is perpendicular to the wall.

**2** Now, think about what happens when you move your end of the rope in a steady, up-and-down motion. You create a wave in the rope. The wave has a shape that looks like a sideways letter S repeating many times.

The highest points of the wave are called crests. The lowest points are called troughs. The distance between any two crests or any two troughs is called the **wavelength.** The amplitude of the wave is the distance from a crest or trough of the wave to the resting position.

## Frequency and Wavelength

As you move the rope up and down, you make crests and troughs that travel along the rope. The number of crests or troughs that pass a given point in one second is related to the frequency of the wave. The **frequency** (FREE kwun see) of a wave is the number of wavelengths that pass a given point in one second. The frequency of the wave on the rope is also equal to the number of times each second that your hand moves up, down, and up again.

**3** If you move your end of the rope more quickly, the frequency of the wave increases. Then the crests and troughs of the wave become closer together on the rope. This means that as the frequency of a wave increases, the wavelength decreases. The same is true for all waves, including light waves.

**4** If you move the end of the rope more slowly, the crests and troughs become more spread out. This means that the wavelength increases as the frequency decreases. This is true for all waves, including light waves. The lower a light wave's frequency, the greater its wavelength will be.

**Reading Check** How does the wavelength change as the frequency decreases?

**Figure 2** Waves are described by their frequency, wavelength, and amplitude.

**Explain** why the wavelength is shorter in the fourth drawing than in the third drawing.

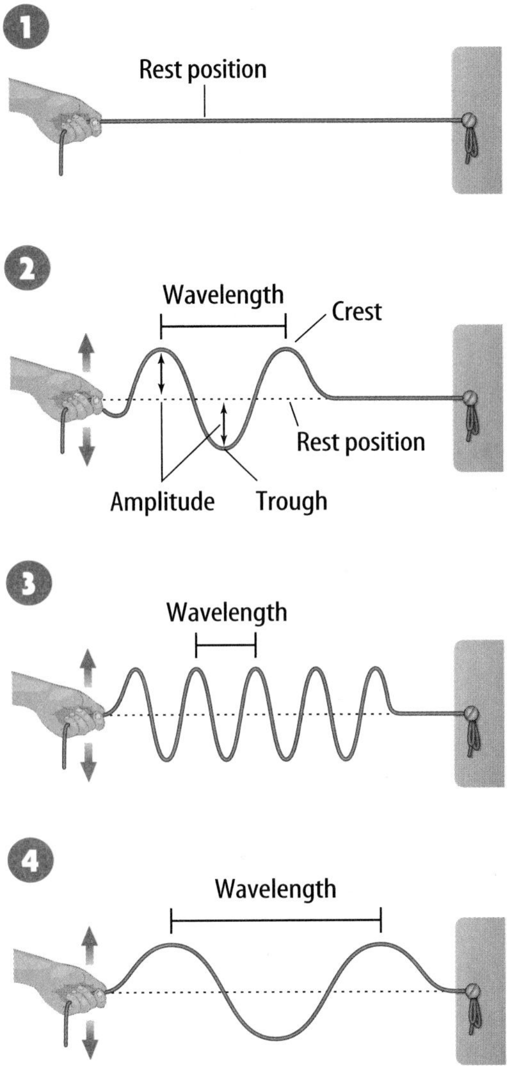

Light travels through solid glass.

Light travels through liquid water.

Light travels through air, a gas.

**Figure 3** To reach the boy's eye, a light ray reflected from the fish travels through a liquid, a solid, and a gas.

**SCIENCE USE V. COMMON USE**

**medium**

*Science Use* a material through which something moves. *Light waves don't need a medium in which to travel.*

*Common Use* being between two extremes or amounts, intermediate. *He listened to the CD at a medium volume.*

## Electromagnetic Waves

When you think of waves, you might think of ocean waves or waves transferred along a rope. In these examples, the substance through which the wave moves is called the **medium.** The medium through which ocean waves move is water. The medium through which the rope wave moves is the material that makes up the rope.

Light can travel through different mediums. As shown in **Figure 3,** light can travel through solids, liquids, and gases. Unlike water waves or waves on a rope, however, light can travel through empty space where there is no matter. Light is an electromagnetic wave, which is a type of wave that can travel in empty space as well as in matter.

# The Electromagnetic Spectrum

Like waves on a rope, electromagnetic waves have a range of wavelengths and frequencies. The entire range of electromagnetic waves of different wavelengths and frequencies is called the **electromagnetic spectrum** (ih lek troh mag NEH tik • SPEK trum).

## A Range of Wavelengths

As shown in **Figure 4,** the electromagnetic spectrum includes all electromagnetic waves arranged from those with the longest wavelengths to those with the shortest wavelengths. Because frequency increases as wavelength decreases, the electromagnetic spectrum is also arranged in order of increasing frequency.

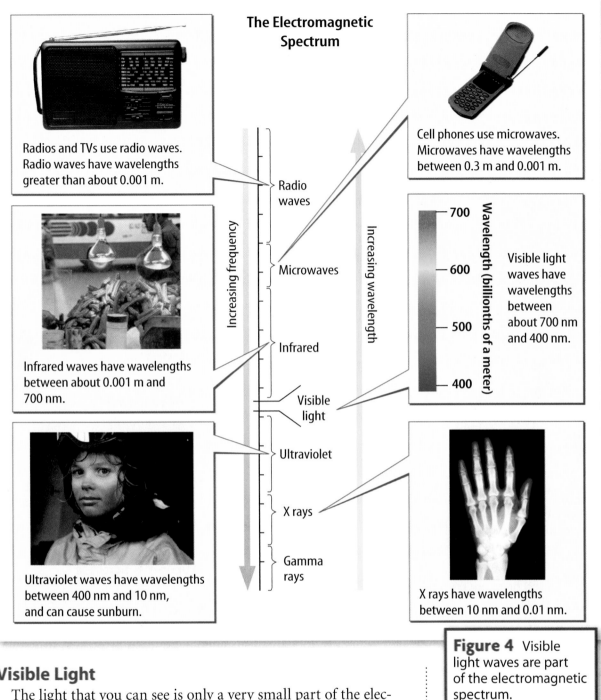

**The Electromagnetic Spectrum**

Radios and TVs use radio waves. Radio waves have wavelengths greater than about 0.001 m.

Cell phones use microwaves. Microwaves have wavelengths between 0.3 m and 0.001 m.

Infrared waves have wavelengths between about 0.001 m and 700 nm.

Visible light waves have wavelengths between about 700 nm and 400 nm.

Ultraviolet waves have wavelengths between 400 nm and 10 nm, and can cause sunburn.

X rays have wavelengths between 10 nm and 0.01 nm.

Increasing frequency

Increasing wavelength

Radio waves
Microwaves
Infrared
Visible light
Ultraviolet
X rays
Gamma rays

Wavelength (billionths of a meter)
700
600
500
400

**Figure 4** Visible light waves are part of the electromagnetic spectrum.

## Visible Light

The light that you can see is only a very small part of the electromagnetic spectrum. **Figure 4** shows the visible light spectrum, which is the range of electromagnetic waves human eyes can detect. Visible light has wavelengths that are so short they are usually measured in units of nanometers (nm). One nanometer equals one billionth of a meter. The wavelengths of visible light waves **range** from about 700 nm to about 400 nm, which is about 100 times smaller than the width of a human hair. Colors that you can see depend on the wavelengths of the light waves that enter the eye.

 **Figure 4** What wavelength of light is red? What wavelength of light is blue?

**ACADEMIC VOCABULARY**
range (RAYNJ)
*(verb)* to change or differ within limits
*From sunrise to sunset, the temperature ranged from 10°C to 25°C.*

# Visible Light and the Electromagnetic Spectrum

The light that human eyes can see is only a small part of an electromagnetic spectrum. The entire electromagnetic spectrum ranges from waves with wavelengths of thousands of meters to waves whose wavelength is less than the width of an atom. In fact, the electromagnetic spectrum has no upper or lower limits. All electromagnetic waves, whether part of the visible spectrum or some other part of the electromagnetic spectrum, transfer energy as they travel from one place to another.

# LESSON 1 Review

## Summarize

Create your own lesson summary as you design a **study web.**

1. **Write** the lesson title, number, and page numbers at the top of a sheet of paper.

2. **Scan** the lesson to find the **red** main headings.

3. **Organize** these headings clockwise on branches around the lesson title.

4. **Review** the information under each **red** heading to design a branch for each **blue** subheading.

5. **List** 2–3 details, key terms, and definitions from each **blue** subheading on branches extending from the main heading branches.

 ELA6: R 2.4

## Standards Check

### Using Vocabulary

1. Define *electromagnetic spectrum* in your own words. **6.a**

2. The _____ is the material through which a wave travels.

### Understanding Main Ideas

3. **State** two different kinds of electromagnetic waves. **6.a**

4. **Describe** the relationship between wavelength and frequency. **6.a**

5. **Organize** Copy and fill in the graphic organizer below. In each oval, list a different part of the electromagnetic spectrum. **6.a**

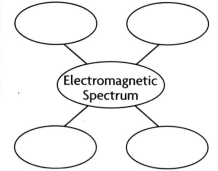

Electromagnetic Spectrum

6. In which does light travel the fastest? **6.a**
   A. air
   B. empty space
   C. diamonds
   D. light always travels at the same speed

7. **Give an example** of an electromagnetic wave that has a wavelength longer than visible light. **6.a**

### Applying Science

8. **Predict** how the speed of a light wave changes as it travels from the Sun, through Earth's atmosphere, to a fish in the ocean. **6.a**

9. **Defend the statement** "Electromagnetic waves transfer energy." Give two examples of how electromagnetic waves cause changes in materials. **6.a**

## Science Online

For more practice, visit **Standards Check** at <u>ca7.msscience.com</u>.

Color   ca7.msscience.com   Brain POP

# Applying Math

## Scientific Notation

6.a, 6.e

MA7: NS 1.1, NS 1.2, MR 2.5

Scientific notation is a way to write large and small numbers. A number written in scientific notation has the form $M \times 10^N$.

To convert a large number to scientific notation, move the decimal point to the left until there is only one nonzero digit to the left of the decimal point. Then N is the number of places you moved the decimal point and is a positive number.

To convert a small number to scientific notation, move the decimal point to the right until there is only one nonzero digit to the left of the decimal point. Then N is the number of places you moved the decimal point and is a negative number.

### Examples

To write the number 92,700 in scientific notation, follow these steps:

**1** Write the number in scientific notation form with a decimal point at the end: $92,700. \times 10^N$

**2** Count the number of places you move the decimal point until there is only one nonzero digit to the left of the decimal point. Here, the decimal point moves four places to the left: $9.2700 \times 10^N$

**3** The decimal point moved four places to the left, so N = 4: $9.2700 \times 10^4$

**4** Delete the zeros at the end of the number: $9.27 \times 10^4$

To write the number 0.0013 in scientific notation, follow these steps:

**1** Write the number in scientific notation form: $0.0013 \times 10^N$

**2** Count the number of places you move the decimal point until there is only one nonzero digit to the left of the decimal point. Here, the decimal point moves three places to the right: $0001.3 \times 10^N$

**3** The decimal point three places to the right, so N = −3: $0001.3 \times 10^{-3}$

**4** Delete the zeros at the beginning of the number: $1.3 \times 10^{-3}$

### Practice Problems

1. The wavelength of an electromagnetic wave is 100,000 m. Express this wavelength in scientific notation.
2. The wavelength of an X ray is 0.000000001 m. Express this wavelength in scientific notation.

**Science** nline

For more math practice, visit **Math Practice** at ca7.msscience.com.

# DataLab

# Can you identify waves in the electromagnetic spectrum?

The wavelengths of waves in the electromagnetic spectrum range from large numbers to small numbers. One way to write large or small numbers is to use scientific notation. For more help in using scientific notation, see the Applying Math feature on the previous page.

## Data

Copy the data table below and complete the second column.

| Wavelengths of Different Waves | | | |
|---|---|---|---|
| Wave Number | Wavelength in Decimal Form (nm) | Wavelength in Scientific Notation (nm) | Type of Electromagnetic Wave/Color of Visible Light |
| 1 | 560 | | |
| 2 | 5,500 | | |
| 3 | 71 | | |
| 4 | 420 | | |
| 5 | 10,800 | | |

## Data Analysis

1. **Use Figure 4** on page 429 to determine the type of electromagnetic wave represented in each row. If the wave is in the visible spectrum, identify its color.

2. **Determine** the wavelength, in scientific notation, of a wave whose wavelength is 10 times longer than wave #3.

 **Science Content Standards**

**6.a** Students know visible light is a small band within a very broad electromagnetic spectrum.

**6.b** Students know that for an object to be seen, light emitted by or scattered from it must be detected by the eye.

**6.c** Students know light travels in straight lines if the medium it travels through does not change.

**6.f** Students know light can be reflected, refracted, transmitted, and absorbed by matter.

**6.g** Students know the angle of reflection of a light beam is equal to the angle of incidence.

## Reading Guide

### What *You'll Learn*

▶ **Describe** what happens to light when it interacts with matter.

▶ **State** the law of reflection.

▶ **Distinguish** between refraction and reflection.

### Why *It's Important*

The way light interacts with matter affects how objects look.

### Vocabulary

absorption
transmission
scattering
refraction
law of reflection

### Review Vocabulary

**energy:** the ability to cause change (Grade 6)

# Light and Matter

**Main Idea** Light interacts with matter in different ways.

**Real-World Reading Connection** When you look around the room, light that enters your eyes comes from different objects. You might see sunlight passing through the glass in a window or your reflection in a mirror. How does the light from these objects reach your eyes?

## The Interaction of Light and Matter

Have you ever seen a pinball machine? When the ball is launched, it enters a field of obstacles. It then rolls in straight lines until it hits a bumper. Then it bounces in a different direction. Sometimes the ball goes into a hole and then is shot out a short time later. Light rays behave in some similar ways. When light rays hit matter, they can be absorbed by the matter, be reflected, or pass right through the material.

All electromagnetic waves, including light, transfer energy from one place to another. **Figure 5** shows an industrial laser that uses the energy carried by infrared waves to cut through steel. When light waves hit a material, some of the energy carried by the light waves is transferred to the atoms or molecules in the material. Atoms can absorb some of this energy so that the material becomes warmer. Atoms can also absorb some of the light energy and then emit new light waves.

**Figure 5** The energy carried by infrared waves from this laser causes the steel to melt.

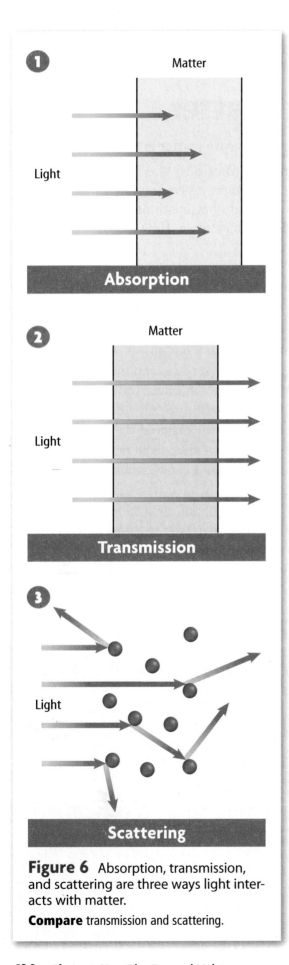

**Figure 6** Absorption, transmission, and scattering are three ways light interacts with matter.

**Compare** transmission and scattering.

### ❶ Absorption of Light

On a sunny day, an asphalt parking lot can be very hot. The asphalt is hot because some of the energy carried by sunlight is absorbed by the asphalt. As shown in **Figure 6,** when light rays hit a material, some of the light ray's energy is transferred to the atoms in the material. This transfer of energy can cause the temperature of the material to increase. The process of transferring light energy to the atoms or molecules in a material is called **absorption** (ub SORP shun).

The amount of energy absorbed when light rays strike a material depends on the types of atoms in the material. The amount of energy absorbed also depends on the wavelengths of light. The atoms in asphalt absorb more energy from sunlight than the atoms in grass. As a result, the asphalt becomes hotter than grass.

### ❷ Transmission of Light

When you look through a window, you see objects on the other side of the glass. Light waves from these objects pass through the glass and enter your eyes. Instead of being absorbed by the glass, these light waves are transmitted through the glass. **Transmission** occurs when light waves strike a material and pass through it. Whether light waves are transmitted or absorbed by a material depends on the wavelength of the light waves that strike the material. Some materials, like glass, transmit only certain wavelengths. Other materials do not transmit any light waves.

### ❸ Scattering of Light

Have you ever noticed dust particles in a beam of sunlight? When the light waves in a sunbeam strike a dust particle, two things happen. First, they are absorbed by the dust particle, and then they are emitted. The light rays that are emitted travel in all directions. **Scattering** occurs when a material causes light waves traveling in one direction to travel in all directions. When the light waves in a sunbeam strike a dust particle, they are scatted in all directions. You see the dust particle as a bright speck of light when some of these scattered light waves enter your eye.

**Opaque**

**Translucent**

**Transparent**

## Opaque, Transparent, and Translucent Materials

The three candleholders in **Figure 7** are made of different materials. These materials absorb, transmit, and scatter light in different ways. The candleholder on the left is made from an opaque material. An opaque material only absorbs and reflects light—no light is transmitted through it. The middle candleholder is translucent. A translucent material allows some light to pass through, but scatters light so you cannot see clearly through it. The candleholder on the right is transparent—it transmits nearly all the light that strikes it.

## The Speed of Light in Different Materials

Light waves and all electromagnetic waves travel through empty space at a speed of about 300,000 km/s. This speed is called the speed of light. No object or wave can move faster than the speed of light in empty space.

However, when light waves travel in matter, they move more slowly. **Figure 8** compares the speed of light in different materials. Light waves slow down in a material because they interact with the atoms and molecules in the material.

 **Reading Check** Under what conditions does light travel fastest?

**Figure 7** The amount of light absorbed, reflected, and transmitted is different for opaque, transparent, and translucent objects.

**Compare** the amount of light that is transmitted through these three different candleholders.

**Figure 8** Light travels at different speeds in different materials.

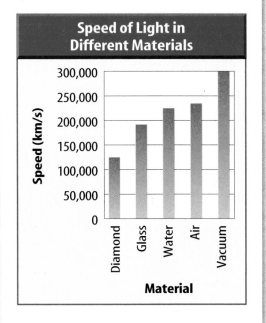

**Speed of Light in Different Materials**

Speed (km/s)

| Diamond | Glass | Water | Air | Vacuum |

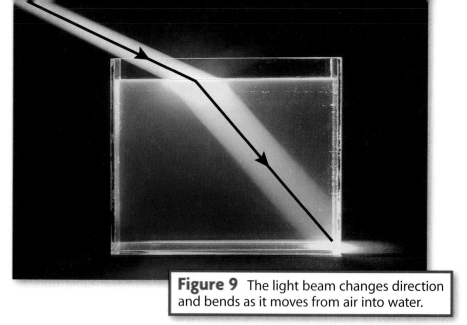

**Figure 9** The light beam changes direction and bends as it moves from air into water.

# Refraction

When light rays move from one medium to another, such as from air to water as shown in **Figure 9,** they can change direction. **Refraction** (rih FRAK shun) occurs when a light ray changes direction when it moves from one material into another.

## Refraction and Speed Changes

Why does the light beam in **Figure 9** change direction? Light waves change direction, or refract, whenever they change speed in moving from one medium into another. The light beam bends because light waves slow down as they move from air into water. The greater the difference in speed between the two materials, the greater the amount of refraction. However, refraction does not occur for waves that are traveling perpendicular to the boundary between the materials. **Figure 10** shows how the refraction of light waves causes a straw in water to look like it is broken.

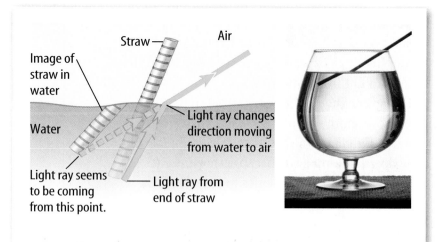

**Figure 10** The straw looks broken because light waves bend as they move from water into air.

**Figure 11** Prisms separate white light into the various colors of the visible spectrum.

## Refraction and the Visible Spectrum

A prism, like the one in **Figure 11,** is a piece of transparent glass or plastic that is usually shaped like a wedge. When light rays pass through the prism, they change direction. Light waves slow down as they move from air into the glass prism. This causes light waves to refract when they enter the prism. Light waves speed up and refract when they move from the prism back into the air.

Refraction produces the rainbow of colors shown in **Figure 11.** White light is a combination of all light waves in the visible light spectrum. When white light passes through the prism, light waves with different wavelengths are refracted by different amounts. Violet light waves have the shortest wavelengths and are bent the most. Red light waves are bent the least.

## White Light

You know that passing white light through a prism separates the white light into the visible light spectrum. But does the process work in reverse? Can you combine different colors of light to make white light? **Figure 12** shows that it is possible to make white light by mixing colored lights. You can also mix colors together to make other colors. For example, where the green and red light overlap, there is yellow light. Red, green, and blue light are called the **primary** colors of light. Almost any color of light can be made by mixing these three colors in different amounts.

**ACADEMIC VOCABULARY**
primary
(*adjective*) of first rank, importance, or value
*A firefighter's primary goal is to save people who are trapped in burning buildings.*

**Figure 12** White light can be made by combining the three primary colors of light.

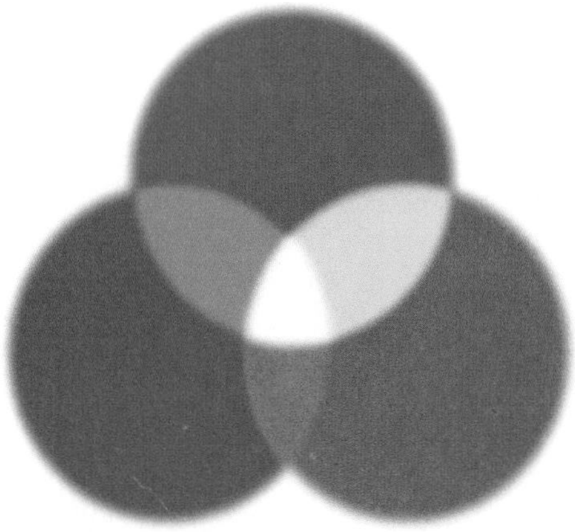

**Figure 13** All light waves obey the law of reflection.
**State** the relationship between the angle of incidence and the angle of reflection.

# Reflection

Light waves usually travel in straight lines in a material or through space. However, light waves can change direction when they speed up or slow down. Light waves also change direction when they are reflected from a surface. When light rays are reflected, the direction of the reflected ray depends on the direction of the incoming light ray that strikes the surface.

 What are the two ways light waves can change direction?

### The Law of Reflection

The direction of a reflected light ray is determined by the law of reflection, as shown in **Figure 13.** The incoming ray and the reflected ray make an angle with a line perpendicular to the surface. The line perpendicular to the surface is called the normal to the surface. The angle of incidence is the angle between the incoming light ray and the normal. The angle of reflection is the angle between the reflected ray and the normal. According to the **law of reflection** (rih FLEK shun), when a light ray is reflected from a surface, the angle of incidence equals the angle of reflection. Light rays reflected from all surfaces always obey the law of reflection.

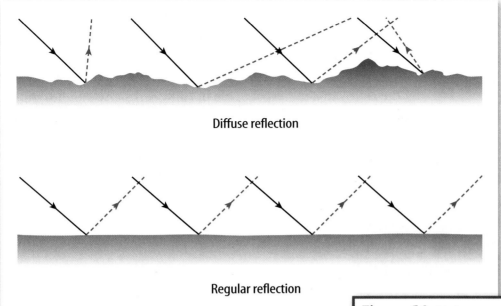
Diffuse reflection

Regular reflection

**Figure 14** Light rays always obey the law of reflection, even if the surface is rough.

## Regular and Diffuse Reflection

Although the surface of a sheet of paper might seem smooth, it's not as smooth as the surface of a mirror. **Figure 14** shows how the rough paper surface reflects light rays in many directions. Each light ray reflected from the uneven surface of the paper obeys the law of reflection. But each one hits a surface that is at a slightly different angle. This means the light rays that are parallel before they hit the surface end up going many different directions after they strike the surface. This reflection from a rough surface is called diffuse reflection.

However, the smooth surface of a mirror reflects parallel light rays so that they remain parallel. Reflection from a mirror is called regular reflection. Whether a surface is rough or smooth, all light rays that strike the surface obey the law of reflection.

 Explain how diffuse reflection is different from regular reflection.

## Reflection and Color

Look around the room. Notice the colors of different objects. Why do some things look red while others appear green? **Figure 15** illustrates why different objects have different colors. As white light strikes an object, some of the light is absorbed and some is reflected. The reflected light is what enters your eyes and causes you to see the object. For example, what makes the flower look red? The flower looks red because the materials in the flower absorb all wavelengths of light except red. The red light is reflected to your eyes, and you see the flower as red.

**Figure 15** The color of an object depends on the wavelengths of light that are reflected by the object.

# What have you learned?

In this lesson, you read about the different ways light can interact with matter. All objects that you see either reflect light or are sources of light. The energy carried by light waves can be absorbed by the atoms in a material. Some of this energy also can be emitted by atoms as new light waves. The interaction of light and matter causes light waves to be reflected and refracted. Light passes through a transparent material, is partially scattered by a translucent object, and does not pass through an opaque object.

# LESSON 2 Review

## Summarize

Create your own lesson summary as you write a script for a **television news report.**

1. **Review** the text after the **red** main headings and write one sentence about each. These are the headlines of your broadcast.

2. **Review** the text and write 2–3 sentences about each **blue** subheading. These sentences should tell *who, what, when, where,* and *why* information about each **red** heading.

3. **Include** descriptive details in your report, such as names of reporters and local places and events.

4. **Present** your news report to other classmates alone or with a team.

 **ELA7: LS 2.2**

##  Standards Check

### Using Vocabulary

1. _____ is the bending of light when it travels from one medium to another. **6.c**

2. State the law of reflection in your own words. **6.g**

### Understanding Main Ideas

3. **Label** a drawing of white light being split into the visible spectrum by a prism. Which color is bent the most? Which is bent the least? **6.f**

4. **Describe** how a light ray travels as it moves through empty space. **6.c**

5. **Identify** Copy and fill in the graphic organizer below to identify three ways light interacts with matter. **6.f**

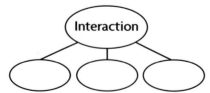

6. What is the process of absorbing light and then reemitting it in a different direction? **6.f**

   **A.** opaque

   **B.** scattering

   **C.** translucent

   **D.** transmission

7. **Give an example** not discussed in the text of a transparent, a translucent, and an opaque object. **6.f**

8. **Compare and contrast** absorption, scattering, and transmission. **6.f**

### Applying Science

9. **Critique** the statement, "The color of an object depends on the wavelengths of light it absorbs." Why is the statement inaccurate? How could you change the statement so it is correct? **6.b**

**Science** nline

For more practice, visit **Standards Check** at ca7.msscience.com.

## Science Content Standards

**6.d** Students know how simple lenses are used in a magnifying glass, the eye, a camera, a telescope, and a microscope.

## Reading Guide

### What *You'll Learn*

▶ **Explain** the function of a lens.

▶ **Analyze** how convex lenses form images.

▶ **Describe** how optical instruments use lenses.

### Why *It's Important*

Lenses can help you see tiny bacteria or giant stars far away in space.

### Vocabulary

lens
convex lens
focal point
focal length

### Review Vocabulary

**optical:** relating to light

# Using Lenses

**Main Idea** Lenses form images by causing light rays to bend.

**Real-World Reading Connection** Have you ever used a camera to take a picture of a friend? All cameras record the light that is emitted or reflected by objects. Cameras, microscopes, and telescopes use lenses to form images that you can see.

## What is a convex lens?

You are probably familiar with different devices that change how you see things. Eyeglasses change the way light is focused on a person's eye. Magnifying lenses and microscopes make very small objects appear to be large. Telescopes and binoculars make objects that are far away appear to be closer. All of these devices use at least one lens to form images. A **lens** is a transparent object with at least one curved side that causes light waves to bend. **Figure 16** shows two different types of lenses.

A lens that bulges outward, such as the one shown in the left photo in **Figure 16,** is called a **convex** (kahn VEKS) **lens.** Parallel light rays passing through a convex lens are bent so they come together, or converge. As shown on the right of **Figure 16,** a concave lens is thinner in the middle than at the edges. Parallel light rays passing through a concave lens spread apart, or diverge.

**Figure 16** All lenses have at least one curved surface and cause light rays to bend.

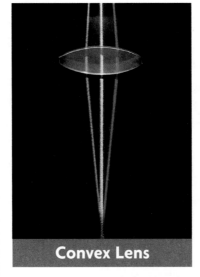
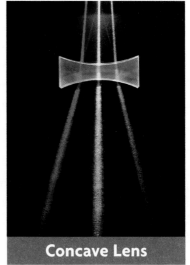

**Convex Lens**          **Concave Lens**

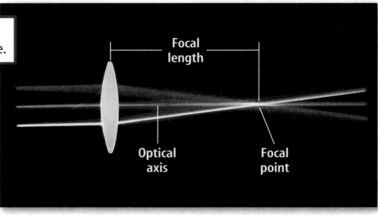

**Figure 17** Light rays passing through convex lenses converge.

Focal length

Optical axis

Focal point

## Light's Path Through a Convex Lens

Convex lenses are usually made out of glass or plastic. Light travels more slowly in both glass and plastic than it does in air. This means that a light ray bends when it slows down as it moves from air into the lens. The light ray bends again when it speeds up as it moves from the lens back into the air.

## Focal Point and Focal Length

**Figure 17** shows several beams of light shining parallel to the optical axis of a convex lens. These beams of light all bend toward the optical axis. The point where all of the beams of light converge is called the **focal** (FOH kuhl) **point.** In a convex lens, all light rays traveling parallel to the optical axis are bent so that they pass through the focal point. The distance from the center of the lens to the focal point is called the **focal length.**

## Image Formation by a Convex Lens

**Figure 18** shows that the image formed by a convex lens depends on the position of an object in relation to the focal point. Notice that the images in the first two panels appear where the light rays converge. The light rays never converge in the third panel. Instead, they diverge from the lens, forming an image that is right-side up, on the same side of the lens as the flower and bigger than the flower.

 **Visual Check** **Figure 18** How is the candle's image different in the bottom panel from the images in the other two panels?

# Visualizing Images Formed by a Convex Lens

## Figure 18

A convex lens can form images of an object that are bigger or smaller than the object. The image can also appear upright or upside down, compared to the object. The type of image formed by a convex lens depends on the location of the object relative to the focal point of the lens.

If the object is more than two focal lengths from the lens, the image formed is upside down and smaller than the object. As the object moves farther from the lens, the image becomes smaller.

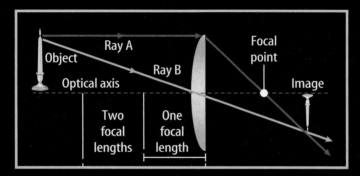

If the object is between one and two focal lengths from the lens, the image is upside down and larger than the object. As the object moves closer to the focal point, the image becomes larger.

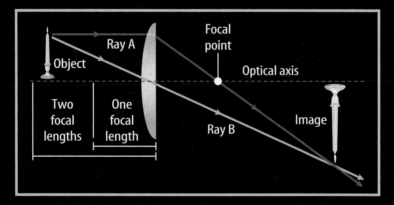

If the object is less than one focal length from the lens, the image is upright and larger than the object. The image becomes smaller as the object moves closer to the lens.

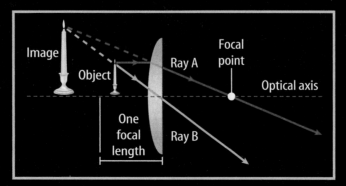

# Optical Instruments

Have you ever thought about why it's so hard to see objects that are far away? An optical instrument uses lenses to focus light and create useful images. Often, an optical instrument acts as a bigger eye by collecting more light than your eyes can collect. It gathers the light and then forms an image that your eyes can see. Different optical instruments do this by combining lenses in various ways.

## Cameras

A typical camera, like the one shown in **Figure 19,** uses several lenses to form an image. The camera is focused by moving the lenses back and forth until a sharp image is formed. The image is smaller than the object and is upside down. In some types of cameras, the image is formed on a section of film. In digital cameras, the image is formed on an electronic light sensor. When you take a picture, the camera shutter opens so that light enters the camera, and the film or the electronic sensor is **exposed.**

If too much light strikes the film or the light sensor, the image formed is overexposed and looks washed out. If too little light enters the camera, the photograph can be too dark. To control the amount of light that reaches the film or the light sensor, cameras have a device called a diaphragm or an aperture. The opening in the aperture becomes larger to let more light into the camera. The aperture opening becomes smaller to reduce the amount of light that enters the camera.

**ACADEMIC VOCABULARY**
expose (ihk SPOHZ)
*(verb)* to make accessible to a particular action or influence
*It is unhealthy to expose your skin to too much sunlight.*

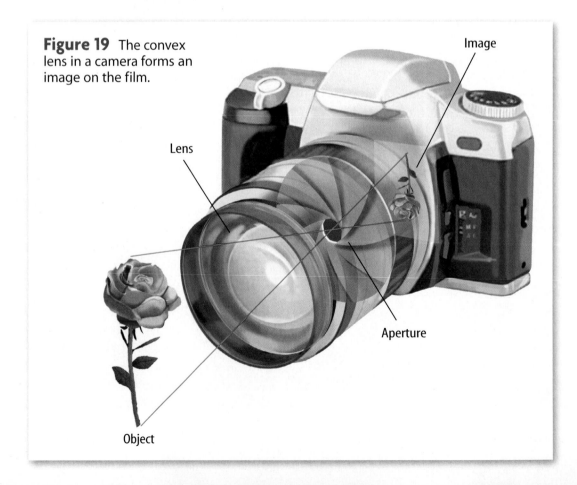

**Figure 19** The convex lens in a camera forms an image on the film.

Image

Lens

Aperture

Object

## Refracting Telescopes

Why is it hard to see far-away objects clearly? As an object gets farther away, less of the light from the object enters the openings in your eyes. As a result, the object appears dimmer and less detailed.

A telescope is an optical instrument that makes far-away objects seem closer. There are two basic types of telescopes. A simple refracting telescope is a combination of two convex lenses in a tube, as shown in **Figure 20.** The larger lens is the objective lens. The objective lens forms an image, which is enlarged by the smaller eyepiece lens.

The objective lens in a refracting telescope is much larger than the opening in a human eye. This means that much more light from a distant object enters the objective lens than would enter an eye. This causes the image formed by the objective lens to be brighter than the image your eye would form. Because the image is brighter, more detail can be seen when the image is magnified. Making the objective lens larger lets more light pass through the lens. Then even clearer images can be formed.

 **Figure 20** What is the function of the eyepiece lens?

## Reflecting Telescopes

The second type of telescope is a reflecting telescope. In a reflecting telescope, the objective lens is replaced with a mirror that has a curved reflecting surface. An image of a distant object is formed inside the telescope tube when light rays are reflected from the curved surface. A simple reflecting telescope is shown in **Figure 21.** Light from a distant object enters one end of the tube and strikes the curved mirror at the other end. The light is reflected from the curved mirror to a flat mirror inside the tube. The flat mirror then reflects the light to an eyepiece lens, which magnifies the image.

 Which mirror in a reflecting telescope is like the convex lens in a refracting telescope?

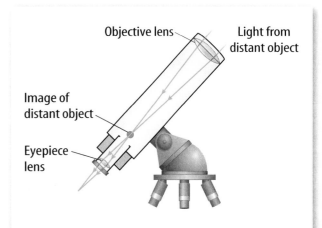

**Figure 20** Refracting telescopes use two convex lenses to form a clear image of a distant object.

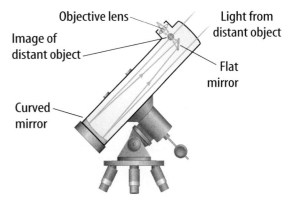

**Figure 21** A reflecting telescope uses a curved mirror to form an image that is magnified by an eyepiece lens.

**Figure 22** The Hale telescope in southern California has a curved mirror that is about 5 m in diameter.

**Figure 23** A simple microscope combines two convex lenses to magnify very small objects.

**Describe** how the eyepiece lens changes the image formed by the objective lens.

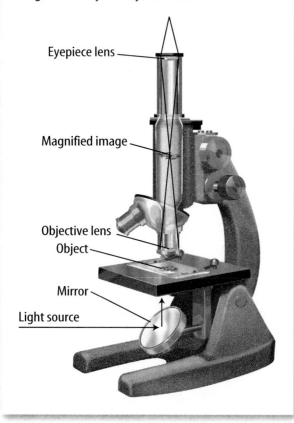

Eyepiece lens

Magnified image

Objective lens
Object

Mirror
Light source

## Large Telescopes

In order to form detailed images of very distant objects, such as planets and galaxies, the objective lens or curved mirror of a telescope must be as large as possible. Because a lens can be supported only around its edges, very large lenses tend to sag due to their weight. However, a large mirror can be supported rigidly on its back side so that it doesn't sag. As a result, the largest telescopes are reflecting telescopes instead of refracting telescopes. **Figure 22** shows one of the largest telescopes in the world, the Hale telescope at Mount Palomar Observatory in southern California.

 Why do large telescopes use mirrors instead of lenses?

## Microscopes

A refracting telescope uses convex lenses to enable distant objects to be seen. A microscope uses convex lenses to make a small object appear larger. **Figure 23** shows a simple microscope. Light from the object passes through the objective lens. The objective lens is positioned so that it forms an enlarged image of the object. The light rays from that image then pass through the eyepiece lens. This lens is positioned so it is closer to the image than one focal length. As a result, the image is made even larger. By using more than one lens, a microscope forms a much larger image than a single lens can produce.

# What have you learned?

A convex lens can form an image by causing light rays to refract. Lenses are used to form images in optical instruments such as cameras, telescopes, and microscopes. Telescopes use lenses and mirrors to collect light from objects that are too distant to be seen. Microscopes use lenses to magnify objects that are too small to see with your eyes alone. In the next lesson, you will read about how lenses can be used to correct some common vision problems.

## LESSON 3  Review

### Summarize

Create your own lesson summary as you organize an **outline**.

1. **Scan** the lesson. Find and list the first **red** main heading.

2. **Review** the text after the heading and list 2–3 details about the heading.

3. **Find** and list each **blue** subheading that follows the **red** main heading.

4. **List** 2–3 details, key terms, and definitions under each **blue** subheading.

5. **Review** additional **red** main headings and their supporting **blue** subheadings. List 2–3 details about each.

 **ELA7:** W 2.5

###  Standards Check

#### Using Vocabulary

1. Define *lens* in your own words. **6.d**

2. Distinguish between *focal point* and *focal length*. **6.d**

#### Understanding Main Ideas

3. **Explain** how the focal length changes as a convex lens becomes flatter. **6.d**

4. **Describe** what happens to light rays that travel parallel to the optical axis as they pass through a convex lens. **6.d**

5. **Compare and Contrast** Copy and fill in the graphic organizer below to compare and contrast details about telescopes. **6.d**

| Telescope | Similarities | Differences |
|-----------|-------------|-------------|
| Reflecting | | |
| Refracting | | |

6. What is the purpose of the aperture in a camera? **6.d**
   - **A.** to invert images
   - **B.** to magnify images
   - **C.** to control the amount of light
   - **D.** to control the image color

7. **Demonstrate** how you could use a convex lens to create an image of an object that is smaller than the original. **6.d**

8. **Compare and contrast** a refracting telescope and a microscope. **6.d**

#### Applying Science

9. **Imagine** you are a scientist studying distant stars. Write a short paragraph describing how your telescope works to a friend who understands light and lenses but doesn't know how telescopes work. Include a drawing of the telescope. **6.d**

**Science Online**

For more practice, visit **Standards Check** at ca7.msscience.com.

### Science Content Standards

**5.g** Students know how to relate the structures of the eye and ear to their functions.

**6.b** Students know that for an object to be seen, light emitted by or scattered from it must be detected by the eye.

**6.d** Students know how simple lenses are used in a magnifying glass, the eye, a camera, a telescope, and a microscope.

**6.e** Students know that white light is a mixture of many wavelengths (colors) and that retinal cells react differently to different wavelengths.

## Reading Guide

### What *You'll Learn*

▶ **Describe** the parts of the human eye.

▶ **Explain** how the parts of the eye form an image.

▶ **Explain** how the eye sees colors.

### Why *It's Important*

Seeing is an important way people learn about the world around them.

### Vocabulary

cornea
pupil
iris
retina
pigment

### Review Vocabulary

**organ:** groups of tissues that work together and perform one or more functions (p. 104)

# The Eye and Vision

**Main Idea** The eye is a complex organ made up of different parts.

**Real-World Reading Connection** Cameras, telescopes, and microscopes all use lenses to form images. Did you know that your eyes also contain lenses? Like other optical instruments, the human eye uses refraction to form images.

## How the Eye Forms an Image

Your eye detects light that is emitted by or reflected from objects. In some ways an eye is similar to a camera, as shown in **Figure 24.** In a camera, light from an object enters the lens. The lens forms an image on the film or light sensor at the back of the camera. The film or light sensor then records the image.

As light enters your eye, lenses in your eye focus light to produce an image on the back of your eye. Special cells at the back of the eye convert the image into electrical signals. These signals then travel to your brain, where they are interpreted as the object you are looking at.

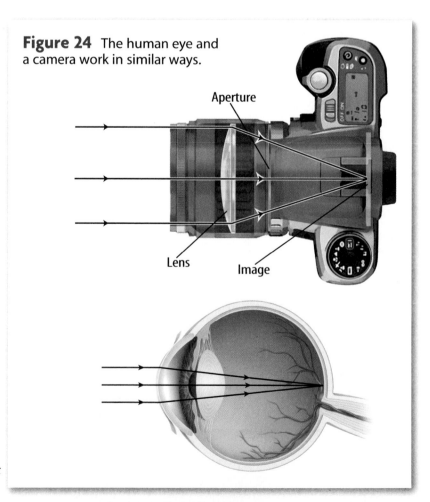

**Figure 24** The human eye and a camera work in similar ways.

Aperture

Lens

Image

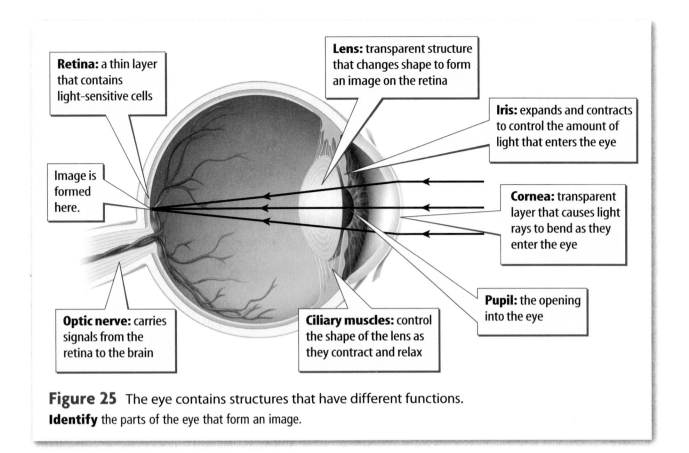

**Retina:** a thin layer that contains light-sensitive cells

**Lens:** transparent structure that changes shape to form an image on the retina

**Iris:** expands and contracts to control the amount of light that enters the eye

**Image is formed here.**

**Cornea:** transparent layer that causes light rays to bend as they enter the eye

**Optic nerve:** carries signals from the retina to the brain

**Ciliary muscles:** control the shape of the lens as they contract and relax

**Pupil:** the opening into the eye

**Figure 25** The eye contains structures that have different functions. **Identify** the parts of the eye that form an image.

## Cornea

**Figure 25** shows the different parts of the human eye. The eye is roughly spherical and is about 2.5 cm in diameter. The outer layer of the eye is called the sclera. The front part of the sclera is clear.

Light enters your eye through the **cornea** (KOR nee uh), which is a clear area of the sclera. The cornea is a convex lens that causes light rays to converge as they enter the eye. Although the eye contains another convex lens that helps focus light rays, most of the refraction of light rays occurs when they enter the cornea.

## Iris

After passing through the cornea, light rays then pass through the pupil. The **pupil** (PYEW pul) is the dark opening into the interior of your eye. The pupil is surrounded by the **iris** (I rus), which is the colored part of your eye behind the cornea. The pupil and the iris are shown in **Figure 26.**

The amount of light that enters the inside of your eye is controlled by the iris. When the light is dim, your iris is small and the pupil is large. This allows more light to enter the interior of your eye. When the light is bright, your iris is larger and your pupil is smaller, so that less light enters your eye.

 Why does the pupil get smaller when the eye is exposed to bright light?

**Figure 26** When the iris becomes smaller, more light enters the eye. When the iris becomes larger, less light enters the eye.

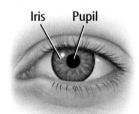

Iris    Pupil

The iris expands in bright light.

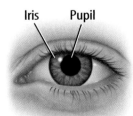

Iris    Pupil

The iris contracts in dim light.

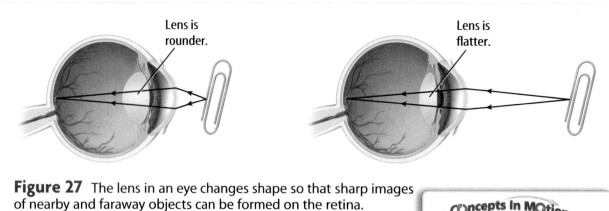

Lens is rounder.

Lens is flatter.

**Figure 27** The lens in an eye changes shape so that sharp images of nearby and faraway objects can be formed on the retina.

**Concepts in Motion**
To see an animation of lens and light movement, visit ca7.msscience.com.

## Lens

After passing through the pupil, light rays pass through the lens. The lens in your eye is convex, like the lens in a magnifying glass. However, instead of being made of rigid glass or plastic, the lens in your eye is **flexible.** The ciliary (SIH lee air ee) muscles attached to the lens change its shape, as shown in **Figure 27.** When you look at objects that are farther away, the muscles contract. This flattens the lens. When you look at objects that are closer, the muscles relax. This makes the lens rounder. By changing its shape, the lens enables sharp images of both nearby and distant objects to be formed on the retina.

## Retina

The light rays that pass through the lens form an image on the retina of the eye. The **retina** is a sheet of light-sensitive cells in the back of the eye. As shown in **Figure 28,** the retina contains two types of cells, called rods and cones. When these cells absorb light energy, chemical reactions occur. These chemical reactions produce nerve impulses that are transmitted to the brain by the optic nerve. Rod cells respond to dim light. Cone cells enable you to see colors but need brighter light to function than rod cells. **Table 1** summarizes the structures in the eye and their functions.

**Figure 28** Rod cells and cone cells line the retina and send signals to the brain when they are hit by light.

**Explain** the function of the rod cells and cone cells.

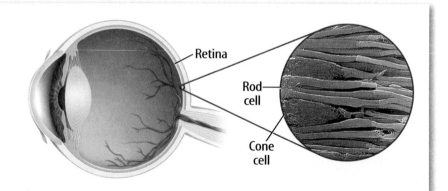

Retina

Rod cell

Cone cell

Concepts In Motion

Interactive Table Organize information about the structures and functions of the eye at ca7.msscience.com.

## Table 1 Parts of the Eye

| Function | Structures | |
|---|---|---|
| To control the amount of light entering the eye | The iris controls the amount of light entering the eye. The opening in the eye is the pupil. The iris contracts in dim light, making the pupil larger, and allowing more light to enter the eye. The iris expands in bright light, making the pupil smaller, and reducing the amount of light that enters the eye. | Iris |
| To form a sharp image on the retina in the back of the eye | The cornea, the lens, and the ciliary muscles produce a sharp image on the retina. The cornea is a convex lens that causes light rays to converge as they enter the eye and reach the lens. The ciliary muscles make the flexible lens flatter or rounder. This enables a sharp image of nearby and far-away objects to be formed on the retina. | Ciliary muscles / Lens / Cornea / Ciliary muscles |
| To convert the light energy that strikes the retina to nerve signals | The retina contains rod cells and cone cells that convert the light energy that strikes them into nerve signals. Rod cells function in dim light and enable objects to be seen at night. Cone cells function in bright light and enable colors to be seen. | Retina / Image / Optic nerve |

# Seeing Color

How do cone cells enable you to see color? You have about seven million cone cells in each retina. Light waves reflected from objects enter the pupil and strike the retina. The response of the cone cells to different wavelengths of light causes you to see objects as having color.

## Three Types of Cone Cells in the Retina

There are three types of cone cells. Each type responds to different wavelengths of light. One type of cone cells responds to the wavelengths of red and yellow light. These cells cause you to see the color red. The second type responds to yellow and green light and causes you to see the color green. The third type responds to blue and violet light and causes you to see the color blue.

 **Reading Check** How are the three types of cone cells different?

Light waves that strike the retina cause the three types of cone cells to send signals to the brain. The brain interprets the combination of the signals from the cone cells as the various colors you see.

## Pigment Colors

Some colors of the objects you see are caused by pigments. A **pigment** is a material used to change the color of other materials or objects. The color of a pigment, such as paint, depends on the wavelengths of the light it reflects. Blue paint reflects blue light and absorbs all other wavelengths. As shown in **Figure 29,** there are three primary pigment colors—magenta, cyan, and yellow. **Figure 29** also shows that each primary pigment color absorbs one of the primary light colors—red, green, or blue—and reflects the other primary colors. Most colors can be made by mixing different amounts of the primary pigment colors.

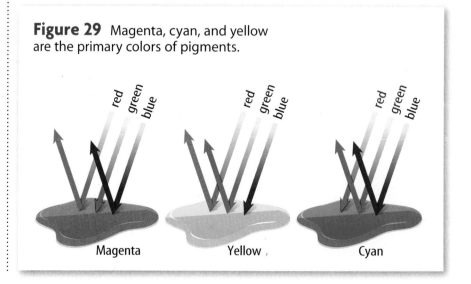

**Figure 29** Magenta, cyan, and yellow are the primary colors of pigments.

Magenta    Yellow    Cyan

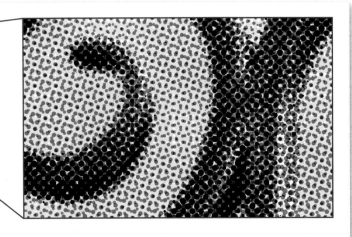

**Figure 30** Small dots of only four colors are used to create all the colors in this book.

**List** the four colors used in four-color printing.

## Color Printing

Look at a color picture in a magazine with a magnifying lens. As shown in **Figure 30,** the picture is formed by many tiny dots of color. Only four colors of dots are used to make all the different colors in the picture. These four colors are usually the primary colors of pigments—magenta, cyan, and yellow—as well as black. The four colors are combined in dots that are too small for the human eye to see clearly. As a result, the light reflected by the dots combines to make all the colors you see in magazines. This book was printed using four-color printing.

## Common Vision Problems

If you have normal vision, you should be able to see objects clearly when they are 25 cm or farther from your eyes. Also, you should be able to detect all colors of visible light. However, some people cannot detect certain colors. Also, many people have problems seeing nearby objects or distant objects.

### Color Deficiency

Take a look at **Figure 31.** Do you see a number? If not, you might have a red-green color deficiency. About 8 percent of males and 0.4 percent of females have a difficult time telling the difference between red and green. People with this deficiency either lack green or red cones or they have green or red cones that do not function correctly.

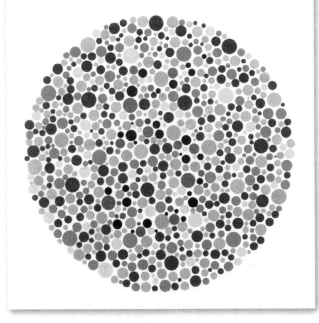

**Figure 31** If you can tell the difference between red and green, you should see the number 5 in this picture.

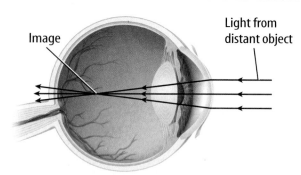

In a nearsighted eye, the eyeball is too long for the lens to form a sharp image of distant objects on the retina.

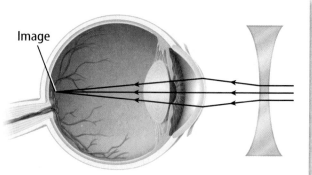

A concave lens in front of a nearsighted eye will diverge the light rays so the image is formed on the retina.

**Figure 32** Nearsightedness can be corrected by placing a diverging lens in front of the eye.

## Nearsightedness

You probably know someone who wears glasses or contacts, or maybe you wear them yourself. Two common vision problems that glasses correct are nearsightedness and farsightedness.

A nearsighted person cannot see faraway objects clearly. As **Figure 32** shows, in a nearsighted eye a sharp image is formed in front of the retina. The image on the retina is blurry. A concave lense causes light rays to diverge before they enter the eye. Then the cornea and the lens can form a sharp image on the retina.

 **Figure 32** Compare the location of the image with and without the diverging lens placed in front of the eye.

## Farsightedness

A person who is farsighted cannot see nearby objects clearly. As shown in **Figure 33,** a sharp image of a nearby object would be formed behind the retina. Glasses with convex lenses make light rays converge more before they enter the eye. Then a sharp image is formed on the retina.

 How does the convex lens placed in front of the eye correct farsightedness?

**Figure 33** Farsightedness can be corrected by placing a converging lens in front of the eye.

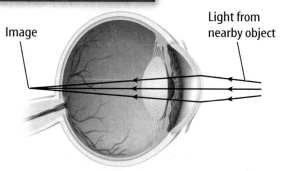

In a farsighted eye, the eyeball is too short for the lens to form a sharp image of nearby objects on the retina.

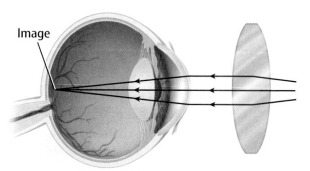

A convex lens in front of a farsighted eye enables a sharp image to be focused on the retina.

# What have you learned?

The eye is a complex light-detecting organ. The iris regulates the amount of light entering the eye, while the cornea and lens focus incoming light to form images. The images fall on the retina, which contains cells whose specialized function is to respond to light of specific wavelengths. These cells then send electrical signals to the brain, where they are processed and perceived as the objects around you.

## LESSON 4 Review

### Summarize

Create your own lesson summary as you write a **newsletter**.

1. **Write** this lesson title, number, and page numbers at the top of a sheet of paper.

2. **Review** the text after the **red** main headings and write one sentence about each. These will be the headlines of your newsletter.

3. **Review** the text and write 2–3 sentences about each **blue** subheading. These sentences should tell *who, what, when, where,* and *why* information about each headline.

4. **Illustrate** your newsletter with diagrams of important structures and processes next to each headline.

 **ELA7: W 2.5**

### Standards Check

#### Using Vocabulary

1. Distinguish between *iris* and *pupil.* **5.g**

2. The _____ is the sheet of light-sensitive cells at the back of the eye. **5.g**

#### Understanding Main Ideas

3. **List,** in order, the structures that light passes through before it reaches the retina. **6.b**

4. **Describe** how the lens in a human eye changes shape as the eye looks at a distant object and then at a closer object. **5.g**

5. **Take Notes** Copy the graphic organizer below and list the function of each part of the eye. **5.g**

| Part | Function |
|------|----------|
| Cornea | |
| Iris | |
| Lens | |
| Retina | |

6. **Explain** the type of eye problem shown below. How does the lens placed in front of the eye help correct the problem? **6.d**

7. **Determine** which cones are involved in seeing the color white. **6.e**

8. **Compare** a camera and the human eye. **5.g**

#### Applying Science

9. **Suggest** why glasses are more common among older people. Use the fact that the lens in the eye becomes less flexible as people age. **5.g**

10. **Justify** the following statement: "The eye is a complex organ made up of many parts." Give specific examples that support the statement. **5.g**

**Science Online**

For more practice, visit **Standards Check** at ca7.msscience.com.

# Lab

# Can a cow teach you about your eyes?

## Materials

paper towels
dissecting kit
dissecting tray
waste bucket
cow's eye

## Safety Precautions

🥽 👕 ☣️ 🧹 💧

### Science Content Standards

**5.g** Students know how to relate the structures of the eye and ear to their functions.

The different parts of the eye have different functions. Some parts move the eye and some parts control the amount of light that enters the eye. Some parts form a sharp image of the object that is being viewed and other parts detect the image and send signals to the brain. Can you sort and classify parts of the eye by function and then find them in the cow's eye?

## Collect Data and Make Observations

1. Read and complete a lab safety form.
2. Fill out the chart to classify parts of the eye according to function.
3. Get the following materials from your teacher: paper towels, a dissecting kit that includes a scalpel, scissors, and tweezers; a dissecting tray or surface, such as a polyurethane cutting board, a waste bucket, and a small bucket with soap and warm water for cleaning up afterward.
4. Get one cow's eye for you and your partner from the supply your teacher has ready and set it on the paper towels in the dissecting pan.
5. Examine the eye to see and feel the following parts: sclera, cornea, muscles that move the eyeball, and optic nerve.
6. Use the dissecting scissors to cut the fat and muscle away from the eye.
7. Cut the eye around the middle with the scissors so you end up with a front half and a back half. Be careful; it is not easy to cut.
8. Look at the front half of the eye first. Try to locate and feel the lens, the back of the iris and the cornea.
9. Carefully make an incision in the cornea; cut until the clear liquid beneath the cornea is released.

10. Remove the cornea and lay it in the dissecting tray. Cut through the cornea; it is made of layers of clear tissue.

11. Pull out the iris, which is between the cornea and the lens. Look for the hole in the center of the iris. This is the pupil that lets light into the eye.

12. Look at the back half of the eyeball and try to find and feel these structures: the retina, the optic nerve, the blind spot where the optic nerve leaves the retina, the fovea, where light is focused (directly behind the pupil near the blind spot).

13. Remove the lens, which is round and looks somewhat clear. Try to look through the lens at some words on a paper.

14. On the inside of the back of the eyeball you should see some blood vessels that are part of a thin film. The film is the retina.

15. Find the spot where the retina is attached at the back of the eye. Find the bundle of nerves that go out of the back of the eye behind this spot. This is the optic nerve.

## Analyze and Conclude

1. **Describe** the functions of the structures you observed in the cow's eye.

2. **Sketch** the appearance of the eye you dissected as it appeared after steps 5, 8, and 12. Draw separate sketches of the cornea and lens.

3. **Explain** how light rays are affected by the structures in the eye as they enter the pupil and strike the retina.

4. **Describe** the appearance of the words on paper when you looked at them through the lens from the cow eye.

5. **Describe** the appearance of the retina in the cow eye.

## Communicate

**Make a Poster** Create a poster that shows each part of the cow eye that you examined. Be sure to use realistic colors for each of the parts. Your poster should also show where these parts are found in a cow eye.

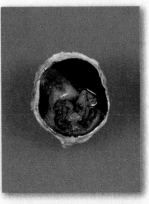

# Real World Science

## So You Want to be a Lighting Technician

Behind the scenes of a dance company or a theater company, lighting technicians work to create interesting effects with light. Lighting technicians also help animate music, dance, theatrical, and art shows. The job requires an understanding of electronics, lights, and computers, a sense for artistry and design, and involves communication with actors, directors, and artists.

Imagine you're a lighting technician working for a theater or a band. Write a journal entry about your experience lighting a show.

## High-Tech Help for the Blind

Science & Technology

More than ten million people worldwide are blind due to retinal degenerative diseases. Scientists have been developing microchip devices that may restore some vision for these people. The picture shows an artificial retina device, consisting of a microchip that is surgically implanted in the retina. The microchip converts the light waves that strike it into electric signals that are carried by the optic nerve to the brain.

Visit **Technology** at ca7.msscience.com to find out more about these devices. Write a 500- to 700-word paper discussing microchip devices, including their components and how they work.

# The Invention of Eyeglasses

More than 2,000 years ago, Seneca, the Roman philosopher, used a glass globe filled with water as a magnifier to read. Around the year A.D. 1000, glass blowers in Italy made reading stones made of solid glass that were are similar to magnifying lenses. Most historians believe monks or craftsmen in Italy produced the first form of eyeglasses around 1285–1289. During the 1700s and 1800s eyeglasses advanced dramatically with the invention of the modern shape, monocles, bifocals, tinting, and more.

Visit **History** at **ca7.msscience.com** to find out more about these inventions. Create a graph that shows the timeline of these inventions. Make sure to label one axis for the invention and one for the appropriate date from A.D. 1700 to 1850.

# The Impact of the Lightbulb on Society

Before the widespread use of lightbulbs, most lighting was done by gas or candles, both of which are fire hazards. Nights were dark as both candles and gas could only provide light in small areas. Gas lights also gave off fumes or leave sooty marks. With the development of the lightbulb and the subsequent electrical wiring of houses and businesses, lighting became both affordable and widespread. Thomas Edison and his company, General Electric, were instrumental in this change.

Visit **Society** at **ca7.msscience.com** to find out more about Thomas Edison, the lightbulb, and how it impacted society. Select one way in which the lightbulb positively impacted society and present a commercial about it. Make sure to give real-world examples of this impact.

**The BIG Idea** Light is a wave that interacts with everything you see.

## Lesson 1 What is light? `6.a, 6.e`

**Main Idea** **Visible light is an electromagnetic wave.**

- Light is a wave that can travel through empty space.
- The spectrum of electromagnetic waves includes many types of waves.
- Visible light takes up a very small part of the electromagnetic spectrum.

- **electromagnetic spectrum** (p. 430)
- **frequency** (p. 429)
- **medium** (p. 430)
- **wavelength** (p. 429)

## Lesson 2 Light and Matter `6.b, 6.c, 6.d, 6.g`

**Main Idea** **Light interacts with matter in different ways.**

- Light rays can be absorbed, transmitted, or scattered by matter.
- Light rays bend when they change speed.
- The angle of reflection is the same as the angle of incidence.
- The color of an object is determined by the wavelengths of light it reflects.

- **absorption** (p. 436)
- **law of reflection** (p. 440)
- **refraction** (p. 438)
- **scattering** (p. 436)
- **transmission** (p. 436)

## Lesson 3 Using Lenses `6.d`

**Main Idea** **Lenses form images by causing light rays to bend.**

- A lens is a transparent object with a curved surface that refracts light.
- Refracting telescopes use lenses to gather and focus light.
- Reflecting telescopes use mirrors to gather light.
- Microscopes use lenses to magnify small objects.

- **convex lens** (p. 443)
- **focal length** (p. 444)
- **focal point** (p. 444)
- **lens** (p. 443)

## Lesson 4 The Eye and Vision `5.g, 6.b, 6.d, 6.e`

**Main Idea** **The eye is a complex organ made up of different parts.**

- The cornea and lens focus light in the eye.
- The iris controls the amount of light entering the eye.
- The image is projected onto the retina in the back of the eye.
- Rod cells in the retina detect light and work best in low light.
- Cone cells detect color and work in bright light.

- **cornea** (p. 451)
- **iris** (p. 451)
- **pigment** (p. 454)
- **pupil** (p. 451)
- **retina** (p. 452)

 **STUDY TO GO** Download quizzes, key terms, and flash cards from ca7.msscience.com.

# Linking Vocabulary and Main Ideas

Use vocabulary terms from page 461 to complete this concept map.

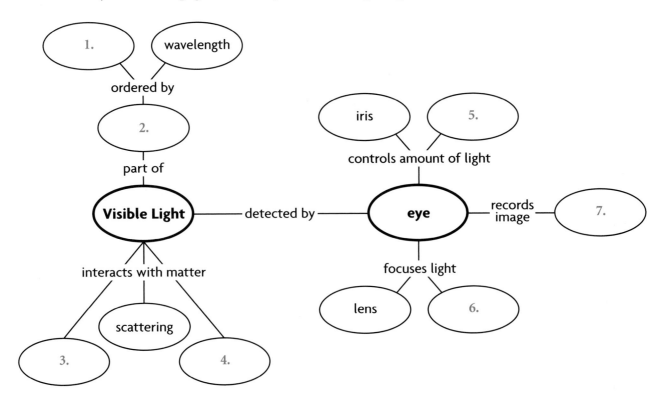

## Using Vocabulary

**Fill in each blank with the correct vocabulary term.**

**8.** _____ is the process of absorption and reemission as light passes through a transparent medium.

**9.** Rod cells and cone cells in the _____ detect light and send electrical signals to the brain.

**10.** The _____ does most of the focusing of light in the eye.

**11.** The _____ gets smaller in bright light and enlarges in dim light.

**12.** The distance between two troughs of a wave is a(n) _____.

**13.** The _____ includes X rays, ultraviolet waves, visible light, infrared light, microwaves, and radio waves.

**14.** The _____ is the spot where light rays converge after passing through a convex lens.

**Science** nline

Visit ca7.msscience.com for:
- ▶ Vocabulary PuzzleMaker
- ▶ Vocabulary eFlashcards
- ▶ Multilingual Glossary

## Checking Concepts

*Choose the word or phrase that best answers the question.*

1. Which property of a wave increases when its frequency decreases? **6.a**
   A. amplitude
   B. crest
   C. speed
   D. wavelength

2. Which correctly shows a ray of light reflecting off a mirror? **6.f**

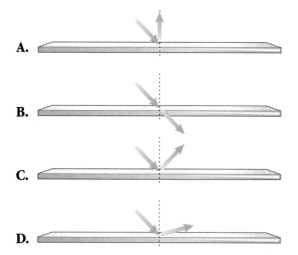

3. What occurs when a light ray strikes the retina and is converted into an electrical signal sent? **6.b**
   A. absorption
   B. reflectance
   C. scattering
   D. transmission

4. What is the order of parts light passes through on its path through the eye? **6.b**
   A. cornea, lens, pupil
   B. lens, pupil, cornea
   C. lens, cornea, pupil
   D. cornea, pupil, lens

5. Which correctly describes the path of a light ray that passes through a convex lens parallel to the major axis? **6.d**
   A. It will pass through the focal point.
   B. It will reflect off the vertical axis.
   C. It will hit the spot where the major axis and the vertical axis cross.
   D. It will pass through the lens and continue along its original path.

6. Which occurs when you see an object? **6.b**
   A. The retina narrows to block out most of the light.
   B. The iris transmits electrical signals to your brain.
   C. The cornea and lens form an image on your retina.
   D. The eyeball moves so that the retina is more than two focal lengths from the lens.

7. Which correctly shows the way light rays are refracted by a convex lens? **6.d**

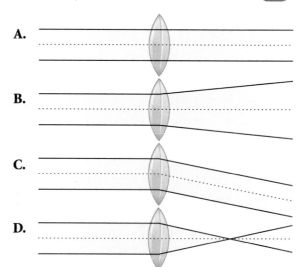

8. Which light waves are refracted the most after passing through a prism? **6.c**
   A. red waves
   B. yellow waves
   C. green waves
   D. blue waves

Science Online Standards Review ca7.msscience.com

## Applying Science

**9. Illustrate** why a rough surface, such as a road, becomes shiny in appearance and a better reflector when it is wet. Draw two diagrams to support your answer. **6.g**

**10. Infer** If the speed of light were the same in all materials, would a lens cause light rays to bend? **6.c**

**11. Suppose** a black plastic bowl and a white plastic bowl are placed in sunlight. After 15 minutes, the temperature of the black bowl is higher than the temperature of the white bowl. Which bowl absorbs more light waves and which bowl reflects more light waves? **6.f**

**12. Compare** the mixing of three pigments to make different colors of paint to how the eye uses three types of cone cells to perceive different colors of light. **6.e**

**13. Create a table** like the one below to classify devices that use different electromagnetic waves. Use examples you can find in your home, school, and community. **6.a**

| Electromagnetic Devices | |
|---|---|
| **Type of Wave** | **Device** |
| Radio waves | |
| Infrared waves | |
| Visible light | |
| X rays | |

### *WRITING in* Science

**14. Write a paragraph** for a camping manual describing how to start a camp fire using a magnifying glass. Imagine you are writing for a friend your age who has not studied convex lenses. Be sure to explain how the lens works and the meanings of the terms *focal point* and *focal length*. **ELA7: W 1.1**

## Cumulative Review

**15. Explain** the importance of blood pressure in the function of the heart. Be sure to define pressure in your explanation. **6.j**

**16. Give an example** of a part in the human body that acts as a lever. Draw a diagram of the part and label the fulcrum. Write a few sentences describing how the body part acts as a lever. **6.i**

## Applying Math

**17.** The wavelength of a microwave is $1 \times 10^{-2}$ m. Express this number as a decimal. **MA7: NS 1.1**

**18.** The wavelength of a light waves is 0.0000006 m. Express this number in scientific notation. **MA7: NS 1.1**

**19.** The wavelength of an infrared wave is $1 \times 10^{-5}$ m. Express this number as a decimal. **MA7: NS 1.1**

**20.** The table below shows the wavelength of some electromagnetic waves.

| Electromagnetic Waves | |
|---|---|
| **Wave** | **Wavelength (m)** |
| Radio wave | 100 |
| Microwave | 0.01 |
| Visible light | $1 \times 10^{-6}$ |

How many times longer is the radio wave than the wave of visible light? **MA7: NS 1.1**

Use the figure below to answer questions 1 and 2.

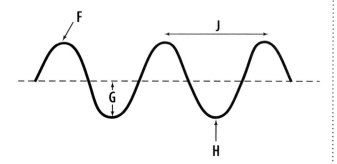

**1** What property of the wave is shown at F?

  A  amplitude

  B  wavelength

  C  crest

  D  trough                                    6.a

**2** What property of the wave is shown at J?

  A  amplitude

  B  wavelength

  C  crest

  D  trough                                    6.a

**3** What property of a light wave determines its color?

  A  wavelength

  B  amplitude

  C  speed

  D  interference                              6.e

**4** What happens when light travels from air into glass?

  A  It speeds up.

  B  It slows down.

  C  It travels at 300,000 km/s.

  D  It travels at the speed of sound.         6.c

Use the figure below to answer questions 5 and 6.

**5** What behavior of light waves lets you see a sharp, clear image of yourself in the water?

  A  refraction

  B  diffraction

  C  reflection

  D  interference                              6.f

**6** Why can't you see a clear image of yourself if the water's surface is rough?

  A  Regular reflection occurs.

  B  Diffuse reflection occurs.

  C  Light rays speed up.

  D  Light rays slow down.                     6.f

**7** **Which is the function of the iris of the eye?**

**A** It blends images to create a sense of distance.

**B** It controls the amount of light entering the eye.

**C** It receives information from the light that enters the eye.

**D** It transmits images to the brain. **5.g**

**8** **The illustration below shows two waves.**

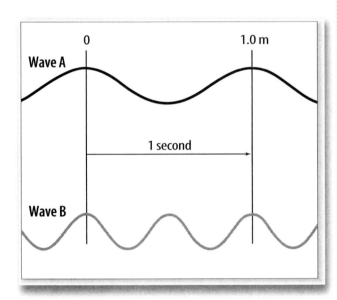

**How does the wave length of wave A compare with the wavelength of wave B?**

**A** The wavelength of A is half as long.

**B** The wavelength of A is the same.

**C** The wavelength of A is twice as long.

**D** The wavelength of A is three times as long. **6.a**

**9** **Why does a leaf look green?**

**A** It reflects green light.

**B** It absorbs green light.

**C** It reflects all colors of light.

**D** It reflects all colors except green. **6.b**

**Use the figure below to answer questions 10 and 11.**

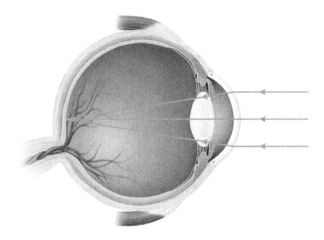

**10** **Which part of the eye gets smaller in bright light?**

**A** cornea

**B** lens

**C** pupil

**D** retina **5.g**

**11** **What is the function of the cornea and lens?**

**A** focus light

**B** protect the center of the eye

**C** convert light to electrical signals

**D** control the amount of light entering the eye **6.d**

**12** **A spoon rests inside a drinking glass that is half filled of water. Which wave behavior explains why the spoon looks like it is broken in the glass of water?**

**A** absorption

**B** refraction

**C** scattering

**D** transmission **6.c**

### CHAPTER 12

# The Ear and Sound

## The BIG Idea

Sound is a wave that interacts with cells in your ear so you can hear noises.

**LESSON 1** `5.g, 7.b`
### Sound
**Main Idea** Sound is a compression wave.

**LESSON 2** `5.g, 7.b, 7.d, 7.e`
### The Ear and Hearing
**Main Idea** The ear detects sound waves that pass through the three parts of the ear and bend small hairs in the inner ear.

## Why are they *so* big?

This animal, the fennec fox, has very large ears in order to hear prey from long distances. The six-inch-long ears enable the smallest sounds to be funneled into the ears. The fennec can hear large insects walking over sand. The large ears also help this desert fox stay cool in the heat—extra heat leaves the fox through the ears.

**Science *Journal*** Make a list of three questions you have about sound and how you perceive it.

## How many sounds can you make?

Almost everyone loves the sound of a bird's song. Not everyone loves the sound of traffic, however.

### Procedure

1. Write down ten sounds you like.

2. Write down ten sounds you don't like.

3. Think of a loud sound and a quiet sound.

4. List five sounds that animals make.

5. Make a concept map or small poster to display your thoughts about sound.

### Think About This

- **Explain** the differences between sounds you like and sounds you dislike.

- **Describe** what you think causes the difference between loud and quiet sounds.

- **Infer** why animals make different sounds.

 5.g, 7.e

 **Science** Online

Visit ca7.msscience.com to:

▶ view **Concepts in Motion**

▶ explore Virtual Labs

▶ access content-related Web links

▶ take the Standards Check

---

 **FOLDABLES** Study Organizer

**Structure and Function** Make the following Foldable to identify the structures of the ear and explain their functions.

▷ **STEP 1 Fold** a sheet of paper in half lengthwise. **Fold** the top down about 2 cm from the top.

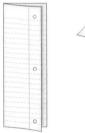

▷ **STEP 2 Unfold** and draw lines along all folds. **Label** as shown.

**Reading** *Skill*

**Interpreting**
As you read this chapter, list the structures of the ear in the first column. Explain the function of each structure in the second column.

# Make Inferences

**①Learn It!** When you make inferences, you draw conclusions that are not directly stated in the text. This means you "read between the lines." You interpret clues and draw upon prior knowledge. Authors rely on a reader's ability to infer because all the details are not always given.

**②Practice It!** Read the excerpt below and pay attention to highlighted words as you make inferences. Use this Think-Through chart to help you make inferences.

Sound waves can reflect off **hard surfaces,** just like a light wave reflects off a shiny surface. A **reflected sound wave** is called an **echo.** The **amount of time** it takes an **echo** to bounce back depends on how far away the reflecting surface is.

—*from page 486*

| Text | Question | Inferences |
|------|----------|------------|
| Hard surfaces | What kind of hard surfaces? | ice, mirrors, pavement |
| Reflected sound wave | How is it reflected? | Is it backward? Is it upside down? |
| Amount of time | How is it measured? | minutes, hours, seconds |

**③Apply It!** As you read this chapter, practice your skill at making inferences by making connections and asking questions.

# Target Your Reading

**Use this to focus on the main ideas as you read the chapter.**

**Reading Tip**

Sometimes you make inferences by using other reading skills, such as questioning and predicting.

**1 Before you read** the chapter, respond to the statements below on your worksheet or on a numbered sheet of paper.

- Write an **A** if you **agree** with the statement.
- Write a **D** if you **disagree** with the statement.

**2 After you read** the chapter, look back to this page to see if you've changed your mind about any of the statements.

- If any of your answers changed, explain why.
- Change any false statements into true statements.
- Use your revised statements as a study guide.

| Before You Read A or D | Statement | After You Read A or D |
|---|---|---|
| | **1** Sounds made with greater energy have greater loudness. | |
| | **2** Sound travels in a wave pattern. | |
| | **3** Hearing damage is irreversible. | |
| | **4** A sound that measures 80 decibels is four times louder than a sound that measures 20 decibels. | |
| | **5** Mice are not able to hear normal human speech. | |
| | **6** Human hearing depends upon tiny hairs. | |
| | **7** The smallest bones in your body are in your ear. | |
| | **8** Hearing damage is caused by sounds over 70 decibels. | |
| | **9** Cats are able to find their way in the dark by listening for the echo of the high-pitched noises they make that humans cannot hear. | |
| | **10** Although you cannot hear very low sounds, you can sense them as they pass through your body. | |

**Science Online**

Print a worksheet of this page at ca7.msscience.com.

## Reading Guide

### What *You'll Learn*

▶ **Describe** the properties of sound waves.

▶ **Explain** what makes sounds loud or soft.

▶ **Compare** high and low sounds.

### Why *It's Important*

You can understand the differences between sounds.

### Vocabulary

compression wave
loudness
amplitude
decibel scale
pitch

### Review Vocabulary

**wavelength:** the distance between any two peaks or troughs on a wave. (p. 427)

# Sound

**Main Idea** Sound is a compression wave.

**Real-World Reading Connection** If you stop reading and pay attention to all of the sounds around you, you will probably hear many different noises. You might hear cars passing by on the street. You might hear voices speaking in another room. Perhaps you will hear someone playing music nearby. There might be the hum of a computer or an air conditioner.

## What is sound?

All of these noises are perceived by your ear as sound. These sounds travel like a ripple travels in water. Every sound has something in common with every other sound. Vibrations make all sounds, and all sounds are transmitted by waves. Have you ever played with a coiled-spring toy like the one in **Figure 1?** If you stretch it out and then give one end a little push, you create a section of coils that are more tightly spaced than the coils in the rest of the spring. You can watch as a region of compressed coils travels all the way to the other side of the spring. In the same way, sound waves compress the molecules through which they travel. These waves travel through a medium, the air, to be received by your ear.

 **Reading Check** What makes sounds?

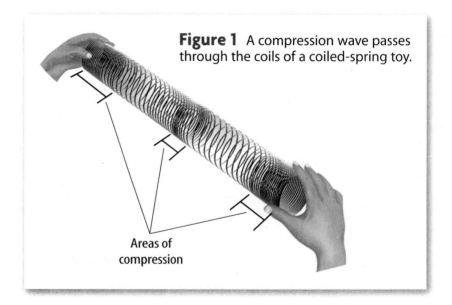

**Figure 1** A compression wave passes through the coils of a coiled-spring toy.

Areas of compression

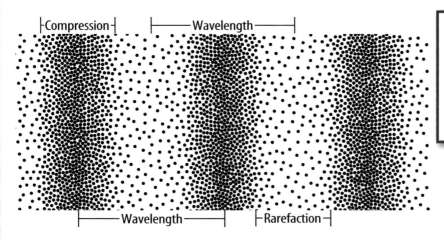

**Figure 2** Sound waves create regions of compression and regions of rarefaction between molecules.

**Describe** the areas of compression and rarefaction in the image using your own words.

## Sound Waves

In the last chapter, you learned that light is a wave. Recall that waves are disturbances that carry energy from one place to another place. Sound is also a wave. When you speak, the vocal cords in your throat vibrate. Your vocal cords move the air in your throat, and the vibrations continue as a wave through the air. The energy that moves one molecule of air is passed on to the next one. The wave moves through the air in your throat to the air surrounding your body and beyond. In this way, energy is transferred from one place to another.

**Compression Waves** Sound waves are called compression waves. In a **compression wave,** particles move back and forth in the same direction the sound wave moves. **Figure 2** illustrates the molecules in a sound wave. In some places of the wave, the molecules are crowded closely together. These areas of high density and pressure are regions of compression. In between two regions of compression, the molecules are spread apart. This area of low density and pressure is a region of rarefaction.

**Wavelength and Frequency** Like other waves, a sound wave has a wavelength and a frequency. The wavelength of a sound wave is the distance between the centers of two regions of compression or the distance between the centers of two regions of rarefaction, as shown in **Figure 2.** Just as for other waves, the frequency is the number of wavelengths that pass a certain point in one second. Recall that frequency is measured in hertz, which is symbolized Hz and represents $1/s$. If a wave has a long wavelength, only a few wavelengths will pass a point in one second, so the wave will have a low frequency. An example of this would be the bass drum: the low notes it produces have a low frequency and a long wavelength and can be felt through your whole body.

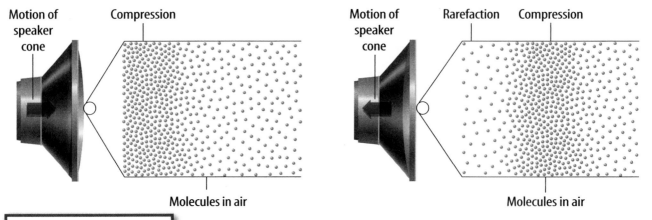

Motion of speaker cone | Compression | Molecules in air

Motion of speaker cone | Rarefaction | Compression | Molecules in air

**Figure 3** The vibrations of a speaker produce the sound that you hear when you are listening to music. When the speaker moves outward, it pushes adjacent molecules closer together, creating a region of compression. When the speaker moves inward, the molecules in the air spread out, creating a region of rarefaction.

ACADEMIC VOCABULARY
complex (kahm PLECKS)
(adjective) complicated in structure; consisting of interconnected parts
The complex road system in the city made it difficult to find the zoo.

## Vibration

Have you ever put your hand on a stereo speaker? If so, you probably felt it vibrating. When an object vibrates, it puts pressure on the surrounding molecules. As the speaker moves outward, as in **Figure 3,** it pushes molecules together and creates a region of compression. When it moves inward, it creates a region of rarefaction, also shown in **Figure 3.** As the speaker continues to vibrate, a series of compressions and rarefactions forms. The compressions and rarefactions move away from the speaker in all directions, creating a sound wave.

 What creates a sound wave?

## Playing in Tune

What does it sound like when you play a musical instrument, such as a violin, that is properly tuned? It probably sounds rich and full. When you play middle C on a violin that has been properly tuned, the string vibrates in a certain pattern that makes the note middle C. However, the vibration of the string is too **complex** to produce just one note at a time. It also produces vibrations that match middle C in the same way that some notes on a scale match each other. This creates a rich sound that you expect from the violin.

What does it sound like when you play a violin that is out of tune? It probably doesn't sound very good. If the primary note, such as middle C, is not quite right, the other vibrations that would normally match it do not blend together. Because the sounds are not organized, this can be considered noise.

 **Figure 3** Using the guideline of this figure, choose a musical instrument and draw how the air molecules move when the instrument is played.

# How loud is it?

You've probably listened to music and had someone say to you, "Your music is too loud. I can't hear myself think!" You've also probably whispered in your quietest voice to a friend and had a teacher say, "Do you want to share that with the group?" What is the difference between a loud noise and a quiet noise?

## Amplitude and Loudness

Loud sound waves generally carry more energy than soft sound waves do. **Loudness** is a person's perception of how much energy a sound wave carries. Because of the structure of the ear, not all sound waves with the same energy have the same loudness. Humans hear sounds with frequencies between 3,000 Hz and 4,000 Hz as louder than other sound waves with the same energy.

Loudness is measured in units called phons. Two sounds of different frequencies produced with different amounts of power will not sound equally loud. Nor will two sounds produced with the same power at different frequencies sound equally loud. The phon takes both frequency and power into account to measure loudness.

The amount of energy a wave carries depends on its amplitude. For a sound wave, **amplitude** (AM plih tood) depends on how spread out the molecules in the regions of compression and rarefaction are, as shown in **Figure 4.** If a sound wave has compressions with molecules that are packed tightly together and rarefactions with molecules that are spaced widely apart, it has a large amplitude. The object that created the wave transferred a lot of energy to the molecules to force them tightly together or to spread them far apart. Sound waves with greater amplitudes carry more energy and sound louder. Sound waves with smaller amplitudes carry less energy and sound quieter.

**WORD ORIGIN**
amplitude
from Latin *amplitudinem;*
means *wide extent, width*

**Figure 4** The amplitude of a sound wave depends on how spread out the particles are in the wave.

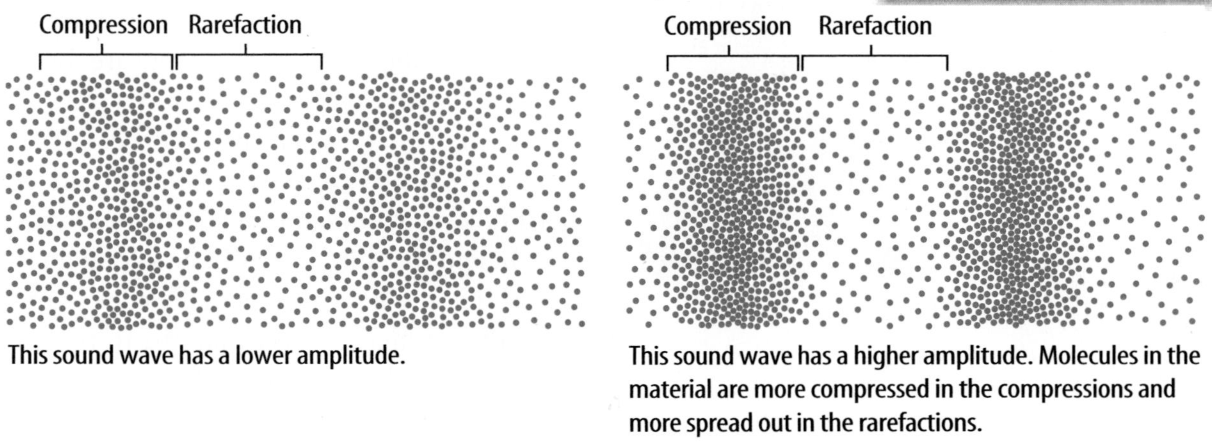

Compression  Rarefaction

This sound wave has a lower amplitude.

Compression  Rarefaction

This sound wave has a higher amplitude. Molecules in the material are more compressed in the compressions and more spread out in the rarefactions.

### WORD ORIGIN

decibel
from Latin *decibus;* means *tenth*

### SCIENCE USE V. COMMON USE

scale

**Science Use** a graduated series or scheme of rank and order. *Water boils at 100° on the Celsius scale.*

**Common Use** an instrument used to weigh objects. *You can use a bathroom scale to determine your weight.*

## The Decibel Scale

Your perception of the amount of energy in a sound wave is measured on the **decibel** (DES uh bel) **scale,** as shown in **Figure 5.** The symbol for a decibel is dB. Because humans can hear sounds over a large range, the decibel scale is based on powers of 10. For example, a sound of 0 decibels is the quietest sound that humans can hear. A sound of 10 decibels has ten times more energy than a sound of 0 dB. A sound that is 20 dB has 100 times more energy. A sound that is 30 dB has 1,000 times more energy.

 **Reading Check** Why is a 20-dB sound not twice as loud as a 10-dB sound?

**Decibels that Damage** Damage to a person's hearing can begin with sounds of about 85 dB. The type of damage depends on the loudness of the sound and the length of time that a person is exposed to the sound. For example, listening to an 85-dB sound for more than eight hours can cause hearing damage. Some everyday sounds that are about 85 dB include garbage disposals, lawn mowers, heavy traffic, and noisy restaurants. Listening to a 110-dB sound for just a minute and a half can cause hearing damage. A car horn, a video arcade, a power saw, and a crying baby all produce sounds of about 110 dB.

**Hearing Protection** How do you protect your hearing? You should wear earplugs or hearing protectors at concerts or when around loud machinery. Workplaces have laws about how long their employees can be exposed to noises between 90 and 115 decibels. Noises above 140 decibels are illegal for worker exposure. Because of the way the decibel scale is constructed, sounds do not add as you might expect. If three people are holding a conversation and suddenly start talking at once, one at 60 dB, another at 65 dB, and the third at 70 dB, how loud do you think it will seem? It actually adds to only 71.5 dB, not much greater than the third person talking alone. However, the effect of three people talking at once is still greater than one person alone.

**Figure 5** The energy that a sound wave carries is measured on the decibel scale.

**Describe** how a 20-dB sound is different than an 70-dB sound.

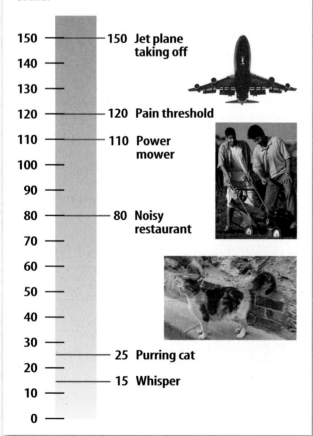

| | |
|---|---|
| 150 | 150 **Jet plane taking off** |
| 140 | |
| 130 | |
| 120 | 120 **Pain threshold** |
| 110 | 110 **Power mower** |
| 100 | |
| 90 | |
| 80 | 80 **Noisy restaurant** |
| 70 | |
| 60 | |
| 50 | |
| 40 | |
| 30 | |
| 20 | 25 **Purring cat** |
| 10 | 15 **Whisper** |
| 0 | |

## Frequency and Pitch

Have you ever been in a car when the driver revved the engine? It makes a higher sound than when the car is idling, because the engine shaft completes more revolutions per minute. Recall that the frequency of a sound is measured by the number of cycles the object causing the sound completes per second. The faster it moves, the higher the frequency is. Pitch corresponds to the frequency of the sound. The **pitch** of a sound is how high or how low it is. The higher the pitch is, the higher the frequency is. The words *pitch* and *frequency* often mean the same.

The human ear can detect sound waves with frequencies between about 64 Hz and 23,000 Hz, shown in **Table 1.** Some animals can hear sounds with even higher frequencies. For example, when a trainer blows a dog whistle, you do not hear anything, but a dog will respond. Dog whistles have frequencies that are higher than the human ear can detect. Other animals that can detect high-frequency sound waves include bats, whales, and dolphins.

| Table 1 Range of Hearing | | |
|---|---|---|
| **Species** | **Scale** | **Approximate Range (Hz)** |
| Human | | 64–23,000 |
| Cat | | 45–64,000 |
| Mouse | | 1,000–91,000 |
| Bat | | 2,000–110,000 |
| Beluga whale | | 1,000–123,000 |
| Elephant | | 16–12,000 |
| Porpoise | | 75–150,000 |
| Tree frog | | 50–4,000 |

## How loud and how low can you go?

Sound is described by its frequency or pitch and by its amplitude. Small children have high-pitched, or high-frequency, voices. Infrasound is sound that has extremely low frequency. Humans cannot hear these sounds, but if they are very loud, that is, having a high amplitude, then we can feel them. Elephants, tigers, giraffes, and some other animals communicate in this low-frequency sound range. Sounds with frequencies that are too high for humans to hear are called ultrasound. Bats and some other animals use ultrasound for echolocation, to map their surroundings.

### Data Collection

Visit ca7.msscience.com to find amplitudes and frequencies of various sounds.

### Data Analysis

1. **Create** a large graph on chart paper and attach it to a wall. Put frequency in hertz along the *x*-axis. Put amplitude in decibels along the *y*-axis.

2. **Plot** data points by writing about the sounds on cue cards and pin the cards at the correct location of frequency and amplitude on the graph.

 5.g, 7.b

 MA7: AF 1.5, MR 2.5

 Try at Home

# What have you learned?

Sound travels by compression waves composed of high- and low-density regions. Vibrations cause these waves by moving molecules closer together and then farther apart. The loudness of a sound wave depends partly upon the amplitude and partly upon the frequency of the sound wave. Your perception of the loudness of a sound is measured on the decibel scale. The pitch of a sound, how high or low it is, depends upon the frequency of the sound.

# LESSON 1 Review

## Summarize

Create your own lesson summary as you design a **visual aid**.

1. **Write** the lesson title, number, and page numbers at the top of your poster.

2. **Scan** the lesson to find the **red** main headings. Organize these headings on your poster, leaving space between each.

3. **Design** an information box beneath each **red** heading. In the box, list 2–3 details, key terms, and definitions from each **blue** subheading.

4. **Illustrate** your poster with diagrams of important structures or processes next to each information box.

 **ELA7:** W 2.5

## Standards Check

### Using Vocabulary

1. **Describe** a compression wave.  5.g

2. The _____ is used to measure the loudness of a sound. 5.g

### Understanding Main Ideas

3. **Give an example** of a sound that has a lower frequency than a siren on a fire engine. 5.g

4. **Discuss** how the spacing of molecules in a sound wave changes if the amplitude of the wave decreases. 5.g

5. **Compare and contrast** frequency and pitch. 5.g

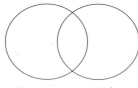

Frequency      Pitch

6. Which is the difference between amplitude and loudness?

   **A.** Amplitude is how a person perceives it; loudness is the amount of energy a wave carries. 5.g

   **B.** Amplitude is how big a wave is, loudness is the amount of sound a wave carries.

   **C.** Amplitude is the amount of energy a wave carries; loudness is how a person perceives it.

   **D.** Amplitude is the amount of sound a wave carries; loudness is how big a wave is.

### Applying Science

7. **Calculate** how long it will take for a sound wave to pass through a window if the speed of sound through glass is 5,640 m/s and the window is 1-cm thick. Use the following equation: time = distance/speed. 5.g

**Science** nline

For more practice, visit **Standards Check** at ca7.msscience.com.

# Applying Math

## City Noise and Bar Graphs

Scientists survey groups of people to find out how they are affected by noise in their neighborhood. The following double-bar graph shows the percentages of noise complaints made in New York City and in the United States in general.

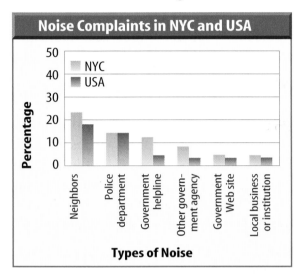

**Noise Complaints in NYC and USA**

NYC
USA

Percentage: 50, 40, 30, 20, 10, 0

Types of Noise: Neighbors, Police department, Government helpline, Other government agency, Government Web site, Local business or institution

## Example

Which group heard the same amount of noise complaints for both New York City and the United States?

**What you know:**
- On the graph, compare the bars for New York City and the United States in the same reporting group.

**What you need to find:**
- Which reporting group has the same value for the United States and New York City?

**Answer:** 14 percent of the people in both New York City and the United States reported their noise complaint to the police department.

## Practice Problems

1. According to the graph, which group received the highest percentage of complaints in the United States?

2. According to the graph, which group received the lowest percentage of complaints in New York City?

**Science** Online

For more math practice, visit **Math Practice** at ca7.msscience.com.

## Science Content Standards

**5.g** Students know how to relate the structures of the eye and ear to their functions.

**7.b** Use a variety of print and electronic resources (including the World Wide Web) to collect information and evidence as part of a research project.

**7.d** Construct scale models, maps, and appropriately labeled diagrams to communicate scientific knowledge (e.g., motion of Earth's plates and cell structure).

**7.e** Communicate the steps and results from an investigation in written reports and oral presentations

## Reading Guide

### What *You'll Learn*

▶ **Describe** the parts of the ear.

▶ **Explain** how the ear detects sound.

### Why *It's Important*

You can better protect your ears if you understand how they work.

### Vocabulary

external ear
auditory canal
tympanic membrane
malleus
incus
stapes
cochlea
echo

### Review Vocabulary

**cartilage:** a strong, flexible tissue made of collagen that gives shape to parts of your body (p. 361)

# The Ear and Hearing

 **Main Idea** The ear detects sound waves that pass through the three parts of the ear and bend small hairs in the inner ear.

**Real-World Reading Connection** You may have used a tape recorder to record sounds. Have you ever thought about how a tape recorder works? In some ways it is similar to your ear, as **Figure 6** shows.

## Functions of the Ear

The outer part of your ear collects sound waves. The microphone connected to a tape recorder serves a similar purpose. Your middle ear passes the sound waves you hear to your inner ear. Similarly, sound waves in digitized form are passed through some wires to the inside of the tape recorder. Finally, your inner ear processes the sound waves into electrical impulses so that your brain can interpret what you hear. A tape recorder records sounds on tape so that they can be played back at a future date.

**Reading Check** Trace the path of a sound from your outer ear to your brain. How does it change as it moves along?

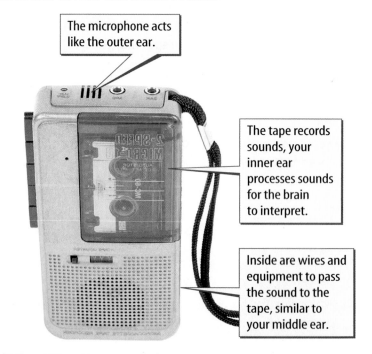

**Figure 6** Your ear detects sound in a way similar to electronic devices that record sounds.

The microphone acts like the outer ear.

The tape records sounds, your inner ear processes sounds for the brain to interpret.

Inside are wires and equipment to pass the sound to the tape, similar to your middle ear.

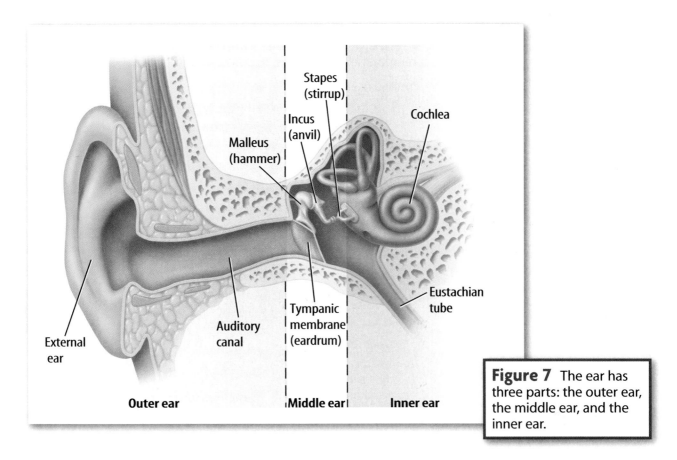

Stapes
(stirrup)

Incus
(anvil)

Malleus
(hammer)

Cochlea

External
ear

Auditory
canal

Tympanic
membrane
(eardrum)

Eustachian
tube

**Outer ear**          **Middle ear**     **Inner ear**

**Figure 7** The ear has three parts: the outer ear, the middle ear, and the inner ear.

## Structures of the Ear

The human ear is made up of the outer ear, the middle ear, and the inner ear, as shown in **Figure 7.** The outer ear includes the **external** ear and the auditory canal; it collects sound waves and transfers them to the middle ear. The middle ear contains the eardrum and three tiny bones that conduct sounds to the inner ear. The inner ear contains intricate structures that detect different frequencies of sounds and sends signals to the brain.

 **Figure 7** Compare the size of the outer, middle, and inner ear.

### The Outer Ear

If someone asked you where your ears are, you would probably point to the visible parts on either side of your head. Technically, these are the external ears, and they are just one part of the outer ear. The **external ear** is made up of folds of cartilage and skin. These folds adjust the sound waves that enter your ear to help the brain interpret the origin of the sound waves.

The other part of the outer ear is called the auditory canal. The **auditory canal** is the part of your ear that collects sound waves from the external ear and passes them to the middle ear. You can easily find the beginning of the auditory canal. It is the opening in your ear that leads into your middle ear.

**ACADEMIC VOCABULARY**

external (eks TUR null)
*(adjective)* located outside or beyond some limits or surface
*The external features of the car—the red and silver colors—were what led us to buy it.*

**Figure 8** The middle ear consists of the tympanic membrane, the malleus, the incus, and the stapes.

Malleus (hammer)

Incus (anvil)

Stapes (stirrup)

Tympanic membrane (eardrum)

Eustachian tube

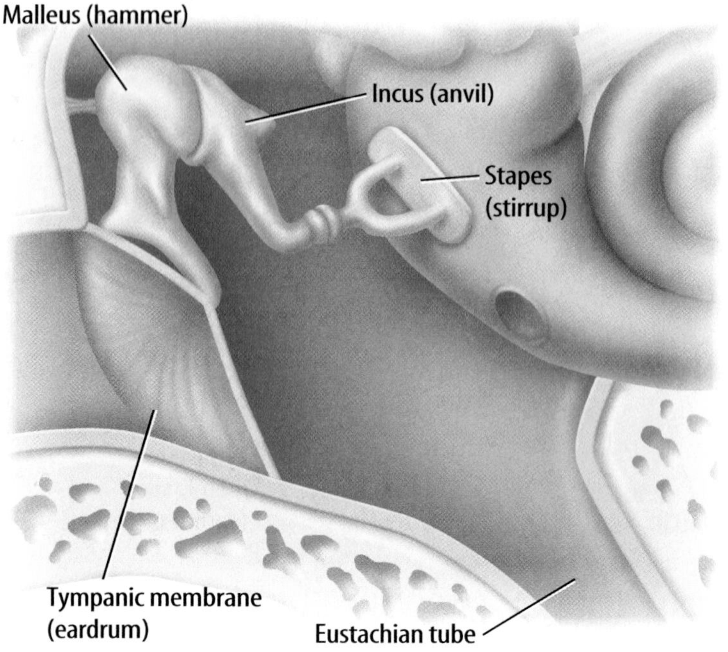

## The Middle Ear

You have probably heard someone say, "Don't listen to such loud music or you'll burst your eardrums." But what exactly are the eardrums? As shown in **Figure 8,** the first part of the middle ear that sound waves reach is called the **tympanic membrane,** more commonly called the eardrum. It is a thin layer of skin that vibrates when sound waves hit it.

The vibrations of the tympanic membrane cause three tiny bones to transmit sound waves through the middle ear to the inner ear, as shown in **Figure 8.** These bones are known by their Latin names: the **malleus** (MAYL ee us), also called the hammer; the **incus,** also called the anvil; and the **stapes** (STAH pehs), also called the stirrup. Two small muscles control the tension on the eardrum and the bones of the middle ear. By changing the tension, these muscles can help protect the eardrum from large vibrations that come from loud sounds.

The malleus, the incus, and the stapes rest in a fluid-filled vessel called the eustachian (you STAY shun) tube. The eustachian tube connects the middle ear to the throat. When you swallow, the pressure is adjusted in your eustachian tube and in your middle ear. This is why it helps to chew gum and swallow or to yawn when the pressure changes on airplanes or in elevators.

 **Reading Check** What helps prevent injury to the eardrum?

WORD ORIGIN

membrane
from Latin *membrum;* means *member of the body*

## The Inner Ear

If you have ever walked through a maze in a cornfield, a cathedral, an amusement park, or a formal garden, you know that a maze is full of twists and turns. Another name for a maze is a *labyrinth*. The inner ear is full of structures with so many twists and turns that it is also called a labyrinth. All the twists and turns in the inner ear allow many sensory cells to be packed into a small space.

When the bones of the middle ear move, they transfer vibrations from the tympanic membrane to the inner ear by way of a membrane called the oval window. The oval window then passes the vibration on to the fluid in the cochlea. The cochlea, shown in **Figure 9,** is a snail-shaped structure. The **cochlea** (KOH klee uh) is lined with sensory cells. These cells sense different frequencies of sound. **Figure 10** shows a diagram of what the cochlea would look like if it were unwound. The sensory cells closest to the middle ear sense high-frequency sound waves. The sensory cells farther from the middle ear sense low-frequency sound waves.

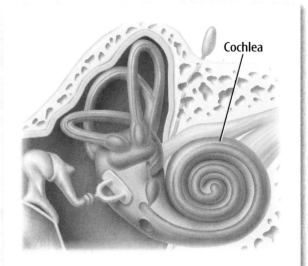

**Figure 9** The cochlea is the part of the inner ear that looks like a snail.

**WORD ORIGIN**····················

cochlea
from Greek *kokhlos;* means *spiral shell*
·····················

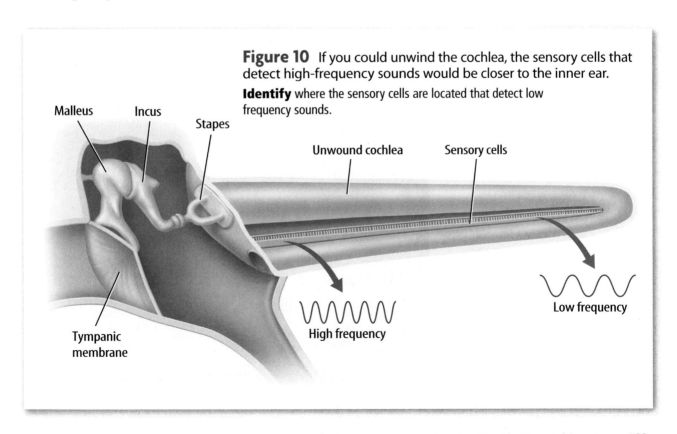

**Figure 10** If you could unwind the cochlea, the sensory cells that detect high-frequency sounds would be closer to the inner ear.

**Identify** where the sensory cells are located that detect low frequency sounds.

Malleus  Incus  Stapes  Unwound cochlea  Sensory cells

Tympanic membrane  High frequency  Low frequency

# Sensing Sound

When you smell or taste something, the signals that are sent to your brain come from chemical changes in your cells. Sound is different. When you hear something, it is because of a movement. As shown in **Figure 11,** all of the sensory cells in the cochlea have little hairs sticking out of them. When a vibration hits the hairs, they bend. The cells react to the bent hairs by sending a signal to the brain.

## Hearing in Humans

Remember that a sound wave is a compression wave. When a sound wave hits the tympanic membrane, it causes a vibration. The vibration is passed to the three tiny bones in your inner ear. The last of these bones, the stapes, vibrates against a part of the cochlea called the oval window. The oval window then passes the vibration on to the fluid in the cochlea.

The vibration of the fluid in the cochlea bends the hairs in the sensory cells. When the hairs bend, a signal is sent to the brain. The brain can tell the frequency of the sound wave by determining the location of the bent hairs. The brain can also determine the loudness of a sound. The farther a hair is deflected, the louder the brain recognizes the sound to be.

 What causes the hairs of the sensory cells to deflect?

**Figure 11** When vibrations bend hairs on sensory cells in the cochlea, they send signals to the brain. Scientists have added false color to this photograph to study whether hairs can be regrown in the cochleas of people who have hearing damage.

# Hearing Damage

Hearing damage can occur in almost any part of the ear. If something happens to prevent sound from being transmitted through the outer and middle ear, conductive hearing loss occurs.

## Effect on Ear Structures

Conductive hearing loss is often caused by colds or allergies that cause a temporary buildup of fluid in the middle ear. This can lead to an infection that puts pressure on the eardrum. When the eardrum does not vibrate properly, vibrations are not passed to the cochlea correctly, so a person cannot hear clearly.

Damage to the cochlea can occur because of aging or from exposure to loud noises. When the hairs on the sensory cells in the cochlea are bent for too long or too much, they can become damaged. This can happen to musicians who spend a lot of time performing at loud concerts, to people who ride motorcycles, or to people who work around loud machinery. Damage to the cochlea is called sensorineural hearing loss.

## Correcting Hearing Damage

Conductive hearing loss can usually be treated. If fluid as a result of infection has accumulated in the middle ear, medicines can clear up the infection. Once the problem is corrected, hearing usually returns to normal.

Sensorineural hearing loss is permanent. It can be corrected only with hearing aids or other devices that increase the ability to hear. People who have badly damaged inner ears can have cochlear implants surgically inserted in their ears, as shown in **Figure 12.** A person with a cochlear implant hears differently from people with normal cochlea, but the implant allows for full communication.

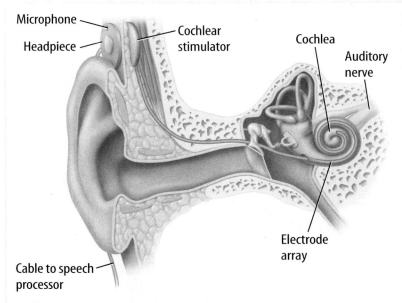

Microphone — Headpiece — Cochlear stimulator — Cochlea — Auditory nerve — Electrode array — Cable to speech processor

**Figure 12** Cochlear implants allow people with severe damage to their inner ears to detect human speech and other sounds so they can communicate normally.

**Determine** which parts of the cochlear implant transmit vibrations instead of the ear.

# Hearing in Other Mammals

Most mammals use a system for hearing that is similar to the hearing system of humans. However, some mammals possess qualities that allow them to hear certain sounds better than humans can.

## Redirecting Sound

Have you ever watched a dog or a cat move its ears around? You might have noticed that these animals rotate their ears very often, especially when they are tracking or hunting. As shown in **Figure 13,** some mammals use their external ears to redirect sound into their auditory canals. This helps them to determine the direction from which the sound is coming and also can help them to detect faint sounds, giving them the ability to hear predators and prey easily.

 How does the shape of the bat's outer ear differ from the shape of a human's outer ear?

## Echolocation

Sound waves can reflect off hard surfaces, just as a light wave reflects off a shiny surface. A reflected sound wave is called an **echo.** The amount of time it takes an echo to bounce back depends on how far away the reflecting surface is.

Some mammals use a method called echolocation, shown in **Figure 14,** to navigate and hunt. Bats, for example, make high-frequency calls and then listen for the echoes. When a bat hears an echo, it can determine the position and identity of objects in its path. Dolphins and whales also use echolocation. By making clicks that bounce off objects in the ocean, they are able to navigate.

 Name two ways certain mammals can use their ears and their hearing that humans cannot.

**Figure 13** Many mammals move their external ears to better collect sounds.

**Identify** animals you have seen live or on television that adjust their external ears to sense sounds better.

# Visualizing Echolocation

**Figure 14**
Many bats emit ultrasonic—very high frequency—sounds. The sound waves bounce off objects, and bats locate prey by returning echoes. Known as echolocation, this technique is also used by dolphins, which produce clicking sounds as they hunt. The diagrams below show how a bat uses echolocation to capture a flying insect.

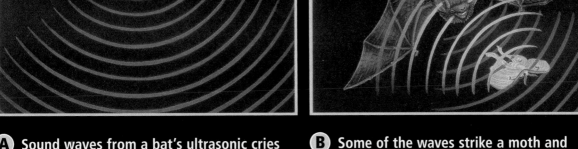

**A** Sound waves from a bat's ultrasonic cries spread out in front of it.

**B** Some of the waves strike a moth and bounce back to the bat.

**C** The bat determines the moth's location by continuing to emit cries, then changes its course to catch the moth.

**D** By emitting a continuous stream of ultrasonic cries, the bat homes is on the moth and captures its prey.

# The Human Ear

The human ear is made up of many tiny parts that work together to interpret sound waves for the brain. Sound is conducted through tiny bones and fluid-filled chambers, where the deflection of tiny hairs determines the type of sound a person hears. Human hearing can be temporarily or permanently damaged by illness or injury to the ears. Treatments can restore permanent hearing loss only partially, so it is important to avoid damage to begin with.

Some animals are able to move their outer ears to better collect sound, and other animals are able to determine the position of objects by the reflection of the sounds the animals make.

# LESSON 2  Review

## Summarize

Create your own lesson summary as you design a **study web**.

1. **Write** the lesson title, number, and page numbers at the top of a sheet of paper.

2. **Scan** the lesson to find the **red** main headings.

3. **Organize** these headings clockwise on branches around the lesson title.

4. **Review** the information under each **red** heading to design a branch for each **blue** subheading.

5. **List** 2–3 details, key terms, and definitions from each **blue** subheading on branches extending from the main heading branches.

 ELA7: W 2.5

##  Standards Check

### Using Vocabulary

1. **Diagram** the inner, middle, and outer ear. Label the external ear, the auditory canal, the tympanic membrane, the bones of the middle ear, and the cochlea. **5.g**

2. **Describe** the function of the middle ear. **5.g**

### Understanding Main Ideas

3. **Infer** why rabbits have such long ears. **5.g**

4. **Discuss** how the inner ear senses sound waves. **5.g**

5. The least amount of hearing loss would occur with damage to the
   A. outer ear
   B. cochlea
   C. stapes
   D. oval window  **5.g**

6. **Sequence** Draw a graphic organizer like the one below about the movement of a sound beginning with the vibration of an object and ending with the brain processing the sound. **5.g**

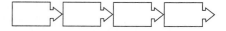

### Applying Science

7. **Design** A cochlear implant is made of human-made parts. If you were designing something that would take the place of a cochlea, what kinds of materials would you use, and why? **5.g**

8. **Hypothesize** If scuba divers come to the surface too quickly they can rupture their eardrums. How would this affect their hearing? **5.g**

**Science Online**

For more practice, visit **Standards Check** at ca7.msscience.com.

# MiniLab

# How does an ear hear?

00:25 minutes

Alexander Graham Bell invented an ear model to study sound. You too can make a mechanical ear and watch it work.

## Procedure

1. Read and complete a lab safety form.

2. Stretch a piece of **plastic wrap** across the end of a long **paper roll** (such as the core of a roll of paper towels or gift wrap) and fasten it with an **elastic band.**

3. What do the bones of your inner ear look like? Design these using **thin cardboard** and attach them in the tube with **tape** to model the bones in your ear.

4. Attach a **disk of shiny foil** to one end of the roll. Attach another shiny disk of foil to the plastic-wrap "eardrum" on the tube. This will complete the middle ear.

5. Make an outer ear from a **cone of cardboard** with a hole at its end. Place it on the inside of the tube.

6. Place the middle of the model of the ear on a box, leaving the ends of the rolls hanging off the front and back.

7. Shine a light onto the shiny foil disk. Ask a partner to talk into the ear. Watch for vibrations as he or she does so.

8. Try out different sounds. Record your observations.

## Analysis

1. **Draw** your model of an ear and draw a model of a human ear. Match up the parts.

2. **Evaluate** your model of an ear. How is it like a human ear? How is it different? How could you improve the model?

##  Science Content Standards

**5.g** Students know how to relate the structures of the eye and ear to their functions.

**7.d** Construct scale models, maps, and appropriately labeled diagrams to communicate scientific knowledge (e.g., motion of Earth's plates and cell structure).

# Lab

## Use the Internet:
# Animal Hearing

### Materials

computer with
  internet access
pen or pencil
paper
poster

### Science Content Standards

**5.g** Students know how to relate the structures of the eye and ear to their function.
**7.b** Use a variety of print and electronic resources (including the World Wide Web) to collect information and evidence as part of a research project.
**7.e** Communicate the steps and results from an investigation in written reports and oral presentations.

## Problem

Cats can identify the size and location of a mouse in the grass by listening to the sounds it makes. Cats have much better hearing than do humans. Sharks can hear sounds in the water up to a kilometer away. How do animals hear? There are many different adaptations and ways that animals receive sound.

## Form a Hypothesis

Form a hypothesis about why different animals hear in different ways. Think about protection, hunting, mating, and communication with other members of their own species.

## Collect Data and Make Observations

1. Brainstorm a concept web containing categories of information about animal hearing.

2. Visit ca7.msscience.com to research information about animal hearing to fit the various categories of your concept web. Consider the Analyze and Conclude questions as you research.

3. Make a table of your research to help you stay organized.

4. Compare your research to that of your classmates. Did they discover something that you did not? Are there animals that they researched that you did not?

5. Create a large concept-web poster to display the class information.

| Animal hearing | | | |
|---|---|---|---|
| **Animal** | **Method of Hearing** | **Special Adaptions** | **Benefit of this Type of Hearing** |
| | | | |
| | | | |
| | | | |
| | | | |
| | | | |

## Analyze and Conclude

1. **Identify** adaptations that certain animals have to give them excellent hearing.
2. **Research** whether the size of an animal's ears affects its hearing and why.
3. **Define** echolocation.
4. **Identify** animals that can hear the highest pitches of sound. Which animals hear the lowest pitches?
5. **Identify** some functions of animal hearing.
6. **Explain** how animals hear under water.
7. **Identify** differences among different types of animal hearing. What are some similarities? Can you group animals according to the types of hearing that they have?
8. **Identify** things that humans have learned about communication and sound by studying animals.
9. **Identify** issues that you have become interested in as a result of your research on this project and that you would like to continue to research.

## Communicate

**WRITING in Science**

Create a three- to six-page report using your research. Use headings to organize your report. Your report can have headings based on the topics you brainstormed in the Analyze and Conclude questions, such as ear size, adaptations, and underwater hearing. Include a concept web on the front page as a table of contents for your report.

# Real World Science

## Become a Speech Therapist

Would you like to help children who have hearing impairments? A language, speech, and hearing specialist teaches students who have trouble hearing, speaking, or understanding speech to communicate better. These specialists involve the student, guardians, and school staff in the therapy. You will need to take science and education classes in high school and college and consider a masters degree.

Visit **Careers** at **ca7.msscience.com** to find out more about what a speech therapist does. **Write** a paragraph about how speech therapists help students. Mention five different places where the work of this specialist might be needed.

## Cochlear Implants

A cochlear implant can allow people who are deaf or hard of hearing to be able to interpret the sounds they hear. It does not amplify the sounds, but it takes them in and sends electronic signals to the brain, which the person can learn to interpret. Pathways associated with hearing are laid early in life, so children and adults who have lost their hearing later are the best candidates for the implants.

Visit **Technology** at **ca7.msscience.com** to learn more about cochlear implants. Pretend you are training a person who has just received a cochlear implant. **Write** a dialogue that addresses three problems these patients experience. How do you address these problems and how does the person react?

# Good Vibrations

Have you ever heard of playing an instrument you don't have to touch? In 1917, Russian musician/engineer Leon Termin invented an instrument that uses the space between it and the body of the performer to alter the pitch and loudness of the tone produced. It was used for background noises in "space alien" movies of the 1940s–1960s. The design and concept influenced people who developed synthesizers and electronic music.

Visit **History** at ca7.msscience.com to find out more about the theremin. Pretend you are at a theremin concert. What sort of pieces are played? What sort of sounds do you hear? Who is performing? **Write** a 300- to 500-word essay that reviews the event and explains how it is different from a usual concert.

# NOISE POLLUTION

Many municipalities have laws that ban noises of certain types, at certain times, or above a certain loudness. Loud noise can disturb thoughts, concentration, and sleep. It can cause a loss of income for businesses and a decline in property value for homeowners. In some instances, loud noise can contribute to hearing damage.

Visit **Society** at ca7.msscience.com to read California's laws on noise. Try to find the laws for your municipality, if any. If a neighbor plays his stereo loudly all the time and makes it hard for you to study, what could you do?

**The BIG Idea** Sound is a wave that interacts with cells in your ear so you can hear noises.

## Lesson 1 Sound
**5.g, 7.b**

**Main Idea** **Sound is a compression wave.**

- Sound is a compression wave.
- Vibrations create sound waves.
- Loudness is a person's ability to judge how much energy a sound wave carries.
- The decibel scale is used to measure the amount of energy in a sound wave.
- A sound with a high pitch has a high frequency.

- **amplitude** (p. 475)
- **compression wave** (p. 473)
- **decibel scale** (p. 476)
- **loudness** (p. 475)
- **pitch** (p. 477)

## Lesson 2 The Ear and Hearing
**5.g, 7.b, 7.d, 7.e**

**Main Idea** **The ear detects sound waves that pass through the three parts of the ear and bend small hairs in the inner ear.**

- The outer ear includes the external ear and the auditory canal.
- The middle ear conducts vibrations to the inner ear.
- The labyrinth, or cochlea, in the inner ear contains sensory cells that send signals to the brain.
- The sensory cells in the cochlea contain hairs that bend when sounds of different frequencies hit them.
- Some mammals use their external ear to redirect sounds.
- Bats, dolphins, and whales use echolocation to navigate and hunt.
- Damage to any of the structures in the ear can cause hearing loss.
- Hearing damage to the middle ear is usually treated with medicine. Damage to the inner ear requires hearing aids or cochlear implants.

- **auditory canal** (p. 481)
- **cochlea** (p. 483)
- **echo** (p. 486)
- **external ear** (p. 481)
- **incus** (p. 482)
- **malleus** (p. 482)
- **stapes** (p. 482)
- **tympanic membrane** (p. 482)

**STUDY TO GO** Download quizzes, key terms, and flash cards from **ca7.msscience.com**.

# Linking Vocabulary and Main Ideas

Use the vocabulary terms from page 494 to complete this concept map.

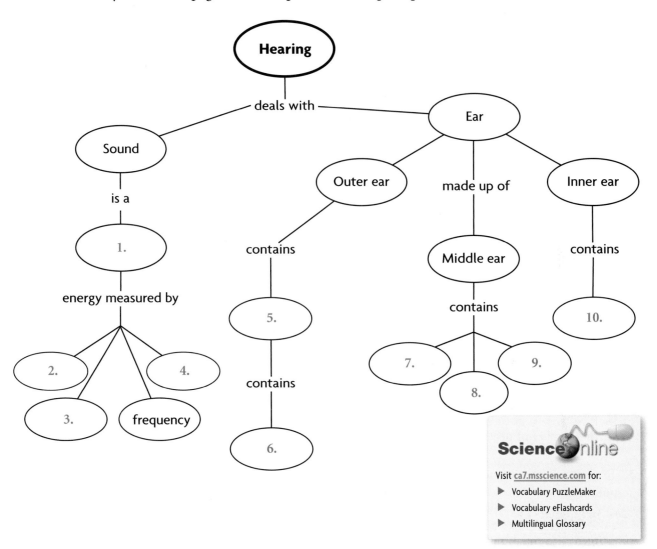

**Science Online**

Visit ca7.msscience.com for:
▶ Vocabulary PuzzleMaker
▶ Vocabulary eFlashcards
▶ Multilingual Glossary

## Using Vocabulary

**Fill in the blanks with the correct vocabulary word or words.**

**11.** The loudness of a sound wave is measured on the _____.

**12.** The _____ separates the outer and middle ear.

**13.** If a wave has regions of _____ that are very tightly packed together, this means the wave carries a lot of energy.

**14.** Hairs on cells in the _____ bend when they are hit by sound waves.

**15.** Horses can easily move their _____, but humans cannot.

**16.** Bats use _____ to hunt for prey.

# Understanding Main Ideas

*Choose the word or phrase that best answers the question.*

1. If these sound waves are traveling at the same speed, which one has a higher frequency?

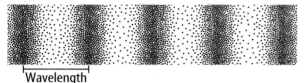

Wavelength

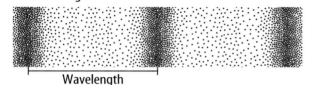

Wavelength

  **A.** the top wave
  **B.** the bottom wave
  **C.** It is impossible to tell from the diagram.
  **D.** Both waves have the same frequency.   `5.g`

2. Which property of waves is not related to how much energy they carry?
  **A.** amplitude
  **B.** loudness
  **C.** pitch
  **D.** the number of decibels it measures   `5.g`

3. To what part of a sound wave is the arrow pointing?

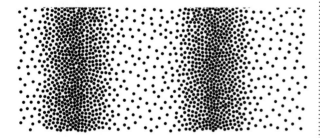

  **A.** a region of compression
  **B.** a region of rarefaction
  **C.** a wavelength
  **D.** a decibel   `5.g`

4. Which property of a sound wave changes as its energy decreases?
  **A.** wavelength
  **B.** frequency
  **C.** pitch
  **D.** amplitude   `5.g`

5. Which is not a bone in the middle ear?
  **A.** stapes
  **B.** incus
  **C.** cochlea
  **D.** malleus   `5.g`

6. What part of the ear is most important for collecting sound waves from the environment?
  **A.** eustachian tube
  **B.** sensory cells
  **C.** tympanic membrane
  **D.** external ear   `5.g`

7. What is a purpose of echolocation?
  **A.** navigation
  **B.** building a shelter
  **C.** camouflage
  **D.** fighting disease   `5.g`

8. To what part of the ear is the arrow pointing?

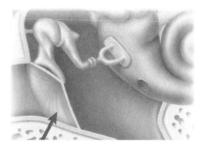

  **A.** tympanic membrane
  **B.** auditory canal
  **C.** cochlea
  **D.** sensory cell   `5.g`

## Applying Science

**9. Imagine** you have an instrument that measures sound in decibels. A sound registers as 50 dB. What kind of sound might it be? Would it be something like the sound of a page of this book turning or more like the sound of a door slamming shut? **5.g**

**10. Explain** how air molecules are affected when the amplitude of a sound wave decreases as it moves farther from the source that created it. **5.g**

**11. Explain** how bats use sound waves for hunting. **5.g**

**12. Compare and contrast** conductive hearing loss and sensorineural hearing loss. **5.g**

**Use the figure below for question 13.**

**13. Describe** the function of the three labeled bones in the diagram below. **5.g**

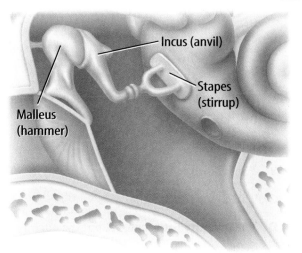

Incus (anvil)

Stapes (stirrup)

Malleus (hammer)

**14. Explain** how a train engine bumping into a line of railroad cars resting on a track is similar to a sound wave. **5.g**

**15. Explain** how two sounds affect your ears when one is 30 dB and the other is 60 dB. Both have a frequency of 15,000 Hz. **5.g**

**16. Infer** how earplugs change the sound waves that a person hears. People who are exposed to loud noises, such as airplane mechanics and musicians, often wear earplugs. **5.g**

*WRITING in* **Science**

**17. Some** cities and townships have laws banning loud noise in certain areas or during certain times. Research noise pollution laws in your area and write a persuasive argument for or against the established regulations. If no such laws exist, propose something appropriate for your area. **ELA7: W 2.4**

## Cumulative Review

**18. Compare** and contrast the path and processing of a sound wave in the ear and a light wave in the eye. **6.c**

**19. Compare and contrast** the geological time scale to the decibel scale. What does each measure? What units are used for each and how do these change with the scale? **4.g**

**20. Recall** how pressure is important in the cardio-pulmonary system. How is pressure also important in the inner ear? **6.j**

## Applying Math

**Use the graph on page 479 to answer questions 21 through 23.**

**21.** According to the graph, which group received the highest percentage of complaints in NYC? **MA7: SP 1.1**

**22.** In NYC, approximately how many times more people complained to their neighbors than complained to the government help line? **MA7: SP 1.1**

**23.** How many groups received less than 10 percent of noise complaints in the USA? **MA7: SP 1.1**

# Standards Assessment

**Use the table below for questions 1 and 2.**

| Decibel Scale | |
|---|---|
| **Sound Source** | **Loudness (dB)** |
| Jet plane taking off | 150 |
| Running lawn mower | 100 |
| Average home | 50 |
| Whisper | 15 |

**1 The table above shows typical sound intensity values on a decibel scale. Which of the following would you expect to be the approximate sound intensity of a noisy restaurant?**

**A** 20 dB

**B** 40 dB

**C** 80 dB

**D** 120 dB

5.g

**2 What sound intensity level would you expect to be painful to most humans?**

**A** 30 dB

**B** 60 dB

**C** 90 dB

**D** 120 dB

5.g

**3 What is the maximum range of sound frequencies that humans can hear?**

**A** 0–150 Hz

**B** 0–200 Hz

**C** 20–5000 Hz

**D** 20–20,000 Hz

5.g

**4 If the intensity of a sound increases by 20 dB, by what factor is the energy carried by the sound wave increased?**

**A** 2 times

**B** 20 times

**C** 100 times

**D** 200 times

5.g

**5 A person produces sound by clapping cymbals together. Describe how you hear the sound the cymbals produce.**

**A** cymbals→inner ear→middle ear→outer ear →brain

**B** cymbals→outer ear→middle ear→inner ear →brain

**C** cymbals→vibrations from the ground →felt in the feet→brain

**D** cymbals→vibrations from the air →felt by skin→brain

5.g

**6 What happens if the person claps the cymbals harder together?**

**A** It makes no difference.

**B** The intensity is higher.

**C** The intensity is lower.

**D** The intensity is unchanged, but the pitch is higher.

5.g

**7 What unit is used to measure frequency?**

**A** decibel

**B** hertz

**C** meters

**D** seconds

5.g



Science Online Standards Assessment ca7.msscience.com

**8** The diagram below shows four different sound waves.

Wave 1

Wave 2

Wave 3

Wave 4

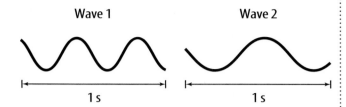

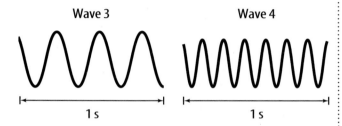

**Which wave will have the loudest sound?**

**A** Wave 1

**B** Wave 2

**C** Wave 3

**D** Wave 4    5.g

**9** Which property of a sound wave determines the pitch of the sound?

**A** amplitude

**B** direction

**C** frequency

**D** speed    5.g

**10** What is the term for how humans perceive sound?

**A** amplitude

**B** frequency

**C** loudness

**D** pitch    5.g

**11** For a sound with a low pitch, what else is always low?

**A** amplitude

**B** frequency

**C** wavelength

**D** wave velocity    5.g

**12** What does the outer ear do to sound waves?

**A** amplifies them

**B** converts them

**C** gathers them

**D** scatters them    5.g

**13** Use the diagram of the ear below to answer the question below.

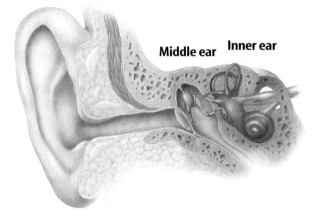

Outer ear

Middle ear  Inner ear

**What part of the ear is damaged by continuous loud noise?**

**A** inner ear

**B** middle ear

**C** outer ear

**D** all of the above    5.g

# The Human Reproductive System

## The BIG Idea

In humans, fertilization and embryo development take place inside a female's body.

### LESSON 1 · 5.d, 7.a
**Reproductive Systems**

**Main Idea** The structures of the human reproductive systems are specialized for the production of offspring.

### LESSON 2
**5.e, 7.a, 7.b, 7.c, 7.d**

**Development Before Birth**

**Main Idea** The normal development of a fetus depends on the good health of its mother.

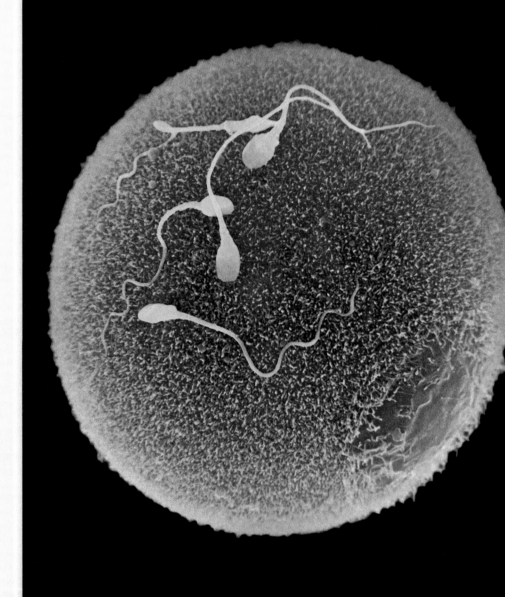

### Sorry, but only one sperm per egg!

This scanning electron microscope image enlarges human sperm cells on a human egg cell thousands of times. You will read in this chapter that after one sperm cell enters an egg cell, other sperm cells cannot.

**Science *Journal*** Imagine that you are a sperm cell entering an egg cell. Describe your journey to the egg cell's nucleus.

## Is it a boy or a girl?

Each human's genetic makeup comes from his or her parents. Who determines a child's gender?

### Procedure

1. Obtain a bag containing two **flat, wooden craft sticks** from your teacher. Open your bag and remove the sticks. You will have sticks labeled $X$ and $X$ (female) or $X$ and $Y$ (male). These are chromosomes.

2. Find someone with the opposite pair. This is your partner.

3. Put your sticks back in your own bag.

4. Each of you should draw a stick from your own bag. Record the letters and the gender of the offspring they represent.

5. Repeat steps 3 and 4 nine more times.

6. Calculate the number of male offspring and the number of female offspring.

### Think About This

- **Infer** which parent determines gender.

- **Compare** the numbers of male offspring and female offspring for the entire class.

 2.b, 7.c

Visit ca7.msscience.com to:

▶ view **Concepts in Motion**

▶ explore Virtual Labs

▶ access content-related Web links

▶ take the Standards Check

**Reproductive Organs**
Make the following Foldable to organize information about the organs of the male and female reproductive systems and functions.

▷ **STEP 1** **Fold** a sheet of paper in half lengthwise. Make the back edge about 2 cm longer than the front edge.

▷ **STEP 2** **Fold** in half again.

▷ **STEP 3** **Unfold** the paper once. **Cut** along the fold of the top flap to make two flaps. **Label** the flaps Male Reproduction and Female Reproduction.

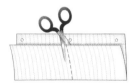

**Monitoring Your Comprehension**
As you read Lesson 1, list each reproductive organ and its function under the appropriate tab.

# Get Ready to Read

## Take Notes

**①Learn It!**  The best way for you to remember information is to write it down, or take notes. Good note-taking is useful for studying and research. When you are taking notes, it is helpful to

- phrase the information in your own words;
- restate ideas in short, memorable phrases;
- stay focused on main ideas and only the most important supporting details.

**②Practice It!**  Make note-taking easier by using a chart to help you organize information clearly. Write the main ideas in the left column. Then write at least three supporting details in the right column. Read the text from Lesson 1 of this chapter under the heading *Egg Production*, on page 508. Then take notes using a chart, such as the one below.

| Main Idea | Supporting Details |
|-----------|--------------------|
|           | 1.<br>2.<br>3.     |
|           | 1.<br>2.<br>3.     |

**③Apply It!**  As you read this chapter, make a chart of the main ideas. Next to each main idea, list at least two supporting details.

# Target Your Reading

Use this to focus on the main ideas as you read the chapter.

**1 Before you read** the chapter, respond to the statements below on your worksheet or on a numbered sheet of paper.

- Write an **A** if you **agree** with the statement.
- Write a **D** if you **disagree** with the statement.

**2 After you read** the chapter, look back to this page to see if you've changed your mind about any of the statements.

- If any of your answers changed, explain why.
- Change any false statements into true statements.
- Use your revised statements as a study guide.

## Reading Tip

Read one or two paragraphs first and take notes after you read. You are likely to take down too much information if you take notes as you read.

**Science Online**

Print a worksheet of this page at ca7.msscience.com.

| Before You Read<br>A or D | Statement | After You Read<br>A or D |
|---|---|---|
| | **1** Every child is genetically related to one male and one female parent. | |
| | **2** A female's reproductive system does not begin producing eggs until she reaches sexual maturity. | |
| | **3** Both males and females begin to lose the ability to reproduce after age 54. | |
| | **4** Millions of sperm fertilize one egg. | |
| | **5** A developing fetus' heart does not begin to beat until after 24 weeks of development. | |
| | **6** The umbilical cord and placenta supply the fetus with oxygen and nutrients from the mother's blood. | |
| | **7** A mother's use of drugs or alcohol can lead to health problems for her child as the child grows and develops. | |

### Science Content Standards

**5.d** Students know how the reproductive organs of the human female and male generate eggs and sperm and how sexual activity may lead to fertilization and pregnancy.

**7.a** Select and use appropriate tools and technology (including calculators, computers, balances, spring scales, microscopes, and binoculars) to perform tests, collect data, and display data.

## Reading Guide

### What *You'll Learn*

▶ **List** the organs of the male and female reproductive systems.

▶ **Compare and contrast** the development of sperm and eggs.

▶ **Sequence** the path traveled by sperm from formation to fertilization.

▶ **Describe** ovulation and the menstrual cycle.

### Why *It's Important*

Knowing how human reproductive systems work will enable you to make well-informed decisions about your reproductive health.

### Vocabulary

| | |
|---|---|
| scrotum | uterus |
| seminiferous tubule | fallopian tube |
| epididymis | follicle |
| penis | ovulation |
| urethra | menstrual cycle |
| vagina | |

# Reproductive Systems

**Main Idea** The structures of the human reproductive systems are specialized for the production of offspring.

**Real-World Reading Connection** It's the first day of school. You notice that some students changed a lot over the summer but others hardly changed at all. Although you and your classmates are about the same ages, you are at different stages of physical development. Your reproductive systems are at different stages of development, too.

## Male Reproductive System

Adult males have many body characteristics that differ from adult females. Men usually have more body hair, deeper voices, and larger, more muscular bodies than women do. These features develop as boys get older and their reproductive systems grow toward maturity.

As you read in Chapter 3, testes (singular, testis) are male animal organs that produce sperm. Human males have two testes, as shown in **Figure 1.** A human male's testes do not begin to produce sperm until his reproductive system matures.

 Which human male reproductive organ produces sperm?

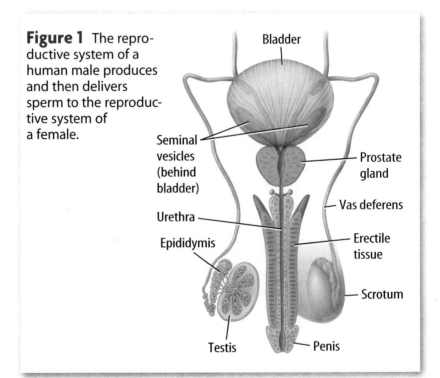

**Figure 1** The reproductive system of a human male produces and then delivers sperm to the reproductive system of a female.

Bladder

Seminal vesicles (behind bladder)

Urethra

Epididymis

Prostate gland

Vas deferens

Erectile tissue

Scrotum

Testis

Penis

## Male Reproductive Organs

The testes are inside a baglike structure called the **scrotum.** It hangs outside the male's body cavity, which keeps the testes slightly cooler than the rest of the body. Normal human body temperature is too warm for sperm production. The cooler temperature in the scrotum enables sperm production.

**Organs of Sperm Production**  The testes contain tightly coiled tubes called **seminiferous tubules** (se mih NIHF rus • TOOB yewlz), where sperm are produced. As shown in **Figure 2,** sperm travel from seminiferous tubules to a storage organ within the scrotum called the **epididymis** (eh puh DIH duh mus). It connects to muscular ducts or tubes called the vas deferens (VAS • DEF uh runz).

**Organs of Sperm Transfer**  The male organ that transfers sperm to a female's reproductive tract is a **penis** (PEE nus). During sexual activity, sperm move from the vas deferens into a short ejaculation (ih ja kyuh LAY shun) duct that connects to a tube called the **urethra** (yoo REE thruh). The urethra extends to the end of the penis and carries sperm out of the body. The urethra also carries urine, but ejaculation and urination never occur at the same time.

When a male is sexually excited, the tissues of the penis fill with blood. This extra blood causes an erection, or firming of the penis. An erection is needed for the penis to enter a female's reproductive tract. During an ejaculation, sperm leave the epididymus, enter the vas deferens, move to the urethra, travel down the urethra, and out the end of the penis. It is important to know that sperm can leave the penis without the male's knowledge, either before ejaculation or during sexual activity that does not result in ejaculation.

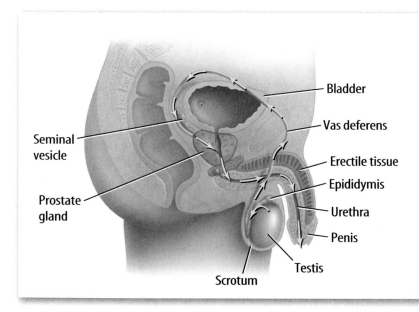

Seminal vesicle

Prostate gland

Scrotum

Testis

Bladder

Vas deferens

Erectile tissue

Epididymis

Urethra

Penis

**Figure 2** Arrows show the path sperm take as they travel from the testes through and finally out of the penis.

**Identify** the male reproductive organs that sperm travel through when ejaculation occurs.

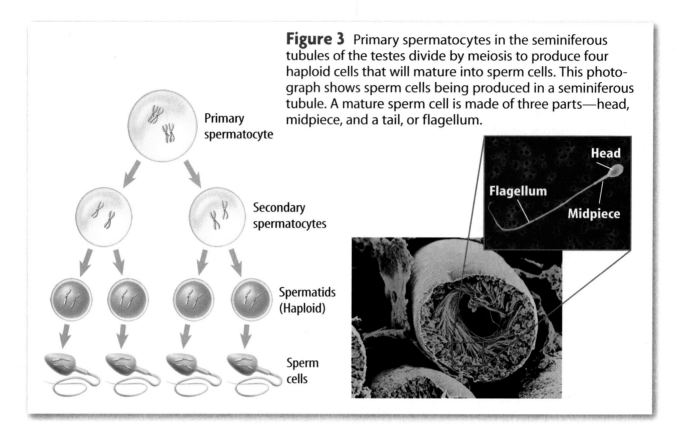

**Figure 3** Primary spermatocytes in the seminiferous tubules of the testes divide by meiosis to produce four haploid cells that will mature into sperm cells. This photograph shows sperm cells being produced in a seminiferous tubule. A mature sperm cell is made of three parts—head, midpiece, and a tail, or flagellum.

## Sperm Production

Males start producing sperm during puberty (PYEW bur tee), which usually begins when they are 10–16 years of age. Sperm production occurs by meiosis in cells that line the seminiferous tubules, as shown in **Figure 3.** It takes 65–75 days to produce a mature sperm cell, also shown in **Figure 3.** A male can continue to make healthy sperm for the rest of his life.

## Sperm and Semen

Each sperm consists of a head, a midpiece, and a tail. The head contains a nucleus, and the midpiece contains mitochondria that release energy. The tail, or flagellum, whips back and forth and propels the sperm forward.

A male ejaculates about 2–5 mL of semen (SEE mun) on average. Semen contains a liquid made by glands in a male's reproductive system and about 100 to 650 million sperm. The seminal vesicles are a pair of glands that makes most of the liquid in semen. They produce a thick, yellowish liquid that contains mucus, ascorbic acid (vitamin C), hormonelike substances that control cell activity, and an enzyme that helps thicken the semen. This liquid also contains sugar that is an energy supply for sperm. The prostate gland also makes some of the liquid in semen. It produces a thin, milky liquid containing enzymes and nutrients.

 Which two glands make the liquid in semen?

# Female Reproductive System

A female's reproductive system produces eggs. This system is also the place where a fertilized egg can grow and develop into a baby. Recall that a male begins producing sperm when he reaches puberty. A female begins producing eggs before she is born.

## Female Reproductive Organs

Unlike a male, all the reproductive organs of a female are located inside her abdomen, as shown in **Figure 4.** Two folds of skin, called labia (LAY bee uh), protect the opening to a female's reproductive system. Beyond the opening, inside the female's body is a thin-walled chamber called the **vagina** (vuh JI nuh). This is where semen is deposited.

**Uterus** Above the vagina, further inside the body, is the **uterus** (YEW tuh rus). It is a thick, muscular organ inside which a fertilized egg can develop. A uterus is normally about the size and shape of a pear, but it enlarges during pregnancy. A tissue called the endometrium (en doh MEE tree um) lines the uterus. The neck, or opening, of the uterus into the vagina is called the cervix (SUR vihks). During childbirth, the cervix gets wider, or dilates. This enables the baby to move into the vagina and out of the mother's body.

**Ovaries and Fallopian Tubes** A pair of organs called ovaries (singular, ovary) produces eggs. An egg released from an ovary moves into a **fallopian tube** (fuh LOH pee un • TOOB) or oviduct that connects the ovary to the uterus, also shown in **Figure 4.** Fertilization usually occurs while the egg is in a fallopian tube. An egg cell has no flagellum, so it cannot move on its own like a sperm cell can. Recall from Chapter 1 that the surface of a cell can have hairlike structures called cilia that move back and forth. The cells on the inside surface of a fallopian tube have cilia. These cilia move an egg toward the uterus.

**WORD ORIGIN**
uterus
from Latin *uterus*; means *womb, belly*

**Figure 4** In the female reproductive system, eggs are produced by meiosis in ovaries. An egg travels from an ovary, into a fallopian tube, then toward the uterus.
**Compare and contrast** the way a sperm moves and the way an egg moves.

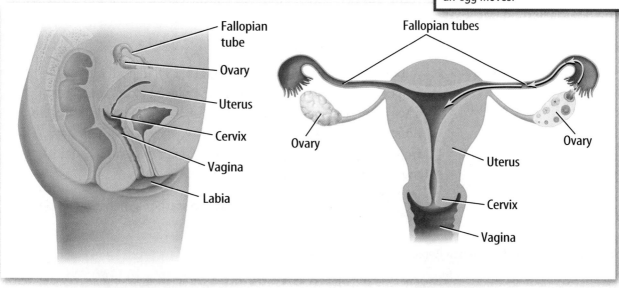

Fallopian tube
Ovary
Uterus
Cervix
Vagina
Labia

Fallopian tubes
Ovary
Ovary
Uterus
Cervix
Vagina

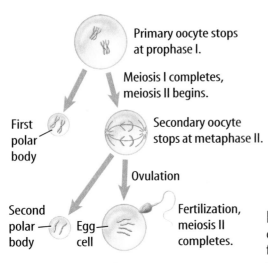

Primary oocyte stops at prophase I.

Meiosis I completes, meiosis II begins.

First polar body

Secondary oocyte stops at metaphase II.

Ovulation

Second polar body — Egg cell

Fertilization, meiosis II completes.

**Figure 5** Polar bodies produced during meiosis disintegrate and do not develop into egg cells. A follicle increases in size as it prepares to release an egg. The bottom of the photograph is a portion of the ovary from which this egg cell was released.

## Egg Production

Cell division by meiosis produces a human egg, as shown in **Figure 5.** Before a female is born, cells in her developing ovaries begin meiosis, but stop at the first phase, prophase I. The cells stopped at prophase I are called primary oocytes (OH uh sites). They remain unchanged until a female begins puberty.

Puberty in a human female usually begins between the ages of 9 and 13. At puberty, a female's body begins producing chemical signals that cause primary oocytes to continue meiosis. However, meiosis stops again at the second stage of meiosis, metaphase II. The cells stopped at metaphase II are called secondary oocytes. Secondary oocytes are the egg cells. A female usually produces only one egg cell every four weeks on average. An egg cell does not complete meiosis until fertilization occurs.

Cells of the ovary surround, protect, and nourish each egg cell. A **follicle** (FAH lih kul) is an egg cell and its surrounding cells. A female at puberty has about 400,000 follicles. The release of an egg from a follicle into a fallopian tube is called **ovulation** (ahv yuh LAY shun), also shown in **Figure 5.**

## Menstrual Cycle

Before a follicle releases an egg, other changes happen in a female's body. The changes that take place before, during, and after ovulation are called the **menstrual** (MEN stroo ul) **cycle.** As illustrated in **Figure 6,** a menstrual cycle lasts about 28 days. The first day of a menstrual **cycle** is the first day of menstrual bleeding, or menstrual flow.

 What event marks the start of a menstrual cycle?

**WORD ORIGIN**

follicle
from Latin *follicus;* means *little bag*

**ACADEMIC VOCABULARY**

cycle (SI kul)
*(noun)* a series of events that repeat
*The cycle of the seasons includes spring, summer, autumn, and winter.*

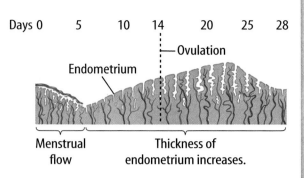

Days 0   5   10   14   20   25   28

Ovulation

Endometrium

Menstrual flow

Thickness of endometrium increases.

**Figure 6** During the menstrual cycle, the endometrium thickens in preparation for possible fertilization and development of a baby.

**Identify** which day of the menstrual cycle ovulation is most likely to happen.

**Menstrual Flow** During the menstrual cycle, the endometrium thickens and the number of blood vessels in it increases to support a fertilized egg. However, if a released egg is not fertilized, the endometrium breaks down and sloughs off. This tissue, some blood, and the unfertilized egg leave the vagina as menstrual flow. Menstrual flow usually lasts four to seven days. After menstrual flow stops, the endometrium thickens and its blood vessels regrow.

**Ovulation** About two weeks after the first day of menstrual flow, ovulation occurs. Usually, only one egg is released from one of a female's ovaries during a menstrual cycle. It takes about 24 to 48 hours for an egg to move down the fallopian tube and into the uterus. If the egg is fertilized, a zygote forms, cell divisions begin, and an embryo begins to develop. When the embryo enters the uterus, it attaches to, or implants in, the endometrium. If this happens, menstrual bleeding does not occur. The absence of menstrual bleeding is usually one of the first signs of pregnancy.

**Hormones** Chemical messengers called hormones regulate the timing of the menstrual cycle and ovulation. Some of the glands and organs that produce hormones, including hormones that regulate menstrual cycles, are shown in **Figure 7** on the following pages.

## Which hormones control ovulation?

The hormones LH and FSH help to control the menstrual cycle and ovulation.

| Day of Cycle | Units of LH in Blood | Units of FSH in Blood |
|---|---|---|
| 1 | 10 | 9 |
| 4 | 15 | 11 |
| 7 | 13 | 11 |
| 10 | 12 | 14 |
| 13 | 13 | 22 |
| 16 | 9 | 17 |
| 19 | 8 | 13 |
| 22 | 6 | 10 |
| 25 | 5 | 9 |
| 28 | 9 | 6 |

*Source: Carlson, Bruce M. Foundations of Embryology. New York: McGraw-Hill. 1996.*

### Data Analysis

1. **Graph** the data. Use different colors to graph LH and FSH.

2. **Highlight** The day of highest hormone concentration is called the LH or FSH surge. Highlight each surge on your graph.

3. **Compare** your graph to **Figure 6.** **Relate** the amounts of LH and FSH to the day of ovulation.

4. **Infer** what might happen if a woman produced too little LH and FSH.

 5.d, 7.a

 Try at Home

MA7: AF 1.5, MR 2.5

# Visualizing Hormones

### Figure 7

Your hormones regulate and coordinate many body functions, from reproduction to growth and development. They circulate in the blood and affect only specific cells. Glands and organs, including the nine shown here, produce hormones.

Melatonin (mel uh TOH nihn) is a hormone that might function as a body clock that regulates sleep/wake patterns. The pineal (PIE nee uhl) gland that is deep within the brain produces melatonin. ▶

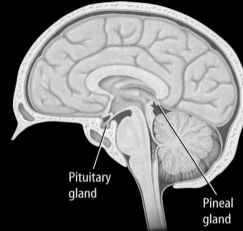

Pituitary gland

Pineal gland

Hormones related to body ▶ activities, from reproduction to growth, are produced by the pituitary (pih TEW uh ter ee) gland. It is about the size of a pea and is attached to the hypothalamus (hi poh THAL uh mus) of the brain.

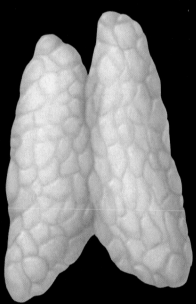

◀ The thymus (THI mus)—a gland in the upper chest behind the sternum—produces hormones that stimulate the production of certain infection-fighting cells.

Testosterone (tes TAHS tuh rohn) ▶ is a hormone that controls the development and maintenance of male sexual traits and plays an important role in the production of sperm. Testes produce testosterone.

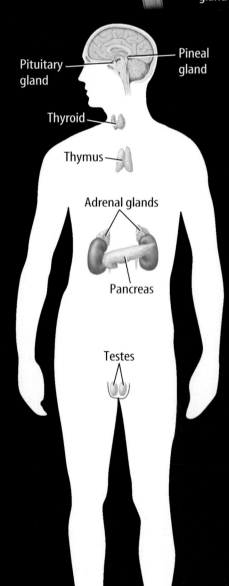

Pituitary gland

Pineal gland

Thyroid

Thymus

Adrenal glands

Pancreas

Testes

*Contributed by National Geographic*

◀ The thyroid gland produces hormones that regulate metabolic rate, control the uptake of calcium by bones, and promote normal nervous system development. It is in the front of the neck below the larynx.

PTH—a hormone that ▶ regulates calcium levels in the body and is essential for life—is produced by the parathyroid glands. They are four small glands attached to the back of the thyroid gland.

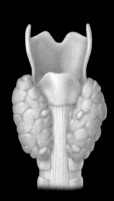

Pituitary gland

Pineal gland

Thyroid

Thymus

Adrenal glands

Pancreas

Ovaries

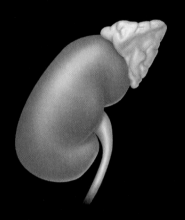

◀ The two adrenal glands produce a variety of hormones. Some play a critical role in helping your body adapt to physical and emotional stress. Others help stabilize blood sugar levels. An adrenal gland is on top of each kidney.

▼ Hormones that help control sugar levels in the blood are produced by the islets of Langerhans—tiny clusters of tissue scattered throughout the pancreas (PAN kree us).

◀ The ovaries produce estrogen (ES truh jun) and progesterone (proh JES tuh rohn). These hormones produce and maintain female sex characteristics and regulate the female reproductive cycle.

## Menopause

Sometime between the ages of 46 and 54, most women stop ovulating and no longer have menstrual cycles. This stage of life is called menopause (MEN uh pawz). Many women begin to lose the ability to reproduce before menopause, as early as their mid-30s. As a woman gets older, the eggs she produces decrease in quality, and it becomes more difficult for her to have a successful pregnancy. An important difference between males and females is that a male's reproductive system continues to function throughout his lifetime, but a female's reproductive system does not.

# Fertilization

Have you ever heard people say they were in the right place at the right time? The same might be said about sperm and fertilization. In humans, for a sperm to fuse with an egg cell, the sperm must swim to the right place—a fallopian tube—and at the right time—near the time of ovulation.

Sperm deposited in or near a female's vagina can swim into her reproductive tract, as shown in **Figure 8.** Most of these sperm will not make it to an egg. Some sperm swim into a fallopian tube that does not contain an egg. Some sperm swim in the opposite direction, away from the fallopian tubes. Other sperm might have genetic or physical defects that prevent them from fertilizing an egg even if they reach it. These facts help explain why millions of sperm are ejaculated to fertilize just one egg.

Normally, only one sperm fertilizes an egg, as shown in **Figure 8.** Once a sperm attaches to an egg, chemical reactions occur that block other sperm from entering the same egg. Sperm can live inside a female's reproductive tract for up to three days. Therefore, a female can become pregnant even if sexual intercourse occurs a couple days before she ovulates.

**SCIENCE USE V. COMMON USE**
fertilization

*Science Use* the joining of a sperm cell and an egg cell, forming a zygote. *Fertilization usually occurs in a woman's fallopian tubes.*

*Common Use* the application of a substance to soil to increase the soil's nutrients. *Fertilization of a garden's soil with aged animal manure can improve plant growth.*

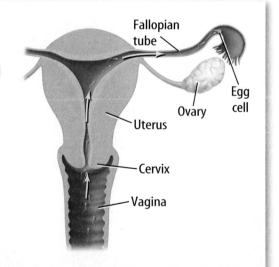

**Figure 8** From the vagina, a sperm must swim through the cervix, into the uterus, and then up a fallopian tube.

**Identify** the structure in which fertilization usually takes place.

# Reproductive Systems Summary

In this lesson, you learned that the male reproductive system includes several organs, such as the testes where sperm are produced. Other male organs contribute fluid to the semen in which sperm move.

The female reproductive system also consists of several organs, including ovaries in which eggs develop. A menstrual cycle lasts about 28 days. It includes the building up of the endometrium, ovulation, and, if fertilization does not take place, menstrual flow. If an egg is fertilized and a zygote implants in the endometrium, the menstrual cycle stops and pregnancy begins.

# LESSON 1 Review

## Summarize

Create your own lesson summary as you organize an **outline**.

1. **Scan** the lesson. Find and list the first **red** main heading.

2. **Review** the text after the heading and list 2–3 details about the heading.

3. **Find** and list each **blue** subheading that follows the **red** main heading.

4. **List** 2–3 details, key terms, and definitions under each **blue** subheading.

5. **Review** additional **red** main headings and their supporting **blue** subheadings. List 2–3 details about each.

 **ELA7:** W 2.5

## Standards Check

### Using Vocabulary

1. Distinguish between *vagina* and *uterus.* **5.d**

2. Write the definition of *menstrual cycle* in your own words. **5.d**

### Understanding Main Ideas

3. Which is not part of the female reproductive system? **5.d**

    A. epididymus

    B. uterus

    C. ovary

    D. endometrium

4. **Compare** the roles of a male and a female in reproduction. **5.d**

5. **Describe** what happens to an egg from ovulation to implantation in the wall of the uterus. **5.d**

6. **Explain** why a male produces millions of sperm when usually only one egg is available to be fertilized? **5.d**

7. What structures move an egg through a fallopian tube? **5.d**

    A. cilia

    B. flagella

    C. muscles

    D. seminal vesicles

8. **Compare** sperm production and egg production. **5.d**

### Applying Science

9. **Create** a table listing the male and female reproductive organs and their functions. **5.d**

10. **Sequence Information** Draw a graphic organizer like the one below to create a time line about the menstrual cycle. **5.d**

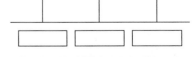

**Science** **O**nline
For more practice, visit **Standards Check** at ca7.msscience.com.

# Applying Math

## Hormone Levels and a Box-and-Whisker Plot

Hormone levels in humans vary within a standard range of normal. A group of ten women had LH levels measured in international units per liter (IU/L), as shown below, a few days following the end of their menstrual cycle.

1.6, 3.3, 4.2, 3.2, 5.3, 9.6, 2.2, 5.4, 5.6, 5.7

### Example

Construct a box-and-whisker plot of this data set.

**1** Order the data set from least to greatest value.

**2** Find the median or the middle value of the data set. Since there is an even number of data values, the median is the average of the two middle values (4.2 and 5.3) or 4.75.

**3** Find the middle value of the lower half of the ordered data—the lower quartile. The lower quartile is 3.2. Find the middle value of the upper half of the ordered data—the upper quartile. The upper quartile is 5.6.

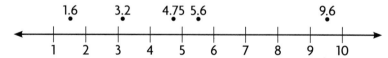

Median = 4.75

1.6, 2.2, 3.2, 3.3, 4.2, 5.3, 5.4, 5.6, 5.7, 9.6

Lower half of data     Upper half of data

**4** Draw a number line. The scale should include the median, the quartiles, and the least (1.6) and greatest (9.6) data values. The last two values are called the lower extreme and the upper extreme. Graph these five values as points above the line.

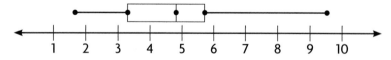

**5** Draw the box and whiskers. Each of the four parts of a box-and-whisker plot contains one fourth of the data.

## Practice Problems

1. Is an LH hormone value of 3.8 closer to the lower quartile or the median?

2. What is the range of these data?

**Science**⬤nline
For more math practice, visit **Math Practice** at ca7.msscience.com.

**Science Content Standards**

**5.e** Students know the function of the umbilicus and placenta during pregnancy.
**Also covers:** 7.a, 7.b, 7.c, 7.d

## Reading Guide

### What *You'll Learn*

▶ **Explain** the importance of the placenta and the umbilical cord to a fetus.

▶ **List** the major developmental stages of a fetus.

▶ **Infer** how a mother's lifestyle can affect her fetus.

### Why *It's Important*

Knowing how a fetus develops helps you understand how important it is for a pregnant woman to take good care of her health.

### Vocabulary

pregnancy          placenta
trimester          umbilical
fetus              cord
prenatal care

### Review Vocabulary

**embryo:** an animal in the early stages of development, before birth

# Development Before Birth

**Main Idea** The normal development of a fetus depends on the good health of its mother.

**Real-World Reading Connection** Did you know that some-one might have taken your picture before you were born? A sonogram uses sound waves to produce a video image of a fetus. It can help a medical provider determine if the fetus is develop-ing normally and whether it is a girl or a boy.

## Fetal Development

Recall from Chapter 3 that all sexually produced organisms begin life as a zygote that forms when a sperm fertilizes an egg. Cell divisions of a human zygote begin about 24 hours after fer-tilization. Cells continue to divide and, after about seven days, a hollow ball of more than 100 cells has formed, as shown in **Figure 9.** This ball of cells is the embryo that implants into the endometrium. After two weeks of growth, the cells begin to arrange themselves into three layers, also shown in **Figure 9.** Different body structures eventually form from each layer. Over a period of about nine months, a human embryo develops into a baby.

 **Reading Check** When do cell divisions of a human zygote begin?

**Figure 9** From the outer layer, nerves and skin develop; from the middle layer, heart, kid-neys, bones, and muscles; and from the inner layer, lungs, liver, and digestive system.

After 7 days

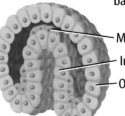

Hollow ball of cells

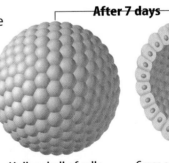

Cross section of hollow ball of cells

— Middle cell layer
— Inner cell layer
— Outer cell layer

After 14 days

## Growth and Development of Body Systems

The development of a baby within a female's uterus is called **pregnancy.** In humans, pregnancy usually lasts for 38 weeks after fertilization, or about 40 weeks after the beginning of the last menstrual cycle. When describing the many changes that take place during pregnancy, it is helpful to divide the nine months of pregnancy into three parts, called **trimesters.**

The first trimester is the first twelve weeks of pregnancy. By the end of the first trimester, an embryo has all the structures that will become the major organ systems of an adult. During the second and third trimesters, an embryo is called a **fetus** (FEE tus). A fetus changes as it continues to develop, as shown in **Table 1.** During the second trimester, the pregnant female can feel the fetus's movements. During the third trimester, the fetus grows rapidly, nearly tripling in size in preparation for birth.

 **Table 1** When might a fetus survive with intensive medical care?

**Concepts In Motion**
Interactive Table  To explore more about the stages of pregnancy, visit Tables at ca7.msscience.com.

### Table 1 Stages of Pregnancy

| Stage | Example | Development |
|---|---|---|
| First trimester | | By the end of the first trimester of pregnancy, an embryo has grown from a microscopic ball of cells to about 7.5 cm long, weighing about 23 g. Its heart is beating, and it can move its arms and legs. |
| Second trimester | | At the end of the second trimester, a fetus is about 25–30 cm long and frequently makes kicking movements. The fetus shown here is about 24 weeks old. A baby born at this stage of development cannot survive without intensive medical care. |
| Third trimester | | During the third trimester, a fetus usually triples in size. This fetus is 36 weeks old. A baby born at this stage of development probably would survive but might require medical care. |

## Premature Babies

Sometimes, infants are born prematurely, before development is complete. Premature babies can have difficulty surviving because some of their organs are not ready to function. The lungs are among the last organs to develop fully. Premature babies must often be cared for in the hospital until their lungs develop completely. Also, premature babies usually have low birth weights. Extremely premature and low birth weight infants can have physical challenges, learning difficulties, or behavioral problems as they grow older.

## Placenta and Umbilical Cord

During development, a growing fetus receives oxygen and nutrients from its mother. A pregnant woman receives carbon dioxide and other wastes from her fetus. This exchange of materials between a pregnant woman and her fetus takes place through a disk-shaped organ called the **placenta** (pluh SEN tuh). A placenta begins to form when an embryo first implants into the endometrium. It develops from tissues of both the fetus and the endometrium. The placenta contains many blood vessels from both the fetus and its mother, but they are not directly connected.

Substances enter and leave the body of a fetus through an **umbilical** (un BIH lih kul) **cord,** as shown in **Figure 11.** The umbilical cord contains two arteries and one vein that connect the fetus to the placenta. When a baby is born, its umbilical cord is cut, but a few inches of it remain attached to the baby's body. This portion of the cord is called the umbilicus (um BIH lih kus). After a few days, the umbilicus dries up and drops off. The place where it was attached to the body is called a navel, or belly button.

 **Reading Check** What is the function of the umbilical cord?

**Figure 10** Nutrients and oxygen move from the mother's blood into the placenta, through the umbilical cord, and then to the fetus. Wastes from the fetus move through the umbilical cord, to the placenta, and then into the mother's blood.

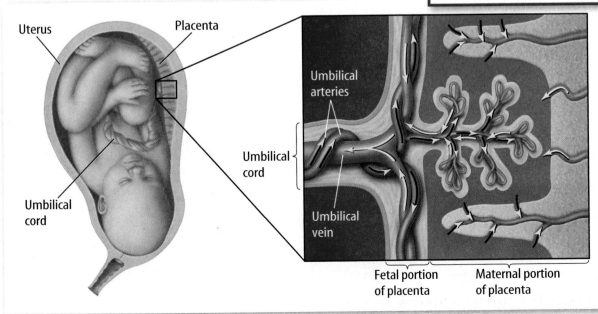

Uterus

Placenta

Umbilical cord

Umbilical arteries

Umbilical cord

Umbilical vein

Fetal portion of placenta

Maternal portion of placenta

# Fetal Health

Everything that happens in a woman's body has an effect on her developing fetus. Anything she does that could harm her health before or during her pregnancy could also harm her fetus. It is important for any woman who might become pregnant to take good care of her health. If she is in good health before she becomes pregnant, she has a better chance of having a healthy pregnancy and a healthy baby.

## Prenatal Care

Health care designed to protect the health of a pregnant woman and prevent problems in her developing fetus is called **prenatal care.** Research has shown that a pregnant woman who receives prenatal care from a certified health care provider has a better chance of delivering a healthy baby. A pregnant woman's prenatal care includes advice and information about nutrition, about viral infections, and about substances that could harm her fetus.

 **Reading Check** Why is prenatal care important?

## Nutrition

All the energy and nutrients a fetus needs for normal development must come from its mother. Vitamins, minerals, proteins, fats, and carbohydrates pass from mother to fetus through the placenta. To support her growing fetus, a pregnant woman needs to eat a healthy diet that includes dairy products, proteins, fruits, vegetables, and whole grains, such as those shown in **Figure 11.**

**Calories**  A pregnant woman is usually advised to add about 300 extra calories a day to her diet. The added calories supply the extra energy needed for the development of the fetus. However, it's best to choose healthy foods and avoid high-calorie foods that contain large amounts of sugar or fat, but few other nutrients.

**Figure 11**  A healthy diet for a pregnant woman includes foods such as those shown here.

**Infer** why it is important for a woman who might become pregnant to consume these types of food.

**Folic Acid** A fetus's spinal cord forms during the first weeks of pregnancy. Without a certain amount of folic acid, a form of vitamin B, spinal cord formation is abnormal. Doctors often recommend that pregnant women take vitamin **supplements** containing folic acid, in addition to eating a balanced diet.

**Caffeine** A pregnant woman should avoid caffeine, or consume it only in small amounts. Caffeine can increase a woman's blood pressure and heart rate, which can be stressful to her fetus.

## Environmental Factors

A pregnant woman can encounter substances in her environment, such as those in **Figure 12,** that present health risks for her fetus. She might inhale harmful substances, consume them with food or water, or absorb them through her skin. These substances can then pass through the placenta and into the fetus. For example, a pregnant woman is usually advised to avoid using pesticides or insect repellents. Chemicals in insecticides and other pesticides can cause premature birth, birth defects, or miscarriage—the loss of an embryo during the first trimester.

Lead is a chemical element sometimes found in air pollution, old paint, and electronics. It can be harmful to anyone, but is especially harmful to a fetus, an infant, or a young child. Pregnant women who have been exposed to high levels of lead have a higher risk of miscarriage, premature delivery, and low birth-weight babies.

**Figure 12** A pregnant woman is advised to avoid substances that could harm her fetus.

# Can folic acid prevent birth defects?

Ten of every 10,000 babies in the United States are born with a neural tube birth defect, such as spina bifida. It occurs when the bones of the spine do not form properly during the first month of pregnancy. The data table below shows how folic acid affects a woman's risk of having a baby with a neural tube defect.

| Effects of Folic Acid Supplements on Neural Tube Defects | | |
| --- | --- | --- |
| Folic Acid Taken Before or During Pregnancy | Babies Born with Neural Tube Defects | Babies Born Without Neural Tube Defects |
| Yes | 6 | 497 |
| No | 21 | 581 |

*from CDC*

## Data Analysis

1. **Calculate** the percentage of babies with neural tube defects born to women who took folic acid.

2. **Calculate** the percentage of babies born with neural tube defects to women who did not take folic acid.

3. **Compare** the percentages of babies with neural tube defects for the two groups.

4. **Analyze** Does folic acid prevent neural tube defects? Explain why or why not.

5. **Conclude** What conclusion can be made from the data?

5.e, 7.a

MA7: NS 1.0, NS 1.3

Try at Home

## Viruses

Viruses can pass from a pregnant woman to her fetus through the placenta or during childbirth. Nearly everyone has had an infection caused by a virus. You've probably had colds, flu, chicken pox, or measles. Other viral illnesses include genital herpes (HUR peez) and AIDS. Some viruses do not cause harm to adults, but they can be very harmful to a fetus or a newborn. For example, the viruses that cause chicken pox and genital herpes can cause birth defects or even death in newborns.

 **Reading Check** Give examples of viral diseases that can harm a fetus.

A virus that is deadly to both adults and newborns is the human immunodeficiency virus (HIV) that causes AIDS. AIDS attacks a person's immune system, limiting the infected person's ability to fight other infections. One out of every four pregnant women infected with HIV passes HIV to her fetus. An HIV-infected pregnant woman can lower the odds of having an HIV-infected baby if she sees a medical provider early, gets good medical care, and takes HIV-fighting medicines.

## Drugs and Alcohol

A pregnant woman should always consult her medical provider before taking any over-the-counter medicine or prescription drug. A medicine that is safe for an adult might not be safe for a developing fetus.

**Nicotine and Alcohol** Nicotine, found in cigarettes, is a drug that has serious negative effects on a fetus. Smoking cigarettes during pregnancy can damage the placenta, and then it cannot deliver normal amounts of oxygen to a fetus. Also, the amount of nutrients passed to the fetus is reduced. A pregnant woman who smokes cigarettes runs a higher risk of having a premature baby. Even second-hand smoke can cause health problems for a fetus. A pregnant woman who drinks alcohol excessively risks having a baby with fetal alcohol syndrome (FAS), like the children shown in **Figure 13.**

**Illegal Drugs** A pregnant woman who uses alcohol or illegal drugs puts herself and her fetus in danger. Illegal drugs, including marijuana, cocaine, and heroin, enter the placenta and then pass into the body of the fetus. Use of these substances increases the chances for miscarriage, premature birth, and low birth weight. They also increase the chances that the child will have behavior problems and learning difficulties as it grows and develops.

Some drugs, such as cocaine and heroin, can cause the death of a fetus. A pregnant woman who shares needles to inject drugs increases her risk of being infected with viruses such as HIV.

**Figure 13** Children born with fetal alcohol syndrome (FAS) have minor physical abnormalities but can have learning difficulties and behavioral problems as adults.

# Development Before Birth Summary

In this lesson, you read that a human zygote develops into a hollow ball of cells that implants into the lining of the endometrium about one week after fertilization. Over the next several weeks, this embryo develops into a fetus that obtains oxygen and nutrients from the mother through the placenta and umbilical cord. A full-term pregnancy lasts about 38 weeks from fertilization.

A pregnant woman can help ensure that her baby has the healthiest possible start to life by getting good prenatal care, eating a nutritious diet, and avoiding exposure to drugs, alcohol, nicotine, and other harmful substances.

# LESSON 2 Review

## Summarize

Create your own lesson summary as you write a script for a **television news report.**

1. **Review** the text after the **red** main headings and write one sentence about each. These are the headlines of your broadcast.

2. **Review** the text and write 2–3 sentences about each **blue** subheading. These sentences should tell *who, what, when, where,* and *why* information about each **red** heading.

3. **Include** descriptive details in your report, such as names of reporters and local places and events.

4. **Present** your news report to other classmates alone or with a team.

 ELA7: W 2.5

## Standards Check

### Using Vocabulary

1. Define prenatal care in your own words. **5.e**

2. Use each term in a separate sentence: *pregnancy* and *fetus.* **5.e**

### Understanding Main Ideas

3. When is the developing **5.e** embryo referred to as a fetus?

   **A.** by the end of week 2
   **B.** by the end of week 4
   **C.** by the end of week 12
   **D.** by the end of week 24

4. **Explain** why it is important for a woman to take good care of her health during pregnancy. **5.e**

5. **Give an example** of a virus that could harm a developing fetus. **5.e**

6. **Distinguish** between the placenta and the umbilical cord. **5.e**

### Applying Science

7. **Develop** a list of healthful foods a woman could add to her diet to increase her daily calorie intake during pregnancy. **5.e**

8. **Assess** the importance of seeing a healthcare professional during pregnancy. **5.e**

9. **Organize Information** Draw a graphic organizer similar to the one below to list substances that could be harmful to a developing fetus. **5.e**

**Science** nline

For more practice, visit **Standards Check** at ca7.msscience.com.

# Use the Internet:
# A Healthy Pregnancy

## Problem

Fetal development takes place in a relatively short amount of time. In just nine months, a functioning human being develops from a zygote formed from the joining of an egg and a sperm. During that time, the fetus receives from its mother through the placenta and umbilical cord everything that it needs to grow and develop into a baby.

## Form a Hypothesis

Develop an explanation for how a woman's lifestyle choices affect the substances that enter the fetus.

## Collect Data and Make Observations

**Research** the fetal development of the organ or organ system your teacher has assigned to you. Use your textbooks, library resources, and ca7.msscience.com. Find the answers to these questions:

1. At what point during a pregnancy does this organ or system begin to develop, function, and become fully developed?

2. Are there specific substances that are harmful to this organ system's development? How do these substances reach the fetus?

3. What nutrients are required for the organ system's development?

4. Are there times during pregnancy when it would be safe for a pregnant woman to
   - drink alcohol?
   - smoke tobacco?
   - use illegal drugs?
   - be exposed to lead or other harmful environmental factors?
   - ignore advice about eating a healthy diet?
5. Do other organs or organ systems develop at the same time? Are they related to the function of your assigned organ or organ system?

## Analyze and Conclude

1. **Sequence** the steps in the development of your assigned organ or organ system.
2. **Describe** hazards to the proper development of your assigned organ or organ system.
3. **Identify** the trimester of pregnancy during which the development of your assigned organ or organ system is particularly sensitive to the hazards listed in question 2.
4. **Explain** how a pregnant woman's lifestyle choices can support the development of your assigned organ or organ system. Are there vitamin supplements she can take? Are there foods or drinks she should avoid?
5. **Infer** from your data what substances are most harmful to the development of your assigned organ or organ system.
6. **Summarize** how your assigned organ or organ system interacts with other developing systems in the body of the fetus.

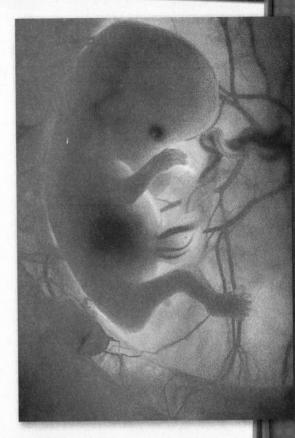

## Communicate

**WRITING in Science**

**Design a Visual Aid** Using the information you have collected, design a visual aid to inform a pregnant woman about ways in which she can protect the health of her developing fetus. Present your information to your class and display the poster in your classroom.

# Real World Science

## The Science of Reproductive Endocrinology

Dr. Arlene Morales is a reproductive endocrinologist who practices in San Diego, California. A reproductive endocrinologist (en duh krih NAH luh jist) is a medical doctor who is a certified obstetrician/gynecologist with advanced training and education in reproductive endocrinology. Reproductive endocrinology is the science that deals with the interaction of the endocrine system and the reproductive system. This highly qualified physician treats infertility and disorders affecting the reproductive health of men, women, and children.

Visit **Careers** at ca7.msscience.com for more information about reproductive endocrinology. Write a list of interview questions you might ask Dr. Morales.

## Ovarian Tissue Transplant

In June 2005, a healthy girl was born to a woman who had an ovarian tissue transplant—the first successful ovarian transplant in the United States. In April 2004, the 24-year-old mother received the ovarian tissue from her identical twin. Both women are shown in the photo to the right. The mother had not had a menstrual period since she was 13 years of age. Her sister had healthy ovaries as evidenced by her three children.

Visit **Technology** at ca7.msscience.com to research additional information about ovarian tissue transplantation. Write a summary paragraph about this procedure. **ELA7: W 2.5**

# The First Test-Tube Baby

In 1978 in England, Louise Brown was the first baby born conceived by *in vitro* fertilization. The *in vitro* process involves extracting an egg/eggs from a female and sperm from a male. The sperm fertilize the egg/eggs and, two to five days later, are implanted into the woman's uterus. Since 1978, approximately 115,000 babies have been born in the United States that were conceived by *in vitro* fertilization.

Visit **History** at ca7.msscience.com for more information about this historic scientific breakthrough. Write a newspaper article announcing this event.

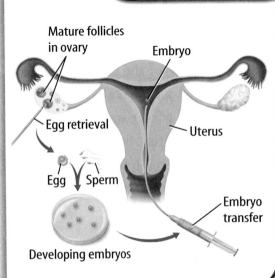

Mature follicles in ovary

Embryo

Egg retrieval

Uterus

Egg    Sperm

Embryo transfer

Developing embryos

# STDs–Sexually Transmitted Diseases

Despite prevention-education efforts and advances in diagnosis and treatment, sexually transmitted diseases remain a major concern for U.S. public health officials. The three most common STDs are chlamydia, gonorrhea, and syphilis. The Centers for Disease Control and Prevention estimates that almost 19 million new cases of STDs are reported annually among 15- to 19-year-olds. This number does not include highly infectious diseases, such as human papillomavirus and genital herpes.

Visit **Society** at ca7.msscience.com for more information about STD prevention. Choose one of the three common STDs and describe its cause, method(s) of transmission, symptoms, treatment, and prevention.

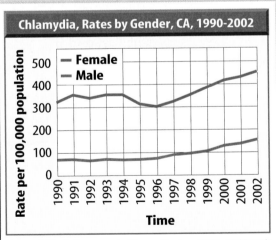

**Chlamydia, Rates by Gender, CA, 1990-2002**

Female
Male

Rate per 100,000 population

500
400
300
200
100
0

1990 1991 1992 1993 1994 1995 1996 1997 1998 1999 2000 2001 2002

**Time**

Source: California Department of Human Services, STD Control Branch

**Standards Study Guide**

**The BIG Idea** In humans, fertilization and embryo development take place inside a female's body.

## Lesson 1 Reproductive Systems

5.d, 7.a

**Main Idea** The structures of the human reproductive systems are specialized for the production of offspring.

- Males produce sperm in their testes continuously throughout their lifetime.
- Female ovaries produce eggs.
- Egg production begins before a female is born.
- Females have a limited number of eggs and reproductive years.
- Sperm swim through a female's reproductive tract to reach an egg.
- Fertilization usually happens in a female's fallopian tubes.
- Only one sperm usually fertilizes an egg.
- Fertilization produces a zygote that develops into an embryo and implants into the uterus.

- **epididymis** (p. 505)
- **fallopian tube** (p. 507)
- **follicle** (p. 508)
- **menstrual cycle** (p. 508)
- **ovulation** (p. 508)
- **penis** (p. 505)
- **scrotum** (p. 505)
- **seminiferous tubule** (p. 505)
- **urethra** (p. 505)
- **uterus** (p. 507)
- **vagina** (p. 507)

## Lesson 2 Development Before Birth

5.e, 7.a, 7.b, 7.c, 7.d

**Main Idea** The normal development of a fetus depends on the good health of its mother.

- Pregnancy usually lasts about 38 weeks.
- The organs and major structures of the fetus begin forming during the first trimester.
- A fetus is dependent on its mother for nutrition and waste removal.
- A mother's prenatal care and lifestyle choices affect the health of her fetus.

- **fetus** (p. 516)
- **placenta** (p. 517)
- **pregnancy** (p. 516)
- **prenatal care** (p. 518)
- **trimester** (p. 516)
- **umbilical cord** (p. 517)

**STUDY TO GO** Download quizzes, key terms, and flash cards from ca7.msscience.com.

**Science Online** Interactive Tutor ca7.msscience.com

# Linking Vocabulary and Main Ideas

Use vocabulary terms from page 526 to complete this concept map.

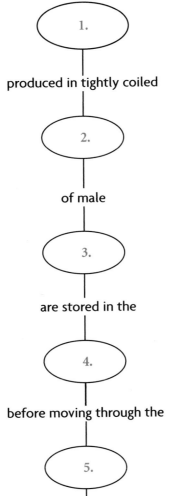

1.

produced in tightly coiled

2.

of male

3.

are stored in the

4.

before moving through the

5.

and deposited in female reproductive tract

**Science** nline

Visit ca7.msscience.com for:
▶ Vocabulary PuzzleMaker
▶ Vocabulary eFlashcards
▶ Multilingual Glossary

## Using Vocabulary

**Fill in each blank with the correct vocabulary term.**

Every 28 days, on average, one of a female's ovaries releases an egg in a process called ____6.____ . Before the egg is released, it and the surrounding protective cells are called a(n) ____7.____ . When released, the egg enters a(n) ____8.____ . If sperm entered a female's ____9.____ and swam into and through the ____10.____ within a few days of egg release, the egg can be fertilized. This results in ____11.____ . The fertilized egg grows and develops into a(n) ____12.____ that is connected to its mother by a(n) ____13.____ . The ____14.____ exchanges materials between the mother and her baby.

## Understanding Main Ideas

*Choose the word or phrase that best answers the question.*

1. What process is the release of an egg into the fallopian tube?
   A. fertilization     `5.d`
   B. meiosis
   C. ovulation
   D. puberty

2. What organ does a male use to deposit sperm in the female reproductive tract?
   A. penis     `5.d`
   B. prostate
   C. seminal vesicle
   D. testis

3. Where does a fetus grow and develop?
   A. fallopian tube     `5.d`
   B. ovary
   C. uterus
   D. vagina

4. Human reproductive organs have different functions.

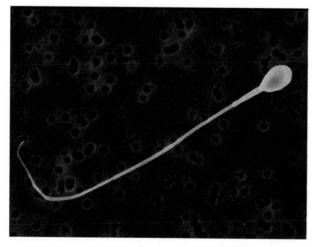

   What organ produces the structure shown above?
   A. ovary     `5.d`
   B. penis
   C. testis
   D. urethra

5. What female reproductive cells stopped at prophase I?
   A. follicle     `5.d`
   B. oocytes
   C. semen
   D. uterus

6. The thickness of a female's endometrium changes in response to other events.

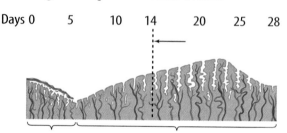

Days 0    5    10    14    20    25    28

   What event is indicated by the arrow?
   A. implantation     `5.d`
   B. menopause
   C. menstrual flow
   D. ovulation

7. Which does not happen in the placenta?
   A. Fetus' blood and mother's blood mix.     `5.d`
   B. Medicines taken by the mother enter fetal blood.
   C. Nutrients and water enter fetal blood.
   D. Wastes from the fetus enter mother's blood.

8. What structure moves a sperm through a female reproductive system?
   A. cilium     `5.d`
   B. flagellum
   C. muscle tissue
   D. seminal vesicle

9. What helps to regulate the timing of the menstrual cycle and ovulation?
   A. semen     `5.d`
   B. endometrium
   C. hormones
   D. follicles

Science  nline   Standards Review ca7.msscience.com

## Applying Science

**10.** **Distinguish** between puberty and menopause. **5.d**

**11.** **Classify** these organs as male or female reproductive structures: ovaries, penis, scrotum, testes, vagina, uterus. **5.d**

**12.** **Create** a cycle map of the events that happen during one female menstrual cycle. **5.d**

**13.** **Explain** the importance of the three cell layers of an embryo, as shown in the diagram below. **5.e**

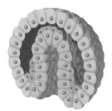

**14.** **Give an example** of a food item a mother should avoid eating in large amounts during pregnancy. **5.e**

**15.** **Diagram** how the blood supply of a fetus relates to the blood supply of the mother. **5.e**

**16.** **Develop** a list of warnings about environmental risk factors for pregnant woman. **5.e**

**17.** **Predict** what might happen if a sperm cell did not have mitochondria. **2.b**

**18.** **Suggest** a reason why the release of only one egg is a benefit to a mother and the fetus that could develop from that egg. **5.d**

**19.** **Hypothesize** why male cyclists who wear tight-fitting pants sometimes produce less sperm than normal. **5.d**

**20.** **Predict** what might happen if a pregnant woman does not include enough folic acid in her diet. **5.e**

### WRITING in Science

**21.** **Write** a paragraph describing how oxygen and nutrients move from a mother's body to the body of a fetus, and how wastes move from the fetus to the mother's body. **ELA7: W 1.3**

## Cumulative Review

**22.** **Give examples** of the classes of levers in the human body. **6.i**

**23.** **Describe** two ways that pressure is important in the body. **6.j**

**24.** **Construct** a diagram of the ear. Label each part and give its function. **5.g**

### Applying Math

A group of ten men had the following levels of testosterone measured in nanomoles per liter (nmol/L). Use the data table below to answer questions 25–28.

| Levels of Testosterone | | | | | |
|---|---|---|---|---|---|
| Participant Number | 1 | 2 | 3 | 4 | 5 |
| Testosterone (nmol/L) | 30.4 | 21.8 | 16.5 | 9.1 | 12.4 |
| Participant Number | 6 | 7 | 8 | 9 | 10 |
| Testosterone (nmol/L) | 35.3 | 19.6 | 16.7 | 24.9 | 25.1 |

**25.** Order the data from smallest to largest. **MA7: SDP 1.3**

**26.** Find the median value of the data set. **MA7: SDP 1.3**

**27.** Find the lower quartile value of the data. **MA7: SDP 1.3**

**28.** Find the upper quartile value of the data. **MA7: SDP 1.3**

**1** **Which is NOT part of the menstrual cycle?**

**A** release of the follicle     5.d

**B** maturing of egg

**C** menopause ends

**D** menstrual flow begins

**2** **When do eggs start to develop in the ovaries?**

**A** before birth     5.d

**B** at puberty

**C** during childhood

**D** during infancy

**Use the illustration below to answer question 3.**

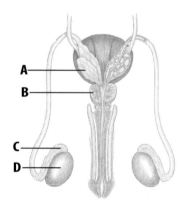

**3** **Which structure produces most of the liquid in semen?**

**A** A     5.d

**B** B

**C** C

**D** D

Preeclampsia is a condition that can develop in a woman after 20 weeks of pregnancy. It involves the development of hypertension or high blood pressure, an abnormal amount of protein in urine, and swelling. Use the table below to answer question 4.

| Preeclampsia Risk in Pregnancy | |
|---|---|
| **Risk Factors** | **Risk Ratio** |
| First pregnancy | 3:1 |
| Mother over 40 years of age | 3:1 |
| Family history of preeclampsia | 5:1 |
| Chronic hypertension | 10:1 |
| Chronic kidney disease | 20:1 |
| Diabetes mellitus | 2:1 |
| Twin birth | 4:1 |

**4** **Which statement does not agree with the data in the table above?**

**A** A pregnant woman with chronic hypertension is at greater risk of developing preeclampsia than a pregnant woman with chronic kidney failure.     5.e

**B** A pregnant woman having her first baby is at greater risk of developing preeclampsia than a pregnant woman with diabetes mellitus failure.

**C** A pregnant woman over 40 years of age is at greater risk of developing preeclampsia than a pregnant woman with family history of preeclampsia.

**D** A pregnant woman with diabetes mellitus is at greater risk of developing preeclampsia than a pregnant woman with twins.

**Use the illustration below to answer questions 5 and 6.**

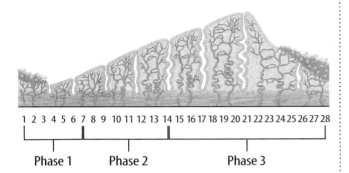

1 2 3 4 5 6 7 8 9 10 11 12 13 14 15 16 17 18 19 20 21 22 23 24 25 26 27 28

Phase 1      Phase 2      Phase 3

**5** **What percentage of the menstrual cycle is phase 3?**

A   10      **5.d**

B   25

C   35

D   50

**6** **What percentage of the menstrual cycle is phase 2?**

A   10      **5.d**

B   25

C   35

D   50

**7** **What is the mixture of sperm and fluid called?**

A   semen      **5.d**

B   testes

C   seminal vesicle

D   epididymis

**8** **If a pregnant woman becomes infected with rubella, a viral disease also known as German measles, the virus can adversely affect the formation of the baby's major organs, such as the heart. When would a rubella infection in a pregnant woman most affect a fetus?**

A   week 8      **5.e**

B   week 20

C   week 32

D   week 37

**Use the graph below to answer questions 9 and 10.**

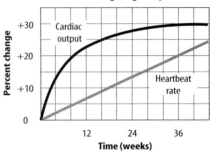

Cardiac Output and Heartbeat Rate During Pregnancy

**9** **Cardiac output increases during pregnancy to keep the fetus supplied with nutrients through the placenta. During which week of pregnancy does cardiac output reach its highest level?**

A   6      **5.e**

B   20

C   24

D   36

**10** **What is the cardiac output of the mother at week 12?**

A   18      **5.e**

B   22

C   28

D   30

## From the Recommended Literature for Science and Math

Are you interested in learning more about the structure and function of living systems and the physical principles associated with them? If so, check out these great books.

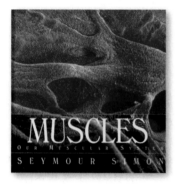

### Nonfiction

**Muscles: Our Muscular System,** by Seymour Simon, describes the nature and work of muscles, the different kinds of muscles in the human body, and the effects of exercise and other activities upon the body system. This book contains full-color photographs. ***The content of this book is related to*** *Science Standard 7.5.*

### Nonfiction

**Bones: Our Skeletal System,** by Seymour Simon, includes photographs, drawings, and X rays to provide basic information about the human skeleton. This book emphasizes the importance of bones in the healthy functioning of the human body. ***The content of this book is related to*** *Science Standard 7.5.*

### Nonfiction

**It's so Amazing! A Book About Eggs, Sperm, Birth, Babies, and Families,** by Robie Harris, answers questions with clear, factual information. This book features an enthusiastic bird and a reluctant bee who narrate the comic cartoon panels and add humor. ***The content of this book is related to*** *Science Standard 7.5.*

### Nonfiction

**Optical Illusion Magic: Visual Tricks & Amusements,** by Michael DiSpezio, explains how we process optical illusions. This book contains illustrations of the human eye and describes how the eye relays information to the brain. ***The content of this book is related to*** *Science Standard 7.6.*

*Choose the word or phrase that best answers the question.*

1. Which is a function of blood?
   A. carries saliva to the mouth
   B. excretes urine from the body
   C. transports nutrients and oxygen to body cells
   D. collects tissue fluid from around cells    **5.b**

2. Which is the site of sperm production?
   A. endometrium
   B. placenta
   C. prostate gland
   D. seminiferous tubules    **5.d**

3. Which is the most important difference between striated and smooth muscle?
   A. Their cells contain different materials.
   B. Their cells have different shapes.
   C. They have different sizes of cells.
   D. They have different functions.    **5.a**

4. The image below shows one organ in the human body.

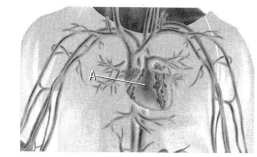

   To which body system does the organ labeled A belong?
   A. circulatory
   B. digestive
   C. respiratory
   D. urinary    **5.b**

5. Why does the lens in the eye change shape?
   A. to control the amount of light entering the eye
   B. to form sharp images in dim light
   C. to form sharp images of distant and nearby objects
   D. to enable colors to be seen    **6.b**

*Write your responses to the following on a sheet a paper.*

6. **Identify** what must happen for a light ray to be refracted as it passes from one medium into another.    **6.f**

7. **Compare** the functions of ovaries and testes.    **5.d**

8. **Explain** why blood sometimes is called "the tissue of life."    **5.b**

9. **Describe** the changes that occur in muscles that do a lot of work. Compare these muscles to the muscles of a person who is inactive most of the time.    **5.c**

10. **Identify** the name of the center point about which a lever rotates.    **6.h**

11. **Draw** a human ear and label the parts.    **5.g**

12. **Explain** how the external ears aid hearing. How is this different in humans and other mammals?    **5.g**

13. **Diagram** how the human body systems are connected to each other.    **5.b**

14. **Design** and complete a comparison chart similar to the one shown comparing the male and female reproductive systems.    **5.d**

| Male | Both | Female |
|---|---|---|
|  |  |  |
|  |  |  |
|  |  |  |
|  |  |  |
|  |  |  |
|  |  |  |

To Students and Their Families,

Welcome to seventh-grade life science. You will begin your journey by learning about the tools that biologists use. Then you will continue with the cells and organisms and you will learn how life evolved on Earth.

Take a few moments each day to review what you have learned about life science. Test your knowledge of each Standard by answering the questions.

Remember, the knowledge and skills you will gain this year will be important beyond the classroom. They will help you to become environmentally aware and to better understand the planet on which you live.

# Table of Contents

**Standard Set 1** Cell Biology . . . . . . . . . . . . . . . . . . . . . . 536

**Standard Set 2** Genetics . . . . . . . . . . . . . . . . . . . . . . . . 538

**Standard Set 3** Evolution . . . . . . . . . . . . . . . . . . . . . . . 540

**Standard Set 4** Earth and Life History . . . . . . . . . . . . . 542

**Standard Set 5** Structure and Function
in Living Systems . . . . . . . . . . . . . . . . . 544

**Standard Set 6** Physical Principles in Living Things . . . . 546

**Standard Set 7** Investigation and Experimentation . . . . 548

**Answers** . . . . . . . . . . . . . . . . . . . . . . . . . . . . . . . . . . 550

## Standard Set 1: Cell Biology

Directions: Select the best answer for each of the following questions.

**1** Which of these statements about cells is true?
   A All cells respond to light.
   B They do not make up most living things.
   C They take in materials from their surroundings.
   D They do not contain any hereditary material.

**2** A cell sample is taken from a certain tissue in a cat and another is taken from a similar tissue in a dog. If the samples were compared using a microscope, which would you expect?
   A Any similarities would depend on the particular species involved.
   B The two samples should be very different.
   C The two samples should be very similar.
   D The two samples should have nothing in common.

**3**
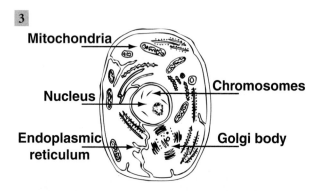

Can you identify this species of animal solely from the cell shown? Why or why not?
   A Yes; this is clearly a cell from a bird.
   B No; but identification would be possible if the diagram were in color.
   C Yes; this is clearly a cell from a human being.
   D No; animal cells share too many similar characteristics.

**4** Unlike most animals, plants do not have skeletons. Which structure in plant cells has a function similar to an animal's skeleton?
   A nucleus
   B vacuole
   C cell membrane
   D cell wall

**5** The diagram below compares organelles and other cell parts found in animal and plant cells.

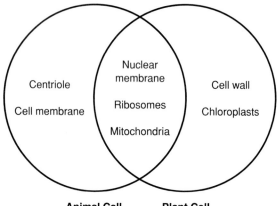

Which organelle or other cell part is incorrectly placed in the diagram?
   A mitochondrion
   B ribosome
   C cell membrane
   D nuclear membrane

**6** Which is found only in animal cells?
   A chloroplasts
   B cytoskeleton
   C cell wall
   D central vacuole

**7** Which is the primary component in the cell wall of a plant cell?
   A carotenoid
   B cellulose
   C chitin
   D chlorophyll

**8** Lila wanted to observe the process of mitosis. She could see mitosis in all cell types *except*
   A cheek.
   B skin.
   C adult nerve.
   D onion skin.

Science Online  Standards Practice  ca7.msscience.com

## Standard Set 1: Cell Biology

Directions: Select the best answer for each of the following questions.

**9** Where are the genes of a plant cell or an animal cell located?

A cytoplasm

B endoplasmic reticulum

C Golgi body

D nucleus

**10** DNA contains all the genetic information about an organism. Which does the acronym DNA mean?

A denatured genetic acid

B deoxyribonucleic acid

C di-nitric acid

D dodecanol nitrous acid

**11** Plant cells contain chloroplasts and mitochondria. Which is the purpose of mitochondria when a cell already has chloroplasts?

A fight diseases

B store vitamins

C help store water

D turn sugars into energy

**12** Chlorophyll is contained in a plant's

A chloroplasts.

B mitochondria.

C roots.

D viruses.

**13** Some plant cells contain chloroplasts, but animal cells do not. Which statement best explains why animal cells can function without chloroplasts?

A Animal cells do not need outside energy.

B Animal cells do photosynthesis using mitochondria.

C Animals have circulatory systems but plants do not.

D Animals obtain energy by consuming other organisms.

**14** The process of mitosis is directly responsible for

A digestion of food.

B excretion of waste.

C reproduction of cells.

D transport of oxygen.

**15** **Observations of Mitosis**

| End of Hour | Number of Cells |
|---|---|
| 1 | 2 |
| 2 | 4 |
| 3 | 8 |
| 4 | ? |

These data were collected by watching a cell go through mitosis many times. If conditions remain constant, how many cells will be present at the end of the fourth hour?

A 8

B 10

C 16

D 32

**16** Which lists the stages of mitosis in the correct order?

A metaphase, anaphase, prophase, telophase

B anaphase, telophase, prophase, metaphase

C telophase, anaphase, metaphase, prophase

D prophase, metaphase, anaphase, telophase

**17** Skin is an organ that functions as a barrier to protect the body from the outside world. Which *best* describes the components that work together to form skin?

A microscopic organisms

B organ systems under the skin

C specialized cells and tissues

D various small organs

**18** After differentiation, most cells lose their ability to become other types of cells. Which cells are the exceptions to this rule?

A brain cells

B plant cells

C retinal cells

D stomach cells

## Standard Set 2: Genetics

Directions: Select the best answer for each of the following questions.

**1** Which type of reproduction shown below requires two parents?

A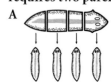

B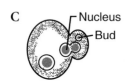

C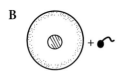

— Nucleus
— Bud

D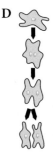

**2** Which is *not* a type of asexual reproduction?
A budding
B fission
C clones
D seeds

**3** Toshiko wants to determine what type of reproduction a particular organism undergoes. She finds that all of the organism's offspring look identical to the original organism. She concludes that this organism reproduces
A asexually.
B frequently.
C rarely.
D sexually.

**4** Which does *not* result in offspring that are identical to the parent?
A budding
B fission
C asexual reproduction
D sexual reproduction

**5** You inherit your mitochondrial DNA solely from whom?
A your father
B your mother
C your maternal grandmother
D your paternal grandmother

**6** Most complex life forms reproduce sexually. Sexual reproduction results in offspring that
A are identical to the mother.
B are identical to their siblings.
C share some traits with each parent but are not identical to either one.
D are identical to one parent

**7** Chimpanzees produce offspring by sexual reproduction. Which type of reproductive cell does the male chimpanzee form?
A egg
B embryo
C ovary
D sperm

**8** A farmer crosses a brown-feathered chicken and a white-feathered chicken. Most of the offspring chickens have white feathers, but some have brown feathers. Which explains the feathers of the offspring?
A Feather color in chickens is not an inherited factor.
B Feather color in chickens is controlled by a combination of heredity and environment.
C One form of the gene for feather color is dominant and the other is recessive.
D Two forms of the gene for feather color exist in these chickens.

Science Online Standards Practice    ca7.msscience.com

## Standard Set 2: Genetics

Directions: Select the best answer for each of the following questions.

**9** A person's natural hair color is due to
A asexual variegation.
B environmental factors.
C genetic variation.
D peer influences.

**10** Maria Rosa crossbreeds two plants, one with red flowers and one with white flowers. Weeks later, all the offspring plants produce red flowers. Maria Rosa determines that the
A red flower allele is dominant.
B white flower allele is dominant.
C red flower is incompletely dominant.
D white flower is incompletely dominant.

**11**

### Observations of Pea Plants

| Trait | Dominant Allele |
| --- | --- |
| Plant height | Tall |
| Flower color | Purple |
| Seed color | Yellow |
| Seed texture | Smooth |

According to the chart, when a pea plant with two purple-flower alleles is mated with a white-flowering pea plant, the offspring will have
A purple flowers.
B tall stems.
C white flowers.
D yellow seeds.

**12** Which are multiple copies or versions of the same gene?
A alleles
B cofactors
C editions
D traits

**13** Which is the function of chromosomes in a cell?
A Chromosomes form part of the cell's defenses against infection.
B Chromosomes give structural support for the cell's nucleus.
C Chromosomes organize the genetic material into discrete units.
D Chromosomes provide energy for the cell's functions.

**14** A mule is the offspring of a horse and a donkey. Most mules have shorter life spans than horses and donkeys and are unable to reproduce. What is the main reason that a mule is rare in nature?
A Most donkeys do not breed.
B The life span of a mule is too short.
C Mules are unable to reproduce.
D Horses and donkeys are two different species.

**15** How many pairs of chromosomes does each human being have?
A 2
B 14
C 23
D 46

## Standard Set 3: Evolution

Directions: Select the best answer for each of the following questions.

**1** Which adaptation helps a penguin survive cold weather?
A black-and-white body coloring
B heavier bones than other birds
C layer of blubber under the skin
D wings that are shaped like flippers

**2** The average annual rainfall in a forest decreases. Over many years, the trees in the forest will *most* likely grow
A bendable trunks.
B deeper roots.
C larger leaves.
D longer stems.

**3** Scientists think that humans originated in Africa and eventually migrated over a period of many years to occupy most habitats on Earth. Which adaptation is *most* likely the result of human migration from an equatorial region to a higher latitude?
A ability to walk on two feet
B changes in shape of skull
C lightened skin color
D loss of body hair

**4** How long does natural selection take to affect a particular species of plants or animals?
A depends on the species
B a few days
C less than one year
D thousands of years

**5** A butterfly population has changed from orange-and-black-colored wings to yellow-and-black-colored wings. This change probably occurred
A because the environment was stable.
B over many generations of butterflies.
C suddenly after a cold winter.
D when the number of flowering plants declined.

**6** Biologists suggest that some squirrels are better able to find food and survive harsh winters than others. They lived through the cold season and passed their genes on to their offspring. This idea supports the idea of
A adaptive radiation.
B artificial selection.
C natural selection.
D use and disuse.

Use the following diagram to answer questions 7–8.

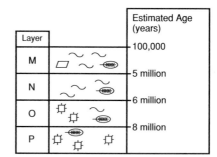

**7** Fossils of an insect species are found in layers O and P, but not in layers M and N. Based on this information, scientists should conclude that the species
A lived in the region for less than 5 million years.
B lived in the region for more than 5 million years.
C disappeared from the region around 6 million years ago.
D disappeared from the region more than 8 million years ago.

**8** Scientists are interested in learning why the insect species is not found in layers M and N. Based only on the fossil record in the diagram above, which hypothesis is most likely to be correct?
A The insects evolved into worms.
B The worm is the adult form of the insect.
C The worms preyed upon the insects.
D The insects were poisoned by a new plant species.

**Science** online   Standards Practice   ca7.msscience.com

## Standard Set 3: Evolution

Directions: Select the best answer for each of the following questions.

**9** The theory that whales evolved from ancestors with legs is most likely based on information gathered from
A DNA analysis.
B embryology research.
C the fossil record.
D population studies.

**10** Which taxon contains the largest number of organisms?
A division
B family
C genus
D order

**11** **Classification of Rabbits**

| Level | Jackrabbit | Cottontail |
|---|---|---|
| Kingdom | Animalia | Animalia |
| Phylum | Chordata | Chordata |
| Class | Mammalia | Mammalia |
| Order | Lagomorpha | Lagomorpha |
| Family | Leporidae | Leporidae |
| Genus | *Lepus* | *Sylvilagus* |
| Species | *californicus* | *floridanus* |

According to the classification table above, which is the lowest taxonomic level that jackrabbits and cottontails have in common?
A class
B family
C genus
D order

**12** Similar classes of living organisms belong to which category?
A family
B genus
C order
D phylum

**13** Who developed the method of classifying organisms according to their characteristics, also known as *systematics*?
A Carolus Linnaeus
B Charles Darwin
C Gregor Mendel
D Thomas Malthus

**14** A change in an ocean current causes the climate on an island to become drier. The grasses that cover the island change from dark green to light brown. Over time, how might a species of green toads respond to these changes?
A Their size will decrease.
B Their size will increase.
C Their coloration will change to brown.
D Their coloration will change to white.

**15** The Gila trout is an endangered fish species of New Mexico. Because of heavy fishing, there has been a dramatic decrease in the population. If overfishing continues, which factor will *most* likely lead to the disappearance of the trout population in this area?
A climatic changes altering the habitat
B competition for food increasing
C reproduction rates declining
D streams becoming overpopulated

**16** While studying inheritance in pea plants, a scientist discovers one plant has smaller pods despite the fact that all its ancestors have long pods. Which best explains why this occurred?
A competition
B isolation
C natural mutation
D natural selection

## Standard Set 4: Earth and Life History

Directions: Select the best answer for each of the following questions.

**1** Which is the principle of using features, phenomena, and processes that are observable today to interpret the past geologic record?

A superposition

B uniformitarianism

C natural selection

D plate tectonics

**2**

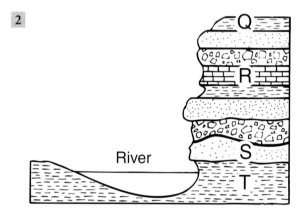

Geologists are currently studying the site pictured above. The rock in layer T is found to have formed at least 6 million years ago. How can scientists study something so old with any confidence?

A Anything older than 10 million years is unreliable, but this rock layer is not that old.

B Nearby water has protected this rock layer without disruption.

C Pressure from all the rock layers above has effectively preserved this layer.

D Physical principles today are identical to the principles that operated long ago.

**3** Why would large volcanic eruptions or asteroid impacts that inject particulate matter into the atmosphere affect Earth's climate?

A Birds choke on the airborne particulate matter and are removed from the skies.

B Increased particulate matter can block sunlight, cooling Earth's climate.

C Oceans absorb the particulate matter, which makes the sea levels rise.

D Particulate matter "scrubs" the atmosphere, making it rain less often.

**4** Which event is too small to disrupt the climate and affect the development of life on Earth?

A a large amount of human industrial activity

B a large and destructive earthquake

C a large volcanic eruption

D the impact of a large asteroid

**5** In 1815–1816, "the year without a summer," ash from a huge volcanic eruption in Indonesia caused global weather fluctuations. In particular, many regions experienced extremely low temperatures. Which was the most likely cause of these atmospheric disturbances?

A Ash from the volcanic eruption prevented sunlight from reaching Earth's surface.

B Debris from the eruption covered the ground and stopped it from radiating energy.

C Gas and ash from the eruption caused snow in tropical regions.

D Lava from the volcano made glaciers melt, and this cooled the oceans and atmosphere.

**6** Which conclusion is valid when comparing fossils found in previously undisturbed strata of sedimentary rock?

A Fossils in the upper strata are older than those in the lower strata.

B Fossils in the upper strata are younger than those in the lower strata.

C Fossils in the upper strata generally are less complex than those in the lower strata.

D There are no fossils in the upper strata that resemble those in the lower strata.

**7** Which is an example of absolute dating?

A calculating the age of a rock layer from the fossils it includes

B calculating the age of a rock by measuring the radioactive decay of certain elements

C calculating the age of a rock relative to the age of a river that cuts through it

D calculating the age of a rock from the location where it was discovered

## Standard Set 4: Earth and Life History

Directions: Select the best answer for each of the following questions.

**8** The half-life of a radioactive isotope is 50 years. How much of a 100-g sample of the isotope will remain after 200 years?

A 3.12 g

B 6.25 g

C 12.5 g

D 25.0 g

**9**

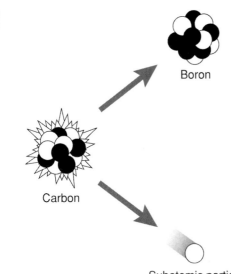

Boron

Carbon

Subatomic particle

The process in the diagram represents

A nuclear fission.

B nuclear fusion.

C radiometric dating.

D spontaneous decay.

**10** Fossils of an ancient reptile, *Mesosaurus*, have been found in rock formations that are now separated by oceans. The reptile could not have crossed these oceans. Which does the presence of the reptile in these rocks suggest about Earth's history?

A The reptile lived on a single landmass that has since split apart.

B Oceans did not exist when the reptile was alive.

C Oceans were once shallow enough for the reptile to wade across.

D Using the fossil record of the reptile is not an accurate way to study Earth's history.

**11** Plate tectonics caused a high mountain range to form over millions of years. Which happens when members of a species are separated on opposite sides of the range?

A Both groups will continue to evolve similarly and remain identical species.

B Both groups will die out eventually because they can't breed with each other.

C Each group will continue to evolve and grow into distinct species.

D One of the groups, unable to breed with the other, will eventually die out.

**12** Why does separating species geographically cause them to evolve differently?

A Individuals cannot interbreed and specific genetic changes are accumulated.

B Isolating species geographically has no effect on their species evolution.

C Trauma from separation affects the genes of each species group.

D When species are separated geographically, they cease to breed and evolve.

**13** Earth's atmosphere changed over time and eventually was able to support plant life. Which is the most likely cause of the change?

A Gases from outer space entered Earth's atmosphere.

B Increased volcanic activity produced a lot of nitrogen and carbon dioxide gas.

C Ozone formed a layer that protects organisms from ultraviolet radiation.

D Sunlight caused oxygen gas to form in the atmosphere.

**14** About 600 million years ago, many different forms of life suddenly appeared on Earth, as shown in the fossil record. What is this event called?

A Cambrian explosion

B Jurassic Park

C K-T extinction

D Paleozoic era

## Standard Set 5: Structure and Function in Living Systems

Directions: Select the best answer for each of the following questions.

**1** Which categories of living things show cellular specialization?
A single-celled organisms
B protozoa
C viruses
D multicellular organisms

**2** Which group consists of only single-celled organisms?
A bacteria
B fungi
C protists
D sponges

**3** Which is *not* an example of cellular differentiation?
A amoebas
B neurons
C muscle tissues
D skeletal bones

**4** The human body is made up of many different specialized organ systems and tissues. What happens if one of these systems fails or is removed?
A The body dies if any organ fails or is removed.
B The body will eventually grow a new replacement organ.
C It depends on the particular organ or system affected.
D Nothing happens because other organs can compensate for the loss of one organ.

**5** Which bones are most responsible for a person's height?

A
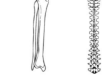
shin bone
thigh bone    backbone

B
skull
arm bone    knee

C
ribcage
arm bones    thigh bone

D
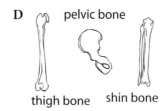
pelvic bone
thigh bone    shin bone

**6** Which attaches a muscle to a bone?
A biceps
B ligaments
C neurons
D tendons

**7** Sperm and testosterone are produced in the
A penis.
B prostate.
C testes.
D urethra.

## Standard Set 5: Structure and Function in Living Systems

Directions: Select the best answer for each of the following questions.

**8**

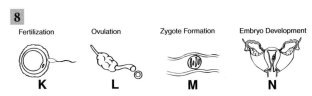

Fertilization    Ovulation    Zygote Formation    Embryo Development

**K**     **L**     **M**     **N**

**Which is the order of stages of the human reproduction cycle?**

A  K, L, M, N

B  K, M, L, N

C  L, K, M, N

D  L, N, M, K

**9**  **Where does fertilization of an egg usually take place?**

A  cilia

B  placenta

C  ovary

D  oviduct

**10**  **Which is the main function of the placenta?**

A  to absorb waste products from the developing fetus

B  to direct the development of the fetus as it grows

C  to make the birth of the fetus easier at the end of pregnancy

D  to nourish and protect the developing fetus

**11**  **Which structure provides a developing fetus with nourishment before birth?**

A  mouth

B  stomach

C  large intestine

D  umbilical cord

**12**  **Why could alcohol consumed by a pregnant woman affect her fetus?**

A  Alcohol can block the flow of nutrients through the umbilical cord.

B  Alcohol can easily pass through the placenta to the developing fetus.

C  Alcohol has no effect on a fetus; the mother's body filters it out.

D  Alcohol in any amount will dissolve the placental tissue.

**13**  **Which is the role of the endosperm in the developing plant embryo?**

A  food source

B  protective shell

C  reproductive organ

D  water storage

**14**  **Which is the function of the anther of a flowering plant?**

A  guides pollen tubes

B  produces ova

C  produces pollen

D  receives pollen

**15**  **Which is *not* a structure found in a flowering plant?**

A  filament

B  pistil

C  stigma

D  umbilicus

**16**  **The tympanic membrane is another term for which structure of the ear?**

A  anvil

B  eardrum

C  earlobe

D  hammer

**17**  **Many different stimuli can affect cells. Which is a typical example of the way certain cells in the human body react directly to bright light?**

A  The body temperature slowly rises.

B  The heart rate decreases.

C  The pupils of the eyes get smaller.

D  The skin glands produce more sweat.

**18**  **Lawrence dissects a fish as his teacher describes a certain part of the fish's eye. The teacher says a tissue at the back of the eye is sensitive to light. The tissue contains two types of cells called rods and cones. Lawrence correctly identifies the part as the**

A  lens.

B  optic nerve.

C  pupil.

D  retina.

## Standard Set 6: Physical Principles in Living Things

Directions: Select the best answer for each of the following questions.

**1** Electromagnetic radiation of a wavelength between 400 nm and 800 nm comprises which part of the spectrum?
A gamma radiation
B microwaves
C radio waves
D visible light

**2**

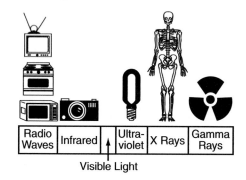

According to this information, which type of electromagnetic energy is used to diagnose broken bones?
A gamma rays
B infrared waves
C radio waves
D X rays

**3** How would the eye perceive an object that emitted or reflected absolutely no light at all?
A The object would appear black.
B The object would be invisible.
C The object would look blurry.
D The object would seem to move.

**4** When visible light is directed at an object, the light is reflected and scattered. Which direction does the reflected light take?
A all directions
B parallel to the light source
C perpendicular to the light source
D directly back to the light source

**5**

Light travels in straight lines, yet the device shown allows us to see around corners and over obstacles. How is this possible?
A Lenses in the device can bend the light.
B Light is still traveling straight, only reflected at certain points.
C Not all light travels in perfectly straight lines.
D When light hits an object, it is no longer required to travel in straight lines.

**6** Why will a pencil placed in a half-full glass of water appear bent?
A The reflected light passes through a different medium.
B The water absorbs some of the reflected light rays.
C The water cools the relatively warm material of the pencil.
D The weight of the water physically bends the pencil.

**7** Some kinds of telescopes contain lenses. The lens of a telescope
A magnifies and focuses the light.
B moves the telescope up and down.
C reflects the light back out to space.
D turns the telescope off and on.

**8** Which does *not* use at least one simple lens?
A computer screen
B digital camera
C human eye
D telescope

## Standard Set 6: Physical Principles in Living Things

Directions: Select the best answer for each of the following questions.

**9** Which are the light receptor cells in the eye that recognize color?

A CLR cells

B color cells

C cone cells

D rod cells

**10** Why does a diffraction grating separate white light into various colors?

A Different wavelengths of light interfere constructively when passed through the grating.

B It is an optical illusion; no separation of colors actually takes place.

C The grating actually adds frequencies to the plain white light.

D The grating alters the electromagnetic nature of white light.

**11**

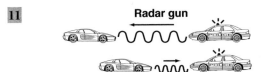

Police can detect speeding motorists with a radar gun. Which property of waves enables them to do this?

A Waves bend when they strike an object.

B Waves bounce back when they strike an object.

C Waves can bend around barriers.

D Waves can combine, travel together, and form a new wave.

**12** Under which condition will refraction not be observed when light passes from one medium to another?

A when light enters the medium at a very large angle

B when light enters the medium at a very small angle

C when light enters the medium parallel to the surface

D when light enters the medium perpendicular to the surface

**13** If a beam of light forms an angle of incidence of 36° on a reflective surface, which is the value of the angle of reflection?

A 18°

B 36°

C 72°

D 90°

**14**

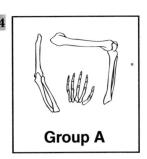 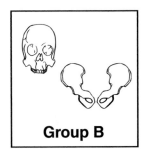

**Group A**          **Group B**

The bones in group A are different from the bones in group B because only the bones in group A have

A calcified joints.

B immovable joints.

C movable joints.

D pivot joints.

**15** Many muscle and bone combinations are models of simple levers. Why is a lever so desirable from a mechanical standpoint?

A to increase output force

B to lengthen life span

C to protect against breaks

D to reduce efficiency

**16** Which is the source of blood pressure in the human body?

A body temperature

B contractions of the heart

C digestive action by the stomach

D electrolytes in the blood

**17** Which keeps the blood from flowing in the wrong direction through the heart?

A blood platelets

B blood pressure

C valves in series

D temperature differential

Directions: Select the best answer for each of the following questions.

**1** Which piece of equipment would be useful for observing mitosis in onion skin?

A

B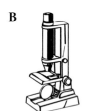

C

D

**2** Which is the *best* tool to gather information quickly about the temperature distribution throughout the Atlantic Ocean?

A barometer
B boat
C radar
D satellite

**3** When scientists complete an experiment, they write detailed papers that describe the experiment, the results, and the conclusions. Then other scientists and experts review the work and decide whether the information is reliable enough to publish in a scientific journal. A research paper might not be published or taken seriously if

A all measurements and data are accurate.
B it details a new scientific discovery.
C it uses only scientific names and terms.
D the results of the experiment cannot be duplicated.

**4** Which of these would be the most reliable source of information on global warming?

A weather forecasts
B newspaper editorials
C Web sites
D articles in a scientific journal

**5** A scientist is studying a compound that is used as a medicine in the treatment of certain skin diseases. The only source of the compound is the leaves of a tropical plant. The scientist plans to try to prepare the same compound in the laboratory. What should be his or her first step in planning the experiment?

A asking a botanist to grow the plant
B interviewing people who have used the medicine
C collecting equipment for the experiment
D searching for information on the preparation of similar compounds

**6** Why is information found in scientific journals generally more reliable than information from individuals?

A Journal articles are always written in English.
B Journal articles must be approved by other scientists.
C Journals are more up-to-date than information on the Internet.
D Journals have been in existence for a long time.

**7** Hernando collected a 50-g soil sample from his garden. He used a sieve to separate the soil from the rocks. There were 5.0 g of rocks. Next, he collected a 150-g soil sample from the same garden and found that it contained 15 g of rocks. He then collected a 300-g soil sample from the same garden and found that it contained 30 g of rocks. Which do the data suggest about the percentage of rocks in Hernando's garden soil?

A It is 5 percent everywhere.
B It is 10 percent everywhere.
C In some places it is 5 percent, in others 10 percent.
D In some places it is 10 percent, in others 15 percent.

## Standard Set 7: Investigation and Experimentation

Directions: Select the best answer for each of the following questions.

**8** Students record the time it takes for three blocks to slide down a metal ramp. The table below shows their data.

**Sliding Blocks on a Ramp**

| Block | Mass (g) | Material | Sliding Time (s) |
|-------|----------|----------|------------------|
| 1 | 100 | Wood | 2.5 |
| 2 | 300 | Plastic | 4.2 |
| 3 | 450 | Iron | 5.1 |

**At this point in the experiment, students should**

A conclude that any 100-g block slides twice as fast as any 450-g block.

B conclude that plastic blocks take 4.2 seconds to slide down ramps.

C conclude that they need more data before they can make a conclusion.

D conclude that wood blocks slide faster than plastic blocks.

**9** You need to deliver a package to your neighbor, but his car is not in the driveway. You think he may be home anyway, although his car is gone. Describe a scientific method to test this hypothesis directly.

A Ask several other neighbors if he is home.

B Knock on his door and see if he answers.

C Leave the package on your doorstep and wait quietly until he sees it.

D Track down the person who currently has his car.

**10** Adela thinks that gravity changes depending on the surface a person stands on. She tests her hypothesis by timing a ball dropped on pavement, grass, soil, and a wooden deck. She finds that gravity is the same on all these surfaces. What can Adela conclude from these results?

A She didn't use the right equipment for her tests.

B Her original hypothesis was incorrect.

C Her watch must be giving an erroneous reading.

D Light and wind affect gravity as much as the surface material.

**11** In the picture of a lightbulb and a globe below, the tilt of Earth's axis can be seen.

How would you use these objects as a model to show how the tilt of Earth's axis causes the change of seasons?

A Spin the globe while the lightbulb is on.

B Move the globe to different positions around the lightbulb.

C Turn the lightbulb on and off as the globe spins.

D Keep the lightbulb on while changing the room's temperature.

**12** Engineers want to study the relationship between wind speed and lift for a new wing design for airplanes. What would be the safest way to study this relationship?

A Study the wing alone in a wind tunnel.

B Study a model of the plane in a wind tunnel.

C Fly a plane with the new wings at several speeds.

D Fly several planes with the new wings at different speeds.

**13** Scientists collect data and draw conclusions. What is the final step of an experiment?

A communicating results

B making an inference

C identifying patterns

D obtaining a patent

# At-Home Standards Practice

The answers for the At-Home Standards Practice presented on the previous pages are listed below. Use this answer key to check your understanding of the Standards. If you need help with a question, use the chapter and lesson reference to go back and review.

## Standard Set 1:
Pages 536–537

1. C Chap. 1, Lesson 1
2. C Chap. 1, Lesson 2
3. D Chap. 1, Lesson 2
4. D Chap. 1, Lesson 2
5. C Chap. 1, Lesson 2
6. B Chap. 1, Lesson 2
7. B Chap. 1, Lesson 2
8. C Chap. 2, Lesson 1
9. D Chap. 2, Lesson 1
10. B Chap. 2, Lesson 1
11. D Chap. 1, Lesson 3
12. A Chap. 1, Lesson 3
13. D Chap. 1, Lesson 3
14. C Chap. 2, Lesson 1
15. C Chap. 2, Lesson 1
16. D Chap. 2, Lesson 1
17. C Chap. 2, Lesson 2
18. B Chap. 2, Lesson 2

## Standard Set 2:
Pages 538–539

1. B Chap. 3, Lesson 1
2. D Chap. 3, Lesson 4
3. A Chap. 3, Lesson 4
4. D Chap. 3, Lesson 1
5. B Chap. 3, Lesson 1
6. C Chap. 3, Lesson 1
7. D Chap. 3, Lesson 1
8. C Chap. 4, Lesson 2
9. C Chap. 4, Lesson 2
10. A Chap. 4, Lesson 2
11. A Chap. 4, Lesson 2
12. A Chap. 4, Lesson 1
13. C Chap. 4, Lesson 1
14. C Chap. 3, Lesson 3
15. C Chap. 3, Lesson 3

## Standard Set 3:
Pages 540–541

1. C Chap. 5, Lesson 2
2. B Chap. 5, Lesson 2
3. C Chap. 5, Lesson 2
4. A Chap. 5, Lesson 1
5. B Chap. 5, Lesson 1
6. C Chap. 5, Lesson 1
7. C Chap. 6, Lesson 1
8. C Chap. 6, Lesson 1
9. C Chap. 6, Lesson 2
10. A Chap. 6, Lesson 4
11. B Chap. 6, Lesson 4
12. D Chap. 6, Lesson 4
13. A Chap. 6, Lesson 4
14. C Chap. 5, Lesson 2
15. C Chap. 5, Lesson 2
16. C Chap. 5, Lesson 2

## Standard Set 4:
Pages 542–543

1. B Chap. 7, Lesson 1
2. D Chap. 7, Lesson 1
3. B Chap. 8, Lesson 1
4. B Chap. 8, Lesson 1
5. A Chap. 8, Lesson 1
6. B Chap. 7, Lesson 1
7. B Chap. 7, Lesson 2
8. C Chap. 7, Lesson 2
9. D Chap. 7, Lesson 2
10. A Chap. 7, Lesson 1
11. C Chap. 6, Lesson 3
12. A Chap. 6, Lesson 3
13. C Chap. 8, Lesson 2
14. A Chap. 8, Lesson 2

## Standard Set 5:
Pages 544–545

1. D Chap. 2, Lesson 2
2. A Chap. 2, Lesson 2
3. A Chap. 2, Lesson 2
4. C Chap. 2, Lesson 2
5. C Chap. 2, Lesson 2
6. D Chap. 9, Lesson 1
7. C Chap. 13, Lesson 1
8. C Chap. 13, Lesson 1
9. D Chap. 13, Lesson 1
10. D Chap. 13, Lesson 2
11. D Chap. 13, Lesson 2
12. B Chap. 13, Lesson 2
13. A Chap. 3, Lesson 2
14. C Chap. 3, Lesson 2
15. D Chap. 3, Lesson 2
16. B Chap. 12, Lesson 2
17. C Chap. 11, Lesson 4
18. D Chap. 11, Lesson 4

## Standard Set 6:
Pages 546–547

1. D Chap. 11, Lesson 1
2. D Chap. 11, Lesson 1
3. B Chap. 11, Lesson 4
4. A Chap. 11, Lesson 2
5. B Chap. 11, Lesson 2
6. A Chap. 11, Lesson 2
7. A Chap. 11, Lesson 3
8. A Chap. 11, Lesson 3
9. C Chap. 11, Lesson 4
10. A Chap. 11, Lesson 2
11. B Chap. 11, Lesson 1
12. D Chap. 11, Lesson 2
13. B Chap. 11, Lesson 2
14. C Chap. 9, Lesson 1
15. A Chap. 9, Lesson 2
16. B Chap. 10, Lesson 2
17. C Chap. 10, Lesson 2

**Standard Set 7:**

Pages 548–549

| 1 | B | Tools of the Scientist |
| 2 | D | Tools of the Scientist |
| 3 | D | Tools of the Scientist |
| 4 | D | Tools of the Scientist |
| 5 | D | Tools of the Scientist |
| 6 | B | Tools of the Scientist |
| 7 | B | Tools of the Scientist |
| 8 | C | Tools of the Scientist |
| 9 | B | Tools of the Scientist |
| 10 | B | Tools of the Scientist |
| 11 | B | Tools of the Scientist |
| 12 | A | Tools of the Scientist |
| 13 | A | Tools of the Scientist |

# Student Resources

## For Students and Parents/Guardians

These resources are designed to help you achieve success in science. You will find useful information on laboratory safety, technology skills, and math skills. In addition, some life science reference materials are found in the Reference Handbook. You'll find the information you need to learn and sharpen your skills in these resources.

# Student Resources Table of Contents

## Science Safety Skill Handbook

**Safety Symbols** ...................................................554
**Safety in the Science Laboratory** ..........................555
   General Safety Rules.........................................555
   Prevent Accidents ............................................555
   Laboratory Work..............................................555
   Laboratory Cleanup .........................................556
   Emergencies ....................................................556

## Technology Skill Handbook

   Hardware Basics ..............................................557
   Storing Your Data............................................557
   Getting Started with Word Processing Programs.....558
   Getting Started with Spreadsheet Programs..........558
   Getting Started with Presentation Programs.........559
   Doing Research with the World Wide Web .............560

## Math Skill Handbook

**Math Review**
   Use Fractions ..................................................561
   Use Ratios ......................................................564
   Use Decimals ..................................................564
   Use Proportions...............................................565
   Use Percentages ..............................................566
   Solve One-Step Equations ................................566
   Use Statistics ..................................................567
   Use Geometry..................................................568
**Science Application**
   Measure in SI..................................................571
   Dimensional Analysis.......................................571
   Precision and Significant Digits .......................573
   Scientific Notation ..........................................573
   Make and Use Graphs......................................574

## Reference Handbook

   Using a Calculator ..........................................576
   Understanding Scientific Terms .......................577
   Use and Care of a Microscope..........................579
   Diversity of Life: Classification of Living Organisms ...........580
   Periodic Table of Elements ..............................584

# Science Safety Skill Handbook

These safety symbols are used in laboratory and field investigations in this book to indicate possible hazards. Learn the meaning of each symbol and refer to this page often. *Remember to wash your hands thoroughly after completing lab procedures.*

| SAFETY SYMBOLS | HAZARD | EXAMPLES | PRECAUTION | REMEDY |
|---|---|---|---|---|
| **DISPOSAL** | Special disposal procedures need to be followed. | certain chemicals, living organisms | Do not dispose of these materials in the sink or trash can. | Dispose of wastes as directed by your teacher. |
| **BIOLOGICAL** | Organisms or other biological materials that might be harmful to humans | bacteria, fungi, blood, unpreserved tissues, plant materials | Avoid skin contact with these materials. Wear mask or gloves. | Notify your teacher if you suspect contact with material. Wash hands thoroughly. |
| **EXTREME TEMPERATURE** | Objects that can burn skin by being too cold or too hot | boiling liquids, hot plates, dry ice, liquid nitrogen | Use proper protection when handling. | Go to your teacher for first aid. |
| **SHARP OBJECT** | Use of tools or glassware that can easily puncture or slice skin | razor blades, pins, scalpels, pointed tools, dissecting probes, broken glass | Practice common-sense behavior and follow guidelines for use of the tool. | Go to your teacher for first aid. |
| **FUME** | Possible danger to respiratory tract from fumes | ammonia, acetone, nail polish remover, heated sulfur, moth balls | Make sure there is good ventilation. Never smell fumes directly. Wear a mask. | Leave foul area and notify your teacher immediately. |
| **ELECTRICAL** | Possible danger from electrical shock or burn | improper grounding, liquid spills, short circuits, exposed wires | Double-check setup with teacher. Check condition of wires and apparatus. Use GFI-protected outlets. | Do not attempt to fix electrical problems. Notify your teacher immediately. |
| **IRRITANT** | Substances that can irritate the skin or mucous membranes of the respiratory tract | pollen, moth balls, steel wool, fiberglass, potassium permanganate | Wear dust mask and gloves. Practice extra care when handling these materials. | Go to your teacher for first aid. |
| **CHEMICAL** | Chemicals that can react with and destroy tissue and other materials | bleaches such as hydrogen peroxide; acids such as sulfuric acid, hydrochloric acid; bases such as ammonia, sodium hydroxide | Wear goggles, gloves, and an apron. | Immediately flush the affected area with water and notify your teacher. |
| **TOXIC** | Substance may be poisonous if touched, inhaled, or swallowed. | mercury, many metal compounds, iodine, poinsettia plant parts | Follow your teacher's instructions. | Always wash hands thoroughly after use. Go to your teacher for first aid. |
| **FLAMMABLE** | Open flame may ignite flammable chemicals, loose clothing, or hair. | alcohol, kerosene, potassium permanganate, hair, clothing | Avoid open flames and heat when using flammable chemicals. | Notify your teacher immediately. Use fire safety equipment if applicable. |
| **OPEN FLAME** | Open flame in use, may cause fire. | hair, clothing, paper, synthetic materials | Tie back hair and loose clothing. Follow teacher's instructions on lighting and extinguishing flames. | Always wash hands thoroughly after use. Go to your teacher for first aid. |

 **Eye Safety** Proper eye protection must be worn at all times by anyone performing or observing science activities.

 **Clothing Protection** This symbol appears when substances could stain or burn clothing.

 **Animal Safety** This symbol appears when safety of animals and students must be ensured.

 **Handwashing** After the lab, wash hands with soap and water before removing goggles

# Safety in the Science Laboratory

## Introduction to Science Safety

The science laboratory is a safe place to work if you follow standard safety procedures. Being responsible for your own safety helps to make the entire laboratory a safer place for everyone. When performing any lab, read and apply the caution statements and safety symbol listed at the beginning of the lab.

## General Safety Rules

1. Complete the *Lab Safety Form* or other safety contract BEFORE starting any science lab.

2. Study the procedure. Ask your teacher any questions. Be sure you understand safety symbols shown on the page.

3. Notify your teacher about allergies or other health conditions which can affect your participation in a lab.

4. Learn and follow use and safety procedures for your equipment. If unsure, ask your teacher.

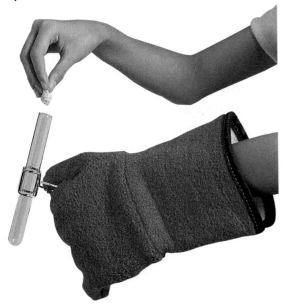

5. Never eat, drink, chew gum, apply cosmetics, or do any personal grooming in the lab. Never use lab glassware as food or drink containers. Keep your hands away from your face and mouth.

6. Know the location and proper use of the safety shower, eye wash, fire blanket, and fire alarm.

## Prevent Accidents

1. Use the safety equipment provided to you. Goggles and a safety apron should be worn during investigations.

2. Do NOT use hair spray, mousse, or other flammable hair products. Tie back long hair and tie down loose clothing.

3. Do NOT wear sandals or other open-toed shoes in the lab.

4. Remove jewelry on hands and wrists. Loose jewelry, such as chains and long necklaces, should be removed to prevent them from getting caught in equipment.

5. Do not taste any substances or draw any material into a tube with your mouth.

6. Proper behavior is expected in the lab. Practical jokes and fooling around can lead to accidents and injury.

7. Keep your work area uncluttered.

## Laboratory Work

1. Collect and carry all equipment and materials to your work area before beginning a lab.

2. Remain in your own work area unless given permission by your teacher to leave it.

**3.** Always slant test tubes away from yourself and others when heating them, adding substances to them, or rinsing them.

**4.** If instructed to smell a substance in a container, hold the container a short distance away and fan vapors towards your nose.

**5.** Do NOT substitute other chemicals/substances for those in the materials list unless instructed to do so by your teacher.

**6.** Do NOT take any materials or chemicals outside of the laboratory.

**7.** Stay out of storage areas unless instructed to be there and supervised by your teacher.

## Laboratory Cleanup

**1.** Turn off all burners, water, and gas, and disconnect all electrical devices.

**2.** Clean all pieces of equipment and return all materials to their proper places.

**3.** Dispose of chemicals and other materials as directed by your teacher. Place broken glass and solid substances in the proper containers. Never discard materials in the sink.

**4.** Clean your work area.

**5.** Wash your hands with soap and water thoroughly BEFORE removing your goggles.

## Emergencies

**1.** Report any fire, electrical shock, glassware breakage, spill, or injury, no matter how small, to your teacher immediately. Follow his or her instructions.

**2.** If your clothing should catch fire, STOP, DROP, and ROLL. If possible, smother it with the fire blanket or get under a safety shower. NEVER RUN.

**3.** If a fire should occur, turn off all gas and leave the room according to established procedures.

**4.** In most instances, your teacher will clean up spills. Do NOT attempt to clean up spills unless you are given permission and instructions to do so.

**5.** If chemicals come into contact with your eyes or skin, notify your teacher immediately. Use the eyewash, or flush your skin or eyes with large quantities of water.

**6.** The fire extinguisher and first-aid kit should only be used by your teacher unless it is an extreme emergency and you have been given permission.

**7.** If someone is injured or becomes ill, only a professional medical provider or someone certified in first aid should perform first-aid procedures.

# Computer Skills

People who study science rely on computer technology to do research, record experimental data, analyze results from investigations, and communicate with other scientists. Whether you work in a laboratory or just need to write a lab report, good computer skills are necessary.

**Figure 1** Students and scientists rely on computers to gather data and communicate ideas.

## Hardware Basics

Your personal computer is a system consisting of many components. The parts you can see and touch are called hardware.

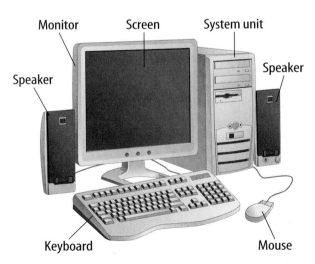

**Figure 2** Most desktop computers consist of the components shown above. Notebook computers have the same components in a compact unit.

Desktop systems, like the one shown in **Figure 2**, typically have most of these components. Notebook and tablet computers have most of the same components as a desktop computer, but the components are integrated into a single, book-sized portable unit.

## Storing Your Data

When you save documents created on computers at your school, they probably are stored in a directory on your school's network. However, if you want to take the documents you have created home, you need to save them on something portable. Removable media, like those shown in **Figure 3**, are disks and drives that are designed to be moved from one computer to another.

**Figure 3** Removable data storage is a convenient way to carry your documents from place to place.

Removable media vary from floppy disks and recordable CDs and DVDs to small solid-state storage. Tiny USB "keychain" drives have become popular because they can store large amounts of data and plug into any computer with a USB port. Each of these types of media stores different amounts of data. Be sure that you save your data to a medium that is compatible with your computer.

## Getting Started with Word Processing Programs

A word processor is used for the composition, editing, and formatting of written material. Word processors vary from program to program, but most have the basic functions shown in **Figure 4**. Most word processors also can be used to make simple tables and graphics.

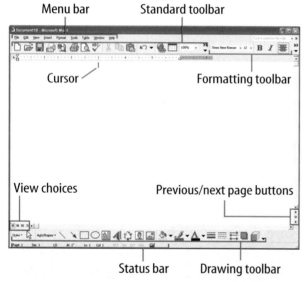

**Figure 4** Word processors have functions that easily allow you to edit, format, view, and save text, tables, and images, making them useful for writing lab reports and research papers.

### Word Processor Tips

- As you type, text will automatically wrap to the next line. Press *Enter* on your keyboard if you wish to start a new paragraph.

- You can move multiple lines of text around by using the *cut* and *paste* functions on the toolbar.

- If you make a typing or formatting error, use the *undo* function on the toolbar.

- Be sure to save your document early and often. This will prevent you from losing your work if your computer turns off unexpectedly.

- Use the *spell-check* function to check your spelling and grammar. Remember that *spell-check* will not catch words that are misspelled to look like other words, such as *cold* instead of *gold*. Reread your document to look for spelling and grammar mistakes.

- Graphics and spreadsheets can be added to your document by copying them from other programs and pasting them into your document.

- If you have questions about using your word processor, ask your teacher or use the program's *help* menu.

## Getting Started with Spreadsheet Programs

A spreadsheet, like the one shown in **Figure 5**, helps you organize information into columns and rows. Spreadsheets are particularly useful for making data tables. Spreadsheets also can be used to perform mathematical calculations with your data. Then, you can use the spreadsheet to generate graphs and charts displaying your results.

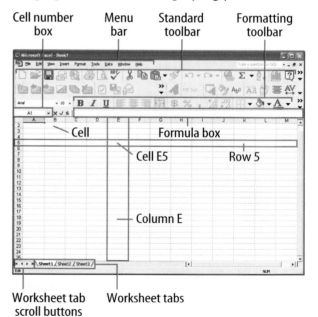

**Figure 5** With formulas and graphs, spreadsheets help you organize and analyze your data.

## Spreadsheet Tips

- Think about how to organize your data before you begin entering data.

- Each column (vertical) is assigned a letter and each row (horizontal) is assigned a number. Each point where a row and column intersect is called a cell, and is labeled according to where it is located. For example: column A, row 1 is cell A1.

- To edit the information in a cell, you must first activate the cell by clicking on it.

- When using a spreadsheet to generate a graph, make sure you use the type of graph that best represents the data. Review the *Science Skill Handbook* in this book for help with graphs.

- To learn more about using your spreadsheet program ask your teacher or use the program's Help menu.

## Getting Started with Presentation Programs

There are many programs that help you orally communicate results of your research in an organized and interesting way. Many of these are slideshow programs, which allow you to organize text, graphs, digital photographs, sound, animations, and digital video into one multimedia presentation. Presentations can be printed onto paper or displayed on-screen. Slideshow programs are particularly effective when used with video projectors and interactive whiteboards, like the one shown in **Figure 6**. Although presentation programs are not the only way to communicate information publicly, they are an effective way to organize your presentation and remind your audience of major points.

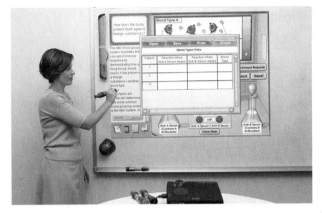

**Figure 6** Video projectors and interactive whiteboards allow you to present information stored on a computer to an entire classroom. They are becoming increasingly common in the classrooms.

## Presentation Program Tips

- Often, color and strong images will convey a point better than words alone. But, be sure to organize your presentation clearly. Don't let the graphics confuse the message.

- Most presentation programs will let you copy and paste text, spreadsheets, art and graphs from other programs.

- Most presentation programs have built-in templates that help you organize text and graphics.

- As with any kind of presentation, familiarize yourself with the equipment and practice your presentation before you present it to an audience.

- Most presentation programs will allow you to save your document in html format so that you can publish your document on a Web site.

- If you have questions about using your presentation software or hardware, ask your teacher or use the program's Help menu.

## Doing Research with the World Wide Web

The Internet is a global network of computers where information can be stored and shared by anyone with an internet connection. One of the easiest ways to find information on the internet is by using the World Wide Web, a vast graphical system of documents written in the computer language, html (hypertext markup language). Web pages are arranged in collections of related material called "Web sites." The content on a Web site is viewed using a program called a Web browser. Web browsers, like the one shown in **Figure 7,** allow you to browse or surf the Web by clicking on highlighted hyperlinks, which move you from Web page to Web page. Web content can be searched by topic using a search engine. Search engines are located on Web sites which catalog key words on Web pages all over the World Wide Web.

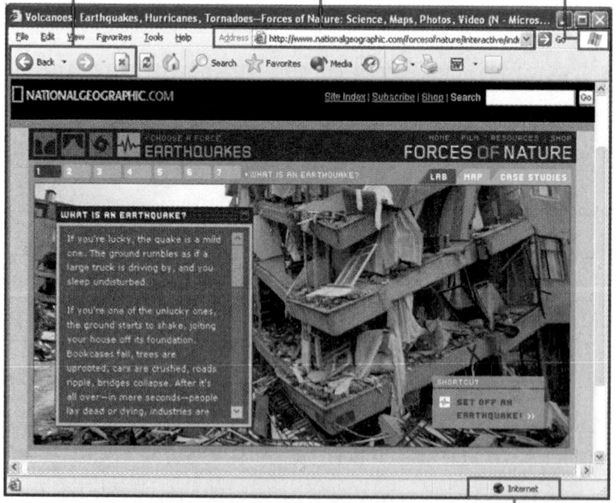

**Figure 7** Web browsers have all the tools you need to navigate and view information on the Web.

## World Wide Web Tips

- Search the Web using specific keywords. For example, if you want to research the element gold don't type *elements* into the search engine.

- When performing a Web search, enclose multiple keywords with quotes to narrow your results to the most relevant pages.

- The first hit your Web search results in is not always the best. Search results are arranged by popularity, not by relevance to your topic. Be patient and look at many links in your search results to find the best information.

- Think critically when you do science research on the Web. Compared to a traditional library, finding accurate information on the Web is not always easy because anyone can create a Web site. Some of the best places to start your research are websites for major newspapers and magazines, as well as U.S. government (*.gov*) and university (*.edu*) Web sites.

- Security is a major concern when browsing the Web. Your computer can be exposed to advertising software and computer viruses, which can hurt your computer's data and performance. *Do not download software at your school unless your teacher tells you to do so.*

- Cite information you find on the Web just as you would books and journals. An example of proper Web citation is the following:
  Menk, Amy J. (2004). *Urban Ecology.* Retrieved January 21, 2005, from McGraw-Hill Web site: http://www.mcgraw-hill.com/papers/urban.html

- The World Wide Web is a great resource for information, but don't forget to utilize local libraries, including your school library.

# Math Review

## Use Fractions  (MA7: NS 1.0, NS 1.2, NS 2.2)

A fraction compares a part to a whole. In the fraction $\frac{2}{3}$, the 2 represents the part and is the numerator. The 3 represents the whole and is the denominator.

**Reduce Fractions** To reduce a fraction, you must find the largest factor that is common to both the numerator and the denominator, the greatest common factor (GCF). Divide both numbers by the GCF. The fraction has then been reduced, or it is in its simplest form.

**Example** Twelve of the 20 chemicals in the science lab are in powder form. What fraction of the chemicals used in the lab are in powder form?

**Step 1** Write the fraction.

$$\frac{part}{whole} = \frac{12}{20}$$

**Step 2** To find the GCF of the numerator and denominator, list all of the factors of each number.

Factors of 12: 1, 2, 3, 4, 6, 12
(the numbers that divide evenly into 12)

Factors of 20: 1, 2, 4, 5, 10, 20
(the numbers that divide evenly into 20)

**Step 3** List the common factors.

1, 2, 4

**Step 4** Choose the greatest factor in the list. The GCF of 12 and 20 is 4.

**Step 5** Divide the numerator and denominator by the GCF.

$$\frac{12 \div 4}{20 \div 4} = \frac{3}{5}$$

In the lab, $\frac{3}{5}$ of the chemicals are in powder form.

**Practice Problem** At an amusement park, 66 of 90 rides have a height restriction. What fraction of the rides, in its simplest form, has a height restriction?

**Add and Subtract Fractions with Like Denominators** To add or subtract fractions with the same denominator, add or subtract the numerators and write the sum or difference over the denominator. After finding the sum or difference, find the simplest form for your fraction.

**Example 1** In the forest outside your house, $\frac{1}{8}$ of the animals are rabbits, $\frac{3}{8}$ are squirrels, and the remainder are birds and insects. How many are mammals?

**Step 1** Add the numerators.

$$\frac{1}{8} + \frac{3}{8} = \frac{(1 + 3)}{8} = \frac{4}{8}$$

**Step 2** Find the GCF.

$$\frac{4}{8} \text{ (GCF, 4)}$$

**Step 3** Divide the numerator and denominator by the GCF.

$$\frac{4 \div 4}{8 \div 4} = \frac{1}{2}$$

$\frac{1}{2}$ of the animals are mammals.

**Example 2** If $\frac{7}{16}$ of the Earth is covered by freshwater, and $\frac{1}{16}$ of that is in glaciers, how much freshwater is not frozen?

**Step 1** Subtract the numerators.

$$\frac{7}{16} - \frac{1}{16} = \frac{(7 - 1)}{16} = \frac{6}{16}$$

**Step 2** Find the GCF.

$$\frac{6}{16} \text{ (GCF, 2)}$$

**Step 3** Divide the numerator and denominator by the GCF.

$$\frac{6 \div 2}{16 \div 2} = \frac{3}{8}$$

$\frac{3}{8}$ of the freshwater is not frozen.

**Practice Problem** A bicycle rider is riding at a rate of 15 km/h for $\frac{4}{9}$ of his ride, 10 km/h for $\frac{2}{9}$ of his ride, and 8 km/h for the remainder of the ride. How much of his ride is he riding at a rate greater than 8 km/h?

# Math Skill Handbook

**Add and Subtract Fractions with Unlike Denominators** To add or subtract fractions with unlike denominators, first find the least common denominator (LCD). This is the smallest number that is a common multiple of both denominators. Rename each fraction with the LCD, and then add or subtract. Find the simplest form if necessary.

**Example 1** A chemist makes a paste that is $\frac{1}{2}$ table salt (NaCl), $\frac{1}{3}$ sugar ($C_6H_{12}O_6$), and the remainder is water ($H_2O$). How much of the paste is a solid?

**Step 1** Find the LCD of the fractions.

$$\frac{1}{2} + \frac{1}{3} \text{ (LCD, 6)}$$

**Step 2** Rename each numerator and each denominator with the LCD.

**Step 3** Add the numerators.

$$\frac{3}{6} + \frac{2}{6} = \frac{(3+2)}{6} = \frac{5}{6}$$

$\frac{5}{6}$ of the paste is a solid.

**Example 2** The average precipitation in Grand Junction, CO, is $\frac{7}{10}$ inch in November, and $\frac{3}{5}$ inch in December. What is the total average precipitation?

**Step 1** Find the LCD of the fractions.

$$\frac{7}{10} + \frac{3}{5} \text{ (LCD, 10)}$$

**Step 2** Rename each numerator and each denominator with the LCD.

**Step 3** Add the numerators.

$$\frac{7}{10} + \frac{6}{10} = \frac{(7+6)}{10} = \frac{13}{10}$$

$\frac{13}{10}$ inches total precipitation, or $1\frac{3}{10}$ inches.

**Practice Problem** On an electric bill, about $\frac{1}{8}$ of the energy is from solar energy and about $\frac{1}{10}$ is from wind power. How much of the total bill is from solar energy and wind power combined?

**Example 3** In your body, $\frac{7}{10}$ of your muscle contractions are involuntary (cardiac and smooth muscle tissue). Smooth muscle makes $\frac{3}{15}$ of your muscle contractions. How many of your muscle contractions are made by cardiac muscle?

**Step 1** Find the LCD of the fractions.

$$\frac{7}{10} - \frac{3}{15} \text{ (LCD, 30)}$$

**Step 2** Rename each numerator and each denominator with the LCD.

$$\frac{7 \times 3}{10 \times 3} = \frac{21}{30}$$

$$\frac{3 \times 2}{15 \times 2} = \frac{6}{30}$$

**Step 3** Subtract the numerators.

$$\frac{21}{30} - \frac{6}{30} = \frac{(21-6)}{30} = \frac{15}{30}$$

**Step 4** Find the GCF.

$$\frac{15}{30} \text{ (GCF, 15)}$$

$$\frac{1}{2}$$

$\frac{1}{2}$ of all muscle contractions are cardiac muscle.

**Example 4** Tony wants to make cookies that call for $\frac{3}{4}$ of a cup of flour, but he only has $\frac{1}{3}$ of a cup. How much more flour does he need?

**Step 1** Find the LCD of the fractions.

$$\frac{3}{4} - \frac{1}{3} \text{ (LCD, 12)}$$

**Step 2** Rename each numerator and each denominator with the LCD.

$$\frac{3 \times 3}{4 \times 3} = \frac{9}{12}$$

$$\frac{1 \times 4}{3 \times 4} = \frac{4}{12}$$

**Step 3** Subtract the numerators.

$$\frac{9}{12} - \frac{4}{12} = \frac{(9-4)}{12} = \frac{5}{12}$$

$\frac{5}{12}$ of a cup of flour

**Practice Problem** Using the information provided to you in Example 3 above, determine how many muscle contractions are voluntary (skeletal muscle).

Math Skill Handbook

**Multiply Fractions** To multiply with fractions, multiply the numerators and multiply the denominators. Find the simplest form if necessary.

**Example** Multiply $\frac{3}{5}$ by $\frac{1}{3}$.

**Step 1** Multiply the numerators and denominators.
$$\frac{3}{5} \times \frac{1}{3} = \frac{(3 \times 1)}{(5 \times 3)} = \frac{3}{15}$$

**Step 2** Find the GCF.
$$\frac{3}{15} \text{ (GCF, 3)}$$

**Step 3** Divide the numerator and denominator by the GCF.
$$\frac{3 \div 3}{15 \div 3} = \frac{1}{5}$$

$\frac{3}{5}$ multiplied by $\frac{1}{3}$ is $\frac{1}{5}$.

**Practice Problem** Multiply $\frac{3}{14}$ by $\frac{5}{16}$.

**Find a Reciprocal** Two numbers whose product is 1 are called multiplicative inverses, or reciprocals.

**Example** Find the reciprocal of $\frac{3}{8}$.

**Step 1** Inverse the fraction by putting the denominator on top and the numerator on the bottom.
$$\frac{8}{3}$$

The reciprocal of $\frac{3}{8}$ is $\frac{8}{3}$.

**Practice Problem** Find the reciprocal of $\frac{4}{9}$.

**Divide Fractions** To divide one fraction by another fraction, multiply the dividend by the reciprocal of the divisor. Find the simplest form if necessary.

**Example 1** Divide $\frac{1}{9}$ by $\frac{1}{3}$.

**Step 1** Find the reciprocal of the divisor.
The reciprocal of $\frac{1}{3}$ is $\frac{3}{1}$.

**Step 2** Multiply the dividend by the reciprocal of the divisor.
$$\frac{\frac{1}{9}}{\frac{1}{3}} = \frac{1}{9} \times \frac{3}{1} = \frac{(1 \times 3)}{(9 \times 1)} = \frac{3}{9}$$

**Step 3** Find the GCF.
$$\frac{3}{9} \text{ (GCF, 3)}$$

**Step 4** Divide the numerator and denominator by the GCF.
$$\frac{3 \div 3}{9 \div 3} = \frac{1}{3}$$

$\frac{1}{9}$ divided by $\frac{1}{3}$ is $\frac{1}{3}$.

**Example 2** Divide $\frac{3}{5}$ by $\frac{1}{4}$.

**Step 1** Find the reciprocal of the divisor.
The reciprocal of $\frac{1}{4}$ is $\frac{4}{1}$.

**Step 2** Multiply the dividend by the reciprocal of the divisor.
$$\frac{\frac{3}{5}}{\frac{1}{4}} = \frac{3}{5} \times \frac{4}{1} = \frac{(3 \times 4)}{(5 \times 1)} = \frac{12}{5}$$

$\frac{3}{5}$ divided by $\frac{1}{4}$ is $\frac{12}{5}$ or $2\frac{2}{5}$.

**Practice Problem** Divide $\frac{3}{11}$ by $\frac{7}{10}$.

# Math Skill Handbook

## Use Ratios   `MA7: NS 1.0`

When you compare two numbers by division, you are using a ratio. Ratios can be written 3 to 5, 3:5, or $\frac{3}{5}$. Ratios, like fractions, also can be written in simplest form.

Ratios can represent one type of probability, called odds. This is a ratio that compares the number of ways a certain outcome occurs to the number of possible outcomes. For example, if you flip a coin 100 times, what are the odds that it will come up heads? There are two possible outcomes, heads or tails, so the odds of coming up heads are 50:100. Another way to say this is that 50 out of 100 times the coin will come up heads. In its simplest form, the ratio is 1:2.

**Example 1** A chemical solution contains 40 g of salt and 64 g of baking soda. What is the ratio of salt to baking soda as a fraction in simplest form?

**Step 1**   Write the ratio as a fraction.
$$\frac{\text{salt}}{\text{baking soda}} = \frac{40}{64}$$

**Step 2**   Express the fraction in simplest form. The GCF of 40 and 64 is 8.
$$\frac{40}{64} = \frac{40 \div 8}{64 \div 8} = \frac{5}{8}$$

The ratio of salt to baking soda in the sample is 5:8.

**Example 2** Sean rolls a 6-sided die 6 times. What are the odds that the side with a 3 will show?

**Step 1**   Write the ratio as a fraction.
$$\frac{\text{number of sides with a 3}}{\text{number of possible sides}} = \frac{1}{6}$$

**Step 2**   Multiply by the number of attempts.
$$\frac{1}{6} \times 6 \text{ attempts} = \frac{6}{6} \text{ attempts} = 1 \text{ attempt}$$

1 attempt out of 6 will show a 3.

**Practice Problem** Two metal rods measure 100 cm and 144 cm in length. What is the ratio of their lengths in simplest form?

## Use Decimals   `MA7: NS 1.0, NS 1.2`

A fraction with a denominator that is a power of ten can be written as a decimal. For example, 0.27 means $\frac{27}{100}$. The decimal point separates the ones place from the tenths place.

Any fraction can be written as a decimal using division. For example, the fraction $\frac{5}{8}$ can be written as a decimal by dividing 5 by 8. Written as a decimal, it is 0.625.

**Add or Subtract Decimals**   When adding and subtracting decimals, line up the decimal points before carrying out the operation.

**Example 1** Find the sum of 47.68 and 7.80.

**Step 1**   Line up the decimal places when you write the numbers.
$$\begin{array}{r} 47.68 \\ + \ 7.80 \end{array}$$

**Step 2**   Add the decimals.
$$\begin{array}{r} {\scriptstyle 1\ 1} \\ 47.68 \\ + \ 7.80 \\ \hline 55.48 \end{array}$$

The sum of 47.68 and 7.80 is 55.48.

**Example 2** Find the difference of 42.17 and 15.85.

**Step 1**   Line up the decimal places when you write the number.
$$\begin{array}{r} 42.17 \\ -15.85 \end{array}$$

**Step 2**   Subtract the decimals.
$$\begin{array}{r} {\scriptstyle 3\,11\,1} \\ 42.17 \\ -15.85 \\ \hline 26.32 \end{array}$$

The difference of 42.17 and 15.85 is 26.32.

**Practice Problem** Find the sum of 1.245 and 3.842.

**Multiply Decimals** To multiply decimals, multiply the numbers like numbers without decimal points. Count the decimal places in each factor. The product will have the same number of decimal places as the sum of the decimal places in the factors.

**Example** Multiply 2.4 by 5.9.

**Step 1** Multiply the factors like two whole numbers.
$24 \times 59 = 1416$

**Step 2** Find the sum of the number of decimal places in the factors. Each factor has one decimal place, for a sum of two decimal places.

**Step 3** The product will have two decimal places.
14.16

The product of 2.4 and 5.9 is 14.16.

**Practice Problem** Multiply 4.6 by 2.2.

**Divide Decimals** When dividing decimals, change the divisor to a whole number. To do this, multiply both the divisor and the dividend by the same power of ten. Then place the decimal point in the quotient directly above the decimal point in the dividend. Then divide as you do with whole numbers.

**Example** Divide 8.84 by 3.4.

**Step 1** Multiply both factors by 10.
$3.4 \times 10 = 34, 8.84 \times 10 = 88.4$

**Step 2** Divide 88.4 by 34.

```
        2.6
   34)88.4
      -68
       204
      -204
         0
```

8.84 divided by 3.4 is 2.6.

**Practice Problem** Divide 75.6 by 3.6.

## Use Proportions  MA7: MR 2.5

An equation that shows that two ratios are equivalent is a proportion. The ratios $\frac{2}{4}$ and $\frac{5}{10}$ are equivalent, so they can be written as $\frac{2}{4} = \frac{5}{10}$. This equation is a proportion.

When two ratios form a proportion, the cross products are equal. To find the cross products in the proportion $\frac{2}{4} = \frac{5}{10}$, multiply the 2 and the 10, and the 4 and the 5. Therefore $2 \times 10 = 4 \times 5$, or $20 = 20$.

Because you know that both ratios are equal, you can use cross products to find a missing term in a proportion. This is known as solving the proportion.

**Example** The heights of a tree and a pole are proportional to the lengths of their shadows. The tree casts a shadow of 24 m when a 6-m pole casts a shadow of 4 m. What is the height of the tree?

**Step 1** Write a proportion.
$$\frac{\text{height of tree}}{\text{height of pole}} = \frac{\text{length of tree's shadow}}{\text{length of pole's shadow}}$$

**Step 2** Substitute the known values into the proportion. Let $h$ represent the unknown value, the height of the tree.
$$\frac{h}{6} = \frac{24}{4}$$

**Step 3** Find the cross products.
$h \times 4 = 6 \times 24$

**Step 4** Simplify the equation.
$4h = 144$

**Step 5** Divide each side by 4.
$$\frac{4h}{4} = \frac{144}{4}$$
$$h = 36$$

The height of the tree is 36 m.

**Practice Problem** The ratios of the weights of two objects on the Moon and on Earth are in proportion. A rock weighing 3 N on the Moon weighs 18 N on Earth. How much would a rock that weighs 5 N on the Moon weigh on Earth?

# Math Skill Handbook

## Use Percentages  `MA7: NS 1.7`

The word *percent* means "out of one hundred." It is a ratio that compares a number to 100. Suppose you read that 77 percent of the Earth's surface is covered by water. That is the same as reading that the fraction of the Earth's surface covered by water is $\frac{77}{100}$. To express a fraction as a percent, first find the equivalent decimal for the fraction. Then, multiply the decimal by 100 and add the percent symbol.

**Example 1** Express $\frac{13}{20}$ as a percent.

**Step 1** Find the equivalent decimal for the fraction.

$$
\begin{array}{r}
0.65 \\
20\overline{)13.00} \\
\underline{12\ 0} \\
1\ 00 \\
\underline{1\ 00} \\
0
\end{array}
$$

**Step 2** Rewrite the fraction $\frac{13}{20}$ as 0.65.

**Step 3** Multiply 0.65 by 100 and add the % symbol.
$0.65 \times 100 = 65 = 65\%$

So, $\frac{13}{20} = 65\%$.

This also can be solved as a proportion.

**Example 2** Express $\frac{13}{20}$ as a percent.

**Step 1** Write a proportion.
$$\frac{13}{20} = \frac{x}{100}$$

**Step 2** Find the cross products.
$1300 = 20x$

**Step 3** Divide each side by 20.
$$\frac{1300}{20} = \frac{20x}{20}$$
$65\% = x$

**Practice Problem** In one year, 73 of 365 days were rainy in one city. What percent of the days in that city were rainy?

## Solve One-Step Equations  `MA7: AF 1.4, MR 2.5`

A statement that two expressions are equal is an equation. For example, $A = B$ is an equation that states that $A$ is equal to $B$.

An equation is solved when a variable is replaced with a value that makes both sides of the equation equal. To make both sides equal the inverse operation is used. Addition and subtraction are inverses, and multiplication and division are inverses.

**Example 1** Solve the equation $x - 10 = 35$.

**Step 1** Find the solution by adding 10 to each side of the equation.
$$x - 10 = 35$$
$$x - 10 + 10 = 35 + 10$$
$$x = 45$$

**Step 2** Check the solution.
$$x - 10 = 35$$
$$45 - 10 = 35$$
$$35 = 35$$

Both sides of the equation are equal, so $x = 45$.

**Example 2** In the formula $a = bc$, find the value of $c$ if $a = 20$ and $b = 2$.

**Step 1** Rearrange the formula so the unknown value is by itself on one side of the equation by dividing both sides by $b$.

$a = bc$
$\frac{a}{b} = \frac{bc}{b}$
$\frac{a}{b} = c$

**Step 2** Replace the variables $a$ and $b$ with the values that are given.

$\frac{a}{b} = c$
$\frac{20}{2} = c$
$10 = c$

**Step 3** Check the solution.

$a = bc$
$20 = 2 \times 10$
$20 = 20$

Both sides of the equation are equal, so $c = 10$ is the solution when $a = 20$ and $b = 2$.

**Practice Problem** In the formula $h = gd$, find the value of $d$ if $g = 12.3$ and $h = 17.4$.

## Use Statistics  MA7: SP 1.0

The branch of mathematics that deals with collecting, analyzing, and presenting data is statistics. In statistics, there are three common ways to summarize data with a single number—the mean, the median, and the mode.

The **mean** of a set of data is the arithmetic average. It is found by adding the numbers in the data set and dividing by the number of items in the set.

The **median** is the middle number in a set of data when the data are arranged in numerical order. If there were an even number of data points, the median would be the mean of the two middle numbers.

The **mode** of a set of data is the number or item that appears most often.

Another number that often is used to describe a set of data is the range. The **range** is the difference between the largest number and the smallest number in a set of data.

**Example** The speeds (in m/s) for a race car during five different time trials are 39, 37, 44, 36, and 44.

### To find the mean:

**Step 1** Find the sum of the numbers.

$$39 + 37 + 44 + 36 + 44 = 200$$

**Step 2** Divide the sum by the number of items, which is 5.

$$200 \div 5 = 40$$

The mean is 40 m/s.

### To find the median:

**Step 1** Arrange the measures from least to greatest.

36, 37, 39, 44, 44

**Step 2** Determine the middle measure.

36, 37, <u>39</u>, 44, 44

The median is 39 m/s.

### To find the mode:

**Step 1** Group the numbers that are the same together.

44, 44, 36, 37, 39

**Step 2** Determine the number that occurs most in the set.

<u>44, 44</u>, 36, 37, 39

The mode is 44 m/s.

### To find the range:

**Step 1** Arrange the measures from greatest to least.

44, 44, 39, 37, 36

**Step 2** Determine the greatest and least measures in the set.

<u>44</u>, 44, 39, 37, <u>36</u>

**Step 3** Find the difference between the greatest and least measures.

$$44 - 36 = 8$$

The range is 8 m/s.

**Practice Problem** Find the mean, median, mode, and range for the data set 8, 4, 12, 8, 11, 14, 16.

A **frequency table** shows how many times each piece of data occurs, usually in a survey. **Table 1** below shows the results of a student survey on favorite color.

**Table 1 Student Color Choice**

| Color | Tally | Frequency |
|---|---|---|
| red | IIII | 4 |
| blue | IIII | 5 |
| black | II | 2 |
| green | III | 3 |
| purple | IIII II | 7 |
| yellow | IIII I | 6 |

Based on the frequency table data, which color is the favorite?

# Math Skill Handbook

## Use Geometry MA7: MG 2.0, MG 2.1

The branch of mathematics that deals with the measurement, properties, and relationships of points, lines, angles, surfaces, and solids is called geometry.

**Perimeter** The **perimeter** ($P$) is the distance around a geometric figure. To find the perimeter of a rectangle, add the length and width and multiply that sum by two, or $2(l + w)$. To find perimeters of irregular figures, add the length of the sides.

**Example 1** Find the perimeter of a rectangle that is 3 m long and 5 m wide.

**Step 1** You know that the perimeter is 2 times the sum of the width and length.
$$P = 2(3 \text{ m} + 5 \text{ m})$$

**Step 2** Find the sum of the width and length.
$$P = 2(8 \text{ m})$$

**Step 3** Multiply by 2.
$$P = 16 \text{ m}$$

The perimeter is 16 m.

**Example 2** Find the perimeter of a shape with sides measuring 2 cm, 5 cm, 6 cm, 3 cm.

**Step 1** You know that the perimeter is the sum of all the sides.
$$P = 2 + 5 + 6 + 3$$

**Step 2** Find the sum of the sides.
$$P = 2 + 5 + 6 + 3$$
$$P = 16$$

The perimeter is 16 cm.

**Practice Problem 1** Find the perimeter of a rectangle with a length of 18 m and a width of 7 m.

**Practice Problem 2** Find the perimeter of a triangle measuring 1.6 cm by 2.4 cm by 2.4 cm.

**Area of a Rectangle** The **area** ($A$) is the number of square units needed to cover a surface. To find the area of a rectangle, multiply the length times the width, or $l \times w$. When finding area, the units also are multiplied. Area is given in square units.

**Example** Find the area of a rectangle with a length of 1 cm and a width of 10 cm.

**Step 1** You know that the area is the length multiplied by the width.
$$A = (1 \text{ cm} \times 10 \text{ cm})$$

**Step 2** Multiply the length by the width. Also multiply the units.
$$A = 10 \text{ cm}^2$$

The area is 10 cm².

**Practice Problem** Find the area of a square whose sides measure 4 m.

**Area of a Triangle** To find the area of a triangle, use the formula:
$$A = \frac{1}{2}(\text{base} \times \text{height})$$

The base of a triangle can be any of its sides. The height is the perpendicular distance from a base to the opposite endpoint, or vertex.

**Example** Find the area of a triangle with a base of 18 m and a height of 7 m.

**Step 1** You know that the area is $\frac{1}{2}$ the base times the height.
$$A = \frac{1}{2}(18 \text{ m} \times 7 \text{ m})$$

**Step 2** Multiply $\frac{1}{2}$ by the product of 18 × 7. Multiply the units.
$$A = \frac{1}{2}(126 \text{ m}^2)$$
$$A = 63 \text{ m}^2$$

The area is 63 m².

**Practice Problem** Find the area of a triangle with a base of 27 cm and a height of 17 cm.

**Circumference of a Circle** The **diameter** ($d$) of a circle is the distance across the circle through its center, and the **radius** ($r$) is the distance from the center to any point on the circle. The radius is half of the diameter. The distance around the circle is called the **circumference** ($C$). The formula for finding the circumference is:

$$C = 2\pi r \text{ or } C = \pi d$$

The circumference divided by the diameter is always equal to 3.1415926… This nonterminating and nonrepeating number is represented by the Greek letter $\pi$ (pi). An approximation often used for $\pi$ is 3.14.

**Example 1** Find the circumference of a circle with a radius of 3 m.

**Step 1** You know the formula for the circumference is 2 times the radius times $\pi$.

$$C = 2\pi(3)$$

**Step 2** Multiply 2 times the radius.

$$C = 6\pi$$

**Step 3** Multiply by $\pi$.

$$C \approx 19 \text{ m}$$

The circumference is about 19 m.

**Example 2** Find the circumference of a circle with a diameter of 24.0 cm.

**Step 1** You know the formula for the circumference is the diameter times $\pi$.

$$C = \pi(24.0)$$

**Step 2** Multiply the diameter by $\pi$.

$$C \approx 75.4 \text{ cm}$$

The circumference is about 75.4 cm.

**Practice Problem** Find the circumference of a circle with a radius of 19 cm.

**Area of a Circle** The formula for the area of a circle is:

$$A = \pi r^2$$

**Example 1** Find the area of a circle with a radius of 4.0 cm.

**Step 1** $A = \pi(4.0)^2$

**Step 2** Find the square of the radius.

$$A = 16\pi$$

**Step 3** Multiply the square of the radius by $\pi$.

$$A \approx 50 \text{ cm}^2$$

The area of the circle is about 50 cm².

**Example 2** Find the area of a circle with a radius of 225 m.

**Step 1** $A = \pi(225)^2$

**Step 2** Find the square of the radius.

$$A = 50625\pi$$

**Step 3** Multiply the square of the radius by $\pi$.

$$A \approx 159043.1$$

The area of the circle is about 159043.1 m².

**Example 3** Find the area of a circle whose diameter is 20.0 mm.

**Step 1** You know the formula for the area of a circle is the square of the radius times $\pi$, and that the radius is half of the diameter.

$$A = \pi\left(\frac{20.0}{2}\right)^2$$

**Step 2** Find the radius.

$$A = \pi(10.0)^2$$

**Step 3** Find the square of the radius.

$$A = 100\pi$$

**Step 4** Multiply the square of the radius by $\pi$.

$$A \approx 314 \text{ mm}^2$$

The area of is about 314 mm².

**Practice Problem** Find the area of a circle with a radius of 16 m.

# Math Skill Handbook

**Volume** The measure of space occupied by a solid is the **volume** (*V*). To find the volume of a rectangular solid multiply the length times width times height, or $V = l \times w \times h$. It is measured in cubic units, such as cubic centimeters (cm³).

**Example** Find the volume of a rectangular solid with a length of 2.0 m, a width of 4.0 m, and a height of 3.0 m.

**Step 1** You know the formula for volume is the length times the width times the height.

$V = 2.0\text{ m} \times 4.0\text{ m} \times 3.0\text{ m}$

**Step 2** Multiply the length times the width times the height.

$V = 24\text{ m}^3$

The volume is 24 m³.

**Practice Problem** Find the volume of a rectangular solid that is 8 m long, 4 m wide, and 4 m high.

To find the volume of other solids, multiply the area of the base times the height.

**Example 1** Find the volume of a solid that has a triangular base with a length of 8.0 m and a height of 7.0 m. The height of the entire solid is 15.0 m.

**Step 1** You know that the base is a triangle, and the area of a triangle is $\frac{1}{2}$ the base times the height, and the volume is the area of the base times the height.

$V = \left[\frac{1}{2}(b \times h)\right] \times 15$

**Step 2** Find the area of the base.

$V = \left[\frac{1}{2}(8 \times 7)\right] \times 15$

$V = \left(\frac{1}{2} \times 56\right) \times 15$

**Step 3** Multiply the area of the base by the height of the solid.

$V = 28 \times 15$

$V = 420\text{ m}^3$

The volume is 420 m³.

**Example 2** Find the volume of a cylinder that has a base with a radius of 12.0 cm, and a height of 21.0 cm.

**Step 1** You know that the base is a circle, and the area of a circle is the square of the radius times π, and the volume is the area of the base times the height.

$V = (\pi r^2) \times 21$

$V = (\pi 12^2) \times 21$

**Step 2** Find the area of the base.

$V = 144\pi \times 21$

$V = 452 \times 21$

**Step 3** Multiply the area of the base by the height of the solid.

$V \approx 9,500\text{ cm}^3$

The volume is about 9,500 cm³.

**Example 3** Find the volume of a cylinder that has a diameter of 15 mm and a height of 4.8 mm.

**Step 1** You know that the base is a circle with an area equal to the square of the radius times π. The radius is one-half the diameter. The volume is the area of the base times the height.

$V = (\pi r^2) \times 4.8$

$V = \left[\pi\left(\frac{1}{2} \times 15\right)^2\right] \times 4.8$

$V = (\pi 7.5^2) \times 4.8$

**Step 2** Find the area of the base.

$V = 56.25\pi \times 4.8$

$V \approx 176.71 \times 4.8$

**Step 3** Multiply the area of the base by the height of the solid.

$V \approx 848.2$

The volume is about 848.2 mm³.

**Practice Problem** Find the volume of a cylinder with a diameter of 7 cm in the base and a height of 16 cm.

# Science Applications

## Measure in SI

The metric system of measurement was developed in 1795. A modern form of the metric system, called the International System (SI), was adopted in 1960 and provides the standard measurements that all scientists around the world can understand.

The SI system is convenient because unit sizes vary by powers of 10. Prefixes are used to name units. Look at **Table 2** for some common SI prefixes and their meanings.

### Table 2 Common SI Prefixes

| Prefix | Symbol | Meaning | |
|--------|--------|---------|---------|
| kilo- | k | 1,000 | thousandth |
| hecto- | h | 100 | hundred |
| deka- | da | 10 | ten |
| deci- | d | 0.1 | tenth |
| centi- | c | 0.01 | hundreth |
| milli- | m | 0.001 | thousandth |

**Example** How many grams equal one kilogram?

**Step 1** Find the prefix *kilo-* in **Table 2.**

**Step 2** Using **Table 2,** determine the meaning of *kilo-*. According to the table, it means 1,000. When the prefix *kilo-* is added to a unit, it means that there are 1,000 of the units in a "kilounit."

**Step 3** Apply the prefix to the units in the question. The units in the question are grams. There are 1,000 grams in a kilogram.

**Practice Problem** Is a milligram larger or smaller than a gram? How many of the smaller units equal one larger unit? What fraction of the larger unit does one smaller unit represent?

## Dimensional Analysis  MA7: MG 1.0

**Convert SI Units** In science, quantities such as length, mass, and time sometimes are measured using different units. A process called dimensional analysis can be used to change one unit of measure to another. This process involves multiplying your starting quantity and units by one or more conversion factors. A conversion factor is a ratio equal to one and can be made from any two equal quantities with different units. If 1,000 mL equal 1 L then two ratios can be made.

$$\frac{1,000 \text{ mL}}{1 \text{ L}} = \frac{1 \text{ L}}{1,000 \text{ mL}} = 1$$

One can convert between units in the SI system by using the equivalents in **Table 2** to make conversion factors.

**Example** How many cm are in 4 m?

**Step 1** Write conversion factors for the units given. From **Table 2,** you know that 100 cm = 1 m. The conversion factors are
$$\frac{100 \text{ cm}}{1 \text{ m}} \text{ and } \frac{1 \text{ m}}{100 \text{ cm}}$$

**Step 2** Decide which conversion factor to use. Select the factor that has the units you are converting from (m) in the denominator and the units you are converting to (cm) in the numerator.
$$\frac{100 \text{ cm}}{1 \text{ m}}$$

**Step 3** Multiply the starting quantity and units by the conversion factor. Cancel the starting units with the units in the denominator. There are 400 cm in 4 m.
$$4 \text{ m} = \frac{100 \text{ cm}}{1 \text{ m}} = 400 \text{ cm}$$

**Practice Problem** How many milligrams are in one kilogram? (Hint: You will need to use two conversion factors from **Table 2.**)

# Math Skill Handbook

| Table 3 Unit System Equivalents | |
|---|---|
| **Type of Measurement** | **Equivalent** |
| **Length** | 1 in = 2.54 cm <br> 1 yd = 0.91 m <br> 1 mi = 1.61 km |
| **Mass and weight*** | 1 oz = 28.35 g <br> 1 lb = 0.45 kg <br> 1 ton (short) = 0.91 tonnes (metric tons) <br> 1 lb = 4.45 N |
| **Volume** | $1\ in^3 = 16.39\ cm^3$ <br> 1 qt = 0.95 L <br> 1 gal = 3.78 L |
| **Area** | $1\ in^2 = 6.45\ cm^2$ <br> $1\ yd^2 = 0.83\ m^2$ <br> $1\ mi^2 = 2.59\ km^2$ <br> 1 acre = 0.40 hectares |
| **Temperature** | $°C = \dfrac{(°F - 32)}{1.8}$ <br> K = °C + 273 |

*Weight is measured in standard Earth gravity.

**Convert Between Unit Systems** **Table 3** gives a list of equivalents that can be used to convert between English and SI units.

**Example** If a meterstick has a length of 100 cm, how long is the meterstick in inches?

**Step 1** Write the conversion factors for the units given. From **Table 3,** 1 in = 2.54 cm.

$$\frac{1\ in}{2.54\ cm} \quad and \quad \frac{2.54\ cm}{1\ in}$$

**Step 2** Determine which conversion factor to use. You are converting from cm to in. Use the conversion factor with cm on the bottom.

$$\frac{1\ in}{2.54\ cm}$$

**Step 3** Multiply the starting quantity and units by the conversion factor. Cancel the starting units with the units in the denominator. Round your answer to the nearest tenth.

$$100\ \cancel{cm} \times \frac{1\ in}{2.54\ \cancel{cm}} = 39.37\ in$$

The meterstick is about 39.4 in long.

**Practice Problem 1** A book has a mass of 5 lb. What is the mass of the book in kg?

**Practice Problem 2** Use the equivalent for in and cm (1 in = 2.54 cm) to show how $1\ in^3 \approx 16.39\ cm^3$.

## Precision and Significant Digits  MA7: 2.7

When you make a measurement, the value you record depends on the precision of the measuring instrument. This precision is represented by the number of significant digits recorded in the measurement. When counting the number of significant digits, all digits are counted except zeros at the end of a number with no decimal point such as 2,050, and zeros at the beginning of a decimal such as 0.03020. When adding or subtracting numbers with different precision, round the answer to the smallest number of decimal places of any number in the sum or difference. When multiplying or dividing, the answer is rounded to the smallest number of significant digits of any number being multiplied or divided.

**Example** The lengths 5.28 and 5.2 are measured in meters. Find the sum of these lengths and record your answer using the correct number of significant digits.

**Step 1**  Find the sum.

| | |
|---|---|
| 5.28 m | 2 digits after the decimal |
| + 5.2 m | 1 digit after the decimal |
| 10.48 m | |

**Step 2**  Round to one digit after the decimal because the least number of digits after the decimal of the numbers being added is 1.

The sum is 10.5 m.

**Practice Problem 1** How many significant digits are in the measurement 7,071,301 m? How many significant digits are in the measurement 0.003010 g?

**Practice Problem 2** Multiply 5.28 and 5.2 using the rule for multiplying and dividing. Record the answer using the correct number of significant digits.

## Scientific Notation

Many times numbers used in science are very small or very large. Because these numbers are difficult to work with scientists use scientific notation. To write numbers in scientific notation, move the decimal point until only one non-zero digit remains on the left. Then count the number of places you moved the decimal point and use that number as a power of ten. For example, the average distance from the Sun to Mars is 227,800,000,000 m. In scientific notation, this distance is $2.278 \times 10^{11}$ m. Because you moved the decimal point to the left, the number is a positive power of ten.

The mass of an electron is about 0.000 000 000 000 000 000 000 000 000 000 911 kg. Expressed in scientific notation, this mass is $9.11 \times 10^{-31}$ kg. Because the decimal point was moved to the right, the number is a negative power of ten.

**Example** Earth is 149,600,000 km from the Sun. Express this in scientific notation.

**Step 1**  Move the decimal point until one non-zero digit remains on the left.
1.496 000 00

**Step 2**  Count the number of decimal places you have moved. In this case, eight.

**Step 2**  Show that number as a power of ten, $10^8$.

Earth is $1.496 \times 10^8$ km from the Sun.

**Practice Problem 1** How many significant digits are in 149,600,000 km? How many significant digits are in $1.496 \times 10^8$ km?

**Practice Problem 2** Parts used in a high performance car must be measured to $7 \times 10^{-6}$ m. Express this number as a decimal.

**Practice Problem 3** A CD is spinning at 539 revolutions per minute. Express this number in scientific notation.

## Make and Use Graphs

**MA7:** AF 1.5, AF 3.3, SP 1.2, MR 2.5

Data in tables can be displayed in a graph—a visual representation of data. Common graph types include line graphs, bar graphs, and circle graphs.

**Line Graph** A line graph shows a relationship between two variables that change continuously. The independent variable is changed and is plotted on the *x*-axis. The dependent variable is observed, and is plotted on the *y*-axis.

**Example** Draw a line graph of the data below from a cyclist in a long-distance race.

| Table 4 Bicycle Race Data | |
|---|---|
| **Time (h)** | **Distance (km)** |
| 0 | 0 |
| 1 | 8 |
| 2 | 16 |
| 3 | 24 |
| 4 | 32 |
| 5 | 40 |

**Step 1** Determine the *x*-axis and *y*-axis variables. Time varies independently of distance and is plotted on the *x*-axis. Distance is dependent on time and is plotted on the *y*-axis.

**Step 2** Determine the scale of each axis. The *x*-axis data ranges from 0 to 5. The *y*-axis data ranges from 0 to 50.

**Step 3** Using graph paper, draw and label the axes. Include units in the labels.

**Step 4** Draw a point at the intersection of the time value on the *x*-axis and corresponding distance value on the *y*-axis. Connect the points and label the graph with a title, as shown in **Figure 8.**

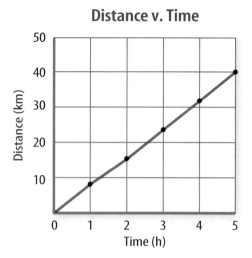

**Distance v. Time**

**Figure 8** This line graph shows the relationship between distance and time during a bicycle ride.

**Practice Problem** A puppy's shoulder height is measured during the first year of her life. The following measurements were collected: (3 mo, 52 cm), (6 mo, 72 cm), (9 mo, 83 cm), (12 mo, 86 cm). Graph this data.

**Find a Slope** The slope of a straight line is the ratio of the vertical change, rise, to the horizontal change, run.

$$\text{Slope} = \frac{\text{vertical change (rise)}}{\text{horizontal change (run)}} = \frac{\text{change in } y}{\text{change in } x}$$

**Example** Find the slope of the graph in **Figure 8.**

**Step 1** You know that the slope is the change in *y* divided by the change in *x*.

$$\text{Slope} = \frac{\text{change in } y}{\text{change in } x}$$

**Step 2** Determine the data points you will be using. For a straight line, choose the two sets of points that are the farthest apart.

$$\text{Slope} = \frac{(40 - 0)\text{ km}}{(5 - 0)\text{ h}}$$

**Step 3** Find the change in *y* and *x*.

$$\text{Slope} = \frac{40\text{ km}}{5\text{ h}}$$

**Step 4** Divide the change in *y* by the change in *x*.

$$\text{Slope} = \frac{8\text{ km}}{\text{h}}$$

The slope of the graph is 8 km/h.

**Bar Graph** To compare data that does not change continuously you might choose a bar graph. A bar graph uses bars to show the relationships between variables. The x-axis variable is divided into parts. The parts can be numbers such as years, or a category such as a type of animal. The y-axis is a number and increases continuously along the axis.

**Example** A recycling center collects 4.0 kg of aluminum on Monday, 1.0 kg on Wednesday, and 2.0 kg on Friday. Create a bar graph of this data.

**Step 1** Select the x-axis and y-axis variables. The measured numbers (the masses of aluminum) should be placed on the y-axis. The variable divided into parts (collection days) is placed on the x-axis.

**Step 2** Create a graph grid like you would for a line graph. Include labels and units.

**Step 3** For each measured number, draw a vertical bar above the x-axis value up to the y-axis value. For the first data point, draw a vertical bar above Monday up to 4.0 kg.

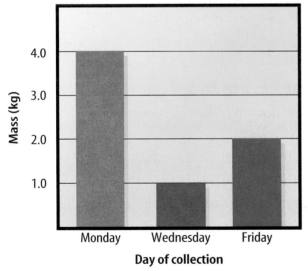

**Aluminum Collected During Week**

**Practice Problem** Draw a bar graph of the gases in air: 78% nitrogen, 21% oxygen, 1% other gases.

**Circle Graph** To display data as parts of a whole, you might use a circle graph. A circle graph is a circle divided into sections that represent the relative size of each piece of data. The entire circle represents 100%, half represents 50%, and so on.

**Example** Air is made up of 78% nitrogen, 21% oxygen, and 1% other gases. Display the composition of air in a circle graph.

**Step 1** Multiply each percent by 360° and divide by 100 to find the angle of each section in the circle.

$$78\% \times \frac{360°}{100} = 280.8°$$

$$21\% \times \frac{360°}{100} = 75.6°$$

$$1\% \times \frac{360°}{100} = 3.6°$$

**Step 2** Use a compass to draw a circle and to mark the center of the circle. Draw a straight line from the center to the edge of the circle.

**Step 3** Use a protractor and the angles you calculated to divide the circle into parts. Place the center of the protractor over the center of the circle and line the base of the protractor over the straight line.

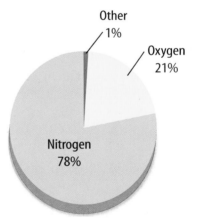

Other
1%

Oxygen
21%

Nitrogen
78%

**Practice Problem** Draw a circle graph to represent the amount of aluminum collected during the week shown in the bar graph to the left.

# Using a Calculator

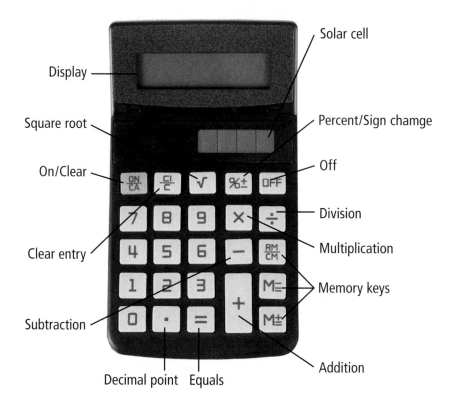

Solar cell

Display

Percent/Sign chamge

Square root

Off

On/Clear

Division

Multiplication

Clear entry

Memory keys

Subtraction

Addition

Decimal point    Equals

- Read the problem very carefully. Decide if you need the calculator to help you solve the problem.
- Clear the calculator by pressing the clear key when starting a new problem.
- If you see an E in the display, clear the error before you begin.
- If you see an M in the display, clear the memory and the calculator before you begin.
- If the number in the display is not one of the answer choices, check your work. You may have to round the number in the display.
- Your calculator will NOT automatically perform the correct order of operations.
- When working with calculators, use careful and deliberate keystrokes, and always remember to check your answer to make sure that it is reasonable. Calculators might display an incorrect answer if you press the keys too quickly.
- Check your answer to make sure that you have completed all of the necessary steps.

# Understanding Scientific Terms

This list of prefixes, suffixes, and roots is provided to help you understand science terms used throughout this textbook. The list identifies whether the prefix, suffix, or root is of Greek (*G*) or Latin (*L*) origin. Also listed is the meaning of the prefix, suffix, or root and a science word in which it is used.

| ORIGIN | MEANING | EXAMPLE |
|---|---|---|
| **A** | | |
| ad (L) | to, toward | adaxial |
| aero (G) | air | aerobic |
| an (G) | without | anaerobic |
| ana (G) | up | anaphase |
| andro (G) | male | androecium |
| angio (G) | vessel | angiosperm |
| anth/o (G) | flower | anthophyte |
| anti (G) | against | antibody |
| aqu/a (L) | of water | aquatic |
| archae (G) | ancient | archaebacteria |
| arthro, artio (G) | jointed | arthropod |
| askos (G) | bag | ascospore |
| aster (G) | star | Asteroidea |
| autos (G) | self | autoimmune |
| **B** | | |
| bi (L) | two | bipedal |
| bio (G) | life | biosphere |
| **C** | | |
| carn (L) | flesh | carnivore |
| cephalo (G) | head | cephalopod |
| chlor (G) | light green | chlorophyll |
| chroma (G) | pigmented | chromosome |
| cide (L) | to kill | insecticide |
| circ (L) | circular | circadian |
| cocc/coccus (G) | small and round | streptococcus |
| con (L) | together | convergent |
| cyte (G) | cell | cytoplasm |
| **D** | | |
| de (L) | remove | decompose |
| dendron (G) | tree | dendrite |
| dent (L) | tooth | edentate |
| derm (G) | skin | epidermis |
| di (G) | two | disaccharide |

| ORIGIN | MEANING | EXAMPLE |
|---|---|---|
| dia (G) | apart | diaphragm |
| dorm (L) | sleep | dormancy |
| **E** | | |
| echino (G) | spiny | echinoderm |
| ec (G) | outer | ecosystem |
| endo (G) | within | endosperm |
| epi (G) | upon | epidermis |
| eu (G) | true | eukaryote |
| exo (G) | outside | exoskeleton |
| **F** | | |
| fer (L) | to carry | conifer |
| **G** | | |
| gastro (G) | stomach | gastropod |
| gen/(e)(o) (G) | kind | genotype |
| genesis (G) | to originate | oogenesis |
| gon (G) | reproductive | archegonium |
| gravi (L) | heavy | gravitropism |
| gymn/o (G) | naked | gymnosperm |
| gyn/e (G) | female | gynoecium |
| **H** | | |
| hal(o) (G) | salt | halophyte |
| hapl(o) (G) | single | haploid |
| hemi (G) | half | hemisphere |
| hem(o) (G) | blood | hemoglobin |
| herb/a(i) (L) | vegetation | herbivore |
| heter/o (G) | different | heterotrophic |
| hom(e)/o (G) | same | homeostasis |
| hom (L) | human | hominid |
| hydr/o (G) | water | hydrolysis |
| **I** | | |
| inter (L) | between | internode |
| intra (L) | within | intracellular |
| is/o (G) | equal | isotonic |

| ORIGIN | MEANING | EXAMPLE |
|--------|---------|---------|
| **K** | | |
| kary (G) | nucleus | eukaryote |
| kera (G) | hornlike | keratin |
| **L** | | |
| leuc/o (G) | white | leukocyte |
| logy (G) | study of | biology |
| lymph/o (L) | water | lymphocyte |
| lysis (G) | break up | dialysis |
| **M** | | |
| macr/o (G) | large | macromolecule |
| meg/a (G) | great | megaspore |
| meso (L) | in the middle | mesophyll |
| meta (G) | after | metaphase |
| micr/o (G) | small | microscope |
| mon/o (G) | only one | monocotyledon |
| morph/o (G) | form | morphology |
| **N** | | |
| nema (G) | a thread | nematode |
| neuro (G) | nerve | neuron |
| nod (L) | knot | nodule |
| nomy(e) (G) | system of laws | taxonomy |
| **O** | | |
| olig/o (G) | small, few | oligochaete |
| omni (L) | all | omnivore |
| orni(s) (G) | bird | ornithology |
| oste/o (G) | bone formation | osteocyte |
| ov (L) | an egg | oviduct |
| **P** | | |
| pal(a)e/o (G) | ancient | paleontology |
| para (G) | beside | parathyroid |
| path/o (G) | suffering | pathogen |
| ped (L) | foot | centipede |
| per (L) | through | permeable |
| peri (G) | around, about | peristalsis |
| phag/o (G) | eating | phagocyte |
| phot/o (G) | light | photosynthesis |
| phyl (G) | race, class | phylogeny |
| phyll (G) | leaf | chlorophyll |
| phyte (G) | plant | epiphyte |
| pinna (L) | feather | pinnate |

| ORIGIN | MEANING | EXAMPLE |
|--------|---------|---------|
| plasm/o (G) | to form | plasmodium |
| pod (G) | foot | gastropod |
| poly (G) | many | polymer |
| post (L) | after | posterior |
| pro (G) (L) | before | prokaryote |
| prot/o (G) | first | protocells |
| pseud/o (G) | false | pseudopodium |
| **R** | | |
| re (L) | back to original | reproduce |
| rhiz/o (G) | root | rhizoid |
| **S** | | |
| scope (G) | to look | microscope |
| some (G) | body | lysosome |
| sperm (G) | seed | gymnosperm |
| stasis (G) | remain constant | homeostasis |
| stom (G) | mouthlike opening | stomata |
| syn (G) | together | synapse |
| **T** | | |
| tel/o (G) | end | telophase |
| terr (L) | of Earth | terrestrial |
| therm (G) | heat | endotherm |
| thylak (G) | sack | thylakoid |
| trans (L) | across | transpiration |
| trich (G) | hair | trichome |
| trop/o (G) | a change | gravitropism |
| trophic (G) | nourishment | heterotrophic |
| **U** | | |
| uni (L) | one | unicellular |
| **V** | | |
| vacc/a (L) | cow | vaccine |
| vore (L) | eat greedily | omnivore |
| **X** | | |
| xer/o (G) | dry | xerophyte |
| **Z** | | |
| zo/o (G) | living being | zoology |
| zygous (G) | two joined | homozygous |

# Use and Care of a Microscope

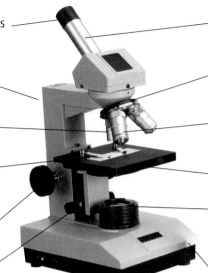

**Eyepiece** Contains magnifying lenses you look through.

**Arm** Supports the body tube.

**Low-power objective** Contains the lens with the lowest power magnification.

**Stage clips** Hold the microscope slide in place.

**Coarse adjustment** Focuses the image under low power.

**Fine adjustment** Sharpens the image under high magnification.

**Body tube** Connects the eyepiece to the revolving nosepiece.

**Revolving nosepiece** Holds and turns the objectives into viewing position.

**High-power objective** Contains the lens with the highest magnification.

**Stage** Supports the microscope slide.

**Light source** Provides light that passes upward through the diaphragm, the specimen, and the lenses.

**Base** Provides support for the microscope.

## Caring for a Microscope

1. Always carry the microscope holding the arm with one hand and supporting the base with the other hand.

2. Don't touch the lenses with your fingers.

3. The coarse adjustment knob is used only when looking through the lowest-power objective lens. The fine adjustment knob is used when the high-power objective is in place.

4. Cover the microscope when you store it.

## Using a Microscope

1. Place the microscope on a flat surface that is clear of objects. The arm should be toward you.

2. Look through the eyepiece. Adjust the diaphragm so light comes through the opening in the stage.

3. Place a slide on the stage so the specimen is in the field of view. Hold it firmly in place by using the stage clips.

4. Always focus with the coarse adjustment and the low-power objective lens first. After the object is in focus on low power, turn the nosepiece until the high-power objective is in place. Use ONLY the fine adjustment to focus with the high-power objective lens.

## Making a Wet-Mount Slide

1. Carefully place the item you want to look at in the center of a clean, glass slide. Make sure the sample is thin enough for light to pass through.

2. Use a dropper to place one or two drops of water on the sample.

3. Hold a clean coverslip by the edges and place it at one edge of the water. Slowly lower the coverslip onto the water until it lies flat.

4. If you have too much water or a lot of air bubbles, touch the edge of a paper towel to the edge of the coverslip to draw off extra water and draw out unwanted air.

# Diversity of Life: Classification of Living Organisms

A six-kingdom system of classification of organisms is used today. Two kingdoms—Kingdom Archaebacteria and Kingdom Eubacteria—contain organisms that do not have a nucleus and that lack membrane-bound structures in the cytoplasm of their cells. The members of the other four kingdoms have a cell or cells that contain a nucleus and structures in the cytoplasm, some of which are surrounded by membranes. These kingdoms are Kingdom Protista, Kingdom Fungi, Kingdom Plantae, and Kingdom Animalia.

## Kingdom Archaebacteria

one-celled; some absorb food from their surroundings; some are photosynthetic; some are chemosynthetic; many are found in extremely harsh environments including salt ponds, hot springs, swamps, and deep-sea hydrothermal vents

## Kingdom Eubacteria

one-celled; most absorb food from their surroundings; some are photosynthetic; some are chemosynthetic; many are parasites; many are round, spiral, or rod-shaped; some form colonies

## Kingdom Protista

**Phylum Euglenophyta** one-celled; photosynthetic or take in food; most have one flagellum; euglenoids

**Phylum Bacillariophyta** one-celled; photosynthetic; have unique double shells made of silica; diatoms

**Phylum Dinoflagellata** one-celled; photosynthetic; contain red pigments; have two flagella; dinoflagellates

**Phylum Chlorophyta** one-celled, many-celled, or colonies; photosynthetic; contain chlorophyll; live on land, in freshwater, or salt water; green algae

**Phylum Rhodophyta** most are many-celled; photosynthetic; contain red pigments; most live in deep, saltwater environments; red algae

**Phylum Phaeophyta** most are many-celled; photosynthetic; contain brown pigments; most live in saltwater environments; brown algae

**Phylum Rhizopoda** one-celled; take in food; are free-living or parasitic; move by means of pseudopods; amoebas

**Kingdom Eubacteria**
*Bacillus anthracis*

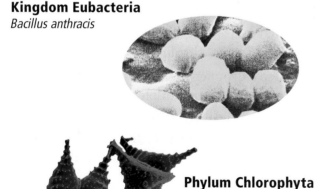

**Phylum Chlorophyta**
*Desmids*

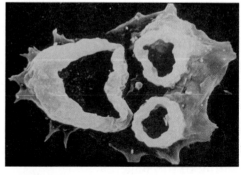

**Amoeba**

**Phylum Zoomastigina** one-celled; take in food; free-living or parasitic; have one or more flagella; zoomastigotes

**Phylum Ciliophora** one-celled; take in food; have large numbers of cilia; ciliates

**Phylum Sporozoa** one-celled; take in food; have no means of movement; are parasites in animals; sporozoans

**Phylum Myxomycota**
Slime mold

**Phyla Myxomycota and Acrasiomycota** one- or many-celled; absorb food; change form during life cycle; cellular and plasmodial slime molds

**Phylum Oomycota** many-celled; are either parasites or decomposers; live in freshwater or salt water; water molds, rusts and downy mildews

## Kingdom Fungi

**Phylum Zygomycota** many-celled; absorb food; spores are produced in sporangia; zygote fungi; bread mold

**Phylum Ascomycota** one- and many-celled; absorb food; spores produced in asci; sac fungi; yeast

**Phylum Basidiomycota** many-celled; absorb food; spores produced in basidia; club fungi; mushrooms

**Phylum Deuteromycota** members with unknown reproductive structures; imperfect fungi; *Penicillium*

**Phylum Mycophycota** organisms formed by symbiotic relationship between an ascomycote or a basidiomycote and green alga or cyanobacterium; lichens

**Phylum Oomycota**
*Phytophthora infestans*

**Lichens**

## Kingdom Plantae

**Divisions Bryophyta** (mosses), **Anthocerophyta** (hornworts), **Hepaticophyta** (liverworts), **Psilophyta** (whisk ferns) many-celled nonvascular plants; reproduce by spores produced in capsules; green; grow in moist, land environments

**Division Lycophyta** many-celled vascular plants; spores are produced in conelike structures; live on land; are photosynthetic; club mosses

**Division Arthrophyta** vascular plants; ribbed and jointed stems; scalelike leaves; spores produced in conelike structures; horsetails

**Division Pterophyta** vascular plants; leaves called fronds; spores produced in clusters of sporangia called sori; live on land or in water; ferns

**Division Ginkgophyta** deciduous trees; only one living species; have fan-shaped leaves with branching veins and fleshy cones with seeds; ginkgoes

**Division Cycadophyta** palmlike plants; have large, featherlike leaves; produces seeds in cones; cycads

**Division Coniferophyta** deciduous or evergreen; trees or shrubs; have needlelike or scalelike leaves; seeds produced in cones; conifers

**Division Gnetophyta** shrubs or woody vines; seeds are produced in cones; division contains only three genera; gnetum

**Division Anthophyta** dominant group of plants; flowering plants; have fruits with seeds

## Kingdom Animalia

**Phylum Porifera** aquatic organisms that lack true tissues and organs; are asymmetrical and sessile; sponges

**Phylum Cnidaria** radially symmetrical organisms; have a digestive cavity with one opening; most have tentacles armed with stinging cells; live in aquatic environments singly or in colonies; includes jellyfish, corals, hydra, and sea anemones

**Phylum Platyhelminthes** bilaterally symmetrical worms; have flattened bodies; digestive system has one opening; parasitic and free-living species; flatworms

**Division Bryophyta**
Liverwort

**Division Anthophyta**
Tomato plant

**Phylum Platyhelminthes**
Flatworm

**Phylum Chordata**

**Phylum Nematoda** round, bilaterally symmetrical body; have digestive system with two openings; free-living forms and parasitic forms; roundworms

**Phylum Mollusca** soft-bodied animals, many with a hard shell and soft foot or footlike appendage; a mantle covers the soft body; aquatic and terrestrial species; includes clams, snails, squid, and octopuses

**Phylum Annelida** bilaterally symmetrical worms; have round, segmented bodies; terrestrial and aquatic species; includes earthworms, leeches, and marine polychaetes

**Phylum Arthropoda** largest animal group; have hard exoskeletons, segmented bodies, and pairs of jointed appendages; land and aquatic species; includes insects, crustaceans, and spiders

**Phylum Echinodermata** marine organisms; have spiny or leathery skin and a water-vascular system with tube feet; are radially symmetrical; includes sea stars, sand dollars, and sea urchins

**Phylum Chordata** organisms with internal skeletons and specialized body systems; most have paired appendages; all at some time have a notochord, nerve cord, gill slits, and a post-anal tail; include fish, amphibians, reptiles, birds, and mammals

## PERIODIC TABLE OF THE ELEMENTS

Columns of elements are called groups. Elements in the same group have similar chemical properties.

Gas
Liquid
Solid
Synthetic

Element — Hydrogen
Atomic number — 1
Symbol — H
Atomic mass — 1.008
State of matter

The first three symbols tell you the state of matter of the element at room temperature. The fourth symbol identifies elements that are not present in significant amounts on Earth. Useful amounts are made synthetically.

| 1 | 2 | 3 | 4 | 5 | 6 | 7 | 8 | 9 |
|---|---|---|---|---|---|---|---|---|
| **1** Hydrogen 1 **H** 1.008 | | | | | | | | |
| **2** Lithium 3 **Li** 6.941 | Beryllium 4 **Be** 9.012 | | | | | | | |
| **3** Sodium 11 **Na** 22.990 | Magnesium 12 **Mg** 24.305 | | | | | | | |
| **4** Potassium 19 **K** 39.098 | Calcium 20 **Ca** 40.078 | Scandium 21 **Sc** 44.956 | Titanium 22 **Ti** 47.867 | Vanadium 23 **V** 50.942 | Chromium 24 **Cr** 51.996 | Manganese 25 **Mn** 54.938 | Iron 26 **Fe** 55.845 | Cobalt 27 **Co** 58.933 |
| **5** Rubidium 37 **Rb** 85.468 | Strontium 38 **Sr** 87.62 | Yttrium 39 **Y** 88.906 | Zirconium 40 **Zr** 91.224 | Niobium 41 **Nb** 92.906 | Molybdenum 42 **Mo** 95.94 | Technetium 43 **Tc** (98) | Ruthenium 44 **Ru** 101.07 | Rhodium 45 **Rh** 102.906 |
| **6** Cesium 55 **Cs** 132.905 | Barium 56 **Ba** 137.327 | Lanthanum 57 **La** 138.906 | Hafnium 72 **Hf** 178.49 | Tantalum 73 **Ta** 180.948 | Tungsten 74 **W** 183.84 | Rhenium 75 **Re** 186.207 | Osmium 76 **Os** 190.23 | Iridium 77 **Ir** 192.217 |
| **7** Francium 87 **Fr** (223) | Radium 88 **Ra** (226) | Actinium 89 **Ac** (227) | Rutherfordium 104 **Rf** (261) | Dubnium 105 **Db** (262) | Seaborgium 106 **Sg** (266) | Bohrium 107 **Bh** (264) | Hassium 108 **Hs** (277) | Meitnerium 109 **Mt** (268) |

The number in parentheses is the mass number of the longest-lived isotope for that element.

Rows of elements are called periods. Atomic number increases across a period.

The arrow shows where these elements would fit into the periodic table. They are moved to the bottom of the table to save space.

**Lanthanide series**

| Cerium 58 **Ce** 140.116 | Praseodymium 59 **Pr** 140.908 | Neodymium 60 **Nd** 144.24 | Promethium 61 **Pm** (145) | Samarium 62 **Sm** 150.36 |
|---|---|---|---|---|

**Actinide series**

| Thorium 90 **Th** 232.038 | Protactinium 91 **Pa** 231.036 | Uranium 92 **U** 238.029 | Neptunium 93 **Np** (237) | Plutonium 94 **Pu** (244) |
|---|---|---|---|---|

Metal

Metalloid

Nonmetal

The color of an element's block tells you if the element is a metal, nonmetal, or metalloid.

**Science Online**

Visit ca7.msscience.com for updates to the periodic table.

| | | | 13 | 14 | 15 | 16 | 17 | 18 |
|---|---|---|---|---|---|---|---|---|
| | | | | | | | | Helium 2 He 4.003 |
| | | | Boron 5 B 10.811 | Carbon 6 C 12.011 | Nitrogen 7 N 14.007 | Oxygen 8 O 15.999 | Fluorine 9 F 18.998 | Neon 10 Ne 20.180 |
| 10 | 11 | 12 | Aluminum 13 Al 26.982 | Silicon 14 Si 28.086 | Phosphorus 15 P 30.974 | Sulfur 16 S 32.065 | Chlorine 17 Cl 35.453 | Argon 18 Ar 39.948 |
| Nickel 28 Ni 58.693 | Copper 29 Cu 63.546 | Zinc 30 Zn 65.409 | Gallium 31 Ga 69.723 | Germanium 32 Ge 72.64 | Arsenic 33 As 74.922 | Selenium 34 Se 78.96 | Bromine 35 Br 79.904 | Krypton 36 Kr 83.798 |
| Palladium 46 Pd 106.42 | Silver 47 Ag 107.868 | Cadmium 48 Cd 112.411 | Indium 49 In 114.818 | Tin 50 Sn 118.710 | Antimony 51 Sb 121.760 | Tellurium 52 Te 127.60 | Iodine 53 I 126.904 | Xenon 54 Xe 131.293 |
| Platinum 78 Pt 195.078 | Gold 79 Au 196.967 | Mercury 80 Hg 200.59 | Thallium 81 Tl 204.383 | Lead 82 Pb 207.2 | Bismuth 83 Bi 208.980 | Polonium 84 Po (209) | Astatine 85 At (210) | Radon 86 Rn (222) |
| Darmstadtium 110 Ds (281) | Roentgenium 111 Rg (272) | Ununbium * 112 Uub (285) | | Ununquadium * 114 Uuq (289) | | | | |

✱ The names and symbols for elements 112–114 are temporary. Final names will be selected when the elements' discoveries are verified.

| Europium 63 Eu 151.964 | Gadolinium 64 Gd 157.25 | Terbium 65 Tb 158.925 | Dysprosium 66 Dy 162.500 | Holmium 67 Ho 164.930 | Erbium 68 Er 167.259 | Thulium 69 Tm 168.934 | Ytterbium 70 Yb 173.04 | Lutetium 71 Lu 174.967 |
|---|---|---|---|---|---|---|---|---|
| Americium 95 Am (243) | Curium 96 Cm (247) | Berkelium 97 Bk (247) | Californium 98 Cf (251) | Einsteinium 99 Es (252) | Fermium 100 Fm (257) | Mendelevium 101 Md (258) | Nobelium 102 No (259) | Lawrencium 103 Lr (262) |

Reference Handbook

# Glossary/Glosario

**Cómo usar el glosario en español:**
1. Busca el término en inglés que desees encontrar.
2. El término en español, junto con la definición, se encuentran en la columna de la derecha.

## Pronunciation Key

Use the following key to help you sound out words in the glossary.

| | | | |
|---|---|---|---|
| a . . . . . . . . . . . . . . . back (BAK) | | ew . . . . . . . . . . . . food (FEWD) | |
| ay . . . . . . . . . . . . . day (DAY) | | yoo. . . . . . . . . . . . pure (PYOOR) | |
| ah. . . . . . . . . . . . . father (FAH thur) | | yew . . . . . . . . . . . few (FYEW) | |
| ow . . . . . . . . . . . . flower (FLOW ur) | | uh . . . . . . . . . . . . comma (CAH muh) | |
| ar . . . . . . . . . . . . . car (CAR) | | u (+ con) . . . . . . . rub (RUB) | |
| e . . . . . . . . . . . . . . less (LES) | | sh. . . . . . . . . . . . . shelf (SHELF) | |
| ee . . . . . . . . . . . . . leaf (LEEF) | | ch. . . . . . . . . . . . . nature (NAY chur) | |
| ih . . . . . . . . . . . . . trip (TRIHP) | | g . . . . . . . . . . . . . . gift (GIHFT) | |
| i (i + com + e). . . . idea (i DEE uh) | | j . . . . . . . . . . . . . . gem (JEM) | |
| oh. . . . . . . . . . . . . go (GOH) | | ing. . . . . . . . . . . . . sing (SING) | |
| aw . . . . . . . . . . . . soft (SAWFT) | | zh. . . . . . . . . . . . . vision (VIH zhun) | |
| or . . . . . . . . . . . . . orbit (OR buht) | | k. . . . . . . . . . . . . . cake (KAYK) | |
| oy. . . . . . . . . . . . . coin (COYN) | | s . . . . . . . . . . . . . . seed, cent (SEED, SENT) | |
| oo. . . . . . . . . . . . . foot (FOOT) | | z . . . . . . . . . . . . . . zone, raise (ZOHN, RAYZ) | |

✳ Academic Vocabulary

| English | A | Español |
|---|---|---|

**absorption/anther**

absorción/antera

**absorption:** the process of transferring light energy to the atoms or molecules in a material (p. 436)

**adaptation:** inheritance of traits that allow an organism to survive in a particular environment (p. 216)

**allele:** each form of a gene with different information (p. 177)

**amniote:** an organism that lays watertight eggs called amniotic eggs (p. 329)

**amplitude:** in a compression wave, the degree to which particles are spread out in areas of compression and rarefaction (p. 475)

✳ **analogous:** being or related to (p. 253)

**anaphase:** the third stage of mitosis, in which the sister chromatids of each replicated chromosome begin to separate (p. 92)

**angiosperm:** flowering seed plant (p. 138)

**anther:** tip of a stamen where pollen grains form (p. 138)

**absorción:** proceso de transferencia de energía luminosa a los átomos o moléculas de la materia (p. 436)

**adaptación:** herencia de rasgos que permite a un organismo sobrevivir en un medio ambiente determinado (p. 216)

**alelo:** cada una de las formas de un gen con diferente información (p. 177)

**amniota:** organismo que pone huevos a prueba de agua denominados huevos amnióticos (p. 329)

**amplitud:** en una onda de compresión, nivel de dispersión de las partículas en áreas de compresión y rarefacción (p. 475)

**análogo:** estar relacionado con algo (p. 253)

**anafase:** tercera etapa de la mitosis, en la cual las cromátidas hermanas de cada cromosoma replicado comienzan a separarse (p. 92)

**angiosperma:** planta de semilla que produce flores (p. 138)

**antera:** punta del estamen donde se forman los granos de polen (p. 138)

# Glossary/Glosario

**artery:** vessel that carries the blood away from the heart to the organs in the body (p. 399)

**asexual reproduction:** the production of offspring by one parent without the joining of a sperm and an egg; offspring are genetically identical to the parent organism (p. 151)

✳ **assign:** to appoint to a duty or task (p. 100)

**asthma:** a common long-term disease that causes swelling of the airways to the lungs, often triggered by environmental factors (p. 396)

**ATP:** adenosine triphosphate (uh DEN uh seen • tri FAHS fayt) or molecules of usable cellular energy (p. 68)

**atrium:** one of two upper chambers of the heart that receives the blood (p. 398)

**auditory canal:** the channel in your external ear that collects sound waves and passes them to the middle ear (p. 481)

**arteria:** conducto que transporta la sangre desde el corazón a los órganos del cuerpo (p. 399)

**reproducción asexual:** producción de descendencia por un solo progenitor sin la unión de un espermatozoide y un óvulo; la descendencia es genéticamente idéntica al organismo progenitor (p. 151)

**asignar:** nombrar para la realización de una función o tarea (p. 100)

**asma:** enfermedad común prolongada que ocasiona dilatación de las vías respiratorias que van a los pulmones, a menudo desatada por factores ambientales (p. 396)

**ATP:** trifosfato de adenosina, o moléculas de energía celular utilizable (p. 68)

**aurícula:** cada una de las dos cavidades superiores del corazón que reciben la sangre (p. 398)

**canal auditivo:** canal del oído externo que capta las ondas de sonido y las transfiere al oído medio (p. 481)

## B

**behavioral adaptation:** an adaptation in which a specific action, such as nest building, allows a species to survive in its environment (p. 223)

**bone:** a hard tissue made of cells, collagen, and calcium (p. 360)

**breathing:** the process of air entering and exiting your lungs (p. 393)

**budding:** a type of asexual reproduction in which a new organism forms on a parent organism, breaks off, and then lives on its own (p. 153)

**adaptación conductista:** adaptación mediante la cual una acción determinada, como la construcción de nidos, permite a una especie sobrevivir en su medio ambiente (p. 223)

**hueso:** tejido duro formado por células, colágeno y calcio (p. 360)

**respiración:** proceso de entrada y salida de aire hacia y desde los pulmones (p. 393)

**germinación:** tipo de reproducción asexual mediante el cual se forma un nuevo organismo en un organismo progenitor, se separa de éste y luego vive independientemente (p. 153)

## C

**camouflage:** a structural adaptation that allows an organism to blend in with its surroundings (p. 221)

**capillary:** microscopic blood vessel that delivers oxygen and nutrients to the cells and picks up carbon dioxide and other waste products (p. 399)

**carbohydrate:** stores energy that can be released quickly through chemical reactions in cells; made of one sugar molecule, a pair of sugar molecules, or a chain of sugar molecules (p. 54)

**cardiovascular disease:** deterioration of the heart and blood vessels (p. 400)

**cartilage:** a strong, flexible tissue made of collagen that gives shape to parts of your body (p. 361)

**camuflaje:** adaptación estructural que permite a un organismo confundirse con el ambiente que lo rodea (p. 221)

**capilar:** vaso sanguíneo microscópico que transporta oxígeno y nutrientes a las células y toma el dióxido de carbono y otros productos de desecho (p. 399)

**carbohidratos:** compuestos que almacenan energía que puede liberarse rápidamente mediante reacciones químicas de las células; están formados por una molécula de azúcar, por un par de moléculas de azúcar o por una cadena de moléculas de azúcar (p. 54)

**enfermedad cardiovascular:** deterioro del corazón y vasos sanguíneos (p. 400)

**cartílago:** tejido fuerte y flexible formado por colágeno que imparte la forma a las partes del cuerpo (p. 361)

# Glossary/Glosario

**cast:** a type of fossil that forms when crystals fill a mold or sediments wash into a mold and harden into rock (p. 248)

**catastrophic event:** an event that causes a drastic change on Earth resulting in the loss of many lives or species (p. 318)

**cell cycle:** life cycle of a cell that includes phases of growth and development and reproduction (p. 88)

**cell differentiation:** a process in which cells become different types of cells (p. 100)

**cell membrane:** flexible covering that surrounds every cell (p. 56)

**cell plate:** a disk formed between the two new nuclei of a plant cell that is dividing (p. 94)

**cell theory:** theory that all organisms are made of one or more cells, the cell is the smallest unit of life, and all new cells come from preexisting cells (p. 49)

**cellular respiration:** a series of chemical reactions that transforms the energy in food molecules to usable cellular energy (p. 68)

**cell wall:** a rigid wall that surrounds the cell outside its cell membrane; found in plants, fungi, and some bacteria (p. 58)

**centromere:** a region near the middle of each chromatid that holds together the sister chromatids (p. 90)

**chloroplast:** organelle that uses light energy to make food from water and carbon dioxide (p. 61)

**chromosome:** structure made of long chains of DNA (p. 60)

**circulatory system:** a system of tissues and vessels that transports blood through the body (p. 397)

**clast:** individual sediment piece or rock particle (p. 287)

**cloning:** usually refers to a method of asexual reproduction developed by scientists and performed in laboratory experiments; produces identical individuals from a cell or from a cluster of cells taken from a multicellular organism (p. 155)

**cochlea (KOH klee uh):** a snail-shaped structure in the inner ear that has sensory cells that detect different frequencies of sound (p. 483)

**codominance:** the interaction of two alleles in which both alleles can be observed in the phenotype (p. 185)

**comparative anatomy:** the study of similarities and differences in the structures of organisms (p. 252)

✳ **complex:** complicated in structure; consisting of interconnected parts (pp. 184, 474)

**compression wave:** a repeating motion that moves particles back and forth in the same direction that the energy moves (p. 473)

**enyesado:** tipo de fósil que se forma cuando los cristales llenan un molde o los sedimentos fluyen hacia un molde y se solidifican formando una roca (p. 248)

**evento catastrófico:** evento que ocasiona un cambio drástico en La Tierra y cuya consecuencia es la pérdida de muchas vidas o especies (p. 318)

**ciclo celular:** ciclo vital de una célula que incluye fases de crecimiento, desarrollo y reproducción (p. 88)

**diferenciación celular:** proceso mediante el cual las células se convierten en diferentes tipos de células (p. 100)

**membrana celular:** cubierta flexible que rodea a las células (p. 56)

**lámina celular:** disco que se forma entre los dos nuevos núcleos de una célula vegetal en proceso de división (p. 94)

**teoría celular:** teoría que sugiere que todos los organismos están formados por una o más células, que la célula es la unidad más pequeña de la vida, y que las nuevas células provienen de células preexistentes (p. 49)

**respiración celular:** serie de reacciones químicas que transforman la energía contenida en las moléculas de los alimentos en energía celular utilizable (p. 68)

**pared celular:** pared rígida que rodea a la célula en el exterior de la membrana celular; se halla en las plantas, en los hongos y en algunas bacterias (p. 58)

**centrómero:** región cercana al centro de cada cromátida que mantiene unidas a las cromátidas hermanas (p. 90)

**cloroplasto:** organelo que usa la energía luminosa para elaborar alimentos a partir de agua y dióxido de carbono (p. 61)

**cromosoma:** estructura formada por largas cadenas de ADN (p. 60)

**sistema circulatorio:** sistema de tejidos y vasos que transportan la sangre a través del cuerpo (p. 397)

**fragmento de roca:** trozos individuales de sedimentos o partículas de rocas (p. 287)

**clonación:** normalmente un método de reproducción asexual desarrollado por los científicos y realizado en experimentos de laboratorio; produce individuos idénticos a partir de una célula o de un grupo de células tomadas de un organismo multicelular (p. 155)

**cóclea:** estructura en forma de caracol del oído interno que contiene células sensoriales que detectan diferentes frecuencias de sonido (p. 483)

**codominancia:** interacción de dos alelos mediante la cual ambos pueden observarse en el fenotipo (p. 185)

**anatomía comparativa:** estudio de las similitudes y diferencias entre las estructuras de los organismos (p. 252)

**complejo:** que posee una estructura complicada; que está formado por partes interconectadas (pp. 184, 474)

**onda de compresión:** proceso repetitivo que hace mover a las partículas en la misma dirección de la energía (p. 473)

# Glossary/Glosario

✳ **concentration:** the measure of how much of a given substance is mixed with another substance (p. 401)

✳ **confirm:** to give approval to (p. 298)

**constant:** a factor in an experiment that remains the same (p. 29)

✳ **contract:** to make a smaller size by squeezing or forcing together (p. 364)

**contraction:** the shortening of a muscle or muscle fiber (p. 364)

**control group:** the part of a controlled experiment that contains all of the same variables and constants as the experimental group but the independent variable is not changed (p. 29)

**convergent evolution:** the independent evolution in similar environments of similar species but with no common ancestor (p. 259)

**convex lens:** a lens that bulges outward and causes light rays passing through it to converge (p. 443)

**cornea:** a convex lens located at the front of the eye (p. 451)

**critical thinking:** comparing what you already know with the explanation you are given in order to decide if you agree with it or not (p. 21)

**cyanobacteria:** single-celled, blue-green algae that are thought to be the first organisms (p. 327)

✳ **cycle:** a series of events that repeat (p. 508)

**cytokinesis:** the final stage of cell division when the cytoplasm of the cell divides (p. 91)

**cytoplasm:** a thick fluid on the inside of a cell, made mostly of water (p. 59)

**cytoskeleton:** a network of fibers inside a cell that functions during muscle contraction, cell division, cell movement, and maintenance of cell shape (p. 59)

**concentración:** medida de la cantidad de una sustancia determinada que se mezcla con otra (p. 401)

**confirmar:** aprobar (p. 298)

**constante:** factor que permanece invariable en un experimento (p. 29)

**contraer:** reducción del tamaño mediante compresión o forzando la unión (p. 364)

**contracción:** acortamiento de un músculo o de una fibra muscular (p. 364)

**grupo de control:** parte de un experimento controlado que contiene las mismas variables y constantes que el grupo experimental, pero en el que la variable independiente no se cambia (p. 29)

**evolución convergente:** evolución independiente de especies similares que no tienen un ancestro común en ambientes similares (p. 259)

**lente convexa:** lente con la parte prominente hacia afuera que hace que los rayos de luz pasen a través de ella para converger (p. 443)

**cornea:** lente convexa ubicada en la parte frontal del ojo (p. 451)

**pensamiento crítico:** comparación de lo que sabemos con la explicación que recibimos para decidir si estamos de acuerdo o no con ella (p. 21)

**bacterias fotosintéticas:** algas verdiazules unicelulares que se cree fueron los primeros organismos (p. 327)

**ciclo:** serie de eventos que se repiten (p. 508)

**citoquinesis:** etapa final de la división celular en que se divide el citoplasma celular (p. 91)

**citoplasma:** líquido espeso del interior de la célula, compuesto mayormente de agua (p. 59)

**citoesqueleto:** red de fibras en el interior de la célula que funciona durante la contracción muscular, la división celular, el movimiento celular y el mantenimiento de la forma de las células (p. 59)

## D

**data:** factual information used as a basis for reading, discussion, or calculation (p. 19)

**daughter cell:** two cells that form when the cytoplasm and its components divide (p. 94)

**decibel scale:** a calibrated set of values used to judge the loudness of a sound (p. 476)

**dependent variable:** the factor that you measure or observe during an experiment (p. 29)

**diagram:** a scientific illustration that explains a process or the logical relationship between objects or ideas (p. 22)

✳ **differentiate:** to show a difference between two or more things (p. 154)

**datos:** información factual que se usa como base para la lectura, discusión o cálculo (p. 19)

**célula hija:** cada una de las dos células que se forman cuando el citoplasma y sus componentes se dividen (p. 94)

**escala de decibeles:** conjunto de valores calibrados que se usan para determinar la intensidad de un sonido (p. 476)

**variable dependiente:** factor que se mide u observa durante un experimento (p. 29)

**diagrama:** ilustración científica que explica un proceso o la relación lógica que existe entre objetos o ideas (p. 22)

**diferenciar:** mostrar una diferencia entre dos o más cosas (p. 154)

# Glossary/Glosario

**diploid:** a eukaryotic cell that contains a complete set of homologous chromosome pairs (p. 129)

**dominant:** a genetic factor that blocks another genetic factor (p. 175)

**diploide:** célula eucariota que contiene un juego completo de pares de cromosomas homólogos (p. 129)

**dominante:** factor genético que bloquea a otro (p. 175)

## E

**echo:** a reflected sound wave, often used in the detection of objects (p. 486)

**ectotherm:** an animal that relies on its environment to regulate its body temperature (p. 334)

**egg:** haploid reproductive cell produced by female reproductive organs (p. 126)

**electromagnetic spectrum:** the entire range of electromagnetic waves of different wavelengths and frequencies (p. 430)

**embryo:** immature diploid organism that developed from the zygote (p. 137)

**embryology:** the science of the development of embryos from fertilization to birth (p. 254)

**endotherm:** animals that generate and regulate internal body heat (p. 334)

**epididymis (eh puh DIH duh mus):** sperm storage organ in a male reproductive system (p. 505)

**establish:** to put beyond doubt (p. 90)

**eukaryotic (yew kayr ee AH tik) cell:** a cell with a nucleus and other organelles (p. 64)

**evidence:** an outward sign (p. 70)

**evolution:** change in an species over time (p. 210)

**experimental group:** the part of a controlled experiment used to study relationships between variables you are interested in knowing more about (p. 29)

**expose:** to make accessible to a particular action or influence (p. 446)

**extension:** the straightening of a limb that increases the angle between the bones of the limb (p. 366)

**external:** located outside or beyond some limits or surface (p. 481)

**external ear:** the fold of cartilage and skin that makes up the most visible part of your ear (p. 481)

**extinct:** no longer existing (p. 224)

**eco:** onda de sonido reflejada que se usa a menudo para detectar objetos (p. 486)

**ectotérmico:** animal que depende de su ambiente para regular su temperatura corporal (p. 334)

**óvulo:** célula reproductiva haploide producida por los órganos reproductores femeninos (p. 126)

**espectro electromagnético:** rango completo de ondas electromagnéticas de diferentes longitudes de onda y frecuencias (p. 430)

**embrión:** organismo diploide inmaduro que se desarrolla a partir del zigoto (p. 137)

**embriología:** ciencia que estudia el desarrollo del embrión, desde la fertilización hasta el nacimiento (p. 254)

**endotérmico:** animal que genera y regula su calor corporal interno (p. 334)

**epidídimo:** órgano del sistema reproductor masculino que almacena los espermatozoides (p. 505)

**establecer:** demostrar más allá de la duda (p. 90)

**eucariota:** célula que posee núcleo y otros organelos (p. 64)

**evidencia:** señal exterior (p. 70)

**evolución:** cambio experimentado por una especie a través del tiempo (p. 210)

**grupo experimental:** parte de un experimento controlado que se usa para estudiar las relaciones entre las variables que se desea investigar (p. 29)

**exponer:** hacer accesible a una acción o influencia determinada (p. 446)

**extensión:** enderezamiento de una extremidad que aumenta el ángulo entre los huesos de la misma (p. 366)

**externo:** ubicado fuera o más allá de algunos límites o de alguna superficie (p. 481)

**oído externo:** pliegue de cartílago y piel que forma la parte más visible del oído (p. 481)

**extinto:** que ya no existe (p. 224)

## F

**fallopian (fa LOH pee un) tube:** tubelike structure of a female reproductive system that connects each ovary to the uterus (p. 507)

**trompa de Falopio:** estructura en forma de tubo del sistema reproductor femenino que conecta a cada ovario con el útero (p. 507)

# Glossary/Glosario

**fermentation:** a chemical process that releases energy from food molecules; it begins and ends in the cytoplasm and does not involve mitochondria or use oxygen (p. 69)

**fertilization:** fusion of a sperm cell with an egg cell to produce a zygote (p. 126)

**fetus:** the term used for the embryo after the first trimester (p. 516)

**filament:** a long stalk that supports the anther and connects it to the base of the flower (p. 138)

**first-class lever:** a lever in which the resistance and effort forces are placed on the opposite side of the fulcrum (p. 370)

**fission:** asexual reproduction in bacteria (p. 152)

**flexible:** capable of being bent (p. 452)

**flexion:** the bending of a limb that decreases the angle between the bones of the limb (p. 366)

**focal length:** distance from the center of the lens to the focal point (p. 444)

**focal point:** point where rays of light that enter a convex lens parallel to the optical axis converge (p. 444)

**follicle:** egg and surrounding cells that protect and nourish it (p. 508)

**fossil:** the naturally preserved remains, imprints, or traces of organisms that lived long ago (p. 244)

**fossil record:** the history of all known fossils and their placements in the formation of rocks and positions in time (p. 250)

**frequency:** the number of times something vibrates back and forth in a given length of time (p. 429)

**fruit:** structure that contains seeds produced by a flowering plant; develops from the ovary of the flower (p. 139)

**fulcrum:** a fixed point around which a lever pivots (p. 368)

**fermentación:** proceso químico que libera energía a partir de las moléculas de alimentos; comienza y termina en el citoplasma y no involucra a las mitocondrias ni utiliza oxígeno (p. 69)

**fertilización:** fusión de una célula de espermatozoide con un óvulo para producir un zigoto (p. 126)

**feto:** término usado para referirse al embrión después del primer trimestre (p. 516)

**filamento:** pedúnculo largo que apoya a la antera y la conecta a la base de la flor (p. 138)

**palanca de primera clase:** palanca en la cual las fuerzas de resistencia y esfuerzo se colocan en el lado opuesto del fulcro (p. 370)

**fisión:** reproducción asexual de las bacterias (p. 152)

**flexible:** que tiene la capacidad de doblarse (p. 452)

**flexión:** inflexión de una extremidad que reduce el ángulo entre los huesos de la misma (p. 366)

**distancia focal:** distancia que hay desde el centro de la lente al punto focal (p. 444)

**punto focal:** punto donde convergen los rayos de luz que entran a una lente convexa paralela al eje óptico (p. 444)

**folículo:** el óvulo y las células que lo rodean para protegerlo y alimentarlo (p. 508)

**fósil:** residuos, huellas o trazas de organismos que vivieron hace muchos años y que han sido conservados por medios naturales (p. 244)

**registro de fósiles:** historia de todos los fósiles conocidos y su colocación en la formación de las rocas, así como su posición a través del tiempo (p. 250)

**frecuencia:** número de veces que algo vibra en un período de tiempo determinado (p. 429)

**fruto:** estructura que contiene las semillas producidas por una planta que florece; se desarrolla a partir del ovario de la flor (p. 139)

**fulcro:** punto fijo alrededor del cual gira/rota una palanca (p. 368)

## G

**gene:** a section of DNA that has information about a specific trait of an organism (p. 177)

**generation:** a group of organisms that represents one step in a line from an ancestor (p. 211)

**genetic disorder:** a genetic or chromosomal mutation that is inherited (p. 188)

**genetics:** the study of how traits of organisms are passed from parents to offspring (p. 173)

**genotype:** alleles that make up an organism (p. 177)

**geographic isolation:** a type of evolution that occurs when populations of species are divided or separated by a physical barrier (p. 259)

**gen:** sección de ADN que contiene información sobre un rasgo específico de un organismo (p. 177)

**generación:** grupo de organismos que representa un paso en una línea a partir de un ancestro (p. 211)

**trastorno genético:** mutación genética o cromosómica que se hereda (p. 188)

**genética:** estudio de cómo los rasgos de los organismos son transferidos de los progenitores a su descendencia (p. 173)

**genotipo:** los alelos que forman un organismo (p. 177)

**aislamiento geográfico:** tipo de evolución que ocurre cuando las poblaciones de especies se dividen o separan a causa de una barrera física (p. 259)

# Glossary/Glosario

✳ **global:** relating to the entire world (p. 319)

**glycolysis (gli KAH lih sis):** the first step of cellular respiration that occurs in a cell's cytoplasm (p. 68)

**gonad:** specialized reproductive organ of animals that produces sperm or eggs (p. 144)

**gymnosperm:** plants that produce naked seeds and no flowers (p. 337)

**global:** relativo al mundo entero (p. 319)

**glicólisis:** primer paso de la respiración celular que ocurre en el citoplasma de la célula (p. 68)

**gónada:** órgano reproductor especializado de los animales que produce espermatozoides u óvulos (p. 144)

**gimnosperma:** planta que produce semillas desnudas y no produce flores (p. 337)

## H

**half-life:** the time it takes a given amount of a radioactive isotope to decay to half its original mass (p. 296)

**haploid:** eukaryotic cell containing only one chromosome from each homologous pair (p. 129)

**heart:** the organ of the circulatory system that pumps the blood throughout the circulatory system (p. 398)

**heart attack:** the result of insufficient blood flow to the heart, often resulting in tissue damage or the heart stopping beating (p. 400)

**heredity:** the passing of traits from parents to offspring (p. 172)

**heterozygous:** two alleles for a gene having different information (p. 178)

**homeostasis:** the ability of an organism to keep its internal conditions within certain limits (p. 51)

**homologous chromosome:** a pair of similar chromosome (p. 89)

**homologous structure:** parts of organisms that are similar in origin and structure; they are the result of evolution and can indicate how closely two or more species share common ancestors (p. 253)

**homozygous:** two alleles for a gene having the same information (p. 178)

**hypertension:** blood pressure above the normal range (p. 410)

**hypothesis:** a tentative explanation that can be tested with a scientific investigation (pp. 19, 28)

**vida media:** tiempo que tarda una cantidad determinada de un isótopo radiactivo en desintegrarse hasta llegar a la mitad de su masa original (p. 296)

**haploide:** célula eucariota que contiene un solo cromosoma de cada par homólogo (p. 129)

**corazón:** órgano del sistema circulatorio que bombea la sangre a través del sistema circulatorio (p. 398)

**ataque cardiaco:** resultado de un flujo sanguíneo insuficiente al corazón, ocasionado a menudo por daño a los tejidos, o porque el corazón deja de latir (p. 400)

**herencia:** transferencia de rasgos de los progenitores a su descendencia (p. 172)

**heterocigótico:** que posee los dos alelos de un gen con diferente información (p. 178)

**homeostasis:** capacidad de un organismo de mantener sus condiciones internas dentro de ciertos límites (p. 51)

**cromosoma homólogo:** par de cromosomas similares (p. 89)

**estructura homóloga:** partes de un organismo similares en cuanto a origen y estructura; son el resultado de la evolución y pueden indicar qué tan relacionadas están dos o más especies con respecto a ancestros comunes (p. 253)

**homocigótico:** que posee los dos alelos de un gen con la misma información (p. 178)

**hipertensión:** presión arterial por arriba del nivel normal (p. 410)

**hipótesis:** explicación tentativa que puede ponerse a prueba mediante una investigación científica (pp. 19, 28)

## I

**incomplete dominance:** alleles that produce a phenotype that is a blended form of the parents' phenotypes (p. 185)

**incus:** a tiny, anvil-shaped bone in the middle ear that transmits sounds, along with the malleus and stapes (p. 482)

**independent variable:** a factor in an experiment that is manipulated or changed by the investigator to observe how it affects a dependent variable (p. 29)

**dominancia incompleta:** condición causada por alelos que producen un fenotipo que es una forma combinada de los fenotipos de los progenitores (p. 185)

**yunque:** hueso pequeño del oído medio, en forma de yunque, que transmite sonidos junto con el martillo y el estribo (p. 482)

**variable independiente:** factor que el investigador manipula o cambia en un experimento para observar cómo afecta a una variable dependiente (p. 29)

**index fossil:** the fossilized remains of an organism that existed over vast areas for a short period of time (p. 316)

**inference:** a logical conclusion based on the information that is available to you (p. 16)

**internet resources:** Web pages, PDF documents, and other electronic documents that are available to anyone with a computer and an internet connection (p. 17)

**interphase:** the phase of a cell cycle in which a cell is preparing to reproduce (p. 88)

✳ **interpret:** to explain the meaning of (p. 220)

**iris:** the colored part of the eye, located behind the cornea (p. 451)

**isotope:** atoms of a given element that have the same number of protons but different numbers of neutrons (p. 294)

**fósil índice:** restos fosilizados de un organismo que existió en áreas muy extensas durante un período corto de tiempo (p. 316)

**inferencia:** conclusión lógica basada en la información que está disponible (p. 16)

**recursos de internet:** páginas Web, documentos en formato pdf y otros documentos electrónicos a disposición de cualquier persona con una computadora y una conexión de internet (p. 17)

**interfase:** fase del ciclo celular en la cual la célula se prepara para reproducirse (p. 88)

**interpretar:** explicar el significado de algo (p. 220)

**iris:** parte de color del ojo, ubicada detrás de la córnea (p. 451)

**isótopos:** átomos de un elemento determinado que poseen el mismo número de protones pero números diferentes de neutrones (p. 294)

**J**

**joint:** the connections between bones (p. 361)

**articulación:** conexiones entre los huesos (p.361)

**L**

**law of independent assortment:** the factors for one trait separate independently of how factors for other traits separate (p. 176)

**law of reflection:** when a light ray is reflected from a surface, the angle of incidence equals the angle of reflection (p. 440)

**law of segregation:** the two factors for each trait segregate or separate from each other during meiosis when gametes form (p. 176)

**lens:** a transparent object with at least one curved side that causes light waves to bend (p. 443)

**lever:** a simple machine made of anything rigid that pivots around a fixed point (p. 368)

**life science:** the scientific study of living things (p. 2)

**light microscope:** uses light and one or more lenses to enlarge an image of something (p. 48)

**lipid:** a large molecule that does not dissolve in water (p. 54)

**lithification:** the process of changing sediment into rock (p. 288)

**loudness:** a person's perception of how much energy a sound wave carries (p. 475)

**ley de la variedad independiente:** ley que establece que los factores correspondientes a un rasgo se separan independientemente de cómo se separan los factores de otros rasgos (p. 176)

**ley de la reflexión:** ley que establece que cuando un rayo de luz se refleja desde una superficie, el ángulo de incidencia es igual al ángulo de reflexión (p. 440)

**ley de la segregación:** ley que establece que los dos factores correspondientes a cada rasgo se segregan o separan uno del otro durante la meiosis al formarse los gametos (p. 176)

**lente:** objeto transparente con al menos un lado curvo que hace que se flexionen las ondas luminosas (p. 443)

**palanca:** máquina simple hecha de cualquier material rígido que gira/rota alrededor de un punto fijo (p. 368)

**ciencias de la vida:** estudio científico de los seres vivos (p. 2)

**microscopio de luz:** instrumento que utiliza la luz y una o más lentes para agrandar una imagen (p. 48)

**lípido:** molécula grande que no se disuelve en agua (p. 54)

**litificación:** proceso mediante el cual el sedimento se transforma en roca (p. 288)

**intensidad del sonido:** percepción por parte de una persona de la cantidad de energía que contiene una onda de sonido (p. 475)

# Glossary/Glosario

**lungs:** the organs in the pulmonary system in which gas exchange occurs (p. 393)

**pulmones:** órganos del sistema respiratorio donde ocurre el intercambio de gases (p. 393)

## M

**malleus:** a tiny, hammer-shaped bone in the middle ear that transmits sounds, along with the incus and stapes (p. 482)

**mass extinction:** the dying off of many different species over a short period of geologic time (p. 318)

**mechanical advantage:** the ability of a machine to increase the amount of force put into the machine (p. 373)

**medium:** the substance through which a wave moves (p. 430)

**meiosis:** the division of a cell and its nucleus that produces haploid daughter cells (p. 128)

**menstrual cycle:** the changes that take place in a female's body before, during, and after ovulation; lasts about 28 days (p. 508)

**metamorphosis:** developmental process in which the form of an animal's body changes as it grows from egg to adult (p. 147)

**metaphase:** the second stage of mitosis, in which the replicated chromosomes move to the middle of the cell and the pairs of sister chromatids line up end to end across the center of the cell (p. 92)

**method:** a way of doing something (p. 174)

**mimicry:** an adaptation that allows one species to look like or act like another species in order to fool a third species (p. 222)

**mitochondrion (plural, mitochondria):** organelle that transforms the usable energy in food molecules (p. 61)

**mitosis (mi TOH sus):** a process in which the nucleus of the cell divides (p. 91)

**modify:** to make minor changes (p. 62)

**mold:** a type of fossil that forms as an imprint or cavity in a rock (p. 248)

**multiple alleles:** genes that have more than two alleles (p. 185)

**muscle:** tissue made of long cells that contract (p. 364)

**martillo:** hueso pequeño del oído medio, en forma de martillo, que transmite sonidos junto con el yunque y el estribo (p. 482)

**extinción masiva:** muerte de muchas especies diferentes en un período corto de tiempo geológico (p. 318)

**ventaja mecánica:** capacidad de una máquina de aumentar la cantidad de fuerza aplicada a ella (p. 373)

**medio:** sustancia a través de la cual se mueve una onda (p. 430)

**meiosis:** división de una célula y su núcleo que produce células hijas haploides (p. 128)

**ciclo menstrual:** cambios que tienen lugar en el cuerpo femenino antes, durante y después de la ovulación; dura aproximadamente 28 días (p. 508)

**metamorfosis:** proceso de desarrollo en el cual la forma del cuerpo de un animal cambia a medida que crece desde el huevo hasta convertirse en adulto (p. 147)

**metafase:** segunda etapa de la mitosis durante la cual los cromosomas replicados se mueven hacia el centro de la célula, y los pares de cromátidas hermanas se alinean de extremo a extremo en el centro de la célula (p. 92)

**método:** manera de hacer algo (p. 174)

**mímica:** tipo de adaptación que permite a una especie parecerse a otra o actuar como otra para engañar a una tercera especie (p. 222)

**mitocondria:** organelo que transforma la energía utilizable contenida en las moléculas de los alimentos (p. 61)

**mitosis:** proceso mediante el cual se divide el núcleo de una célula (p. 91)

**modificar:** realizar cambios menores (p. 62)

**molde:** tipo de fósil que se forma como huella o cavidad en una roca (p. 248)

**alelos múltiples:** genes que tienen más de dos alelos (p. 185)

**músculo:** tejido formado por células largas que se contraen (p. 364)

## N

**naturalist:** a person who studies the natural world including plants, rocks, and animals (p. 210)

**natural selection:** the process by which organisms, with traits that help them adapt to a changing environment, are able to successfully reproduce (p. 216)

**naturalista:** persona que estudia el mundo natural, incluyendo las plantas, las rocas y los animales (p. 210)

**selección natural:** proceso mediante el cual los organismos que poseen rasgos que los ayudan a adaptarse a un medio ambiente cambiante pueden reproducirse con éxito (p. 216)

# Glossary/Glosario

* **network:** a system of lines or channels that connect with each other (p. 144)

**nucleic (noo KLAY ihk) acid:** long chains of molecules called nucleotides (p. 54)

**nucleus (plural, nuclei):** an organelle that contains the genetic material—a chemical code for making all the molecules of a cell, often called the control center of the cell (p. 60)

**red:** sistema de líneas o canales que se conectan unos con otros (p. 144)

**ácido nucleico:** largas cadenas de moléculas denominadas nucleótidos (p. 54)

**núcleo:** organelo que contiene el material genético; código químico para elaborar todas las moléculas de una célula, denominado a menudo el centro de control de la célula (p. 60)

## O

**opinion:** a personal view, belief, feeling, or claim about something (p. 18)

**organ:** groups of tissues that work together and perform one or more functions (p. 104)

**organelle:** compartment in the cytoplasm that has a specific function (p. 59)

**organ system:** organs that work together and perform one or more functions (p. 105)

**ovary:** portion of the pistil of the flower that contains ovules; develops into a fruit; the egg producing gonad of female animals (pp. 138, 144)

**ovulation:** process in which an egg is released from an ovary (p. 508)

**ovule:** portion of the ovary of the flower that contains eggs; develops into a seed (p. 137)

**opinión:** perspectiva, creencia o sentimiento personal, o una afirmación sobre algo (p. 18)

**órgano:** grupos de tejidos que funcionan en conjunto y llevan a cabo una o más funciones (p. 104)

**organelo:** compartimiento del citoplasma que tiene una función específica (p. 59)

**sistema de órganos:** órganos que funcionan en conjunto y llevan a cabo una o más funciones (p. 105)

**ovario:** parte del pistilo de una flor que contiene óvulos; se transforma en fruto; la gónada de las hembras de los animales que produce óvulos (pp. 138, 144)

**ovulación:** proceso mediante el cual el ovario libera un óvulo (p. 508)

**óvulo:** parte del ovario de la flor que contiene óvulos; se transforma en semilla (p. 137)

## P

**paleontologist:** a scientist who studies fossils (p. 244)

* **parallel:** extending in the same direction without meeting and everywhere equidistant (p. 288)

**pedigree:** a model that shows the genetic traits that were inherited by members of a family tree (p. 184)

**penis:** the male organ that transfers sperm to a female's reproductive tract (p. 505)

* **period:** an amount of time (p. 410)

**permineralization:** a fossilization process in which groundwater deposits minerals in empty spaces of an organism's original hard structures and preserves them (p. 246)

**phenotype:** observable traits and all characteristics of an organism (p. 177)

**photosynthesis:** a series of chemical reactions in some organisms that uses light energy and makes food (p. 70)

**pigment:** a material used to change the color of other materials or objects (p. 454)

**pistil:** female reproductive organ of a flower; includes stigma, style, ovary, and ovules (p. 138)

**paleontólogo:** científico que estudia los fósiles (p. 244)

**paralelo:** que se extiende en la misma dirección sin encontrarse y equidistante en todos los puntos (p. 288)

**genealogía:** modelo que muestra los rasgos genéticos heredados por los miembros de un árbol genealógico (p. 184)

**pene:** órgano masculino que transfiere los espermatozoides al tracto reproductor femenino (p. 505)

**período:** una cantidad de tiempo (p. 410)

**permineralización:** proceso de fosilización mediante el cual el agua subterránea deposita minerales en los espacios vacíos de las estructuras duras originales de un organismo y las conserva (p. 246)

**fenotipo:** rasgos observables y todas las características de un organismo (p. 177)

**fotosíntesis:** serie de reacciones químicas en algunos organismos que usan la energía luminosa y elaboran alimentos (p. 70)

**pigmento:** material que se usa para cambiar el color de otros materiales u objetos (p. 454)

**pistilo:** órgano reproductor femenino de una flor; incluye estigma, estilo, ovario y óvulos (p. 138)

# Glossary/Glosario

**pitch:** the measure of how high or low a sound is, based upon its frequency (p. 477)

**placenta:** a disc-shaped organ in the uterus that develops from tissues of both the fetus and the endometrium; exchanges materials between the mother and the fetus (p. 517)

**pneumonia:** an infection of the lungs caused by viruses, bacteria, fungi, or parasites (p. 394)

**pollen grain:** contains the male haploid structure of a seed plant; has a hard, protective outer covering, contains nutrients, and produces sperm cells (p. 136)

**pollen tube:** a tube that grows from a pollen grain and delivers the sperm to the ovule (p. 139)

**pollination:** when pollen grains land on a female reproductive structure of a plant that is the same species as the pollen grain (p. 137)

**polygenic inheritance:** when multiple genes determine the phenotype of a trait (p. 187)

✳ **portion:** limited part set apart from the whole (p. 326)

**prediction:** to say in advance what will happen next in a sequence of events (pp. 19, 28)

**pregnancy:** period of development from fertilized egg until birth; usually last about 38 weeks in humans (p. 516)

**prenatal care:** health care aimed at maintaining the health of a pregnant woman and preventing health problems in her developing fetus (p. 518)

**pressure:** force measured per unit area (p. 405)

✳ **primary:** of first rank, importance, or value (p. 439)

**primate:** an animal with opposable thumbs and eyes that look directly forward; evolved during the Eocene epoch (p. 338)

**print resources:** books, newspapers, popular magazines and peer-reviewed journals (p. 17)

**procedure:** a sequence of instructions used to gather data in a scientific investigation (p. 31)

✳ **process:** a series of natural activities (p. 50)

✳ **prohibit:** to prevent from doing something (p. 259)

**prokaryotic (proh kayr ee AH tik) cell:** a cell without a nucleus and other organelles (p. 64)

**prophase:** the first phase of mitosis in which the DNA that makes up a replicated chromosome twists into tight coils (p. 92)

**protein:** folded chain or a group of folded chains of molecules called amino acids (p. 53)

**pterosaur:** flying reptile not related to a dinosaur (p. 333)

**pulmonary system:** the tissues and organs that bring the air in and out of your body to exchange oxygen and carbon dioxide (p. 392)

**tono:** medida de cuán agudo o bajo es un sonido, basada en su frecuencia (p. 477)

**placenta:** órgano en forma de disco del útero que se desarrolla a partir de tejidos del feto y del endometrio; realiza intercambio de materiales entre la madre y el feto (p. 517)

**neumonía:** infección de los pulmones ocasionada por virus, bacterias, hongos o parásitos (p. 394)

**grano de polen:** parte que contiene la estructura haploide masculina de una planta de semillas; posee una cubierta exterior dura protectora, contiene nutrientes y produce espermatozoides (p. 136)

**tubo de polen:** tubo que crece a partir de un grano de polen y lleva los espermatozoides al óvulo (p. 139)

**polinización:** proceso en el que los granos de polen se depositan en una estructura reproductora femenina de una planta que es de la misma especie que el grano de polen (p. 137)

**herencia poligénica:** condición en la que múltiples genes determinan el fenotipo de un rasgo (p. 187)

**porción:** parte limitada separada del todo (p. 326)

**predicción:** establecimiento de lo que va a suceder próximamente en una secuencia de eventos (pp. 19, 28)

**embarazo:** período de desarrollo desde el óvulo fertilizado hasta el nacimiento; normalmente dura aproximadamente 38 semanas en los humanos (p. 516)

**cuidado prenatal:** cuidado de la salud cuyo propósito es mantener la salud de una mujer embarazada e impedir problemas de salud en el feto (p. 518)

**presión:** fuerza medida por unidad de superficie (p. 405)

**primario:** de primer orden, importancia o valor (p. 439)

**primate:** animal con pulgares opuestos y ojos que miran directamente hacia delante; evolucionaron durante la época del Eoceno (p. 338)

**recursos impresos:** libros, periódicos, revistas populares y publicaciones revisadas por compañeros (p. 17)

**procedimiento:** secuencia de instrucciones que se usa para recabar datos en una investigación científica (p. 31)

**proceso:** serie de actividades naturales (p. 50)

**prohibir:** impedir que se haga algo (p. 259)

**célula procariota:** célula que no posee núcleo y otros organelos (p. 64)

**profase:** primera fase de la mitosis en la cual el ADN que forma un cromosoma replicado se tuerce para formar rollos firmes (p. 92)

**proteína:** cadena plegada o grupo de cadenas plegadas de moléculas denominadas aminoácidos (p. 53)

**pterosaurio:** reptil volador no relacionado con el dinosaurio (p. 333)

**sistema pulmonar:** tejidos y órganos que llevan el aire hacia y desde el cuerpo para intercambiar el oxígeno y el dióxido de carbono (p. 392)

# Glossary/Glosario

**Punnett square:** a model used to predict possible geno-types and phenotypes of offspring (p. 182)

**pupil:** the dark opening into the interior of the eye (p. 451)

**cuadro de Punnett:** modelo que se usa para predecir posibles genotipos y fenotipos de la descendencia (p. 182)

**pupila:** abertura oscura del interior del ojo (p. 451)

## Q

**qualitative observation:** descriptions of the natural world using words (pp. 16, 30)

**quantitative observation:** descriptions of the natural world using numbers (pp. 16, 30)

**observación cualitativa:** descripción del mundo natural mediante palabras (pp. 16, 30)

**observación cuantitativa:** descripción del mundo natural mediante números (pp. 16, 30)

## R

**radioactive decay:** when an unstable atomic nucleus changes to another nucleus by emitting particles and energy (p. 294)

✳ **range:** to change or differ within limits (p. 431)

**recessive:** a genetic factor that is hidden by the presence of a dominant factor (p. 175)

**refraction:** occurs when a light ray changes direction as it passes from one material to another (p. 438)

**regeneration:** a type of asexual reproduction in animals; produces a new organism from part of an animal's body (p. 154)

**relative age:** an estimation of age made by comparing position or characteristics of two objects (p. 289)

**relaxation:** the lengthening of inactive muscle or muscle fibers (p. 364)

**retina:** sheet of light-sensitive cells at the back of the eye (p. 452)

**ribosome:** a small structure without membrane, that builds proteins (p. 60)

**rock cycle:** the series of processes that change rock from one form into another (p. 286)

**desintegración radiactiva:** proceso que ocurre cuando un núcleo atómico inestable se transforma en otro núcleo al emitir partículas y energía (p. 294)

**fluctuar:** variar o diferir dentro de ciertos límites (p. 431)

**recesivo:** factor genético que se oculta por la presencia de un factor dominante (p. 175)

**refracción:** fenómeno que ocurre cuando un rayo de luz cambia de dirección al pasar de un material a otro (p. 438)

**regeneración:** tipo de reproducción asexual de los animales; produce un nuevo organismo a partir de una parte del cuerpo de un animal (p. 154)

**edad relativa:** cálculo estimado de edad que se hace al comparar la posición o las características de dos objetos (p. 289)

**relajación:** alargamiento de un músculo o fibras musculares inactivas (p. 364)

**retina:** lámina de células sensibles a la luz ubicadas en la parte posterior del ojo (p. 452)

**ribosoma:** estructura pequeña sin membrana que elabora proteínas (p. 60)

**ciclo de la roca:** serie de procesos que transforman una roca en otra (p. 286)

## S

**scale:** a ratio of the measurements of an original object to the measurements of a model (p. 23)

**scale model:** three-dimensional representation of an object that is proportionately larger or smaller than the actual object (p. 23)

**scattering:** occurs when a material causes light waves traveling in one direction to travel in all directions (p. 436)

**science:** the process of studying nature at all levels and the collection of information that is created through this process (p. 2)

**escala:** proporción entre las medidas de un objeto original y las medidas de un modelo (p. 23)

**modelo de escala:** representación tridimensional de un objeto que es proporcionalmente mayor o más pequeño que el objeto real (p. 23)

**dispersión:** ocurre cuando un material hace que las ondas luminosas que viajan en una dirección viajen en todas direcciones (p. 436)

**ciencia:** proceso mediante el cual se estudia la naturaleza a todos niveles, y la recopilación de información que se crea en este proceso (p. 2)

# Glossary/Glosario

**scientific law:** a rule that describes a pattern in nature (p. 6)

**scientific theory:** an explanation of things or events that is based on knowledge gained from many observations and investigations (p. 6)

**scrotum:** baglike sac that contains the testes; hangs outside the male's body cavity (p. 505)

**second-class lever:** a lever in which the resistance force is located between the fulcrum and the effort forces (p. 370)

**seed:** consists of an embryo and a food supply, protected inside an outer covering; develops from an ovule after fertilization (p. 137)

**seminiferous tubules:** tightly coiled tubes inside the testes in which sperm cells are produced by meiosis (p. 505)

**sex chromosomes:** chromosomes that contain genes that determine an organism's gender (p. 186)

**sexual reproduction:** a form of reproduction; combining genetic material in two different cells; producing an offspring (p. 126)

**shock:** inability of the body to supply enough oxygen to meet tissue requirements (p. 410)

**sister chromatid:** copy of a chromosome made during S-phase of cell cycle (p. 90)

**skeletal system:** the hard, supportive structures within your body, mostly made of bone (p. 360)

**\* specific:** relating to or being an example of a certain kind of thing (p. 135)

**sperm:** haploid reproductive cell produced by the male reproductive organs (p. 126)

**spore:** a haploid reproductive structure (p. 135)

**\* stable:** resistant to change of position or condition (p. 370)

**stamen:** male reproductive organ of a flower; includes anther and filament (p. 138)

**stapes:** a tiny, stirrup-shaped bone in the middle ear that transmits sounds, along with the incus and malleus (p. 482)

**stem cell:** cells that are able to produce different types of cells (p. 102)

**stigma:** the tip of the pistil where pollen lands (p. 138)

**stratum (plural, strata):** layers of rock (p. 289)

**stroke:** death of brain tissue due to a blocked or ruptured blood vessel (p. 400)

**structural adaptation:** an adaptation that is expressed in a physical body structure (p. 221)

**\* structure:** any part of an organism (p. 246)

**ley científica:** regla que describe un patrón de la naturaleza (p. 6)

**teoría científica:** explicación de circunstancias o eventos basada en el conocimiento obtenido a través de muchas observaciones e investigaciones (p. 6)

**escroto:** estructura en forma de saco que contiene los testículos; pende fuera de la cavidad corporal masculina (p. 505)

**palanca de segunda clase:** palanca en la cual la fuerza de resistencia se encuentra entre el fulcro y las fuerzas de esfuerzo (p. 370)

**semilla:** estructura que consiste en un embrión y es una fuente de alimentos, y está protegida por una cubierta; se desarrolla a partir de un óvulo después de la fertilización (p. 137)

**túbulos seminíferos:** tubos firmemente enrollados en el interior de los testículos donde se producen los espermatozoides mediante la meiosis (p. 505)

**cromosomas sexuales:** cromosomas que contienen los genes que determinan el sexo de un organismo (p. 186)

**reproducción sexual:** forma de reproducción; combinación del material genético en dos células diferentes; producción de descendencia (p. 126)

**conmoción:** incapacidad del cuerpo para suministrar oxígeno en cantidades suficientes para satisfacer las necesidades de los tejidos (p. 410)

**cromátida hermana:** copia de un cromosoma producido durante la fase S del ciclo celular (p. 90)

**sistema esquelético:** estructura dura, de apoyo del cuerpo, formada principalmente por huesos (p. 360)

**específico:** relacionado con algo o que constituye un ejemplo de un tipo determinado de objeto (p. 135)

**espermatozoide:** célula reproductora haploide producida por los órganos reproductores masculinos (p. 126)

**espora:** estructura reproductiva haploide (p. 135)

**estable:** resistente al cambio de posición o condición (p. 370)

**estambre:** órgano reproductor masculino de una flor; incluye antera y filamento (p. 138)

**estribo:** hueso pequeño del oído medio, en forma de estribo, que transmite sonidos junto con el yunque y el estribo (p. 482)

**célula madre:** célula que tiene la capacidad de producir diferentes tipos de células (p. 102)

**estigma:** punta del pistilo donde se deposita el polen (p. 138)

**estrato:** capas de rocas (p. 289)

**embolia:** muerte del tejido cerebral debido a un vaso sanguíneo bloqueado o roto (p. 400)

**adaptación estructural:** adaptación que se expresa en una estructura física del cuerpo (p. 221)

**estructura:** cualquier parte de un organismo (p. 246)

# Glossary/Glosario

**style:** the long tube of the pistil that connects the stigma and the ovary (p. 138)

**suffocation:** a condition in which oxygen is not able to be delivered to the lungs or the body (p. 394)

**superposition:** the theory that undisturbed layers of rock have the oldest layers on the bottom and the youngest on the top (p. 289)

✳ **supplement:** something that adds to something else (p. 518)

**systematics:** the modern study of classification which mostly uses DNA and molecular biology to identify related organisms (p. 264)

**estilo:** tubo largo del pistilo que conecta al estigma y al ovario (p. 138)

**sofocación:** condición en la cual no puede llevarse el oxígeno a los pulmones o al cuerpo (p. 394)

**superposición:** teoría que afirma que los estratos imperturbados de rocas poseen las capas más antiguas en la parte inferior y las más jóvenes en la parte superior (p. 289)

**suplemento:** componente que se añade a algo (p. 518)

**sistemática:** estudio moderno de clasificación que usa básicamente el ADN y la biología molecular para identificar organismos relacionados (p. 264)

**telophase:** the final phase of mitosis, in which a new membrane forms around each set of chromosomes, creating two identical nuclei (p. 92)

**tendon:** the tissue that connects bone to muscle and does not stretch very much (p. 366)

**testes (TES teez):** male gonads; produce sperm (p. 144)

**third-class lever:** a lever in which the effort force is located between the fulcrum and resistance force (p. 370)

**tissue:** similar cells that work together and perform a function (p. 103)

**transmission:** occurs when light waves strike a material and pass through it (p. 436)

**trimester:** one-third of the nine-month term of a human pregnancy (p. 516)

**tympanic membrane:** a thin layer of skin that separates the outer and middle ear, commonly called the eardrum (p. 482)

**telofase:** fase final de la mitosis en la cual se forma una nueva membrana alrededor de cada juego de cromosomas y se producen dos núcleos idénticos (p. 92)

**tendón:** tejido que conecta el hueso al músculo y que posee poca elasticidad (p. 366)

**testículos:** gónadas masculinas que producen espermatozoides (p. 144)

**palanca de tercera clase:** palanca en la cual la fuerza de esfuerzo se encuentra entre el fulcro y la fuerza de resistencia (p. 370)

**tejido:** células similares que funcionan en conjunto y realizan una función (p. 103)

**transmisión:** fenómeno que ocurre cuando las ondas luminosas chocan con un material y pasan a través de él (p. 436)

**trimestre:** un tercio del período de nueve meses del embarazo humano (p. 516)

**membrana timpánica:** capa fina de piel que separa al oído externo del oído medio, denominada comúnmente tímpano (p. 482)

**umbilical cord:** organ that connects a fetus to the placenta; carries food and oxygen from placenta to fetus and carries wastes from fetus to placenta (p. 517)

**uniformitarianism:** the idea that Earth processes that are at work today were also working on Earth in the past (p. 285)

**urethra:** extends through the length of the penis and transports semen as well as urine (p. 505)

**uterus:** thick, muscular, pear-shaped organ of a female reproductive system, located above the vagina, where a fertilized egg can develop into a baby (p. 507)

**cordón umbilical:** órgano que conecta al feto con la placenta; transporta alimentos y oxígeno de la placenta al feto y lleva los desechos del feto a la placenta (p. 517)

**uniformismo:** idea de que los procesos actuales de La Tierra también tenían lugar en La Tierra del pasado (p. 285)

**uretra:** órgano que se extiende a lo largo del pene y transporta semen y orina (p. 505)

**útero:** órgano grueso, muscular, en forma de pera, del sistema reproductor femenino, ubicado sobre la vagina, donde un óvulo fertilizado puede desarrollarse para convertirse en un feto (p. 507)

# Glossary/Glosario

**vagina:** a thin-walled chamber in the female reproductive tract where semen is deposited (p. 507)

**variable:** any factor in a scientific investigation that can have more than one value (p. 29)

✱ **variety:** the quality of having different forms (p. 329)

✱ **vary:** to make different (p. 127)

**vein:** vessel that carries blood back to the heart (p. 399)

**ventricle:** the two lower chambers of the heart that pump the blood out of the heart (p. 398)

**vertebrate:** animal with a backbone (p. 329)

**vagina:** cámara de pared fina del tracto reproductor femenino donde se deposita el semen (p. 507)

**variable:** factor de una investigación científica que puede tener más de un valor (p. 29)

**variedad:** calidad de tener diferentes formas (p. 329)

**variar:** volver diferente (p. 127)

**vena:** conducto que transporta la sangre de vuelta al corazón (p. 399)

**ventrículo:** cada una de las dos cavidades inferiores del corazón que bombean la sangre hacia el cuerpo (p. 398)

**vertebrado:** animal que posee una columna vertebral (p. 329)

**wavelength:** the distance between any two crests or troughs on a wave (p. 429)

**longitud de onda:** distancia entre dos crestas o depresiones de una onda (p. 429)

**zygote:** diploid cell formed by the fusion of one egg and one sperm cell; develops into a new organism (p. 126)

**zigoto:** célula diploide formada por la fusión de un óvulo y un espermatozoide; se desarrolla para convertirse en un nuevo organismo (p. 126)

Italic numbers = illustration/photo    **Bold numbers** = vocabulary term
*lab* = indicates a page on which the entry is used in a lab
*act* = indicates a page on which the entry is used in an activity

# A

**Abdominal Thrust, 395**

**Absolute age**, calculating, 297

**Absorption, 436;** light interacting with matter, *436*

**Acid cloud**, basalt flow, 321

**Activities**, 469; Applying Math, 67, 80, 165, 199, 218, 237, 273, 309, 349, 413, 421, 433, 465, 497, 529; Applying Science, 55, 66, 72, 80, 133, 142, 149, 157, 165, 180, 190, 199, 217, 227, 237, 251, 256, 260, 265, 273, 291, 299, 309, 323, 331, 339, 349, 367, 375, 403, 411, 421, 432, 442, 449, 457, 465, 478, 488, 497, 513, 521, 529; Science Online, 47, 55, 66, 72, 78, 79, 123, 125, 133, 142, 149, 157, 162, 163, 169, 171, 180, 181, 190, 196, 197, 207, 209, 217, 218, 227, 234, 235, 251, 256, 260, 261, 265, 270, 271, 281, 283, 291, 299, 306, 307, 310, 313, 315, 323, 331, 339, 347, 357, 359, 367, 375, 382, 383, 389, 391, 403, 411, 413, 418, 419, 425, 427, 432, 433, 442, 449, 457, 462, 463, 471, 478, 488, 494, 495, 501, 503, 513, 521, 526, 527; Writing in Science, 75*lab*, 80, 165, 193*lab*, 199, 267*lab*, 273, 309, 343, 385, 415*lab*, 421, 465, 491*lab*, 497, 523, 529

**Adaptation, 252;** behavioral, 223; blending with environment, 220, *220;* structural, 221, 222; type(s) of, 221

**Adapting**, inability, 226

**Adrenal gland**, 511

**Air**, pollution triggering asthma, 396; pressure, 406, *406,* 407; pulmonary system, *392,* 392

**Airplane**, changing pressure, 482

**Airway**, in asthma patient, *396;* narrowing, 396

**Alcohol**, during pregnancy, 520

**Algae**, first plant developing, 330

**Allele, 177;** color blindness, *186;* multiple, 185; Punnett square, 183, *183;* representing, 178

**Allergen**, asthma, 396

**Alternating**, generation, 134, *134*

**Alveoli**, 402, *402;* breathing, 393

**Alveolus.** *See* alveoli

**Amber**, original-material fossil, 248

**Amino acid**, sequence, 53

**Ammonite**, cast, *248*

**Amniote, 329**

**Amoeba**, *99,* 99

**Amphibian**, evolving in Mesozoic era, 333; reproducing, 329

**Amplitude**, *429,* 429, **475;** of a sound wave, *475;* Word Origin, 475

**Amylase**, 53*tab*

**Analogous structure, 253**

**Analyze and Conclude**, 75*lab,* 109*lab,* 159*lab,* 193*lab,* 231*lab,* 267*lab,* 303*lab,* 343*lab,* 379*lab,* 415*lab,* 459*lab,* 491*lab,* 523*lab*

**Anaphase**, mitosis, *92, 93;* meiosis I and II, 130, *131*

**Anatomy**, animal. *See* Animal anatomy, comparative, **252**, plant. *See* Plant anatomy

**Ancient life**, Paleozoic era, *317,* 317; studying, 344

**Angiosperm, 138,** 332; life cycle, 139, *139;* Mesozoic era, *337,* 337; reproducing, 138; Word Origin, 139

**Angle of incidence**, 440

**Angle of reflection**, 440

**Animal**, bacteria-eating, 327; breeding, 127; cloning, 156, 161; developing embryo, 146; evolving, 241*lab;* fertilizing, 144; hearing sound, *486,* 486, 490–491*lab;* illness, 160; regeneration, 154; reproducing, 149; reproductive organ, 143; vertebrate, 329

**Animal anatomy**, 144, *144*

**Animal cell**, *59,* 59; cytokinesis, *94;* Golgi apparatus, 62, *62*

**Animal tissue**, *103*

**Anther, 138,** *139*

**Anti-evolutionist**, Owen, Sir Richard, 233

**Anvil.** *See* Incus

**Aorta**, blood flow, 409

**Apatosaurus**, Triassic period, 334

**Appendage**, cell, 58

**Appendix.** *See* Glossary; Math Skill Handbook; Credits; Reference Handbook; Science Skill Handbook; Technology Skill Handbook

**Applying Math**, 67, 80, 115, 165, 181, 199, 218, 237, 261, 273, 309, 341, 349, 413, 421, 433, 465, 497, 529

**Applying Science**, 55, 66, 72, 80, 95, 107, 115, 133, 142, 149, 157, 165, 180, 190, 199, 217, 227, 237, 251, 256, 260, 265,

273, 291, 299, 309, 323, 331, 339, 349, 367, 375, 385, 403, 411, 421, 432, 442, 449, 457, 465, 478, 488, 497, 513, 521, 529

**Archaeopteryx**, bird species from Jurassic period, *336,* 336

**Archean eon**, Precambrian time, *317,* 326; rock, 326; stromatolite, 327

**Archimedes**, Greek mathematician, 368

**Area**, finding for chest of drawers, 218*act;* finding for wash stand, 218*act;* surface, 81*act*

**Aristotle**, classifying organism, 262

**Artery, 399,** *399;* blood flow, 409

**Asexual reproduction, 151;** advantage, *151,* 151; disadvantage, 152; type(s) of, 152–156

**Assign, 100**

**Asteroid**, climate change, 319; mass extinction, 318, 322

**Asthma**, 394, **396,** 417

**Atherosclerosis**, damaging blood vessel, *410*

**Athlete**, with asthma, 396

**Atmosphere, 405**

**Atmospheric pressure**, 405, 407

**Atom**, 294; absorbing energy, 435

**ATP (Adenosine Triphosphate), 68**

**Atria, 398**

**Atrium**, blood flow, *409,* 409; chamber of heart, *398,* 398; contracting, 408, *408*

**Auditory canal, 481,** *481*

# B

**Bacteria**, decomposing organism, 64; pneumonia, 394; studying evolution of, 268; surviving high temperature, 64

**Ball**, pressure, 406

**Ball-and-socket joint**, 362, *363tab*

**Ballerina**, toe pressure, 406

**Basalt flow**, 321; global cooling, 321; producing gas, 321

**Bat**, echolocation, 486, *487,* 487

**Beach**, forming, 285, *285*

**Beagle.** *See* HMS Beagle

**Begonia leaf**, differentiated cell, 102, *102*

**Behavioral adaptation**, 223

**Belly button**, 517

**Big Idea**, 44, 78, 84, 112, 122, 162, 168, 196, 206, 234, 240, 270, 280, 306, 312,

**Biological evidence of evolution**
356, 382, 388, 418, 424, 468, 494, 500, 526

**Biological evidence of evolution.** *See* Evolution, biological evidence of

**Biologist**, evolutionary, 232

**Biology**, molecular, 255

**Bird**, descendent of dinosaur, 334; Jurassic period, 336

**Birth**, premature, 517

**Birth defect**, folic acid for preventing, 519*lab*

**Bladder**, male human body, *504*

**Blending inheritance**, 172

**Blind**, helping, 460

**Blindness**, color, *186*

**Blood**, component(s) of, 397, 397*tab*; pumping, 398; pumping within heart, *408*, 408; type(s) of, 185, 185*tab*; vessel, 399

**Blood cell**, 101; red, *56*

**Blood pressure**, 405; horse, 417; problem(s) with, 410

**Blood vessel**, *399*; damaging blood vessel, *410*; pressure, 407

**Blue Baby Syndrome**, **416**

**Bog body**, *293*, *293*

**Bone**, 360, 360; interacting with muscle, 366*lab*; as lever, 374; stem cell, 102

**Brain cell**, 100, *100*

**Branching diagram**, 265*lab*. *See* Dichotomous key

**Breathing**, 393, *393*, 402

**Breeding**, selective, 127, 214, *214*

**Bristlecone pine**, gymnosperm, 137, *137*

**Bronchi**, *402*; breathing, 393

**Bronchiole**, *402*, 402; in asthma patient, *396*; breathing, 393

**Bronchus.** *See* bronchi

**Budding**, asexual reproduction, 153

**Butterfly**, Quino checkerspot, 51, *51*

## C

**Cactus**, evolving, *259*

**Cactus finch**, 213, *213*

**Caffeine**, during pregnancy, 519

**Calcite**, forming fossil, 246

**Calcium**, keeping bone(s) hard, 361; strengthening collagen fiber, 360

**Calculating**, bird species, 229*lab*; cooling Earth, 293; female offspring v. male offspring, 501*lab*; half-life, 296, *296*, 300*lab*; lever output force, 375*act*; mechanical advantage of a level, 376*lab*, 379*lab*; percentage of cells with visible DNA, 54*lab*; percent-age of neural tube defect, 519*lab*; percentage of phenotype, 191*lab*, 193*lab*; ratio of peas, 176*lab*; sound wave passing through window, 478*act*

**Calculator**, 228*lab*; Using, 576

**California**, asthma, 417; Gold Rush, 305; population with asthma, 396

**California poppy plant**, genetic information, 127

**California Standards Assessment.** *See* Standards Assessment

**Calorie**, 518

**Cambrian explosion**, 328

**Cambrian period**, Cambrian explosion, 328; Paleozoic era, *328*

**Camera**, 446; working like a human eye, *450*, 450

**Camouflage**, structural adaptation, 221

**Candleholder**, light interacting with matter, *437*, 437

**Capillary**, **399**, *399*, 402, *402*

**Carbohydrate**, 54

**Carbon dioxide**, exposing to, 394; form-ing carbonic acid, 287; releasing from burning plant, 322; waste product, 392

**Carbon film**, *247*, 247

**Carbonization**, *247*, 247

**Cardiac muscle cell**, 101

**Cardiac muscle tissue**, 364

**Cardiopulmonary system**, illness affect-ing, 404*lab*

**Cardiovascular disease**, **400**, *400*; pre-venting, 402

**Career.** *See* Real World Science

**Car jack**, as lever, *373*, 373

**Cartilage**, **361**; covering bone end, *361*

**Casein**, 53*tab*

**Cast**, *248*, **248**

**Cat**, hearing sound, 486

**Catastrophe**, Word Origin, 318

**Catastrophic event**, **318**

**Cell**, **48**; appendage, 58; blood, 101; brain, 100, *100*; chemistry, 52; cone, *451*; connective tissue, 101; cytoplasm, 59, *59*; diploid, 129; of embryo, *515*, 515; eukaryotic, 65, *65*; growing, 51; haploid, 129; human, 101; liver, *100*, 100; mitochondria, 61, *61*; mitotic division, 153; modeling, 65*lab*; mol-ecule, 52; muscle, 101, 364; observing DNA, 54*lab*; organizing, 50; plant, *49*; prokaryotic, 64, 65, *65*; respiratory, 58; rod, *451*; sensory, 483; shape, 56, *56*; size, *48*, 48; skin, 91, *91*; stem, 102; structure, 63*tab*; type(s) of, 64, 65; using atom(s) and molecule(s), 52; wall, 58, *58*, 63*tab*

**Cell cycle**, **88**; interphase, 88, *88*; phase(s) of, 91*tab*; zebra fish egg, 89, *89*

**Cell differentiation**, **100**

**Cell division**, identical cell(s), 90; mito-sis, 91, 92; result of, 94

**Cell membrane**, **56**, *57*, 57; cell struc-ture, 63*tab*; prokaryotic cell, 64

**Cell plate**, **94**

**Cell theory**, **49**

**Cell wall**, **58**, *58*

**Cellular energy**, releasing, 70*tab*

**Cellular respiration**, **68**; carbon dioxide, 392; plant cell, 89; steps of, 69

**Cenozoic era**, Geologic time scale, *338*; ocean life, 338; Phanerozoic eon, 317, *317*; plant population, 338; seven epoch(s), 338

**Central vacuole**, cell structure, 63*tab*; large organelle in plant cell, 62

**Centromere**, **90**

**Cervix**, female reproductive organ, 507, *507*

**Champosaur**, extinct aquatic reptile, 335, *335*

**Characteristic**, physical of animal, 143, *143*

**Check.** *See* Reading Check; Visual Check

**Chemical weathering**, *287*, 287

**Chlorophyll**, 70, *70*

**Chloroplast**, **61**, *61*; cell structure, 63*tab*; DNA (deoxyribonucleic acid), 65; existing on its own, 65; photosyn-thesis, 71, *71*

**Choking**, abdominal thrust, *395*, 395; causing suffocation, 394

**Cholesterol**, damaging blood vessel, *410*; steroid, 54

**Chow chow**, phenotype, *177*

**Chromosome**, **60**; chart of, *186*, 186; G1 and G2 phase, 90; homologous, 177, *177*; human being, 60; meiosis, 128, 130, *131*; mitosis, 92; sex, 186; sheep, *60*

**Cigarette**, during pregnancy, 520

**Cilia**, **58**, *58*; cell structure, 63*tab*; female reproduction, 507

**Ciliary muscle**, *451*

**Cilium.** *See* Cilia

**Circulatory system**, **397**; pressure, 407; preventing problem(s), 402; problem(s) in, 400, *400*; Word Origin, 397; working with pulmonary system, 401, *401*

**Classification system**, classmate, 266–267*lab*; historic, 262; living things, 263*tab*, 580; modern method, 264

**Classmate**, classifying, 266–267*lab*

**Clast**, moving, 287

**Climate**, changing, 345; mass extinction, 318, 319

**Cloning, 155;** animal, 156, 161; plant, 155

**Clotting**, platelet causing, 397

**Cocaine**, during pregnancy, 520

**Cochlea, 483,** *483;* damaging, 485

**Cochlear implant**, *485,* 485, 492

**Cockroach**, Silurian period, 329

**Codominance, 185**

**Cold**, congestion, 394

**Collagen**, protein forming strong fiber, 360

**Collect Data and Make Observations**, 74, 108, 158, 192, 230, 266, 302, 342, 378, 414, 458, 490, 544. *See also* Data Collection

**Color**, deficiency, 455; pigment, 454; primary, 455; printing, 455, *455;* reflection, *441,* 441; seeing in the dark, 454*lab;* wavelength range, 439, *439*

**Color blindness**, allele, *186*

**Communicate**, oral presentations, 77, 108*lab,* 111; written reports, 751*lab,* 76, 77, 160, 161, 266, 524

**Comparative anatomy, 252**

**Complex, 184,** 474

**Compression**, amplitude, 475; forming, 474

**Compression wave**, *472,* **473;** amplitude, *475*

**Computers.** *See* Use the Internet Labs

**Concave lens**, 443, *443*

**Concentration, 401**

**Concept map**, 78, 112, 162, 196, 234, 270, 306, 346, 382, 418, 462, 469*lab,* 494, 526

**Concepts in Motion**, *63tab,* 71, 105, 131, 140, 258, 263, 363, 397, 409, 516*tab*

**Conclude.** *See* Analyze and Conclude

**Cone**, reproductive structure, *137,* 137

**Cone cell**, 451, *451;* type(s) of, 454

**Congestion**, from cold, 394

**Conifer**, gymnosperm, 137

**Connective tissue cell**, 101

**Construct**, diagrams and label, 108*lab,* 111, 414–415, 489

**Continental drift**, *257,* 257

**Continental shield**, *298,* 298

**Contract, 364**

**Contraction, 364;** of the heart, 408; muscle, 364, 365

**Convergent evolution, 259**

**Convex lens**, 443, *443;* camera, 446, *446;* forming clear image, *447;* forming image, *444,* 444, 445

**Coral**, building on skeleton, *319;* invertebrate, 328

**Cord**, umbilical, 517

**Cornea**, *451,* **451**

**Crest**, wave, *429,* 429

**Cretaceous period**, mass extinction, 320, 322; Mesozoic era, *317,* 332, *333*

**Crocodile**, evolving in Mesozoic era, 333

**Cross**, Science Use v. Common Use, 175

**Cross-pollination**, pea plant, 174, *174*

**Crystal**, forming, 286

**Cyanobacteria, 327;** releasing oxygen into atmosphere, 327

**Cyanobacterium (*Spirulina plantesis*),** photosynthetic membrane, *98*

**Cycle, 508**

**Cystic fibrosis, 188**

**Cytochrome *c*,** establishing common ancestor(s), *255,* 255

**Cytokinesis, 91,** *94*

**Cytoplasm**, cytokinesis, 91; fermentation, 69; meiosis, 130, *131; Volvox* colony, *99;* Word Origin, **59**

**Cytoskeleton**, *59,* **59;** cell structure, *63tab;* meiosis, 130, *131;* vesicle, 62

# D

**Darwin**, Charles, 210, *210;* natural selection, 216, *216;* observing geographic isolation, 259

**Data analysis**, 54*lab,* 96*lab,* 148*lab,* 176*lab,* 191*lab,* 229*lab,* 255*lab,* 300*lab,* 324*lab,* 327*lab,* 376*lab,* 402*lab,* 434*lab,* 477*lab,* 509*lab,* 519*lab*

**Data**, display. *See* Display date

**DataLab**, Can folic acid prevent birth defects?, 519; Can you identify waves in the electromagnetic spectrum?, 434; Can you see a genotype?, 191; Data Collection, 255; How can you observe DNA in a cell?, 54; How does illness affect the cardiopulmonary system?, 402; How does your garden grow?, 96; How fast do they grow?, 148; How Long Until It's All Gone?, 300; How loud and how low can you go?, 477; How many bird species live near you?, 229; Peas, Anyone?, 176; What is the mechanical advantage of a lever?, 376; What makes the best fossils?, 327; Which hormones control ovulation?, 509; Which organisms return first following a catastrophic event?, 324

**Dating**, accurate, 295

**Daughter cell, 94**

**Deccan Traps**, basalt flow in India, 321

**Decibel**, Word Origin, 476

**Decibel scale**, 476, *476*

**Decomposition**, of organism, *245,* 245

**Degrading**, habitat, 233

**Dendrochronology**, 295

**Deoxyribonucleic acid.** *See* DNA

**Deposition**, sedimentary rock, 287

**Depositional environment**, 288

**Design Your Own**, Can you apply the principles of natural selection to island species?, 230–231; Model and Invent, Build Your Own Levers, 378–379; Model and Invent, Design an Organ, 108–109; Model and Invent, Erosion Stoppers, 302–303; Model and Invent, What happens when the cardiopulmonary system breaks down?, 414–415; Use the Internet, A Healthy Pregnancy, 522–523; Use the Internet, What makes you unique?, 192–193

**Developing**, cell cycle, 88; external, 146, *146;* human being, 51; internal, 148; Quino checkerspot butterfly, *51*

**Devonian period**, mass extinction, 319; Paleozoic era, *317*

**Diaphragm**, 393, *393,* 402; moving in chest cavity, 407

**Diatom**, reproducing asexually, 153, *153*

**Dichotomous key**, creating, 264*lab*

**Differentiate, 154**

**Differentiated Human Cells**, *102*

**Diffuse reflection**, *441,* 441

**Dinosaur**, evolving in Triassic period, 333; Mesozoic era, 317, *317*

***Diplodocus,*** becoming extinct, 337; Triassic period, 334

**Diploid**, generation, 135; plant, *139*

**Diploid cell**, creating, *129;* human body, 134; maintaining, 129; meiosis, 132

**Diploid moss generation**, *135*

**Display data**, 54*lab,* 74*lab,* 76, 96*lab,* 148*lab*

**Dissecting**, cow eye, 458*lab*

**Diversity**, evolution, 217

**Diversity of Life: Classification of Living Organisms**, 580

**DNA (deoxyribonucleic acid)**, chloroplast, 65; chromosome, 60, 177; genetic information, 54; mitochondria, 65; observing in a cell, 54*lab;* organism, 264; prokaryotic cell, 64

**Dog**, gestation, 148; hearing sound, 486, 486; selective breeding, 214; skeletal system, *106*

# Index

**Dog whistle**, hearing, 477

**Dolan, Tom,** athlete with asthma, 396

**Dolly,** sheep cloning, *156,* 156

**Dolphin,** echolocation, 486

**Dominance,** type(s) of, 184–185; Word Origin, 185

**Dominant, 175**

**Dove,** selective breeding, *214*

**Dragonfly,** Silurian period, 329

**Draw conclusions.** *See* Analyze and Conclude

**Drift,** continental, 257

**Drugs,** during pregnancy, 520

**Duck-billed platypus,** external development, 146, *146*

## E

**Ear,** detecting sound, *480;* detecting sound wave, 477; function of, 478; hearing dog whistle, 477; hearing sound, 476, 481, *481,* 489*lab;* structure(s) of, *481. See also* Inner ear; Middle ear; Outer ear

**Eardrum,** 481, *481. See also* Tympanic membrane

**Earth,** age of, 293, 297; changing, 292*lab;* studying rock, 304; surface, 281*lab*

**Echo, 486**

**Echolocation,** 486

***E. coli,*** prokaryotic cell, *65;* reproducing asexually, 152

**Ectotherm,** 334

**Ediacaran fauna,** soft-bodied organism, 328

**Effort force,** 369, *373,* 373

**Egg, 126;** chromosome, 129, *129;* embryo, 146, *146;* external development, *146,* 146; female reproduction, 507, *507;* producing, *508,* 508; sexual reproduction disadvantage, 128

**Ejaculation,** pathway of sperm, 505

**Elasmosaurus,** extinct aquatic reptile, *335,* 335

**Electromagnetic spectrum,** 430, *431;* identifying wave(s), 434*lab*

**Electromagnetic wave,** 430; transferring energy, 435

**Electron,** *294,* 294

**Electron microscope,** 49, *49*

**Element,** 294

**Elephant,** gestation, 148

**Elephant seal,** dominance, *128*

**Embryo, 136,** *139,* 515; developing, 254, *515,* 515; developing animal, 146; evidence of evolution, *254;* implanting, 509

**Embryology,** 254

**Emit, 428**

**Endometrium,** 507; embryo implanting, *515,* 515; thickening, *509,* 509

**Endoplasmic reticulum,** attaching to, 60; cell structure, 63*tab*

**Endotherm,** 334

**Energy, 68,** 435; carrying sound wave, 476, *476;* glycolysis, 68; light, 52, *61,* 61; processing, *61,* 61; Science Use v. Common Use, 52; transferring, *52;* wave carrying, *428,* 428

**Environment,** affecting phenotype, 188, 189; changing, 220; depositional, 288; factor affecting population growth, 215; living and nonliving things, *50,* 50

**Environmental Standards,** correlations to, crop pollination, 139; dispersal of seeds, 140–141; genetic diversity, 225; invasive exotic organisms, 225; natural vegetation pollination, 139–141

**Eocene epoch,** Geologic time scale, *338;* primate, grass and flowering plant evolving, 338

**Epididymis, 505;** male reproductive organ, *504*

**Epoch,** division of era, 317

**Era,** 317

**Erectile tissue,** male reproductive organ, *504*

**Erosion,** mountain, *285,* 285; stopping, 302–303*lab*

**Escherichia bacteria,** prokaryotic cell, 64

**Establish, 90**

**Estrogen,** regulating female reproductive cycle, 511

**Eukaryote, 126;** meiosis, 128; reproducing asexually, 152; sexual reproduction, 127; single-cell organism, 99

**Eukaryotic,** Word Origin, 65

**Eukaryotic cell, 64,** *65,* 88; yeast, 65

**Eustachian tube,** *482,* 482

**Event,** unscrambling, 313*lab*

**Evidence, 70**

**Evolution, 210,** 244; biological evidence of, 210–227, 252–256; classifying organism, 265; diversity, 217; early hypothesis, 269; natural selection, 252; observing, 268; of life on Earth, 244–260, 325–339

**Evolutionary biologist,** 232

**Evolution museum,** Galápagos Island, 269

**Exercise,** preventing disease, 402; triggering asthma, 396

**Exhalation,** 393, *393;* pressure during, 407, *407*

**Exploring,** the unknown, 74–75*lab*

**Exposed, 446**

**Extension,** 366

**External, 481**

**External development,** egg, 146, *146*

**External ear,** 481, *481*

**External fertilization,** 145, *145*

**Extinct, 224,** 325

**Extinction,** causing, 224–226, 226*tab;* Devonian period, 319; fossil record, 322; habitat, 233; mass, **318,** *318;* pattern, 323; Permian Period, 330, *330;* reptile, 335. *See also* Mass extinction

**Eye,** dissecting cow, 458*lab;* forming image, 450, *450;* part(s) of, 451–453, *453,* 453*tab;* working like a camera, *450,* 450

**Eyeglasses,** correcting vision, *456,* 456; inventing, 461

## F

**Factor,** 175

**Fallopian tube, 507;** female reproductive organ, *507*

**Fantailed pigeon,** selective breeding, *214*

**Farsightedness,** *456,* 456

**Fat,** lipid, 54

**Female reproductive structure,** 136

**Female reproductive system,** *507,* 507; organs of, 507

**Fermentation, 69**

**Fern,** growing, *135*

**Fertilization, 126,** 512; angiosperm life cycle, 139; animal, 144; controlling in pea plant, 174; external, 145, *145;* gestation, 148; internal, 145; life cycle of flowering plant, *139;* mitosis, 135; Science Use v. Common Use, 512; self-, *174,* 174; sexual reproduction, 128

**Fetal alcohol syndrome (FAS),** *520,* 520

**Fetus, 516;** developing, *515,* 515, 517; drugs and alcohol, 520; health, 517; nutrition, 518

**Filament, 138,** *139;* muscle, 364, 365, *365*

**Finch,** 212, *212, 213,* 213

**First-class lever, 370,** 371*tab;* human body, 372

**First trimester,** pregnancy, 516, 516*tab*

**Fish,** age, 345; bony, 329

**Fission,** asexual reproduction, 152; bacterium growing, *152;* Word Origin, 152

**Flagella**, 58, cell structure, 63*tab;* prokaryotic cell, 64

**Flexible**, 361, 451

**Flexion**, 366

**Flower**, anatomy of, 139; of common plant, 140*tab;* reproducing, *138,* 138

**Flowering plant**, life cycle, *139*

**Flowerless seed plant**, reproducing, 137

**Fluid**, building up in lung, 394

**Focal length**, 444

**Focal point**, 444

**Foldables**, 45, 85, 123, 169, 207, 241, 281, 313, 357, 389, 425, 469, 501

**Folic acid**, during pregnancy, 519; preventing birth defect, 519*lab*

**Follicle**, *508,* 508; Word Origin, 508

**Food**, healthy for pregnancy, *518,* 518; transforming to energy, 68

**Food web**, transferring energy, *52*

**Force**, 369

**Fossil**, *244, 244,* 284; age, 249; dinosaur, 334; forming, 245, *245, 246, 246,* 249*lab;* index, 316; index criteria, 316*tab;* original-material, 248, *248;* plant as carbon film, *247,* 247; record, 289; recording history, 325; relative age, 289; supporting evolution, *252*

**Fossil record**, 250; extinction rate, 322

**Frequency**, *429, 429;* detecting in inner ear, 483, *483;* hearing sound, 475; pitch, 477; sound wave, 473

**Frill-backed pigeon**, selective breeding, *214*

**Frog**, evolving in Mesozoic era, 333; external, *145;* external fertilization, 145

**Fruit**, 139, *139;* of common plant, 140, 140*tab*

**Fulcrum**, 368; Word Origin, 369

**Fungi.** *See* Fungus

**Fungus**, pneumonia, 394

## G

**Galápagos Islands**, evolution museum, 269

**Galápagos tortoise**, 212

**Garden**, growing, 96*lab*

**Gas**, in atmosphere, *321,* 321; basalt flow, 321; causing suffocation, 394; exchange, 401

**Gender**, sex chromosome, *186,* 186

**Gene**, 177; determining horse coat color, 187, *187;* trait, 187

**Generation**, 211; alternating, 134, *134;* diploid, 135; haploid, 135; pedigree, *184,* 184; trait skipping, 172

**Genetic disorder**, 188; human, 188*tab*

**Genetic diversity**, losing, 225

**Genetic material**, blending inheritance, 172; guinea pig, 126, 127

**Genetics**, Mendel, Gregor, 173; Word Origin, 173

**Genetic testing**, 232

**Genetic variation**, 215, *215;* California poppy plant, 127

**Genome**, 54

**Genotype**, 177; Punnett square, 182; ratio of, *183;* representing, 178; seeing, 191*lab;* type of, *178,* 178

**Geographic isolation**, 259

**Geologic processes**, 284–285

**Geologic time scale**, 316; determining beginning and ending of unit, 318, *318;* radiometric dating, 344; used today, *317,* 317

**Geology**, 284–291, 293–299

**Gestation**, 148

**Gliding joint**, 362, 363*tab*

**Global**, 319

**Global cooling**, asteroid, 322; basalt flow, 321; mass extinction, 320

**Global warming**, mass extinction, 319

**Glycolysis**, 68

**Golgi apparatus**, 62, *62;* cell structure, 63*tab*

**Golden retriever**, mating, *127*

**Gold Rush**, 305

**Gondwanaland**, resulting from Pangaea splitting, 332, **332**

**Graph**, average growth of cuttings, 159*lab;* average growth of seedlings, 159*lab;* changing systolic blood pressure, 413*act;* dependent variables, 404*lab;* growing fetus, 148*lab;* half-life, 300*lab;* hormone controlling menstrual cycle, 509*lab;* human trait, 193*lab;* vital signs, 404*lab*

**Grass**, evolving in Eocene epoch, 338

**Gravity**, moving clast, 287

**Green algae**, first plant developing, 330

**Ground finch**, *213,* 213

**Growing**, cell cycle, 88; garden, 96*lab;* human being, 51; Quino checkerspot butterfly, *51*

**Growth phase**, interphase, *88,* 88

**Guinea pig**, genetic material, *126,* 126, 127

**Gymnast**, using major muscle group, *372*

**Gymnosperm**, 337; reproducing, 137

## H

**Habitat**, 219; degradation and extinction, 233; losing, 224

**Hadeon eon**, Precambrian time, *317,* 326

**Hair**, bending in cochlea, *484,* 484

**Hales, Reverend Stephen**, measuring blood pressure of horse, 417

**Hale telescope**, *448*

**Half-life**, 296; radioactive isotope, 296*tab*

**Hammer.** *See* Malleus

**Handbook(s).** *See* Glossary; Math Skill Handbook; Credits; Reference Handbook; Science Skill Handbook; Technology Skill Handbook

**Haploid**, generation, 135, *139;* Word Origin, 129

**Haploid cell**, angiosperm life cycle, 139; creating, 129, *129*

**Hawaii**, basalt flow, *321, 321*

**Hearing**, animal, 490–491*lab;* damaging, 476, 485; mammal, *486,* 486; range, 477*tab*

**Hearing aid**, 485

**Heart**, 398; pulmonary system, *392;* pumping in one direction, 408, *409,* 409; transplant, 416

**Heart attack**, 400, *400*

**Hemoglobin**, 53*tab;* red blood cell, 398

**Heredity**, 172; maternal, 187; polygenic, 187; sex-linked, 186; trait, *176,* 176

**Heroin**, during pregnancy, 520

**Hertz**, measuring frequency, 473

**Heterozygous**, 178; Word Origin, 178

**Hinge joint**, 362, 363*tab*

**History.** *See* Real World Science

**HIV.** *See* Human immunodeficiency virus

*HMS Beagle,* 210; voyage, 211, *211*

**Holocene epoch**, Quaternary period, *317,* 317

**Homeostasis**, 51; maintaining, 53

**Hominid group**, evolving in Cenozoic era, 338

**Homologous**, Word Origin, 89, 253

**Homologous chromosomes**, 89, 129; allele of gene, 177, *177;* separating, *178,* 178

**Homologous structure**, *253,* 253

*Homo sapien,* hominid group, 338

**Homozygous**, 178; separating, *179,* 179; Word Origin, 178

**Hormone**, 509; controlling ovulation, 509*lab;* regulating body function, 510–511

**Horse**, blood pressure, 417

**Human being**, Cenozoic era, 317, *317;* gestation, 148; growing, 51

**Human body**, joint(s) in, 362, 363*tab;* lever, 371*tab*

**Human cell**, differentiated, 101

**Human ear.** *See* Ear

**Human immunodeficiency virus (HIV),** 520

**Human organ.** *See* organ; organ system

**Human sexual activity,** 505

**Hutton, James,** *284;* uniformitarianism, 285

**Hybrid,** 175

**Hybridization,** systematics, 264

**Hydra,** reproducing, *153,* 153

**Hypertension, 410**

**Hypothesis,** asteroid hitting Earth during Cretaceous period, 322; changing heart rate and breathing rate, 389*lab;* forming, 74*lab,* 108*lab,* 158*lab,* 193*lab,* 230*lab,* 266*lab,* 302*lab,* 324*lab,* 342*lab,* 378*lab,* 414*lab,* 490*lab,* 522*lab;* photosynthesis of a leaf, 73*lab*

## I

**Iceberg,** breaking off glacier, *320*

**Ichthyosaur,** extinct aquatic reptile, 335, *335*

**Igneous rock,** *286,* 286; radiometric dating, 297

**Illegal drugs,** during pregnancy, 520

**Image,** changing, 444*lab;* forming by a convex lens, 444, *444,* 445

**Immovable joint,** 362, 363*tab*

**Immune system,** 520; fighting infection, 397. *See* Human immunodeficiency virus (HIV)

**Implant,** cochlear, *485,* 485, 492

**Incomplete dominance, 185**

**Incus,** *482,* **482**

**Independent assortment,** law of, **176,** 179

**Index fossil, 316;** criteria, 316*tab*

**Infant,** premature, 517

**Infection,** fighting, 397; pneumonia, *394,* 394

**Inhalation,** *393,* 393; pressure during, *407,* 407

**Inheritance,** maternal, 187; polygenic, **187**

**Inherited trait,** 175

**Inner ear,** *483,* 483; comparing to tape recorder, *480;* detecting different frequencies of sound, 481; processing sound wave, 480; structure(s) of, *481*

**Instrument,** playing in tune, 474

**Insulin,** 53*tab*

**Internal development,** 148

**Internal fertilization,** 145

**Internet.** *See* Science Online; Using the Internet

**Interphase, 88;** cellular respiration, 89; onion root cell, *89;* phase(s) of, 90; stage(s) of, 91*tab*

**Interpret,** 220

**Invertebrate,** Mesozoic era, 333

**Invertebrate marine organism,** Paleozoic era, *317,* 317

**Invertebrate organism,** Proterozoic eon, 328

**Involuntary muscle,** 364

**Ion,** in blood, 397

**Iris,** *451,* **451**

**Iron,** forming fossil, 247

**Islets of Langerhans,** 511

**Isolation,** 258; geographic, 259; observing geographic, 259

**Isotope, 294;** radioactive decay, 296

**Italy,** Mt. Vesuvius eruption, 320

## J

**Jelly,** invertebrate, 328

**Joint, 361;** human body, 363*tab;* type(s) of, 362; Word Origin, 361

**Joyner-Kersee, Jackie,** athlete with asthma, 396

**Jurassic period,** Mesozoic era, 332, *333*

## K

**Kalanchoe plant,** propagating, 154, *154*

**Kangaroo,** gestation, 148, *148*

**Karyotype,** *60*

**Keratin,** 53*tab*

**Kingdom,** determining, 263

**Kudzu plant,** growing rapidly, *225;* preventing erosion, 225

## L

**Lab,** Can a cow teach you about your eyes?, 458–459; Classifying the Students in Your Class, 266–267; DataLab, 54, 96, 148, 176, 191, 229, 255, 300, 324, 327, 376, 402, 434, 477, 509, 519; Design Your Own, 522–523, 192–193, 230–231, 378–379, 108–109, 302–303, 414–415; Exploring the Unknown, 74–75; Launch Lab, 45, 85, 123, 169, 207, 241, 281, 313, 357, 389, 425, 469, 501; MiniLab, 65, 103, 132, 249, 327, 444; Plant Propagation, 158–159; Try at Home DataLab, 96, 148, 176, 191, 229, 255, 324, 376, 404, 434, 477, 509, 519; Try at Home Launch Lab, 313; Try at Home MiniLab, 73, 228, 264, 292, 340, 366, 412, 438, 454, 489; Use the Internet, Animal Hearing, 490–491; Use the Internet, How has California changed over geologic time?, 342–343

**Labia,** female reproductive organ, *507*

**Labyrinth,** inner ear, 483

**Lactic acid fermentation,** 69

**Ladybug,** metamorphosis, 147, *147*

**Language Arts Standards,** correlations to, 55, 66, 72, 86, 95, 107, 133, 142, 149, 157, 180, 190, 193*lab,* 207, 217, 227, 241, 251, 256, 260, 265, 273, 291, 299, 313, 314, 323, 331, 339, 343, 367, 375, 385, 389, 403, 411, 415, 432, 442, 449, 457, 460, 461, 465, 478, 488, 497, 501, 513, 521

**Larynx,** breathing, 393

**Launch Lab,** Can you make an animal evolve?, 241; Can you make a rainbow?, 425; Does your pulse change?, 389; How are events unscrambled?, 313; How does reproduction happen?, 123; How many sounds can you make?, 469; How well can you predict?, 169; Is it a boy or a girl?, 501; Is it easy to lift?, 357; What are we made of?, 45; What attracts insects to certain flowers?, 207; What is Earth's surface life?, 281; When is division not a math problem?, 85

**Laurasia,** resulting from Pangaea splitting, 332, **332**

**Lava,** flowing across Hawaii, 321, *321*

**Law of independent assortment, 176,** 179

**Law of reflection, 440,** *440;* obeying, 441

**Law of segregation, 176,** 178

**Layering,** rock, *289,* 289

**Leaf,** differentiated cell, 102, *102;* tissue layer(s), 104, *104*

**Lens, 443,** *451;* changing shape, 451, *451*

**Lesson Review,** 55, 66, 72, 95, 107, 133, 142, 149, 157, 180, 190, 217, 227, 251, 256, 260, 265, 291, 299, 323, 331, 339, 367, 375, 403, 411, 432, 442, 449, 457, 478, 488, 513, 521

**Levels of organization.** *See* Organization, levels of

**Lever, 368;** advantage in the body, 372; building, 378–379*lab;* class(es) of, 369, 370; human body, 371*tab,* 374; mechanical advantage, 373; seesaw, *368;* speed advantage, 374; Word Origin, 369

**Life**, ancient, *317, 317*; middle, 317, *317*; recent, 317, *317*

**Life cycle**, flowering plant, *139*; of organism, 245, *245*

**Life stage**, generation, *134*

**Ligament**, connecting bone(s), 361, *361*

**Light**, angle of incidence of, 440; angle of reflection of, 440; bending, *443, 444*; changing direction, *438*, 438; interacting with matter, 435, 436, *436*; speed, *437*, 437; traveling, 430, *430*; visible, 431

**Lightbulb**, inventing, 461

**Light energy**, making plant food, 52, *61*, 61

**Lighting technician**, 460

**Light microscope**, **48**, 49

**Light ray**, bending, 443; obeying law of reflection, 441; reflecting, *440*, 440

**Light wave**, 428, *428*; absorbing energy, 435; law of reflection, *440*, 440; striking retina, 454

**Linnaeus, Carolus,** classification system, 262

**Lion**, physical characteristic, *143*

**Lipid**, 54

**Lithification**, **288**

**Lithospheric plate**, **257**

**Liver cell**, *100*; filtering blood, 100

**Living things**, classifying, 263*tab*

**Loudness**, **475**; brain determining, *484*, 484

**Lung**, 393, *402*; gas exchange, 402; pulmonary system, *392*

**Lysosome**, cell structure, 63*tab*; vacuole in animal cell, 62

# M

**Machines**, simple and joints, 362

**Macromolecule**, 53

**Magma**, forming crystal, 286

**Magnifying glass**, 443

**Main Idea**, 48, 56, 68, 88, 98, 126, 134, 143, 151, 172, 182, 210, 219, 244, 252, 257, 262, 284, 293, 316, 325, 332, 360, 368, 392, 405, 428, 435, 443, 450, 472, 480, 504, 515. *See also* Understanding Main Ideas

**Male reproductive structure**, 136

**Malleus**, *482*, **482**

**Mammal**, developing embryo, *146*, 146; evolving in Mesozoic era, 333, *336*, 336; hearing sound, 486, *486*; Mesozoic era, *317*, 317; physical characteristic, 143

**Map**, continental shield, *298*. *See also* Concept map

**Marijuana**, during pregnancy, 520

**Marine organism**, Invertebrate, 317, *317*

**Mass extinction**, **318**, *318*; asteroid, 318, 322; climate change, 318, 319; Cretaceous period, 320, 322; Devonian period, 319; global cooling, 320; global warming, 319; Permian Period, 321, *330*, 330; Triassic period, 337

**Maternal inheritance**, 187

**Mathematics.** *See* Applying Math

**Matter**, interacting with light, 435, *437*, 437

**Mechanical advantage**, **373**; of lever, 376*lab*

**Medium**, **430**; Science Use v. Common Use, 430

**Meiosis**, **504**; animal, 144, *144*; cell division, 508; chromosome, *129*, 129; comparing to mitosis, 132, 132*tab*; diploid parent cell, 132; eukaryote, 128; phase(s) of, 130, *131*; Word Origin, 128

**Melatonin**, 510

**Membrane**, cell, 56, 57, *57*; Word Origin, 482

**Mendel, Gregor,** controlling fertilization, 174; father of genetics, 173

**Menopause**, 512

**Menstrual cycle**, *508*, **508**; thickening endometrium, *509*, 509

**Menstrual flow**, *509*, 509

**Mesozoic era**, 332, *333*; flowering plant, *337*; invertebrate, 333; Phanerozoic eon, 317, *317*; plant population, 337

**Metamorphic rock**, *286*, 286; determining age, 297

**Metamorphosis**, Word Origin, **147**

**Metaphase**, mitosis, *92*, *93*, 508; meiosis I and II, 130, *131*

**Meteorite**, age of, 341*act*; killing dinosaur(s), *322*; radiometric dating, 298

**Method**, **174**

**Mexico**, Yucatan Peninsula, *322*, 322

**Microfossil**, *244*

**Microphone**, comparing to outer ear, 480, *480*

**Microscope**, convex lens, 448, *448*; electron, *49*, 49; light, **48**, 49; modern, 49; use and care of, 579

**Middle ear**, containing eardrum, 481, *481*; passing sound wave, *480*, 480; structure(s) of, *482*, 482

**Middle life**, Mesozoic era, 317, *317*

**Mimicry**, species to species, *222*; structural adaptation, 222

**Mineral**, calcium, 360; depositing, *247*, 247; history of gold, 305

**MiniLab**, How can you create a dichotomous key?, 264; How can you model a cell?, 65; How can your population have the strongest, longest-lasting survivors?, 228; How can you see photosynthesis?, 73; How do bones and muscles interact?, 366; How does an ear hear?, 489; How does Earth Change over time?, 292; How does Earth change over time?, 327; How does the cardiopulmonary system work?, 412; How does the image change?, 444; How do fossils form?, 249; How do you see colors in the dark?, 454; What does Meiosis look like?, 132; What happened here?, 340; What is the mechanical advantage of a lever?, 376; What's in a tissue?, 103; Why does the pencil look broken?, 438

**Mirror**, regular reflection, 441

**Mitochondria**, 360; cell, 61; cell structure, 63*tab*; cellular respiration, 69; DNA (deoxyribonucleic acid), 65; existing on its own, 65; muscle cell, 364, 365, *365*; trait inheritance, *187*

**Mitosis**, **91**, 134; cell division, 153; comparing to meiosis, 132, 132*tab*; diploid parent cell, 132; meiosis, 130; phase(s) of, 92, *93*; result of, 94; Word Origin, 91

**Mitotic cell division**, asexual reproduction, 153

**Mitotic phase**, reproduction, 88, *88*; stage(s) of, 91*tab*

**Model and Invent.** *See* Design Your Own, Model and Invent

**Modify**, 62

**Mold**, 248, *248*

**Molecular biology**, 255

**Molecule**, amino acid, 53; cell, 52; macromolecule, 53; passing through cell, *57*, 57; protein, 53; sugar, 54; water, *53*

**Moon**, radiometric dating, 298; surface, *298*

**Mosasaur**, extinct aquatic reptile, 335, *335*

**Moss**, growing, *135*; life cycle, 135

**Motion**, Concepts in. *See* Concepts in Motion

**Mountain**, erosion, 285

**Mount St. Helens**, volcanic eruption, *320*

**Mouse**, gestation, 148
**Mouth**, breathing, 393
**Mt. Vesuvius**, volcanic eruption, 320
**Mucus**, causing infection, 394
**Multiple allele, 185**
**Muscle**, 101, **364;** contraction, 364, 365; fiber contracting, 103; heart, 408; interacting with bone, 366*lab;* opposing, 366, *366;* type(s) of, 364
**Muscle cell**, 101
**Muscle tissue**, type(s) of, 364
**Musculoskeletal system**, 360–367
**Music**, loudness, 475
**Musical instrument**, playing in tune, 474
**Mutation, 182**

**Naturalist, 210**
**Natural Selection**, 213, **216;** applying to island species, 230–231*lab;* caused by environmental change, 220; Darwin theory, 215; step(s) of, 216; theory of evolution, 252
**Navel**, 517
**Nearsightedness**, 456, *456*
**Negative end**, water molecule, 53
**Neogene period**, Tertiary period, 317, *317*
**Nerve cell**, 56*;* muscle contracting, 364; signaling, 56
**Network, 144**
**Neutron**, 294, *294*
**Nicotine**, during pregnancy, 520
**Noise ordinance**, 493
**Nose**, breathing, 393
**Nucleic acid, 54**
**Nucleotide**, long chain of molecule(s), 54
**Nucleus, 60,** *294;* cell structure, 63*tab;* cell type, 64; meiosis, 130, *131;* mitosis, 91; muscle fiber, 364; radiation, 294
**Nutrition**, fetal, 518; for pregnancy, *518*

**Offspring**, potential, *183,* 183
**One-trait model**, 183, *183*
**Oocyte**, 508
**Optical, 443**
**Optical instrument**, type(s) of, 446–448
**Optic nerve**, *451*
**Ordinance**, noise, 493
**Ordovician era**, iceberg breaking off glacier, *320*

**Ordovician Period**, Geologic time scale, *317;* mass extinction, 320; ocean floor, 329, *329*
**Organ, 104,** 143, 450; animal reproductive, 143, 144; designing, 108–109*lab;* female reproductive, 507, *507;* male reproductive, 504, *504. See also* Organ system
**Organelle**, 59
**Organism**, adapting, 220; alternating diploid and haploid generation, 134; ancient, 327; asexual reproduction, 151; classifying, 262, 736; decomposing, 64, 245, *245,* 246; DNA, 264; functioning, *106;* genetic material, 126; growing, 51; increasing in complexity, 328; invertebrate, 328; invertebrate marine, 317, *317;* maintaining homeostasis, 51; moving by cilia, 58; multicellular, 100, 106; organizing, 50; phenotype, 177; prokaryote, 98; protein functioning in, 53; reproducing, 51; single cell, *64;* soft-bodied, 328; surviving Permian mass extinction, 332; *Volvox* colony, *99*
**Organization**, characteristic of life, 50; for structure and function, 98–99; levels of, 103–107
**Organ system, 105,** 105*tab;* depending on other organ(s), 106, *106. See also* Organ
**Origin**, Word. *See* Word Origin
**Original-material fossil**, *248,* 248
**Outer ear**, *481;* collecting sound wave, 480, 481; comparing to microphone, *480*
**Oval window**, 483
**Ovary**, 138, *139;* angiosperm life cycle, 139; female reproductive organ, *507;* producing estrogen and progesterone, 511
**Ovulation, 508,** *508, 509,* 509; hormone controlling, 509*lab*
**Ovule, 136;** angiosperm life cycle, 139
**Owen, Sir Richard,** anti-evolutionist, 233
**Oxygen**, decrease in level of, 319; level in Earth's early atmosphere, 326; photosynthesis, 71; pulmonary system, *392,* 392; supplying body, *401,* 401; transporting within blood, 398, 399, *399*
**Ozone**, increasing, 327; during Precambrian time, *326*

**P**

**Paleogene period**, Tertiary period, 317, *317*

**Paleontologist, 244**
**Paleontology**, 316; Word Origin, 245
**Paleozoic era**, Geologic time scale, *328;* invertebrate, 329; ocean floor, 329, *329;* Phanerozoic eon, *317,* 317; plant, 330
**Pancreas**, 511
**Pangaea**, land mass splitting, **332,** 332
**Parasite**, pneumonia, 394
**Parathyroid gland**, 511
**Parthenogenesis**, Ernest Everett Just, 161
**Peacock**, physical characteristic, *143*
**Pea plant**, phenotype, 178; trait, 177; trait(s) of, 173, *173*
**Pedigree**, 182, *184,* **184**
**Penis, 505;** male reproductive organ, *504*
**Pennsylvanian period**, amniote, 329; Geologic time scale, *317*
**Percentage**, calculating cells with visible DNA, 54*lab;* calculating phenotype, 191*lab;* cells in mitosis and cell division, 96*lab;* probability in inheritance, 181*act*
**Period, 410;** division of era, 317
**Periodic Table of the Elements, 584**
**Permian Period**, Geologic time scale, *317;* mass extinction, 321, 330, *330*
**Permineralization, 246;** leg bone, *246*
**Petrified wood**, fossilizing tree, *246,* 246
**Phanerozoic eon**, era(s) within, 317, *317*
**Pharynx**, *402;* breathing, 393
**Phenotype**, 177; environment, 188; pedigree indicating, 184; Punnett square, 182; ratio of, *183*
**Phospholipid**, lipid, 54
**Phosphorus**, keeping bone(s) hard, 361
**Photosynthesis, 70;** cellular respiration, *71;* cyanobacterium (*Spirulina plantesis*), 98; diatom, 153; making oxygen, 71; seeing, 73; Word Origin, 71
**Photosynthetic membrane**, cyanobacterium (*Spirulina plantesis*), 98
**Physical weathering**, 287, *287*
**Pig**, guinea, 126, *126,* 127
**Pigeon**, selective breeding, *214*
**Pigment, 454**
**Pigmentation**, 70, *70*
**Pistil, 138,** *139;* angiosperm life cycle, 139
**Pitch, 477**
**Pituitary gland**, 510
**Pivot joint**, 362, 363*tab*
**Pivot point**, 372
**Placenta, 517**
**Plane**, changing pressure, 482

**Plant**, breeding, 127; California poppy, 127; cloning, 155; common, 140*tab;* cutting, 154; disease-free, 160; evolving, *259,* 259; flowering, 338; fossil, 247, *247;* kalanchoe, 154, *154;* kudzu, *225,* 225; life cycle, *134,* 134, *139;* Paleozoic era, 330; reproducing, 142; selective breeding, 127, 214; using light energy for food, 52

**Plant anatomy**, 135–137

**Plant cell**, *49;* cellular respiration, 89; cytokinesis, *94;* differentiating, 102; Golgi apparatus, *62,* 62; onion root, 89, *89;* shape, 56; wall, *58,* 58; xylem, *56*

**Plant organ**, 104

**Plant tissue**, *103*

**Plant tissue culture**, 155, *155*

**Plasma**, level in blood, 397

**Platelet**, 101; function, 397, 397*tab*

**Plate tectonics**, relating to evolution, 257, 260

**Platypus**, duck-billed, *146,* 146

**Pleistocene epoch**, Quaternary period, 317, *317*

**Plesiosaur**, extinct aquatic reptile, 335, *335*

**Pneumonia, 394;** lung with, *394*

**Poinsettia**, asexual reproduction, *151,* 151

**Pollen grain, 136**

**Pollen tube,** *139,* **139**

**Pollination,** 136; cross-, *174,* 174

**Pollution**, triggering asthma, 396

**Polonium**, 294, *294*

**Polygenic inheritance, 187**

**Poppy plant**, genetic variation, 127

**Population, 210;** environmental factor, 215; growing, 215; strongest, long-lasting survivor, 228*lab*

**Portion, 326**

**Positive end**, water molecule, 53

**Precambrian time**, fossil record, 325; Geologic time scale, *317,* 326

**Pregnancy, 516;** avoiding harmful substance(s), 519, *519;* healthy, 522–523*lab;* stage(s) of, 516*tab*

**Premature**, birth, 517

**Prenatal care, 518**

**Prescription drug**, during pregnancy, 520

**Pressure, 405;** changes in, 482; changing, 406; contraction of heart, 408; equation for finding, 406; pulmonary system, 407, *407;* Science Use v. Common Use, 406; toe in ballerina, 406. *See also* Blood pressure

**Primary, 439**

**Primate, 338**

**Printing**, color, *455,* 455

**Prism**, refracting light, 439, *439*

**Probability**, in inheritance, 181*act*

**Process, 50**

**Progesterone**, regulating female reproductive cycle, 511

**Prohibit, 259**

**Prokaryote, 151;** reproducing asexually, 152; single-cell organism, 98

**Prokaryotic cell,** *64,* **64,** 98; E. coli, *65*

**Propagating**, plant, 154, *154,* 158*lab*–159

**Prophase**, mitotis, *92, 93,* 508; meiosis I and II, 130, *131*

**Prostate gland**, male reproductive organ, *504*

**Protein, 53;** in blood, 397; chromosome, 177; collagen, 360; hemoglobin, 398; muscle contracting, *365;* type(s) of, 53*tab*

**Proterozoic eon**, invertebrate organism, 328; Precambrian time, *317,* 326

**Protist,** 99; *Volvox,* 99, *99*

**Proton**, 294, *294*

**Pterosaur, 333;** skimming water, *333*

**Puberty**, female, 508; male, 506

**Pulmonary system, 392,** *392;* pressure in, *407,* 407; preventing problem(s), 402; problem(s) of, 394; working with circulatory system, 401, *401*

**Pulse**, changing, 389*lab*

**Punnett square, 182,** *183,* 183

**Pupil, 451,** *451*

**Pyrite**, forming fossil, 247

### Q

**Quaternary period**, Cenozoic era, *317,* 317

**Quino checkerspot butterfly**, changing, 51, *51*

### R

**Radiation, 293**

**Radioactive decay**, 294

**Radiometric dating**, 297, 344, age of meteorite and moon, 298; calculating absolute age, 297; lab setting, *297*

**Rainbow**, making, 425*lab*

**Rainwater**, dissolving limestone, 287, *287*

**Range, 431**

**Rarefaction,** *473;* forming, 474

**Ratio**, calculating peas, 176*lab*

**Ray**, of light, *440,* 440

**Reading Check**, 50, 52, 54, 59, 61, 64, 89, 91, 92, 94, 105, 127, 128, 135, 147, 148, 152, 155, 173, 177, 179, 184, 187, 212, 215, 221, 223, 224, 245, 247, 249, 250, 255, 263, 287, 288, 293, 296, 319, 321, 326, 327, 333, 361, 362, 364, 366, 369, 370, 372, 374, 393, 394, 396, 398, 401, 402, 405, 407, 408, 410, 429, 437, 440, 441, 447, 448, 451, 454, 472, 474, 476, 480, 482, 484, 486, 504, 506, 508, 515, 517, 518, 520

**Real-World Reading Connection**, 48, 56, 68, 88, 98, 126, 134, 143, 151, 172, 182, 210, 219, 244, 252, 257, 262, 284, 293, 316, 325, 332, 360, 368, 392, 405, 428, 435, 443, 450, 472, 480, 504, 515

**Real World Science**, 76–77, 110–111, 160–161, 194–195, 232–233, 268–269, 304–305, 344–345, 380–381, 416–417, 460–461, 492–493, 524–525

**Recent life**, Cenozoic era, 317, *317*

**Recessive, 175**

**Record**, fossil, 289

**Recorder**, taping sound, 480, *480*

**Red blood cell**, 101; function, 397, 397*tab;* hemoglobin, 398

**Reference Handbook**, Diversity of Life: Classification of Living Organisms, 580, Periodic Table of the Elements, 584; Use and Care of a Microscope, 579; Using a Calculator, 576; Understanding Scientific Terms, 577

**Reflecting telescope**, forming magnified image, *447,* 447

**Reflection**, angle of, 440; color, 441, *441;* law of, *440,* 440

**Refracting telescope**, 447; forming clear image, *447*

**Refraction, 438;** moving light through prism, 439, *439*

**Regeneration, 154**

**Regular reflection**, 441, *441*

**Relative age, 289;** fossil, 289

**Relaxation, 364**

**Replacement**, permineralization, 247

**Reproduce**, Science Use v. Common Use, 128

**Reproducing**, cell cycle, 88

**Reproduction**, animal, 149; asexual, 151; disadvantage, 128; organ(s) of, 144; sexual, 126

**Reproductive phase**, mitotic phase, *88,* 88

**Reproductive structure**, 136

# Index

**Reproductive system**, female, *507, 507;* male, *504,* 504

**Reptile**, evolving in Mesozoic era, 333; extinction, 335

**Resistance force**, 369

**Respiration, 392,** 402

**Respiratory cell**, 58

**Rest position**, wave, *429, 429*

**Retina, 452,** *451;* light wave striking, 454

**Review.** *See* Lesson Review; Standards Review

**Rib**, 393, *393*

**Ribonucleic acid (RNA)**, making protein, 54

**Ribosome, 60;** attaching to endoplasmic reticulum, *60;* cell structure, 63*tab*

**Rock**, age of, 289; carrying through history, 305; forming, 284, *284;* studying, 304; type(s) of, 286

**Rock cycle, 286,** *286*

**Rock dove**, selective breeding, *214*

**Rod cell**, 451, *451*

## S

**Saddle joint**, 362, 363*tab*

**Salamander**, breeding, 258, *258*

**Salmonella bacteria**, prokaryotic cell, 64

**Sand dollar**, changing, 325*tab*

**Sandstone**, forming, *285;* layering, 289

**Scale**, geologic time, 316, 318, *318;* geologic time used today, 317, *317;* Science Use v. Common Use, 476

**Scattering, 436;** light interacting with matter, *436*

**Science**, Writing in. *See* Writing in Science

**Science Online**, 47, 55, 66, 72, 78, 79, 85, 87, 95, 107, 112, 113, 123, 125, 133, 142, 149, 157, 162, 163, 169, 171, 180, 181, 190, 196, 197, 207, 209, 217, 218, 227, 234, 235, 241, 243, 251, 256, 260, 261, 265, 270, 271, 281, 283, 291, 299, 306, 307, 310, 313, 315, 323, 331, 339, 346, 347, 357, 359, 367, 375, 382, 383, 389, 391, 403, 411, 413, 418, 419, 425, 427, 432, 433, 442, 449, 457, 462, 463, 464, 469, 471, 478, 488, 494, 495, 501, 503, 513, 521, 526, 527

**Scientific notation**, electromagnetic spectrum, 433*act;* life on Mars, 341; wavelength, 434*act,* 465*act*

**Scientific Terms**, Understanding, 577

**Scorpionfly**, comparing to true-fly, *252,* 252

**Scrotum, 505;** male reproductive organ, *504*

**Seal**, elephant, *128*

**Sea star**, reproducing asexually, *154*

**Sea urchin**, reproduction, 128, *128*

**Second-class lever, 370,** 371*tab;* human body, 372

**Second trimester**, pregnancy, 516, 516*tab*

**Sediment**, sorting, *288*

**Sedimentary rock, 286,** 286; deposition, 288; forming, 287; lithification, 288; transporting, 287

**Seed, 136;** angiosperm life cycle, *139,* 139; of common plant, 140, 140*tab;* dispersing, 141

**Seed plant**, flowering, 138, *138;* flowerless, 137; reproducing, 136, *136*

**Seesaw**, children on, *368*

**Segregation**, law of, **176,** 178

**Selective breeding**, *214,* 214; sexual reproduction, 127

**Semen**, 506

**Seminal vesicle**, male reproductive organ, 504

**Seminiferous tubules, 505**

**Sensory cell**, 483

**Sex chromosome, 186**

**Sexual activity.** *See* Human sexual activity

**Sexual reproduction, 126;** disadvantage, 128; fertilization, 128; selective breeding, 127

**Sheep**, cloning, *156,* 156

**Shock, 410**

**Siberian Traps**, basalt flow in Siberia, 321; releasing ash and sulfur, 330

**Silica**, crystallizing, 247; forming fossil, 246

**Silurian period**, Geologic time scale, *317;* Paleozoic era, 329

**Sister chromatid, 90;** meiosis, 130, *131;* mitosis, 92

**Skeletal muscle**, *365,* 365

**Skeletal muscle cell**, 101

**Skeletal muscle tissue**, 364

**Skeletal system**, *360, 360;* function, 361

**Skin cell**, 91, *91*

**Smoking**, preventing disease, 402

**Smooth muscle cell**, 101

**Smooth muscle tissue**, 364

**Snail shell**, mold, *248*

**Society.** *See* Real World Science

**Soft-bodied organism**, Ediacaran fauna, 328

**Sound**, making, 469*lab;* sensing, 484

**Sound wave**, amplitude, *475,* 475; carrying energy, *476,* 476; causing vibration, 484; compression wave, 473;

creating compression, *473;* detecting in inner ear, 483, *483;* echo, 486; echolocation, *487,* 487

**Species, 262;** competition, 225; grouping and naming, 262; survival of, 127, 215–217, 224–227, 229*lab,* 247

**Specific, 135**

**Spectrometer**, mass, 344

**Speech therapist**, becoming, 492

**Speed**, of light, *437,* 437; and refraction of light, 438, *438*

**Sperm**, 126, *139, 506;* angiosperm life cycle, 139; chromosome, *129,* 129; moving, *135;* pathway through female body, 512, *512;* pathway through male body, 505, *505;* producing, 504, 506; sexual reproduction disadvantage, 128

**Spermatocyte**, *506*

**Sponge**, invertebrate, 328; Science Use v. Common Use, 329

**Spore, 135**

**Stable, 370**

**Stamen, 138,** *139*

**Standardized Test Practice.** *See* Standards Assessment

**Standards Assessment**, 82–83, 116–117, 166–167, 200–201, 238–239, 274–275, 310–311, 350–351, 386–387, 422–423, 466–467, 498–499, 530–531

**Standards Review**, 79–81, 113–115, 163–165, 197–199, 235–237, 271–273, 307–309, 347–349, 383–385, 419–421, 463–465, 495–497, 527–528

**Standards Study Guide**, 78, 112, 162, 196, 234, 270, 306, 346, 382, 418, 462, 494, 526

**Stapes, 482,** *482*

**Stem cell, 102**

**Steno, Nicolas**, superposition, 289

**Steno's Principle(s)**, 290*tab*

**Steroid**, lipid, 54

**Stigma, 138,** *139;* angiosperm life cycle, 139

**Stirrup.** *See* Stapes

**Strata, 289**

**Streptomyces bacteria**, prokaryotic cell, 64

**Stress**, damaging blood vessel, *410*

**Stroke,** *400,* **400**

**Stromatolite**, forming, 327

**Structural adaptation**, 221

**Structure, 246;** homologous and analogous, 253, *253;* Vestigial, 254

**Study Guide**, 78, 112, 162, 196, 234, 270, 306, 346, 382, 418, 462, 494, 526

**Style, 138,** *139;* angiosperm life cycle, 139

**Suffocation, 394;** abdominal thrust, *395*, 395

**Sugar**, molecule, 54; as plant food, 61

**Sun**, providing energy for organism, 52

**Superposition**, principle of, **289**

**Supplement, 518, 519**

**Surface area**, finding for a solid, 81*act*

**Surgery**, Vivien Thomas, 416

**Syndrome**, Blue Baby, 416

**System.** *See* Circulatory system; Immune System; Musculoskeletal System; Organ system; Pulmonary system

**Systematics, 264**

**Systemic circulation,** *399, 399*

## T

**Table**, bird species, 229*lab;* Calculating Half-Life, 300*lab;* cardiopulmonary system, 412*lab,* 414*lab;* Cells in mitosis and cell division, 96*lab;* Cell Structure, 63; Classification of Living Things, 263; Compare and Contrast unknown cell, 75*lab;* Comparison of Meiosis and Mitosis, 132; Components in Whole Blood, 397; Electromagnetic Devices, 465*act;* Electromagnetic Waves, 465*act;* Flowers, Fruits, and Seeds of Common Plants, 140; Half-Lives of Selected Radioactive Isotopes, 296; hormone controlling menstruation, 509*lab;* Human ABO Blood Types, 185; Human Organ System, 105; Human Traits, 192*lab;* Illustrated Table of Some Causes of Slow Extinction, 226; Index Fossil Criteria, 316; Joints in the Human Body, 363; Levers in the Human Body, 371; mechanical advantage of a lever, 376*lab;* Parts of the Eye, 453; Pea Traits Studied by Mendel, 173; Phases of the Cell Cycle, 92; Processes that Release Cellular Energy, 70; Range of Hearing, 477; Sand Dollar Changes, 325; Some Human Genetic Disorders, 188; Species that Lived in California, 342*lab;* Stages of Pregnancy, 516; Steno's Principles, 290; time range of fossils, 261*act;* Types of Proteins, 53; Wavelengths of Different Waves, 434*lab*

**Tape recorder**, comparing to middle ear, *480,* 480; taping sound, 480, *480*

**Technician**, lighting, 460

**Technology.** *See* Real World Science

**Tectonic cycle,** *286*

**Tectonics**, plate, 260

**Telescope**, Hale, 448; lens of, 447; parts of, 447; type(s) of, 447, 448

**Telophase**, mitosis, 92, *93;* meiosis, 130, *131*

**Temperature**, bacteria surviving, 64; forming rock, 286; global cooling, 320; global warming, 319; human being maintaining, 51; regulating body, 334

**Tendon,** *361,* **366**

**Tension**, controlling in Middle ear, 482

**Tertiary period**, Cenozoic era, *317,* 317

**Testing**, genetic, 232

**Testis**, male reproductive organ, 504, *504*

**Testosterone**, 510

**Test Practice.** *See* Standards Assessment

**Theory**, cell, **49**

**Therapist**, speech, 492

***Thermus thermophilus* bacteria, 64**

**Third-class lever, 370,** 371*tab*

**Third trimester**, pregnancy, 516, 516*tab*

**Threatened**, Science Use v. Common Use, 225

**Thrust**, abdominal, 395; abdominal thrust, *395*

**Thymus**, 510

**Thyroid gland**, 511

**Time scale**, geologic, 316, 318, *318;* geologic used today, 317; radiometric dating, 344

**Tire**, pressure, *405,* 405

**Tissue, 103;** muscle, 364; organ, *104;* Science Use v. Common Use, 103

**Toe**, pressure, 406

**Tortoise,** *212;* Galápagos, 212

**Trachea**, breathing, 393

**Trait**, heredity, 176, *176;* passing, 172; pea plant, 173, *173;* predicting, 182; skipping generation, *172*

**Transmission, 436;** light interacting with matter, *436*

**Transplanting**, heart, 416

**Transportation**, sedimentary rock, 287

**Tree**, evolving in Devonian period, 330, *330;* petrified wood, *246,* 246

**Tree finch**, 213, *213*

**Tree ring**, accurate dating, 295, *295*

**Triassic period**, mass extinction, 337; Mesozoic era, 332, *333*

**Trilobite**, Cambrian period, 328; changing body structure, *328*

**Trimester, 516,** 516*tab*

**Triple-beam balance**, 12

**Trough**, wave, *429,* 429

**True-fly**, comparing to scorpionfly, 252, *252*

**Try at Home DataLab,** 255; Can folic acid prevent birth defects?, 519; Can you identify waves in the electromagnetic spectrum?, 434; Can you see a genotype?, 191; How does illness affect the cardiopulmonary system?, 404; How does your garden grow?, 96; How fast do they grow?, 148; How loud and how low can you go?, 477; How many bird species live near you?, 229; Peas, Anyone?, 176; Which hormones control ovulation?, 509; Which organisms return first following a catastrophic event?, 324

**Try at Home Launch Lab,** How are events unscrambled?, 313

**Try at Home MiniLab,** How can you create a dichotomous key?, 264; How can your population have the strongest, longest-lasting survivors?, 228; How can you see photosynthesis?, 73; How do bones and muscles interact?, 366; How does an ear hear?, 489; How does Earth change over time?, 292; How does the cardiopulmonary system work?, 412; How do you see colors in the dark?, 454; What happened here?, 340; What is the mechanical advantage of a lever?, 376; Why does the pencil look broken?, 438

**Tune**, playing in, 474

**Turtle**, evolving in Mesozoic era, 333

**Twin(s)**, genetically identical, 151; genetic material, 127

**Two-trait model, 183,** *183*

**Tympanic membrane, 482,** *482*

## U

**Ultraviolet ray**, harmful, 326; ozone, 327

**Umbilical cord,** *517,* 517

**Understanding Main Ideas,** 55, 66, 72, 79, 80, 95, 107, 114, 133, 142, 149, 157, 164, 180, 190, 198, 217, 227, 236, 251, 256, 260, 265, 272, 291, 299, 308, 323, 331, 339, 348, 367, 375, 384, 403, 411, 420, 432, 442, 449, 457, 478, 488, 496, 513, 521, 528

**Uniformitarianism, 285**

**Unknown**, exploring, 74*lab*

**Urchin**, sea, *128,* 128

**Urethra, 505;** male human body, *504*

**Use and Care of a Microscope, 579**

Index

**Use the Internet**, Animal Hearing, 490–491; How has California changed over geologic time?, 342–343; What makes you unique?, 192–193. *See also* Design Your Own, Use the Internet

**Using a Calculator**, 576

**Using Vocabulary**, 55, 66, 72, 95, 107, 113, 133, 142, 149, 157, 163, 180, 190, 197, 217, 235, 251, 256, 260, 265, 271, 291, 299, 307, 323, 331, 339, 347, 367, 375, 383, 403, 411, 419, 432, 442, 449, 457, 463, 478, 488, 495, 513, 521, 527

**Uterus**, **507;** female reproductive organ, *507;* Word Origin, 507

## V

**Vacuole**, lysosome, 62; in plant cell, *62;* storage organelle, 62

**Vagina**, *507;* female reproductive organ, *507*

**Valve**, heart, 408; preventing blood backflow, 408, *408,* 409, *409*

**Variety**, **329**

**Vary**, **127**

**Vascular plant**, evolving, 330

**Vas deferens**, male reproductive organ, *504*

**Vein**, *399,* 399; blood flow, 409

**Ventricle**, blood flow, 409, *409;* chamber of heart, *398,* 398; contracting, 408, *408*

**Vertebrate**, **329;** Paleozoic era, 329

**Vesicle**, male reproductive organ, *504*

**Vessel**, blood, *399,* 399

**Vesicle**, 62; cell structure, *63tab*

**Vestigial structure**, 254

**Vibration**, bending hair in cochlea, 484, *484;* making sound, 472; of a stereo speaker, *474,* 474; transferring to inner ear, 483

**Virus**, pneumonia, 394; during pregnancy, 520

**Visible light**, wavelength range, 431

**Vision**, common problem(s), 455–456

**Visual Check**, 49, 65, 70, 90, 92, 127, 132, 134, 140, 175, 185, 216, 220, 222, 223, 317, 320, 322, 325, 328, 362, 364, 370, 374, 394, 406, 431, 444, 447, 474, 481, 486, 516

**Visualizing**, Abdominal Thrusts, 395; Accurate Dating with Tree Rings, 295; Cell Membrane, 57; Differentiated Human Cells, 101; Echolocation, 487; Extinct Reptile, 335; Hormones, 510–511; Images Formed by a Convex Lens, 445; Interactions of Genes and the Environment, 189; Isolation, 258; Muscle Contractions, 365; Natural Selection, 213; Seed dispersal, 141

**Vocabulary**, 48, 56, 68, 88, 98, 126, 134, 143, 172, 182, 210, 219, 244, 252, 262, 284, 293, 316, 325, 332, 360, 368, 392, 405, 428, 435, 443, 450, 472, 504, 515. *See also* Using Vocabulary

**Volcanic haze effect**, global cooling, 321

**Volcano**, **316;** basalt flow in Hawaii, *321;* climate change, 319; mass extinction, 318, 320

**Volume**, finding for a solid, 81*act;* water affecting erosion, 303*lab*

**Voluntary muscle**, 364

*Volvox,* protist colony, 99, *99*

## W

**Warbler finch**, *213,* 213

**Water**, main ingredient, 53

**Water cycle**, *286*

**Water molecule**, *53*

**Water wave**, *428,* 428

**Wave**, compression, *472;* electromagnetic, 430; light, *428,* 428; part(s) of, 429; sound, 473, *473;* water, 428, *428*

**Wavelength**, 429, *429,* **472;** range, 430, *430, 439,* 439; sound wave, 473; visible light, *431*

**Wax**, lipid, 54

**Weathering**, **287;** chemical, 287; physical, 287

**Web**, food, *52*

**Wegener, Alfred,** continental drift, 257

**Whale**, echolocation, 486; evolving in Cenozoic era, 338

**Whistle**, hearing dog whistle, 477

**White blood cell**, 101; function, 397, *397tab*

**White light**, 439; passing through prism, *439,* 439

**Woodpecker finch**, 213, *213*

**Wooly mammoth**, preserving in ice, *248,* 248

**Word Origin**, amplitude, 475; angiosperm, 139; catastrophe, 318; circulatory system, 397; cytoplasm, 59; decibel, 476; dominance, 185; Eukaryotic, 65; fission, 152; fulcrum, 369; genetics, 173; heterozygous, 178; homologous, 89, 253; homozygous, 178; joint, 361; lever, 369; meiosis, 128; membrane, 482; metamorphosis, 147; paleontology, 245; Photosynthesis, 71; uterus, 507

**Work**, **368;** Science Use v. Common Use, 373

**World Wide Web.** *See* Science Online, Use the Internet, Real World Science

**Writing in Science**, 75*lab,* 80, 115, 165, 193*lab,* 199, 267*lab,* 273, 309, 343*lab,* 385, 415*lab,* 421, 465, 491*lab,* 497, 523*lab,* 529

## X

**X ray**, lung, *394,* 394

## Y

**Yeast**, budding, *153,* 153; eukaryotic cell, *65*

**Yolk**, food supply for embryo, *146,* 146

**Yucatan Peninsula**, asteroid impact site, 322, *322*

## Z

**Zygote**, **126,** *139;* cell division, 515; forming, 509

Index

**Magnification Key:** Magnifications listed are the magnifications at which images were originally photographed.

**LM**–Light Microscope

**SEM**–Scanning Electron Microscope

**TEM**–Transmission Electron Microscope

**Acknowledgments:** Glencoe would like to acknowledge the artists and agencies who participated in illustrating this program: Argosy Publishing; Articulate Graphics; Craig Attebery represented by Frank and Jeff Lavaty; Emily Damstra; Gary Hincks; Precision Graphics; Michael Rothman; Zoobotanica.

## Photo Credits

**List of Abbreviations:**

AA=Animals Animals; CBS=Carolina Biological Supply; CB=Corbis-Bettmann; CP=Color-Pic; CMSP=Custom Medical Stock Photo; DRK=DRK Photo; ES=Earth Scenes; FPG=FPG International; GH=Grant Heilman Photography; LI=Liaison International; MP=Minden Pictures; OSF=Oxford Scientific Films; PA=Peter Arnold, Inc.; PR=Photo Researchers; PT=Phototake, NYC; SPL=Science Photo Library; SS=Science Source; TSM=The Stock Market; TSA=Tom Stack & Associates; TSI=Tony Stone Images; VU=Visuals Unlimited

**Cover** Greg Probst/Getty Images; **viii** Geoff Bryant/Photo Researchers; **viiii** Galen Rowell/CORBIS; **x** Gerald & Buff Corsi/Visuals Unlimited; **xi** Joseph Sohm/ChromoSohm Media Inc./Photo Researchers; **xviii** CORBIS; **2** (t)Getty Images, (c)Louie Psihoyos/CORBIS, (b)Getty Images; **4** (t)Science VU/USGS/Visuals Unlimited, (c)CORBIS, (b)Lawrence Migdale/SPL/Photo Researchers; **5** Supreme Council for Antiquities/Handout/Reuters/CORBIS; **7** (t)Matt Meadows (b)Amos Morgan/Getty Images; **8** (t)Steve Cole/Getty Images (b)Andrew Lambert Photography/Photo Researchers; **9** (t)Matt Meadows, (b)Horizons Companies; **10** Horizons Companies; **11** Matt Meadows; **12** Matt Meadows; **14** (t)CORBIS, (c b)Matt Meadows; **16** Icon Images; **17** CORBIS; **20** (t)CORBIS, (b)Getty Images; **21** Michael Newman/PhotoEdit; **23** Toby Talbot/AP/Wide World Photos; **28** (l)Keith Brofsky/Getty Images, (r)Getty Images; **30** CORBIS; **31** Jan Suttle/Life File/Getty Images; **34** Jeff Greenberg/PhotoEdit; **36** Bettmann/CORBIS; **37** Leland Bobbe/Getty Images; **38** Karen Kasmauski/CORBIS; **39** (t)David Young-Wolff/PhotoEdit, (c)Ed Eckstein/CORBIS, (b)Neil Borden/Photo Researchers; **40** (t)Doug Menuez/Getty Images, (b)Jon Feingersh/Zefa/CORBIS; **41** (t)Image Source/Alamy (b)Laura Sifferlin; **42** (t)Steve Hamblin/Alamy; **42-43** (bkgd)Eurelios/PhotoTake NYC; **43** (tl)Quest/SPL/Photo Researchers, (tr)Neil Borden/Photo Researchers, (b)Digital Instruments/Veeco/Photo Researchers; **44** SPL/Photo Researchers; **45** Matt Meadows; **49** Marilyn Schaller/Photo Researchers; **50** CORBIS; **51** AP/Wide World Photos; **54** Michael Dalton, Fundamental Photographs, NYC; **57** Stephen R. Wagner; **58** (t)Biophoto Associates/Photo Researchers, (b)ISM/Phototake NYC; **59** Ed Reschke/Peter Arnold, Inc.; **60** (t)Leonard Lessin/Peter Arnold, Inc., (bl)Dr. P. Motta & Dr. T. Naguro/Photo Researchers, (br)Don W. Fawcett/Photo Researchers; **61** (t)Dr. P. Motta & Dr. T. Naguro/Photo Researchers, (b)Dr. Jeremy Burgess/Photo Researchers; **62** (t)Biology Media/Photo Researchers, (b)Dr. Henry Aldrich/Visuals Unlimited; **64** Francois Franceschi and the Max Planck

Institute; **65** (tr)Matt Meadows, (c)David Fankhauser, (bc)Astrid & Hanns-Frieder Michler/Photo Researchers; **70** Wes Walker/Lonely Planet Collection/Getty Images; **73-74** Matt Meadows; **75** Horizons Companies; **76** (t)Yoav Levy/PhotoTake NYC, (b)Thomas Deerinck/Visuals Unlimited; **77** (t)Dr. Fred Hossler/Visuals Unlimited, (b)Ramin Yazdani; **80** SPL/Photo Researchers; **83** P. Motta & T. Naguro/Science Photo Library/Photo Researchers; **84** Don Savant; **85** Matt Meadows; **89** (t)Dr. Richard Kessel & Dr. Gene Shih/Visuals Unlimited, (b)Carolina Biological Supply Company PhotoTake NYC; **91** Dr. David M. Phillips/Visuals Unlimited; **93** (t)Michael Abbey/Visuals Unlimited, (others)John D. Cunningham/Visuals Unlimited; **94** (l)RMF/Visuals Unlimited, (r)Robert Calentine/Visuals Unlimited; **98** (l)A.B. Dowsett/Photo Researchers, (r)Michael Abbey/Photo Researchers; **99** (t)Michael Abbey/Visuals Unlimited, (b)James M. Bell/Photo Researchers; **100** (l)Dr. Dennis Kunkel/Visuals Unlimited, (r)David McCarthy/Photo Researchers; **101** (t)Ken Eward/Science Source/Photo Researchers, (c)Cabisco/Visuals Unlimited, (bl)Quest/SPL/Photo Researchers, (bc)Robert Knauft/Biology Media/Photo Researchers, (br)Eric Grave/Science Source/Photo Researchers; **102** Jerome Wexler/Visuals Unlimited; **104** Eye of Science/SPL/Photo Researchers; **106** Tomek Sikora/Zefa/CORBIS; **108** (t)Matt Meadows, (b)Tim Fuller; **109** Tim Fuller; **110** (t)Boston College, (b)Custom Medical Stock Photo; **111** (t)SPL/Photo Researchers (b)Coalition on Donation; **114** John D. Cunningham/Visuals Unlimited; **116** Cabisco/Visuals Unlimited; **118** (tl)Doug Martin, (tr bl br)StudiOhio; **119** Cabisco/Visuals Unlimited; **120-121** (bkgd)Will & Deni McIntyre/Photo Researchers; **120** Luther Burbank Home & Gardens/Santa Rosa, CA; **121** (t)Henry T. Kaiser/PictureQuest, (b)Roslin Institute; **122** Art Wolfe/Photo Researchers; **126** Carolyn A. McKeone/Photo Researchers; **127** (t)Joseph Sohm/ChromoSohm Media, Inc./Photo Researchers, (b)CORBIS; **128** (l)Andrew J. Martinez/Photo Researchers, (r)Tim Fiitzharris/Minden Pictures; **129** (tl)Nature's Images/Photo Researchers, (bl)Nature's Images/Photo Researchers, (br)Jeremy West/Getty Images; **131** (t to b)Science VU/Visuals Unlimited, (2 3 4 7)Visuals Unlimited/John D. Cunningham; **131** (5 6 8)Carolina Biological Supply/Phototake - NYC; **132** Horizons Companies; **135** (l)John Anderson/Animals Animals, (r)David M. Dennis/Animals Animals; **136** Eye of Science/Photo Researchers; **137** (cw from top)Stephen Ingram/Earth Scenes, Dr. Daniel Nickrent/Southern Illinois University, Timothy D. Ives, Gerald & Buff Corsi/Visuals Unlimited; **138** (l)Horizons Companies, (r)Lightwave Photography, Inc./Animals Animals; **140** (l to r, t to b)Patty Murray/Animals Animals, Alan & Linda Detrick/Photo Researchers, Color-Pic/Earth Scenes, Brad Mogen/Visuals Unlimited, Walter H. Hodge/Peter Arnold, Inc., Doug Steley/Alamy, Renee Morris/Alamy, AGStockUSA, Inc./Alamy Images, USDA/Photo Researchers, Adam Jones/Photo Researchers, CORBIS, Josh Westrich/Zefa/CORBIS; **141** (tl)Kevin Shafer/CORBIS, (tr)Tom & Pat Leeson, (c)Dwight Kuhn, (bl)Darryl Torckler/Stone, (br)Dwight Kuhn; **143** (t)Leonard Lee Rue III/Photo Researchers, (b)F.J. Hiersche/Photo Researchers; **144** (l)John Pointier/Animals Animals, (r)Doug Wechsler/Earth Scenes; **145** Michael & Patricia Fogden/CORBIS; **146** (t)Jean-Phillipe Varin/Photo Researchers, (b)Marie Read/Earth Scenes; **148** Alan Root/OSF/Earth Scenes; **151** Age fotostock/SuperStock; **152** CNRI/Photo Researchers; **153** (tl)Wim van Egmond/Visuals Unlimited, (tr)Horizons Companies, (bl)Ed Reschke/Peter Arnold, Inc., (br)Dr. Richard Kessel & Dr. C. Y. Shih/Visuals Unlimited; **154** (tl)Bernard Photo Productions/Earth Scenes, (tr)Maurice Nimmo/SPL/Photo Researchers, (b)Franklin Viola/Earth Scenes; **156** Roslin Institute; **158-159** Horizons Companies; **160** (t)Paddy Ryan/Animals Animals, (b)Jim Richardson/CORBIS; **161** (t)SPL/Photo Researchers, (b)Alison Van Eenennaam, PhD; **166** (l)Barry L. Runk/Grant Heilman, (r)R. Kessel/G. Shih/Visuals Unlimited; **168** LWA/JDC/CORBIS; **169** Horizons Companies; **172** Science & Society Picture Library; **173** Malcolm Gutter/Visuals Unlimited; **177** Henry T. Kaiser/PictureQuest; **182** Michael Newman/PhotoEdit; **184** (l)Maya Barnes/The Image Works, (r)Bill Aron/PhotoEdit; **185** (l)Peter Smithers/CORBIS, (c)Bill Ross/CORBIS, (r)Geoff Bryant/Photo Researchers; **186** Biophoto Associates/Photo Researchers; **187** Jennifer Thompson; **189** (tl)June Green/Alamy Images, (tr)CORBIS, (c)Carolyn A. McKeone/Photo Researchers, (bl br)Hania Arensten-Berdys/www.gardensafari.net, ; **193** Aaron Haupt; **194** (t)Cary Wolinsky/IPN/Aurora Photos, (b)Jim Richardson/CORBIS; **195** (t)CORBIS, (b)Tom Pantages/Alamy Images; **199** Horizons Companies; **202** (tl bl br)StudioOhio, (tr)Doug Martin; **204** Bettmann/CORBIS; **204/205** (bkgd)Papilio/Alamy Images; **205** (t)Yva Momatiuk/John Eastcott/Minden Pictures, (b)O. Louis Mazzatenta/National Geographic/Getty Images; **206** James L. Amos/CORBIS; **210** Bettmann/CORBIS; **211** (l)Frans Lanting/Photo Researchers, (r)Barbara Cushman Rowell/DRK Photo; **212** (t)George D. Lepp/CORBIS, (tc)Inga Spence/Visuals Unlimited, (bl)Gerald & Buff Corsi/Visuals Unlimited, (bc)Gibson, Adrienne/Animals Animals, (br)Gerald & Buff Corsi/Visuals Unlimited; **213** (cw from top)Mickey Gibson/Animals Animals, (2 3 4 5)Tui DeRoy/Bruce Coleman, Inc., (6)Stephen R. Wagner; **214** (t)Gary Meszaros/Visuals Unlimited, (c)Mark Stouffer/Animals Animals, (b)Kenneth W. Fink/Photo Researchers; **215** (t)Andy Jackson/Alamy Images, (b)Image Source, Ltd; **219** Michael Nichols/National Geographic Image Collection; **220** S.J. Krasemann/Peter Arnold, Inc.; **221** WorldFoto/Alamy Images; **222** (t)Carol Buchanan/Alamy Images, (c)www.seapics.com, (b)Leszczynski, Zigmund/Earth Scenes; **223** (l)Nelson, Alan G./Earth Scenes, (r)B. G. Thomson/Photo Researchers; **224** Pat Powers and Cherryl Schafer/Getty Images; **225** G. Carleton Ray/Photo Researchers; **226** (t)Milt Putnam/University of Florida, (c)Kevin Schafer/Zefa/Corbis, (b)Insadco Photography/Alamy Images; **231** NASA; **232** Peter Lane Taylor/Visuals Unlimited; **233** (t)Louie Psihoyos/CORBIS, (b)Steve Kaufman/Peter Arnold, Inc.; **236** Mark Stouffer/Animals Animals; **237** Andy Jackson/Alamy Images; **239** Patti Murray/Animals Animals; **240** Layne Kennedy/CORBIS; **241** Horizons Companies; **244** (l)Dr. Richard Kessel & Dr. Gene Shih/Visuals Unlimited, (r)Richard T. Nowitz/PhotoTake NYC; **245** www.offwell.info; **246** (l)Sinclair Stammers/Photo Researchers, (r)PhotoLink/Getty Images; **247** (l)Gregory Dimljian/SPL/Photo Researchers, (r)James L. Amos/CORBIS; **248** (tl)Mark A. Schneider/Visuals Unlimited, (tr)Chris Howes/Wild Places Photography/Alamy Images, (b)Koichi Kamoshida/Getty Images; **249** Horizons Companies; **250** Louie Psihoyos/CORBIS; **252** (l)B. Borrell Casals/Frank Lane Picture Agency/CORBIS, (r)Bill Beatty/Visuals Unlimited; **259** (t)Altrendo Nature/Getty Images, (b)G.D. Carr; **263** (t to b)Stephen J. Krasemann/SPL/Photo Researchers, Claus Meyer/Minden Pictures, OSF/S. Turner/Earth Scenes, Esbin-Anderson/Omni-

Photo Communications, Theo Allofs/CORBIS, Kawika Chetron/Cold Water Images; **266** Geoff Butler; **268** (t)Daniel Morel/Reuters/CORBIS, (b)Dr. Chris Adami/Keck Graduate Institute; **269** (t)Hulton Archive/Getty Images, (b)Tui De Roy/Minden Pictures; **274** PhotoLink/Getty Images; **275** (l)Altrendo Nature/Getty Images, (r)G.D. Carr; **276** (tl tr bl)StudioOhio, (br)Doug Martin; **277** Patti Murray/Animals Animals; **278** (t)Albert Copley/Visuals Unlimited (b)American Institute of Physics/Emilio Segrè Visual Archives; **278/279** (bkgd)Layne Kennedy/CORBIS; **279** D. Parker/Photo Researchers; **280** David Muench/CORBIS; **281** Mediacolors/Alamy Images; **284** Martin Bond/Photo Researchers; **285** (t)Omni-Photo Communications, (c)Sylvester Allred/Fundamental Photographs, NYC, (bl)Americana Images/SuperStock, (br)Rob & Ann Simpson/Visuals Unlimited; **287** (t)Larry Stepanowicz/Visuals Unlimited, (b)CORBIS; **288** (t)David R. Frazier/Photo Researchers, (bl)Wally Eberhart/Visuals Unlimited, (br)Fritz Polking/Visuals Unlimited; **289** Galen Rowell/CORBIS; **290** (t)Ed Reschke/Peter Arnold, Inc., (tc)Keith Mann/Boreal Ltd, (bc)John Crossley, (b)Doug Sokell/Visuals Unlimited; **291** Keith Mann/Boreal Ltd; **293** Chris Lisle/CORBIS; **295** (t)Dr. Jack M. Bostrak/Visuals Unlimited, (b)Dietrich Rose/Zefa/CORBIS; **297** James King-Holmes/SPL/Photo Researchers; **298** NASA/Johnson Space Center; **304** (t)Digital Vision/PunchStock, (b)A. Pasieka/Photo Researchers; **305** (t)George Holton/Photo Researchers, (b)Bettmann/CORBIS; **308** Keith Mann/Boreal Ltd; **312** Scott Berner/Visuals Unlimited; **319** Viola's Photo Visions, Inc./Animals Animals; **320** (t)Alaska Stock, (b)Jim Sugar/CORBIS; **321** USGS/Photo Researchers; **327** (l)Mitsuaki Iwago/Minden Pictures, (r)R. Calentine/Visuals Unlimited; **336** Sally A. Morgan/Ecoscene/CORBIS; **344** (t)Carlos Goldin/Photo Researchers, (b)James King-Holmes/Photo Researchers; **345** (t)The Natural History Museum, London, (b)NASA/Goddard Space Flight Center Scientific Visualization Studio; **349** Alaska Stock; **351** R. Calentine/Visuals Unlimited; **352** StudioOhio; **354** (tl)CORBIS, (tr)John Wang/Getty Images, (b)Hulton-Deutsch Collection/CORBIS; **354/355** (bkgd)Robert Glusic/Getty Images; **355** Steve Powell/Allsport/Getty Images; **356** Chase Jarvis/CORBIS; **357** Thinkstock/Alamy; **360** Anatomical Travelogue/Photo Researchers; **365** (tl)Judy Lutz, (tr)Astrid and Hans-Frieder Michler/Photo Researchers, (bl)Stephen R. Wagner, (br)Lennart Nilsson; **368** Ole Graf/Zefa/CORBIS; **371** (t)Frank Chmura/Alamy, (c)Martin Meissner/AP/Wide World Photos, (b)Tony Freeman/PhotoEdit; **372** Robert Pratta/Reuters/CORBIS; **373** David Young-Wolff/PhotoEdit; **374** Aflo Foto Agency/Alamy; **378** Matt Meadows; **379** Matt Meadows; **380** (t)Ariel Skelley/CORBIS, (b)New Jersey Herald/Claire Sheprow/AP/Wide World Photos; **381** (t)HIP/Art Resource NY, (b)Custom Medical Stock Photo; **386** CORBIS; **388** Lester V. Bergman/CORBIS; **389** James Day Photography Ltd./Getty Images; **393** Tim Fuller; **394** (t)Garry Hunter/Getty Images, (b)ISM/PhotoTake NYC; **395** Richard T. Nowitz; **396** ORBIS; **397** (t)Kenneth Eward/BioGrafx/Photo Researchers, (c)SPL/Photo Researchers, (b)NIBSC/Photo Researchers; **399** Tim Fuller; **402** Tim Fuller; **405** Matt Meadows; **406** (t)Matt Meadows, (b)Horizons Companies; **407** Tim Fuller; **412-415** Matt Meadows; **416** (t)Vivien Thomas by Bob Gee/Oil on Canvas/Aaron Levin/The Alan Mason Chesney Medical Archives of The Johns Hopkins Medical Institutions, (b)Mark Harmel/Time Life Pictures/Getty Images; **417** (t)Bettmann/CORBIS, (b)Nik Wheeler/CORBIS; **421** Horizons Companies;

# PERIODIC TABLE OF THE ELEMENTS

Columns of elements are called groups. Elements in the same group have similar chemical properties.

🎈 Gas

💧 Liquid

⬜ Solid

◉ Synthetic

Element — Hydrogen
Atomic number — 1
Symbol — H
Atomic mass — 1.008
State of matter

The first three symbols tell you the state of matter of the element at room temperature. The fourth symbol identifies elements that are not present in significant amounts on Earth. Useful amounts are made synthetically.

| | 1 | 2 | | 3 | 4 | 5 | 6 | 7 | 8 | 9 |
|---|---|---|---|---|---|---|---|---|---|---|
| 1 | Hydrogen 1 H 1.008 | | | | | | | | | |
| 2 | Lithium 3 Li 6.941 | Beryllium 4 Be 9.012 | | | | | | | | |
| 3 | Sodium 11 Na 22.990 | Magnesium 12 Mg 24.305 | | | | | | | | |
| 4 | Potassium 19 K 39.098 | Calcium 20 Ca 40.078 | Scandium 21 Sc 44.956 | Titanium 22 Ti 47.867 | Vanadium 23 V 50.942 | Chromium 24 Cr 51.996 | Manganese 25 Mn 54.938 | Iron 26 Fe 55.845 | Cobalt 27 Co 58.933 |
| 5 | Rubidium 37 Rb 85.468 | Strontium 38 Sr 87.62 | Yttrium 39 Y 88.906 | Zirconium 40 Zr 91.224 | Niobium 41 Nb 92.906 | Molybdenum 42 Mo 95.94 | Technetium 43 Tc (98) | Ruthenium 44 Ru 101.07 | Rhodium 45 Rh 102.906 |
| 6 | Cesium 55 Cs 132.905 | Barium 56 Ba 137.327 | Lanthanum 57 La 138.906 | Hafnium 72 Hf 178.49 | Tantalum 73 Ta 180.948 | Tungsten 74 W 183.84 | Rhenium 75 Re 186.207 | Osmium 76 Os 190.23 | Iridium 77 Ir 192.217 |
| 7 | Francium 87 Fr (223) | Radium 88 Ra (226) | Actinium 89 Ac (227) | Rutherfordium 104 Rf (261) | Dubnium 105 Db (262) | Seaborgium 106 Sg (266) | Bohrium 107 Bh (264) | Hassium 108 Hs (277) | Meitnerium 109 Mt (268) |

The number in parentheses is the mass number of the longest-lived isotope for that element.

Rows of elements are called periods. Atomic number increases across a period.

The arrow shows where these elements would fit into the periodic table. They are moved to the bottom of the table to save space.

| | | | | | |
|---|---|---|---|---|---|
| Lanthanide series | Cerium 58 Ce 140.116 | Praseodymium 59 Pr 140.908 | Neodymium 60 Nd 144.24 | Promethium 61 Pm (145) | Samarium 62 Sm 150.36 |
| Actinide series | Thorium 90 Th 232.038 | Protactinium 91 Pa 231.036 | Uranium 92 U 238.029 | Neptunium 93 Np (237) | Plutonium 94 Pu (244) |